I&T Collector's Series

FARM TRACTORS

1926-1956

Editorial

Editorial Director
Randy Stephens

Editor
Mike Hall

Technical Editor
C.G. Ewing

Senior Technical Writer
Robert Mills

Inventory/Production Manager
Terry Distin

Lead Editorial Assistant
Elizabeth Couzens

Editorial Assistants
Shirley Renicker
Jon Worley

Marketing

Marketing Director
Chris Charlton

Advertising and Promotions Manager
Katherine Nelms

Advertising Assistant
Wendy Blumenthal

Graphic Designer
Anita Blattner

Sales and Administration

Director of Sales
Dutch Sadler

Accounts Manager
Ted Metzger

Sales Coordinator
Lynn Reynolds

**Customer Service and Administration
Manager**
Joan Jackson

Published by
Intertec Publishing Corporation

President and CEO
Harry A. McQuillen

Executive Vice President
Raymond E. Maloney

Group Vice President
Bill J. Wiesner

I&T Collector's Series
FARM TRACTORS
1926-1956

Cover Photo: Thomas Hart Benton
"Louisianna Rice Fields" 1928
Courtesy of The Brooklyn Museum   Brooklyn, New York
John B. Woodward Memorial Fund

**Compiled from the pages of *The Cooperative Tractor Catalog*
and the *Red Tractor Book***

 **INTERTEC**
PUBLISHING

Mattituck-Laurel Library

Library of Congress Catalog Card Number: 90-055416
International Standard Book Number: 0-89288-389-2

Printed in the United States of America by
Walsworth Press, Marceline, Missouri 64658

Special thanks to Farm Press Publications, Inc.

CONTENTS

PREFACE

The development of the farm tractor owes much of its early impetus to the success of the automobile, which was not built with the farmer in mind. But rural America quickly saw and appreciated the benefits of the motor car in running errands during the busy season. So they bought and used automobiles in much greater numbers than expected of them.

Farmers for more than two generations had been familiar with and dependent on increasingly complex farm machinery. The reaper, which appeared in the 1830's, is often cited as the first great step in agricultural mechanization—but the reaper was relatively simple. The grain binder in the 1870's was much more complex but readily accepted. The first threshing machines appeared about 1840. Threshing was considered the province of the specialist and became more so after the appearance of the steam traction engine about 1870. Although the average farmer left the running of the threshing rig to the specialist, he worked the harvest, trusted it and developed a familiarity with the work and the machines.

This book covers the golden years of the farm tractor development in America—the thirty years between 1926 and 1956. In earlier years, there was a wide diversity in farm tractor design, and most of the manufacturers were small enterprises. By 1926, designs had stabilized along the lines most accepted by the farmer but diversity still existed.

The material for this book is derived from the *Cooperative Tractor Catalog* and *Red Tractor Book*; the annual directories of the *Implement & Hardware Trade Journal* and *Implement & Tractor*—early and later names of the leading trade magazine for the farm equipment industry. The original format for each year's listings has been maintained to preserve the character of the *Cooperative Tractor Catalog* and *Red Tractor Book*.

The 1926 listing included here contains information on all tractors available for sale during that calendar year. The succeeding year listings contain ONLY models introduced during that calendar year.

> NOTE: There is a built-in discrepancy in these listings. The *Cooperative Tractor Catalog* and later *Red Tractor Book* were published early in the calendar year and information from the manufacturer was required about two months before publication date. Often manufacturers would not release the information on new models to be introduced in the spring, so the listings may sometimes run behind actual introduction date.

1926

The 1926 list includes all available current models according to the 1926 *Cooperative Tractor Catalog*, without regard to what year they were first introduced. Twenty-one models of 12 makes are shown.

ADVANCE-RUMELY THRESHER CO., INC.

La Porte, Indiana

The Advance-Rumely "Oil Pull" line was unique in that oil, rather than water was used as an engine coolant, on the theory that a hotter operating temperature would provide increased efficiency with the kerosene fuel used. Coolant temperatures of 200-215° F are accomplished today with a glycol-water mixture and a pressurized system.

Oilpull 25-45   1926-1927

Traction Wheels: Four wheels with two in rear, 57½x18, giving traction and two non-drive in front, 38½x8.

No. of Plows Recommended: Five to six 14-in.

Length: 167 in.; **Width:** 82 in.; **Height:** 107 in.

Turning Radius: 19 ft.

Motor: Own, 7 13/16 x9½, horizontal, valve-in-head, 2 cylinders, removable sleeve.

Lubrication: Mechanical oiler and splash.

Carburetor: Own, 2⅜ in.

Ignition System: High tension.

Cooling System: Pump circulation; oil in system.

Bearings: New Departure, Timken roller and bronze.

Transmission: Spur gear; 2, 2½ and 3 m. p. h. forward; 2½ m. p. h. reverse.

Final Drive: Spur gear enclosed in transmission.

Belt Pulley: 21¾x10; 540 r.p.m. and 3000 feet per minute at normal engine speed.

OILPULL 25-45
Advance-Rumely Thresher Co., Inc., La Porte, Ind.

ALLIS-CHALMERS MANUFACTURING CO.
Milwaukee, Wisconsin

The Allis-Chalmers Manufacturing Co. was an early manufacturing conglomerate, starting business making milling burrs and other milling supplies in the 1850's, expanding into centrifugal pumps, steam engines and electric power components. They built their first tractor in 1914 and established a separate tractor division in 1926. The company was one of the first to equip their engines with renewable cylinder sleeves.

A-C 20-35 Road   1926

Traction Wheels: Four wheels; two in rear, 50x20, giving traction.
Length: 152 in.; **Width:** 90 in.; **Height:** 65 in.; **Weight:** 9500 lbs.
Turning Radius: 12 ft.
Motor: Own, 4¾x6½, overhead valve, 4 cylinders, cast en bloc.
Lubrication: Full pressure.
Carburetor: Schebler, 1½ in.
Ignition System: Eisemann.
Cooling System: Fin and tube radiator and fan.
Bearings: Roller and plain.
Transmission: Enclosed spur gear; 2 to 2½ m.p.h. forward; 2¼ m.p.h. reverse.
Final Drive: Enclosed double reduction.
Belt Pulley: 13½x8; 750 r.p.m. and 2500 feet per minute at normal engine speed.

A-C 20-35 ROAD
Allis-Chalmers Mfg. Co., Milwaukee, Wis.

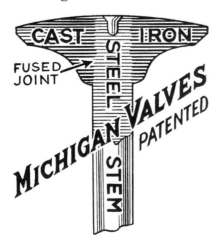

The Improved
Allis-Chalmers Tractor

The Allis-Chalmers Franchise offers dealers a tractor that is easily sold and that stays sold; generous cooperation in sales, service and advertising; financing aid of a most practical nature; discounts worthy of the best efforts of high-grade dealers. Write for full particulars.

**Sales and Service
from
Fifteen Factory
Branches**

The Allis-Chalmers tractor, designed over ten years ago, is a striking example of scientific and practical engineering. So well was it worked out from every angle that the fundamental design has never been changed. It was then and is now, "a tractor ahead of the times."

After watching its performance for a decade, several new improvements have been perfected and are now ready for the trade. None of these changes are radical. They are more in the nature of refinements. Parts that developed the least tendency to weakness over a period of years have been strengthened. The housings have been improved, accessibility increased, simplicity augmented.

Figured on the basis of dependable horsepower per dollar of cost the Allis-Chalmers Tractor is an outstanding achievement, a purchase unrivaled in economy.

The Allis-Chalmers Mfg. Co.

Builders of Power for Over 70 Years

Tractor Division   Milwaukee, Wisconsin

**Better Built by
Engine Builders**

**"Good
Equipment
Makes a Good
Farmer Better"**

**Two sizes—
20-35, 15-25**

AVERY POWER MACHINERY CO.

Peoria, Illinois

The Avery Power Machinery Co. started business as the Avery Planter Co., expanding to include stalk cutters and cultivators. In the 1890's, they included threshers and steam traction engines, which became their leading product. They were early pioneers in the manufacture of farm tractors, entering the market about 1910.

Avery 20-35	1926-1927
Avery 25-50	1926-1932
Avery 45-65	1926-1932
Avery Power Road Maintainer	1926-1932

AVERY 20-35

Avery Power Machinery Co., Peoria, Ill.

Traction Wheels: Four wheels, driving from two rear wheels, 60x16.

No. of Plows Recommended: Four 14-in.

Length: 152 in.; **Width:** 68 in.; **Height:** 80 in.; **Weight:** 7500 lbs.

Turning Radius: 12 ft.

Motor: Own, 4⅞ x 7, horizontal opposed, valve in head, 4 cylinders. cast en bloc.

Lubrication: Internal gear pump.

Carburetor: Kingston double, 1¼-in.

Ignition System: K-W high tension magneto.

Starting System: Impulse starter.

Cooling System: Cellular radiator, pump and fans.

Bearings: Hyatt roller in differential.

Transmission: Spur gear; two speeds; 2⅓ to 4½ m.p.h. forward

Final Drive: Double spur gear.

Belt Pulley: 16x7½; 700-900 r.p.m. at normal engine speed.

Traction Wheels: Four wheels, driving from two rear wheels, 69 x 20.

No. of Plows Recommended: Five to six 14-in.

Length: 176 in.; **Width:** 90½ in.; **Height:** 108 in.; **Weight:** 12500 lbs.

Turning Radius: 20 ft.

Motor: Own, 6¾x8, opposed valve-in-head, 4 cylinders; cast in pairs.

Lubrication: Internal gear pump.

Carburetor: Kingston double, 2 in.

Ignition System: K-W high tension magneto.

Starting System: Impulse starter.

Cooling System: Cellular radiator, pump and fans.

Bearings: Own throughout.

Transmission: Spur gear, two speeds, 2½ to 4 m.p.h forward; 2½ to 3 m.p.h. reverse.

Final Drive: Double spur gear.

Belt Pulley: 22x8½; 600-700 r.p.m.

AVERY 25-50

Avery Power Machinery Co., Peoria, Ill.

AVERY 45-65
Avery Power Machinery Co., Peoria, Ill.

Traction Wheels: Four-wheel, driving from two rear wheels, 87½ x 24.

No. of Plows Recommended: Eight to ten 14-in.

Length: 215 in.; Width: 111½ in.; Height: 121 in.; Weight: 22000 lbs.

Turning Radius: 20½ ft.

Motor: Own; 7¾ x 8, opposed valve-in-head, 4 cylinders, cast en bloc.

Lubrication: Internal gear pump.

Carburetor: Kingston double, 2-in.

Ignition System: K-W high tension magneto.

Starting System: Impulse starter.

Cooling System: Cellular radiator, pump and fans.

Bearings: Own throughout.

Transmission: Spur gear, two speeds, 1¾ to 3⅓ m.p.h. forward; 1¾ to 2⅛ m.p.h. reverse.

Final Drive: Double spur gear.

Belt Pulley: 26x10; 500-600 r.p.m.

Traction Wheels: Four wheels; two traction in rear, 42x8; two non-drive in front, 28x5.

Weight: 5000 lbs.

Turning Radius: 10 ft.

Motor: Waukesha, 3½x4½, vertical, 4 cylinders, cast en bloc.

Lubrication: Full force feed.

Carburetor: Kingston.

Ignition System: High tension magneto with impulse starter.

Cooling System: Perfex cellular radiator.

Bearings: Anti-friction.

Transmission: Enclosed gear; three speeds; 1¾ to 4½ m.p.h. forward; 2½ m.p.h. reverse.

Final Drive: Enclosed double spur gear.

AVERY POWER ROAD MAINTAINER
Avery Power Machinery Co., Peoria, Ill.

The A. D. BAKER CO.

Swanton, Ohio

Baker 22-40

1926-1937

BAKER 22-40
The A. D. Baker Co., Swanton, Ohio.

Traction Wheels: Four wheels with two traction in rear, 54x14-18, and two non-drive in front, 36x6.

No. of Plows Recommended: Three to five 14-in.

Length: 153 in.; Width: 68 in.; Height: 71 in.; Weight: 7290 lbs.

Turning Radius: 14 ft.

Motor: Beaver, 4¾x6, vertical, 4 cylinders, cast in pairs.

Lubrication: Force feed.

Carburetor: Stromberg, 1¾-in.

Ignition System: Bosch high tension magneto with impulse starter.

Cooling System: Centrifugal pump, Automotive fan and Perfex radiator.

Bearings: Roller and ball.

Transmission: Sliding gear; 2 to 4 m.p.h. forward; 2 m.p.h. reverse.

Final Drive: Spur gear.

Belt Pulley: 15½x8½; 700 r.p.m and 2840 ft. per minute at normal engine speed.

BATES MANUFACTURING CO.
Joliet, Illinois

Bates Industrial 25
Bates Industrial 40

1926-1928
1926-1928

BATES INDUSTRIAL 25
Bates Manufacturing Co., Joliet, Ill.

Traction Wheels: Two crawlers full length of tractor, 11-in. wide and 78-in. long.
Length: 103 in.; **Width:** 60 in.; **Height:** 58 in.; **Weight:** 8000 lbs.
Turning Radius: 6 ft.
Motor: Beaver, 4½x6, valve-in-head, 4-cylinders, cast en bloc.
Lubrication: Force feed system.
Carburetor: Kingston.
Ignition System: High tension magneto.
Cooling System: Pump.
Bearings: Ball and roller.
Transmission: Sliding gear; 1.75 to 4.3 m.p.h. forward; 2 m.p.h. reverse.
Final Drive: Spur gear, enclosed and running in oil.

Traction Wheels: Two crawlers, 12 inches wide and 92 inches long.
Length: 122 in.; **Width:** 66 in.; **Height:** 66 in.; **Weight:** 11,000 lbs.
Turning Radius: 7 ft.
Motor: Waukeska, 5x6¼, L-head, 4-cylinders, cast in pairs.
Lubrication: Force feed.
Carburetor: Kingston.
Ignition System: High tension magneto.
Cooling System: Pump.
Bearings: Ball and roller.
Transmission: Sliding gear; 1.4 to 4½ m.p.h. forward; 3¼ m.p.h. reverse.
Final Drive: Spur gear, enclosed and running in oil.

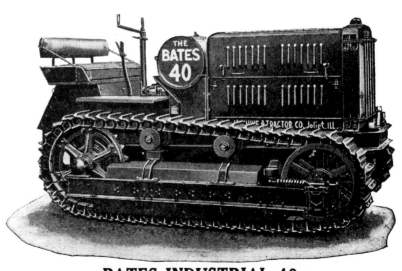

BATES INDUSTRIAL 40
Bates Manufacturing Co., Joliet, Ill.

BRYAN STEAM CORP.

Peru, Indiana

The Bryan steam tractor generated steam by burning kerosene or distillate and seems to be the only steam tractor designed and built for general field work. Production and sales efforts were limited and the company ceased production in 1930.

Bryan (Steam)

1926-1930

BRYAN (STEAM) 20 H.P. AT BELT
Bryan Steam Corporation, Peru, Ind.

Traction Wheels: Four wheels; two non-drive in front 32x6 and two traction in rear 52x12.
No. of Plows Recommended: Three 14 in.
Weight: 5500 lbs.
Turning Radius: 15 ft.
Engine: Stephenson Link valve gear, flyball governor, 2 cylinders, 4x5.
Lubrication: Cylinders by force feed; rear axle and engine as unit in oil.
Steam Generation System: Bryan water tube boiler; 600 lbs. working pressure; 1200 tested pressure; vaporizing burner; kerosene or distillate; 30 gallons fuel capacity; plunger pump; 60 gallons water capacity.
Bearings: Timken roller in front axle, Hyatt roller in rear axle.
Transmission: Own direct, ⅛ to 5 m.p.h. forward.
Differential: Allen self-locking.
Final Drive: Gear.
Belt Pulley: 24x6¾; 300 r.p.m.

The CENTRAL TRACTOR CO.

Greenwich, Ohio

Centaur 10

1926-1930

Traction Wheels: Steel.
No. of Plows Recommended: One 12-in.
Length: 60 in.; **Width:** 30 in.; **Height:** 38 in.; **Weight:** 1,220 lbs.; **Price:** $464.
Turning Radius: 9 ft.
Motor: Le Roi, 3⅛x4¼, vertical, 2 cylinders, cast en bloc.
Lubrication: Pump.
Carburetor: Zenith.
Ignition System: Eisemann, high tension magneto.
Cooling System: Thermo syphon.
Bearings: Bronze.
Final Drive: Chain.
Belt Pulley: 5¼x5; 800 to 1,600 r.p.m.

CENTAUR 10
The Central Tractor Co., Greenwich, Ohio

CENTAUR

An All-Purpose Farm Tractor
—Ideal for Crop Cultivating

THE CENTAUR TRACTOR literally has "the edge" on all competition. Here is a farm tractor that in addition to plowing, harrowing and seed bed preparation, adapts itself **perfectly** to the needs of **cultivating growing row crops of all kinds.**

The CENTAUR TRACTOR is **correctly** built for cultivating. It straddles a row or works between rows—and handles **one or two rows** at a time, thoroughly, quickly and more profitably than a team. Thousands of big-acreage farmers buy CENTAUR to use chiefly for this important operation, yet it can serve every power purpose from plowing to harvesting.

WRITE FOR COMPLETE LITERATURE

Get the facts about this low-priced farm tractor that has been making good for over eight years on thousands of farms. A postal will bring you our dealer proposition and details of our practical "customer finance" plan that makes sales easy. Let us hear from you today.

The Central Tractor Company

DEPT. 00.   GREENWICH, OHIO

HUBER MANUFACTURING CO.

Marion, Ohio

Huber Master Four 25-50   1926

Traction Wheels: Four wheels with two in rear, 60x16, giving traction and two non-drive in front, 38x7.

No. of Plows Recommended: Four 14-in.

Length: 147 in.; **Width:** 86 in.; **Height:** 66 in.; **Weight:** 8,500 lbs.; **Price:** $3,000.

Turning Radius: 10 ft.; **Acres Plowed in 10-hr. Day:** 15.

Motor: Hinkley, 5½x6, valve-in-head, 4 cylinders, cast in pairs.

Lubrication: Pressure through hollow crankshaft.

Carburetor: Zenith, 1¾ in.

Ignition System: Eisemann magneto with impulse starter.

Cooling System: Centrifugal pump, Perfex radiator and Automotive fan.

Bearings: Hyatt and Timken roller.

Transmission: Spur gear completely enclosed; live axle; 2 to 3.18 m.p.h. forward; 1.5 m.p.h. reverse.

Final Drive: Two bull gears on live axle enclosed in transmission case.

Belt Pulley: 13½x8; 1000 r.p.m and 3241 feet per minute at normal engine speed.

HUBER MASTER FOUR 25-50
Huber Manufacturing Co., Marion, Ohio.

JOHN LAUSON MANUFACTURING CO.
New Holstein, Wisconsin

Lauson 16-32   1926-1927
Lauson 20-35   1926-1929
Lauson 20-40   1926-1929

LAUSON 16-32
John Lauson Mfg. Co., New Holstein, Wis.

Traction Wheels: Four-wheel type; two drives in rear, 54x12, and two non-drive in front, 36x6.

No. of Plows Recommended: Three to four, 14-in.

Length: 126 in.; **Width:** 67 in.; **Height:** 63 in.; **Weight:** 5,400 lbs.

Turning Radius: 14 ft.

Motor: Lauson-Beaver, valve-in-head, 4 cylinders, cast en bloc.

Lubrication: Splash and force feed.

Carburetor: Kingston, 1¼-in.

Ignition System: Splitdorf high tension magneto.

Lighting Equipment: Bosch

Cooling System: Perfex radiator, centrifugal pump and Automotive fan.

Bearings: Hyatt and Timken in transmission.

Transmission: Selective gear; 2½ to 3½ m.p.h. forward; 2½ m.p.h. reverse.

Final Drive: Spur gears.

Belt Pulley: 16x7; 680 r.p.m.

Traction Wheels: Four wheels; two in rear, 54x12, giving traction.

No. of Plows Recommended: Four 14-in.

Length: 126 in.; **Width:** 64 in.; **Height:** 66 in.; **Weight:** 7,650 lbs.

Turning Radius: 14 ft.

Motor: Beaver, vertical, 4 cylinders, cast en bloc.

Lubrication: Splash and force feed.

Carburetor: Kingston, 1½-in.

Ignition System: Splitdorf high tension magneto.

Lighting Equipment: Bosch.

Cooling System: Perfex radiator, centrifugal pump and Automotive fan.

Transmission: Sliding gear; 2½ to 3½ m.p.h. forward; 2 m.p.h. reverse.

Final Drive: Spur gear.

Belt Pulley: 17½x8; 600 r.p.m.

LAUSON 20-35
John Lauson Mfg. Co., New Holstein, Wis.

LAUSON 20-40

John Lauson Mfg. Co., New Holstein, Wis.

Traction Wheels: Rear, traction, 54x16, 12 and 20 inch optional; front, non drive, 36x6.

Length: 148 in.; **Width:** 80 in.; **Height:** 72 in.; **Weight:** 8,100 lbs.

Turning Radius: 14 ft.

Motor: Beaver, vertical, 4 cylinders, cast in pairs.

Lubrication: Splash and force feed.

Carburetor: Kingston, 1½ in.

Ignition System: Splitdorf high tension magneto.

Lighting Equipment: Bosch.

Cooling System: Perfex cellular radiator, centrifugal pump and Automotive fan.

Bearings: Hyatt and Timken in transmission.

Transmission: Sliding gear, 2½ to 3½ m.p.h. forward; 2¼ m.p.h. reverse.

Final Drive: Spur gears.

Belt Pulley: 17½x8; 600 r.p.m.

MEAD-MORRISON MANUFACTURING CO.

East Boston, Massachusetts

Mead-Morrison "55"   1926-1929

MEAD-MORRISON "55"
Mead-Morrison Mfg. Co., East Boston, Mass.

Traction Wheels: Crawlers; flexible track; dry type.
No. of Plows Recommended: Four, 14-in.
Length: Open model, 124 in.; **Width:** 62 in.; **Height:** 63 in.; **Weight:** 9,100 lbs.
Turning Radius: 6 ft.; **Acres Plowed In 10-hr. Day:** 17.
Motor: Stearns, 4¾x6½, vertical, overhead valves, 4 cylinders, cast en bloc.
Lubrication: Pressure feed to all crankshaft, piston pin, camshaft and rocker shaft bearings.
Carburetor: Schebler, 1¾-in.
Ignition System: Bosch magneto with impulse starter.
Lighting Equipment: Open model, optional.
Cooling System: Spirex sectional radiator, pump circulation, 60 gal. per min., 24 in. fan and silent chain drive.
Bearings: Ball bearings throughout.
Transmission: Selective spur gear; three speeds and reverse; 2½ to 6¼ m.p.h. forward; 1¾ m.p.h. reverse.
Final Drive: Internal gear to track through driving sprocket.
Belt Pulley: 12x9; 1000 r.p.m. and 3140 feet per minute at normal engine speed.

MINNEAPOLIS THRESHING MACHINE CO.

Hopkins, Minnesota

Minneapolis 17-30 Type A   1926-1928
Minneapolis 17-30 Type B   1926-1928
Minneapolis 22-44   1926-1928
Minneapolis 35-70   1926-1928

Traction Wheels: Four wheels with two drive wheels in rear, 54x12.
Length: 132⅛ in.; **Width:** 75 in.; **Height:** 70½ in.; **Weight:** 6400 lbs.
Turning Radius: 13½ ft.
Motor: Own, 4¾x7, vertical, 4 cylinders, cast en bloc.
Lubrication: Mechanical oil pump and splash.
Carburetor: Schebler, 1½ in.
Ignition System: Bosch high tension.
Cooling System: Modine radiator, centrifugal pump and fan.
Bearings: Hyatt roller.
Transmission: Sliding spur gear, enclosed; approximate 2.35 to 3.09 m.p.h. forward; 2.26 m.p.h. reverse.
Final Drive: Internal gear and pinion.
Belt Pulley: 15½x7½; 825 r.p.m.

MINNEAPOLIS 17-30 TYPE A
Minneapolis Threshing Machine Co., Hopkins, Minn.

MINNEAPOLIS 17-30 TYPE B
Minneapolis Threshing Machine Co., Hopkins, Minn.

Traction Wheels: Four wheels with two in rear, 54x12, giving traction.

Length: 142½ in.; **Width:** 76½ in.; **Height:** 72 in.; **Weight:** 7300 lbs.

Turning Radius: 16 ft.

Motor: Own, 4⅞x7, vertical, 4 cylinders, cast en bloc.

Lubrication: Mechanical oil pump and splash.

Carburetor: Schebler, 1½ in.

Ignition System: Bosch high tension.

Cooling System: Modine tubular radiator, centrifugal pump and fan.

Bearings: Hyatt roller.

Transmission: Sliding spur gear, enclosed, approximate 2.35 to 3.09 m.p.h forward; 2.26 m.p.h. reverse.

Final Drive: Internal gear and pinion.

Belt Pulley: 15½x7½; 825 r.p.m.

Traction Wheels: Four wheels with two drive wheels in rear, 62x20.

Length: 168 in.; **Width:** 85 in.; **Height:** 113 in.; **Weight:** 12,410 lbs.

Turning Radius: 15¼ ft.

Motor: Own, 6x7, horizontal, 4 cylinders, cast in pairs.

Lubrication: Mechanical oil pump and splash.

Carburetor: Kingston, model E, 2 in.

Ignition System: Bosch high tension.

Cooling System: Modine tubular radiator, centrifugal pump and own fan.

Bearings: Plain.

Transmission: All spur gear; 2.6 to 1.98 m.p.h. forward; 1.98 m.p.h. reverse.

Final Drive: Spur gear and pinion.

Belt Pulley: 18½x10⅛; 700 r.p.m.

MINNEAPOLIS 22-44
Minneapolis Threshing Machine Co., Hopkins, Minn.

MINNEAPOLIS 35-70
Minneapolis Threshing Machine Co., Hopkins, Minn.

Traction Wheels: Four wheels; two in rear, 84x30 giving traction.

Length: 207 in.; **Width:** 122 in.; **Height:** 136 in.; **Weight:** 22,500 lbs.

Turning Radius: 20 1/6 ft.

Motor: Own, 7¼x9, horizontal, 4 cylinders, cast in pairs.

Lubrication: Mechanical oil pump and splash.

Carburetor: Kingston, 2½ in.

Ignition System: Bosch high tension.

Cooling System: Own radiator, centrifugal pump and own fan.

Bearings: Plain.

Transmission: All spur gear; 2.45 to 2 m.p.h. forward; 1.68 m.p.h. reverse.

Final Drive: Spur gear and pinion.

Belt Pulley: 24x10¼; 550 r.p.m.

YUBA MANUFACTURING CO.
San Francisco, California

Yuba Ball Tread 25-40   1926-1931

Traction Wheels: Two crawlers in rear; one front wheel.

No. of Plows Recommended: Six 14-in.

Length: 186 in.; **Width:** 73½ in.; **Height:** 61 in.; **Weight:** 9610 lbs.

Turning Radius: 9¼ ft.

Motor: Yuba "Y," 5¼x7; vertical, 4 cylinders, cast in pairs.

Carburetor: Stromberg, 1¼ in.

Ignition System: Bosch high tension magneto.

Lighting: K-W system.

Cooling System: Fan, pump and Modine radiator.

Bearings: Hyatt roller in transmission.

Transmission: Sliding gear, 2.2 to 3¼ m.p.h forward.

Final Drive: Internal gear.

Belt Pulley: 10, 12 or 14x8½, optional.

YUBA BALL TREAD 25-40
Yuba Mfg. Co., San Francisco, Cal.

Schaefer Automatic
(One-Man) Tractor Scraper

SIMPLE – SAFE – STRONG

A good earth-moving tool sold and used extensively the world over since 1921 for Laying-out Allotments, Roads, Parks, Cemeteries, Ball, Golf and Aeroplane Fields, Digging Cellars and Ponds, Leveling Hills and Beaches, Grading around new Schools, Filling Trenches. In Brickyards, Potteries, Fisheries, Etc.

Utilizes draw-bar-pull to best advantage. Requires only a coupling pin to attach it to tractor. **Workmen's Favorite** because it is easily controlled direct from tractor seat. Does more work than several horse-drawn outfits can do. Requires only one man.

Two sizes for light tractors. Five foot width (best seller) hauls in and ahead of bowl (varying with soil conditions) about 16 cubic feet of earth. Four foot size (about 13 cubic feet), recommended to parties who have not used tractors before, and to those who operate under unusual conditions. Two more sizes, six foot and seven foot wide, available for large powerful tractors.

Strong, simple construction. Has but few parts. They are well made. The scraper is specially braced for tractor use. It has high carbon steel blade and reversible shoes.

Correct Assembly

Operation: Slight pull on loading rope tilts blade into ground and loads scraper rapidly. Pulling trip lever forward releases catch and permits tractor to dump the scraper. Earth may be spread instead of dumped by engaging trip lever against either of two extra stops in draw bar. Empty scraper returns on its shoes and falls into loading position again when tractor is backed two feet.

— This tool has merit —

The Gustav Schaefer Wagon Co.
Vehicle Builders Since 1880

4180 Lorain Ave.,   Cleveland, Ohio, U. S. A.

1927

The 1927 list shows 16 models of nine makes not included in the 1926 list. Tractors listed in 1926 may remain current and will not be repeated.

This time period also saw rapid growth in the use of the automobile and a need for better roads in rural areas. The farm equipment industry saw this need and made an effort to satisfy it by designing and building road machinery. The market was not large, but was important to the economy and filled a supply niche until a separate construction machinery market was established.

J. I. CASE PLOW WORKS, INC.

Racine, Wisconsin

Wallis "Certified" 15-27
Wallis Certified Orchard

1927
1927-1928

Traction Wheels: Four wheels with two traction in rear, 48x12, and two non-drive in front, 30x8.

No. of Plows Recommended: Three 14-in.

Length: 132 in.; **Width:** 61 in.; **Height:** 55 in.; **Weight:** 4,096 lbs.

Turning Radius: 14 ft.

Motor: Own, 4⅜x5¾, valve-in-head, 4 cylinders, cast en bloc.

Lubrication: Circulating-splash.

Carburetor: Kingston.

Ignition System: Bosch high tension magneto, with Wallis impulse starter.

Cooling System: Modine tubular radiator, centrifugal pump and fan.

Bearings: New Departure and Timken throughout.

Transmission: Selective sliding gear, 2¾ to 3⅓ m.p.h. forward; 2¾ m.p.h. reverse.

Final Drive: Spur gear.

Belt Pulley: 18½x7; 475 r. p. m. and 2,300 feet per minute at normal engine speed.

WALLIS "CERTIFIED" 15-27

J. I. Case Plow Work, Inc., Racine, Wis.

WALLIS "CERTIFIED" ORCHARD
J. I. Case Plow Work, Inc., Racine, Wis.

Traction Wheels: Four wheels; two in rear, 42x12, giving traction, and two in front, 28x6¼.

No. of Plows Recommended: Three 14-in.

Length: 127 in.; **Width:** 56 in.; **Height:** 50 in.; **Weight:** 3900 lbs.

Turning Radius: 13 ft.

Motor: Own; $4\frac{3}{8}x5\frac{3}{4}$, valve-in-head, 4 cylinders, cast en bloc.

Lubrication: Circulating splash.

Carburetor: Kingston.

Ignition System: Bosch high tension magneto with Wallis impulse starter.

Cooling System: Modine tubular radiator, centrifugal pump and fan.

Bearings: New Departure and Timken throughout.

Transmission: Selective sliding gear; 2.4 to 3.5 m.p.h. forward; 2.4 m.p.h. reverse.

Final Drive: Spur gear.

CATERPILLAR TRACTOR CO.

Peoria, Illinois and San Leandro, California

The Caterpillar Tractor Company was formed in 1925 by the merger of the C. L. Best Tractor Co. of San Leandro, California, and Holt Manufacturing Company of Stockton, California. The company's headquarters were moved to C. L. Best's facilities in Peoria, Illinois.

Caterpillar Thirty	1927-1928
Caterpillar Sixty	1927-1928

Traction Wheels: Two crawlers, 13x68.

No. of Plows Recommended: Four or five 14-in.

Length: 129 in.; **Width:** $59\frac{3}{8}$ in.; **Height:** $58\frac{3}{4}$ in.; **Weight:** 9,115 lbs.; **Price:** $3,000.

Turning Radius: 9 ft.

Motor: Own, $4\frac{3}{4}x6\frac{1}{2}$, vertical, 4 cylinders, cast singly.

Lubrication: Force feed.

Carburetor: Ensign.

Ignition System: Bosch.

Lighting Equipment: Robert Bosch, extra.

Cooling System: Pump.

Bearings: Largely ball and roller, antifriction.

Transmission: Sliding gear, 1.75 to 3.62 m.p.h. forward; 2 m.p.h reverse.

Final Drive: Machine cut gears enclosed in oil bath.

Belt Pulley: 12x8; 850 r.p.m. and 2670 feet per minute at normal engine speed.

"CATERPILLAR" THIRTY
Caterpillar Tractor Co.,
Peoria, Ill., and San Leandro, Cal.

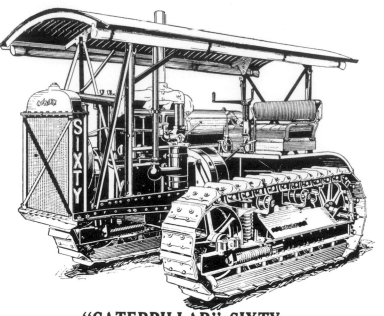

"CATERPILLAR" SIXTY
Caterpillar Tractor Co.,
Peoria, Ill., and San Leandro, Cal.

Traction Wheels: Two crawlers, each 89x16 or 20.

No. of Plows Recommended: Eight to ten 14-in.

Length: 152½ in.; Width: 95 in.; Height: 78 in.; Weight: 19,095 lbs.; Price: $5,000.

Turning Radius: 15 ft.

Motor: Own, 6½x8½ vertical, 4 cylinders, cast singly.

Lubrication: Force feed.

Carburetor: Ensign.

Ignition System: Bosch magneto.

Lighting Equipment: Robert Bosch, extra.

Cooling System: Pump.

Bearings: Largely ball or roller anti-friction.

Transmission: Sliding gear, 1.93 to 3.63 m.p.h. forward and 1.35 m.p.h. reverse.

Final Drive: Machine cut gears, enclosed in oil bath.

Belt Pulley: 16x10; 650 r.p.m. and 2640 feet per minute at normal engine speed.

CLEVELAND TRACTOR CO.

Cleveland, Ohio

Cletrac Model 20K 20-27   1927
Cletrac Model 30A 30-45   1927

CLETRAC MODEL 20K 20-27
Cleveland Tractor Co., Cleveland, O.

Traction: One crawler on each side, 60x9½.

No. of Plows Recommended: Three 14-in.

Length: 99 in.; Width: 48½ in.; Height: 52 in.; Weight: 4390 lbs.

Turning Radius: 9 ft.; Acres Plowed in 10-hr. Day: 10 to 12.

Motor: Own, 4x5½, valve-in-head, 4 cylinders, cast en bloc.

Lubrication: Force feed to crankshaft and connecting rods.

Carburetor: Tillotson, 1¼-in.

Ignition System: Eisemann high tension magneto.

Cooling System: Water pump circulation.

Bearings: Three bronze back babbitt lined on crankshaft.

Transmission: Selective gear; 2¼ to 4½ m.p.h. forward; 1.66 m.p.h. reverse.

Final Drive: Internal gear and pinion.

Belt Pulley: 12x6½; 860 r.p.m. and 2700 feet per minute at normal engine speed.

Traction: One crawler on each side, 70x13.

No. of Plows Recommended: Four 14-in.

Length: 108½ in.; **Width:** 57 in.; **Height:** 57 in.

Turning Radius: 10 ft. 6 in.; **Acres Plowed in 10-hr. Day:** 12 to 14.

Motor: Wisconsin, 4x5, valve-in-head, 6 cylinders, cast en bloc.

Lubrication: Force feed to crankshaft, connecting rods and valve rockers.

Carburetor: Tillotson, 1½ in.

Ignition System: Eisemann high tension magneto.

Cooling System: Water pump circulation.

Bearings: Four bronze back babbitt lined on crankshaft.

Transmission: Selective gear; 2½ to 4¾ m.p.h. forward; 1¾ m.p.h. reverse.

Final Drive: Internal gear and pinion.

Belt Pulley: 15x8½; 690 r.p.m. and 2700 feet per minute at normal engine speed.

CLETRAC MODEL 30A 30-45
Cleveland Tractor Co., Cleveland, O.

ELECTRIC WHEEL CO.

Quincy, Illinois

EWC 5-Ton	1927
EWC "80"	1927

Traction Wheels: Two full length crawlers, each 77-in. ground contact, 12-in. wide.

No. of Plows Recommended: Five to six 14-in.

Length: 124 in.; **Width:** 62 in.; **Height:** 60 in.; **Weight:** 10,102 lbs.

Turning Radius: 7 ft.; **Acres Plowed in 10-hr. Day:** 18 to 21.

Motor: Own, 5¼x6, vertical, 4 cylinders, cast singly.

Lubrication: Full force feed.

Carburetor: Zenith, 1½-in.

Ignition System: Bosch high tension magneto.

Starting and Lighting Equipment: Special equipment.

Cooling System: Radiator, centrifugal pump and fan.

Bearings: Ball and roller.

Transmission: Selective sliding gear; 1.95, 2.9 and 4.4 m.p.h. forward; 2.6 m.p.h. reverse.

Final Drive: Enclosed spur gear.

Belt Pulley: 13¾x7½; 900 r.p.m. and 3000 feet per minute at normal engine speed.

EWC 5-TON
Electric Wheel Co., Quincy, Ill.

EWC "80"
Electric Wheel Co., Quincy, Ill.

Traction Wheels: Two crawlers, each 94-in. ground contact by 16-in. wide.
No. of Plows Recommended: Ten to twelve, 14-in.
Length: 162 in.; **Width:** 90 in.; **Height:** 90 in.; **Weight:** 2,100 lbs.
Turning Radius: 8½ ft.
Motor: Waukesha, 6¾x8, vertical, 4 cylinders, cast in pairs.
Lubrication: Force feed.
Carburetor: Stromberg.
Ignition System: Bosch.
Starting and Lighting Equipment: Extra.
Cooling System: Pump, radiator and fan.
Bearings: Roller and ball anti-friction.
Transmission: Sliding gear; 1.8 to 3.7 m.p.h. forward; 1.7 m.p.h. reverse.
Final Drive: Gears enclosed in oil.
Belt Pulley: Extra.

HART-PARR CO.

Charles City, Iowa

The Hart-Parr Co. is credited with building the first tractor manufacturing plant, and by some with coining the word "tractor," the steam threshing engines of former years being referred to as "traction engines."

Hart-Parr 18-36	1927-1928
Hart-Parr 28-50	1927-1928

Traction Wheels: Four-wheel tractor, with two drive members, 52 x 12, in rear.
No. of Plows Recommended: Three or four 14 to 16-in.
Length: 126 in.; **Width:** 73 in.; **Height:** 61 in.; **Weight:** 6,250 lbs.
Turning Radius: 12 ft.; **Acres Plowed in 10-hr. Day:** 12 to 15.
Motor: Own; 6¾x7; horizontal, 2 cylinders, cast en bloc.
Lubrication: Madison-Kipp force feed lubricator.
Carburetor: Schebler, 1½-in.
Ignition System: Robert Bosch high tension magneto with impulse starter.
Lighting Equipment: To order.
Cooling System: Radiator, centrifugal pump and fan.
Bearings: Roller and ball in transmission and own on drive axle.
Transmission: Selective, sliding spur gear, 2 to 3 m.p.h forward; 2 m.p.h. reverse.
Final Drive: External gear, enclosed.
Belt Pulley: 14x9; 800 r.p.m. and 2,930 feet per minute at normal engine speed.

HART-PARR 18-36
Hart-Parr Co., Charles City, Ia.

HART-PARR 28-50
Hart-Parr Co., Charles City, Ia.

Traction Wheels: Four wheels; two in front, 28x7; two traction in rear, 51⅛x14.

No. of Plows Recommended: Five 14 or 16 in.

Length: 135 in.; **Width:** 88 in.; **Height:** 64½ in.; **Weight,** 18,750 lbs.

Motor: Own, 5¾x6½; horizontal, 4 cylinder, cast in pairs.

Lubrication: Madison-Kipp force feed.

Carburetor: Schebler, 1½ in.

Ignition System: Robert Bosch high tension magneto with impulse starter.

Cooling System: Centrifugal pump, fan and radiator.

Bearings: Roller and ball in transmission and own on drive axle.

Transmission: Selective, sliding spur gear, 2¼ to 3¼ m.p.h. forward; 1⅓ m.p.h. reverse.

Final Drive: Internal gear and master pinions.

Belt Pulley: 14x9; 850 r.p.m. and 3,170 feet per minute at normal engine speed.

HUBER MANUFACTURING CO.

Marion, Ohio

Huber Super Four 20-40	1927-1928
Huber Super Four 25-50	1927-1928

HUBER SUPER FOUR 20-40
Huber Manufacturing Co., Marion. O.

Traction Wheels: Four wheel type; two traction in rear, 56x18.

No. of Plows Recommended: Four 14-in.

Length: 160 in.; **Width:** 84 in.; **Height:** 62 in.; **Weight:** 8,900 lbs.

Turning Radius: 14 ft.; **Acres Plowed in 10-hr. Day:** 15.

Motor: Stearns, 5⅛x6½, overhead valves, 4 cylinders, cast en bloc.

Lubrication: Force feed.

Carburetor: Kingston, 1½-in.

Ignition System: Eisemann high tension magneto with impulse starter.

Cooling System: Perfex radiator.

Bearings: Hyatt and Timken.

Transmission: Selective gears; 2.4 to 3.2 m.p.h. forward; 2 m.p.h. reverse.

Final Drive: Enclosed spur gear, live axle.

Belt Pulley: 15½x8; 666 r.p.m. and 2,677 feet per minute at normal engine speed.

Traction Wheels: Four wheel type; two traction in rear, 56x20.
No. of Plows Recommended: Four to six 14-in.
Length: 160 in.; Width: 88 in.; Height: 62 in.; Weight: 9,200 lbs.
Turning Radius: 14 ft.; Acres Plowed in 10-hr. Day: 15 to 20.
Motor: Stearns, 5½x6½, overhead valves, 4 cylinders, cast en bloc.
Lubrication: Force feed.
Carburetor: Kingston, 1¾-in.
Ignition System: Eisemann high tension magneto with impulse starter.
Cooling System: Perfex radiator.
Bearings: Hyatt and Timken.
Transmission: Selective gears; 2.4 to 3.2 m.p.h. forward; 2 m.p.h. reverse.
Final Drive: Enclosed spur gear, live axle.
Belt Pulley: 15½x8; 666 r.p.m. and 2,677 feet per minute at normal engine speed.

HUBER SUPER FOUR 25-50
Huber Manufacturing Co., Marion, O.

INTERNATIONAL HARVESTER CO. OF AMERICA
Chicago, Illinois

In 1906, McCormick Harvester Co. began tractor production by installing their own one-cylinder engine on a "Morton Manufacturing Co." frame and drive gear. Then in 1907, began work on the "Mogul" tractor line. McCormick and Deering established their own dealer organizations before the "IH" merger, and separate tractor lines were made; "Mogul" for McCormick and "Titan" for Deering.

The International Harvester Co. at this time was the largest farm equipment company and tractor manufacturer in the country. They built the first tractors equipped with power take-off and the first truly general purpose farm tractor, the Farmall line.

McCormick-Deering Farmall   1927-1934

McCORMICK-DEERING FARMALL
International Harvester Co. of America, Chicago, Ill.

Traction Wheels: Four wheel type; two traction in rear, 40x6.
No. of Plows Recommended: Two 14-in.
Length: 123 in.; Width: 86 in.; Height: 67 in.; Weight: 3,650 lbs.
Turning Radius: 8 ft.
Motor: Own, 3¾x5, vertical, valve-in-head, 4 cylinders, cast en bloc.
Lubrication: Splash circulating.
Carburetor: Ensign.
Ignition System: International high tension magneto.
Cooling System: Thermo-syphon.
Bearings: Own make roller in transmission and rear axle.
Transmission: Selective; 2, 3 and 4 m.p.h. forward; 2¾ m.p.h. reverse.
Final Drive: Spur gear.
Belt Pulley: 14x6½; 693 r.p.m. and 2,540 feet per minute at normal engine speed.

McCORMICK-DEERING "FARMALL"
International Harvester Co. of Am., Chicago, Ill.

As You'd Expect

The valves that last longest and cause least trouble in a tractor are the ones that do those very same things in airplanes, automobiles, trucks, motorcycles and speedboats.

Both as original equipment, and also for replacement, Thompson Valves lead all others in all six fields.

Thompson Valves

MINNEAPOLIS STEEL & MACHINERY CO.
Minneapolis, Minnesota

Twin City 17-28   1927-1929
Twin City 27-44   1927-1929

Traction Wheels: Four wheels, two in rear, 50x12, giving traction.

No. of Plows Recommended: Three 14-in.

Length: 134 in.; **Width:** 63 in.; **Height:** 63½ in.; **Weight:** 5,050 lbs.

Turning Radius: 12½ ft.

Motor: Own make, 4 cylinders, 4¼x6, vertical, cast en bloc, removable sleeve.

Lubrication: Pressure feed.

Carburetor: Holley or Schebler, 1¼ in.

Ignition System: Bosch high tension magneto with impulse coupling.

Cooling System: Modine radiator, centrifugal pump and fan.

Bearings: Hyatt roller throughout.

Transmission: Sliding gear; 2.2 to 2.9 m.p.h. forward.

Final Drive: Enclosed spur gear.

Belt Pulley: 16x6½; 650 r.p.m. and 2720 f.p.m. at normal engine speed.

TWIN CITY 17-28
Minneapolis Steel & Machinery Co., Minneapolis, Minn.

TWIN CITY 27-44
Minneapolis Steel & Machinery Co., Minneapolis, Minn.

Traction Wheels: Four wheels; two drivers in rear, 60x20.

No. of Plows Recommended: Five to six, 14-in.

Length: 152 in.; **Width:** 88 in.; **Height:** 73 in.; **Weight:** 8,550 lbs.

Turning Radius: 15 ft.

Motor: Own, 5½x6¾, vertical, valve-in-head, 4 cylinders, cast en bloc, removable sleeve.

Lubrication: Pressure feed.

Carburetor: Schebler 1½ in.

Ignition System: Bosch high tension magneto with impulse starter.

Cooling System: Modine tubular radiator, centrifugal pump and fan.

Bearings: Hyatt throughout.

Transmission: Sliding gear, 2.2 and 2.9 m.p.h. forward; 1.85 m.p.h. reverse.

Final Drive: Enclosed spur gear.

Belt Pulley: 21x8½; 466 r.p.m. and 2560 feet per minute at normal engine speed.

TOWNSEND TRACTOR CO.
Janesville, Wisconsin

Townsend 12-20   1927-1928

Traction Wheels: Four wheels; two in rear, 45x10, giving traction and two non-drive in front, 25x5.

No. of Plows Recommended: Two to three, 14-in.

Length: 112 in.; **Width:** 54 in.; **Height:** 54 in.; **Weight:** 4000 lbs.

Turning Radius: 8 ft.

Motor: Own, 6x8, horizontal, valve-in-head, 2 cylinder.

Lubrication: Force feed oiler.

Carburetor: Own, 2¼ in.

Ignition System: High tension magneto.

Starting and Lighting Equipment: Extra.

Cooling System: Radiator.

Bearings: Plain babbitt.

Transmission: Spur gear; 2½ to 3½ m.p.h. forward; 2 m.p.h. reverse.

Final Drive: Spur gear.

Belt Pulley: 14x7; 475 to 600 r.p.m.

TOWNSEND 12-20
Townsend Tractor Co., Janesville, Wis.

The 1928 list shows 25 models of 13 makes.

ADVANCE-RUMELY THRESHER CO., INC.

La Porte, Indiana

Do All 19.6	1928-1930
Oilpull "W" 20-30	1928-1931
Oilpull "X" 25-40	1928-1931
Oilpull "Y" 30-50	1928-1931
Oilpull "Z" 40-60	1928-1929

Traction Wheels: Four wheels with two in rear, 42x7, giving traction and two non-drive in front, 26x5.

No. of Plows Recommended: Two, 14-in.

Length: 110 in.; **Width:** 82 in.; **Height:** 64 in.; **Weight:** 3,000 lbs.

Turning Radius: 10 ft.; **Acres Plowed in 10-hr. day:** 6.

Motor: Waukesha, $3\frac{1}{2}$x$4\frac{1}{2}$, vertical, L-head, 4 cylinders, cast en bloc.

Lubrication: Pressure.

Carburetor: Zenith, 1-in.

Ignition System: High tension magneto with impulse starter.

Cooling System: Thermo-syphon.

Bearings: Three bearings 2 inches in diameter and 7 inches long.

Transmission: Sliding gear; $2\frac{5}{8}$ to $3\frac{3}{4}$ m.p.h. forward; $2\frac{7}{8}$ m.p.h. reverse.

Final Drive: Enclosed spur gear.

Belt Pulley: 10x$5\frac{1}{2}$; 1,200 r.p.m. and 3,146 feet per minute at normal engine speed.

DO ALL 19.6

Advance-Rumely Thresher Co., Inc., La Porte, Ind.

Traction Wheels: Four wheels, with two in rear, 46x12, giving traction and two non-drive in front, 30x5½.

No. of Plows Recommended: Three 14-in.

Length: 136 in.; **Width:** 55¾ in.; **Height:** 90½ in.

Turning Radius: 15 ft.

Motor: Own; 5⅛x7, horizontal; valve-in-head, 2 cylinders, removable sleeve.

Lubrication: Mechanical oiler and splash.

Carburetor: Own—Secor Higgins, 2⅛ in.

Ignition System: High tension magneto.

Starting: Mechanical.

Cooling System: Pump circulation; oil in system.

Bearings: New Departure, Timken and bronze.

Transmission: Spur gear; 2.2, 2.9 and 3.5 m. p. h. forward; 2.7 m. p. h. reverse.

Final Drive: Spur gear—enclosed in transmission.

Belt Pulley: 16x7½; 825 to 850 r.p.m. and 3400 feet per minute at 825 r.p.m.

OILPULL "W" 20-30
Advance-Rumely Thresher Co., Inc., La Porte, Ind.

Traction Wheels: Two drive wheels in rear, 52x16, and two non-drive in front, 34x7.

No. of Plows Recommended: Four 14-in.

Length: 151 in.; **Width:** 71½ in.; **Height:** 101 in.

Turning Radius: 17 ft.

Motor: Own; 6⅛x8¼, horizontal, valve-in-head, 2 cylinders, removable sleeve.

Lubrication: Mechnical oiler and splash.

Carburetor: Own—Secor Higgins, 2¼ in.

Ignition System: High tension magneto.

Starting Equipment: Mechanical.

Cooling System: Pump circulation; oil in system.

Bearings: New Departure, Timken and bronze.

Transmission: Spur gear; 2.3, 2.9 and 3.5 m. p. h. forward; 2.9 m. p. h. reverse.

Final Drive: Spur gear enclosed in transmission.

Belt Pulley: 18¾x8½; 700 to 725 r.p.m. and 3400 feet per minute at 700 r.p.m.

OILPULL "X" 25-40
Advance-Rumely Thresher Co., Inc., La Porte, Ind.

OILPULL "Y" 30-50
Advance-Rumely Thresher Co., Inc., La Porte, Ind.

Traction Wheels: Four wheels with two in rear, 57½x18, giving traction and two non-drive in front, 38½x8.

No. of Plows Recommended: Five to six 14-in.

Length: 167 in.; **Width:** 82 in.; **Height:** 107 in.

Turning Radius: 19 ft.

Motor: Own, 7⅛x9½, horizontal, valve-in-head, 2 cylinders, removable sleeve.

Lubrication: Mechanical oiler and splash.

Carburetor: Own, 2⁹⁄₁₆ in.

Ignition System: High tension.

Cooling System: Pump circulation; oil in system.

Bearings: New Departure, Timken roller and bronze.

Transmission: Spur gear; 2.3, 2.9 and 3.5 m. p. h. forward; 2.9 m. p. h. reverse.

Final Drive: Spur gear enclosed in transmission.

Belt Pulley: 21¾x10; 610 to 635 r.p.m. and 3400 feet per minute at 610 r.p.m.

Traction Wheels: Four wheel type; two in rear, 64x24, giving traction and two in front, 44x10.

No. of Plows Recommended: Eight to ten 14-in.

Length: 191 in.; Width: 100 in.; Height: 114½ in.

Turning Radius: 22 ft.

Motor: Own; 9x11, horizontal, valve-in-head, 2 cylinders, removable sleeve.

Lubrication: Mechanical oiler and splash.

Carburetor: Own—Secor Higgins, 2¾ in.

Ignition System: High tension magneto.

Starting Equipment: Mechanical.

Cooling System: Pump circulation; oil in system.

Bearings: New Departure, Timken and bronze.

Transmission: Spur gear; 2, 2½ and 3 m. p. h. forward; 2½ m. p. h. reverse.

Final Drive: Spur gear enclosed in transmission.

Belt Pulley: 25x10; 470 r.p.m. and 3000 feet per minute at normal engine speed.

OILPULL "Z" 40-60
Advance-Rumely Thresher Co., Inc., La Porte, Ind.

ATLAS ENGINEERING CO.
Clintonville, Wisconsin

Atlas 30-45

1928

ATLAS 30-45
Atlas Engineering Co., Clintonville, Wis.

Traction Wheels: Four wheel drive; two in front and two in rear, 42x12.

No. of Plows Recommended: Four to six 14 in.

Length: 100 in.; Width: 64 in.; Height: 77 in.; Weight: 8,500 lbs.

Turning Radius: 11 ft.

Motor: Waukesha, 4¾x6¾, 4 cylinders, cast in pairs.

Lubrication: Force feed and splash.

Carburetor: Stromberg M-3, 1½ in.

Ignition System: Eisemann high tension magneto with impulse starter.

Cooling System: Fan, pump and radiator.

Bearings: Timken in wheels; Hyatt in transmission.

Transmission: Sliding gear; 1½ to 5 m.p.h. forward.

Final Drive: Gear.

Belt Pulley: 14x8; 950 r.p.m. and 2600 feet per minute at normal engine speed.

The A. D. BAKER CO.
Swanton, Ohio

Baker 25-50   1928-1937

Traction Wheels: Tour wheels; two traction in rear, 61x18 and two non-drive in front, 39x8.

Length: 159 in.; **Width:** 78 in.; **Height:** 79 in.; **Weight:** 9200 lbs.

Turning Radius: 16 ft.

Motor: Wisconsin, 5½x6½, vertical, valve-in-head, 4 cylinders, cast en bloc.

Lubrication: Full pressure system.

Carburetor: Stromberg, 1½ in.

Ignition System: American Bosch high tension magneto with impulse coupling.

Cooling System: Modine tubular radiator.

Bearings: Hyatt.

Transmission: Enclosed sliding gear, 2 to 3½ m. p. h. forward; 2½ m. p. h. reverse.

Final Drive: Spur gear.

Belt Pulley: 15½x8½; 700-845 r.p.m. and 2840-3422 feet per minute at normal engine speed.

BAKER 25-50
The A. D. Baker Co., Swanton, Ohio.

MILLARD'S IMPLEMENT SERVICE

Millard's Implement Service was established in 1885 and is the oldest and best farm machinery guide in the United States. It lists farm machinery manufacturers throughout the United States, and all jobbers West of the Mississippi river, indicating the lines handled. Millard's is given free to subscribers to the Implement & Hardware Trade Journal at $2.00 per year.

J. I. CASE PLOW WORKS, INC.

Racine, Wisconsin

"America's Foremost Tractor"

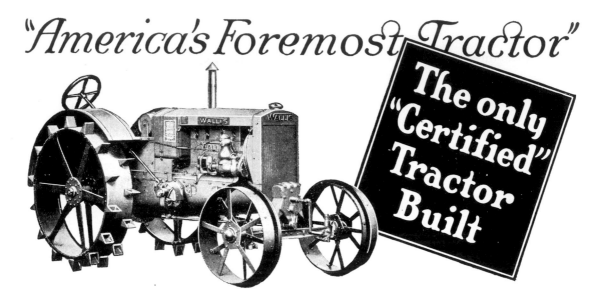

The only "Certified" Tractor Built

WALLIS 20-30 TRACTOR *Certified*

delivers

More Power
for
More Years
and at
Less Expense

—than any other tractor approaching it in Weight and Piston Displacement. 3 plow power, 2 plow weight.

Every Wallis Tractor built in 1927 is "Certified"—bears the signed statement of those responsible for its manufacture that from raw materials to the shipping platform high Wallis standards have been maintained to the letter.

The "Certified" Wallis is the product of development and refinement through 12 years of field service. Wallis manufacturers have directed their energies to building this one type Tractor better and better. The Wallis is recognized as "America's Foremost Tractor."

J. I. CASE PLOW WORKS, Inc.
RACINE, WISCONSIN

Write today for our 1927 Catalog. Learn why you can make more for the effort expended with the Wallis franchise. Some valuable territories still open.

NOTICE: We want the public to know that the WALLIS TRACTOR is built by the J. I. CASE PLOW WORKS, Inc., of Racine, Wisconsin, and is not the product of any other company with "J. I. CASE" as part of its corporate name.

CATERPILLAR TRACTOR CO.

Peoria, Illinois and San Leandro, California

Caterpillar Twenty   1928-1933

Traction Wheels: Two self-laying tracks; 63 in. ground contact; 11 in. wide.
No. of Plows Recommended: Four 14-in.
Length: 115.5 in.; **Width:** 61 in.; **Height:** 60.5 in.; **Weight:** 7,000 lbs.; **Price:** $2,175.
Turning Radius: 10 ft.
Motor: Own, 4x5½, vertical, 4 cylinders, cast singly.
Lubrication: Pressure oiling system.
Carburetor: Ensign.
Ignition System: Eisemann high tension magneto.
Starting and Lighting Equipment: Robert Bosch, extra.
Cooling System: Pump.
Bearings: Largely anti-friction ball and roller.
Transmission: Sliding gear; 1.79 to 4.67 m. p. h. forward; 2.26 m. p. h. reverse.
Final Drive: Machine cut gears enclosed in oil bath.
Belt Pulley: 11½x6½; 1,100 r.p.m. and 3,315 feet per minute at normal engine speed.

"CATERPILLAR" TWENTY
Caterpillar Tractor Co.,
Peoria, Ill., and San Leandro, Calif.

Caterpillar Tractors
For Roadbuilding, Logging and Farming

CLEVELAND TRACTOR CO.

Cleveland, Ohio

Cletrac Model 20 20-27	1928-1931
Cletrac Model 30 30-45	1928-1930
Cletrac "40"	1928-1931
Cletrac "100"	1928-1931

Traction: One crawler on each side, 60x9½.

No. of Plows Recommended: Three 14-in.

Length: 99 in.; Width: 48½ in.; Height: 52 in.; Weight: 4,889 lbs.

Turning Radius: 9 ft.; Acres Plowed in 10-hr. Day: 10 to 12.

Motor: Own, 4x5½, valve-in-head, 4 cylinders, cast en bloc.

Lubrication: Force feed to crankshaft and connecting rods.

Carburetor: Tillotson, 1¼-in.

Ignition System: Eisemann high tension magneto.

Cooling System: Water pump circulation.

Bearings: Three bronze back babbitt lined on crankshaft.

Transmission: Selective gear; 2¼ to 4½ m.p.h. forward; 1.66 m.p.h. reverse.

Final Drive: Internal gear and pinion.

Belt Pulley: 12x6½; 860 r.p.m. and 2700 feet per minute at normal engine speed.

CLETRAC MODEL 20 20-27

Cleveland Tractor Co., Cleveland, O.

Traction: One crawler on each side, 70x13.

No. of Plows Recommended: Four 14-in.

Length: 108½ in.; Width: 57 in.; Height: 57 in.

Turning Radius: 10 ft. 6 in.; Acres Plowed in 10-hr. Day: 12 to 14.

Motor: Wisconsin, 4x5, valve-in-head, 6 cylinders, cast en bloc.

Lubrication: Force feed to crankshaft, connecting rods and valve rockers.

Carburetor: Tillotson, 1½ in.

Ignition System: Eisemann high tension magneto.

Cooling System: Water pump circulation.

Bearings: Four bronze back babbitt lined on crankshaft.

Transmission: Selective gear; 2½ to 4¾ m.p.h. forward; 1¾ m.p.h. reverse.

Final Drive: Internal gear and pinion.

Belt Pulley: 15x8½; 690 r.p.m. and 2700 feet per minute at normal engine speed.

CLETRAC MODEL 30 30-45

Cleveland Tractor Co., Cleveland, O.

Traction Wheels: One crawler on each side, 80x14.

No. of Plow Recommended: Six to eight, 14-in.

Length: 132 in.; Width: 69 in.; Height: 63 in.; Weight: 11,300 lbs.; Price: $3,985.

Turning Radius: 11 ft.

Motor: Wisconsin, 4½x5, valve-in-head, 6 cylinders, cast en bloc.

Lubrication: Force feed to crankshaft, connecting rods and valve rockers.

Carburetor: Schebler, 1¾ in.

Ignition System: Battery, coil and distributor.

Starting and Lighting Equipment: Delco Remy.

Cooling System: Water with pump circulation.

Bearings: Bronze backed, babbitt lined.

Transmission: Selective, sliding gear; 2 to 5.5 m.p.h. forward; 2 m.p.h. reverse.

Final Drive: Internal gear and pinion.

Belt Pulley: 15x13; 855 r.p.m. and 3,300 feet per minute at normal engine speed.

CLETRAC "40"

Cleveland Tractor Co., Cleveland, O.

Traction Wheels: One crawler on each side, 112x19.

No. of Plows Recommended: Twelve to sixteen 14-in.

Length: 198 in.; Width: 96 in.; Height: 86 in.; Weight: 27,450 lbs.; Price: $7,500.

Turning Radius: 17 ft.

Motor: Wisconsin, 6x7, valve-in-head; 6 cylinders, cast in pairs.

Lubrication: Force feed to crankshaft, connecting rods, piston pins and valve rockers.

Carburetor: Schebler, 2-in.

Ignition System: Battery, coil, distributor, two spark.

Starting and Lighting Equipment: Delco Remy.

Cooling System: Water with pump circulation.

Bearings: Bronze backed, babbitt lined.

Transmission: Selective, sliding gear; 1.75 to 4.6 m.p.h. forward; 1.8 m.p.h. reverse

Final Drive: Internal gear and pinion.

Belt Pulley: 24x15; 477 r.p.m. and 3,000 feet per minute at normal engine speed.

CLETRAC "100"
Cleveland Tractor Co., Cleveland, O.

DEERE & CO.

Moline, Illinois

The John Deere Model "D" tractor was a slightly revised and redesignated version of the 15-27 introduced in 1925, and the first tractor carrying the John Deere name. This "Poppin' John" with slight modifications, continued to be built until 1953.

John Deere Model "D" 15-27	1928-1929
John Deere General Purpose 10-20	1928-1929

Traction Wheels: Four wheels with two traction members, 46x12, in rear.

No. of Plows Recommended: Three to four 14-in.

Length: 109 in.; Width: 63 in.; Height: 56 in.; Weight, 4164 lbs.

Turning Radius: 12 ft.; Acres Plowed In 10-hr. Day: 12 to 16.

Motor: Own, 6¾x7; horizontal, 2 cylinders, cast en bloc.

Lubrication: Force feed; gear pump; drilled crankshaft and connecting rods.

Carburetor: Schebler, 1½-in.

Ignition System: Splitdorf high tension magneto.

Starting and Lighting Equipment: Electric lights.

Cooling System: Thermo siphon, Modine radiator and fan.

Bearings: Hyatt roller in differential; Timken roller on axles; ball on spline shaft.

Transmission: Sliding gears 2½ to 3¼ m. p. h. forward; 2 m. p. h. reverse.

Final Drive: Double roller chain.

Belt Pulley: 15x7½; 800 r.p.m. and 3200 ft. per minute at normal engine speed.

JOHN DEERE MODEL "D" 15-27
Deere & Co., Moline, Ill.

JOHN DEERE GENERAL PURPOSE 10-20
Deere & Co., Moline, Ill.

Traction Wheels: Four wheels; two traction in rear, 43¾x8.

No. of Plows Recommended: Two, 14-in.

Length: 114¾ in.; **Width:** 60½ in.; **Height:** 55½ in.; **Weight:** 3600 lbs.

Turning Radius: 8 ft.

Motor: Own, 5¾x6, horizontal, 2 cylinders, cast en bloc.

Lubrication: Pressure; drilled crankshaft.

Carburetor: Schebler, 1½-in.

Ignition System: High tension magneto.

Starting and Lighting Equipment: K-W lighting generator.

Cooling System: Thermo-syphon.

Bearings: Timken and ball.

Transmission: Sliding gear; 2⅓, 3⅛ and 4⅓ m.p.h. forward; 2 m.p.h. reverse.

Final Drive: Chains.

Belt Pulley: 13⅛x6⁷⁄₁₆; 950 r.p.m. and 3200 feet per minute at normal engine speed.

JOHN DEERE "GENERAL PURPOSE" STANDARD TREAD
Deere & Co., Moline, Ill.

PROFIT-MAKERS
For the Dealer—For the Farmer

The John Deere line of tractors includes both the John Deere Model D for the heavier farm jobs and the John Deere General Purpose, the tractor that plants and cultivates three rows at a time besides all the other farm work within its two-plow power range.

The John Deere dealer can now meet the tractor requirements in his territory.

There's satisfaction and profit to the dealer who sells and to the farmer who buys John Deere tractors.

John Deere Plow Co.
Kansas City, Mo. — Omaha, Neb.

GENERAL TRACTOR CO.

Cleveland, Ohio

General 10-12

GENERAL 10-12
General Tractor Co., Cleveland, O.

1928-1931

Traction Wheels: Two, 32x6.

No. of Plows Recommended: One to two.

Length: 120 in.; **Width,** 28-36 in.; **Height,** 51 in.; **Weight:** 1600 lbs.; **Price:** $550.

Turning Radius: 7½ ft.

Motor: Own, 3½x5¼, vertical 4 cycle, 2 cylinders.

Lubrication: Force feed and splash.

Carburetor: Tillotson, 1¼ in.

Ignition System: High tension.

Cooling System: Thermo-syphon.

Bearings: Ball, bronze and roller.

Transmission: Own make planetary type; three drums, forward, reverse and brake; 1 to 3 m.p.h. forward; 2 m.p h. reverse.

Final Drive: Gear.

J. T. TRACTOR CO.

Cleveland, Ohio

"J T" 30-45—With Winch

1928-1929

Traction: Two crawlers, 110x11.

No. of Plows Recommended: Three 14-in.

Length: 137 in.; **Width:** 60 in.; **Height:** 68½ in.; **Weight:** 10,000 lbs.; **Price:** $3,500; **Winch:** $1,000 extra.

Turning Radius: 5 ft.

Motor: Climax K U, 5x6½, vertical, 4 cylinders, cast in pairs.

Lubrication: Pressure system; vane oil pump.

Carburetor: Zenith, 1½-in.

Ignition System: K-W or Apollo magneto with impulse starter.

Lighting Equipment: Prestolite system.

Cooling System: McCord tubular radiator, Oakes fan and centrifugal pump.

Transmission: Selective; 1⅓ to 5 m.p.h. forward; 1¼ m.p.h. reverse.

Final Drive: External ring gear and bull pinion.

Belt Pulley: 10x8; 900 r.p.m. and 2350 feet per minute at normal engine speed.

"J T" 30-45—WITH WINCH
J. T. Tractor Co.. C veland, O.

JOHN LAUSON MANUFACTURING CO.
New Holstein, Wisconsin

Lauson 25-45

1928-1929

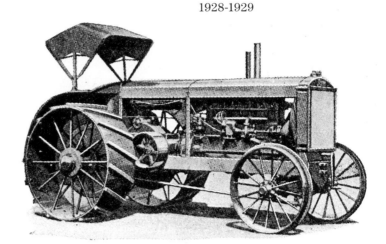

Traction Wheels: Four wheel type; two drivers in rear, 54x16; 20-inch optional; non-drives, 36x6.
No. of Plows Recommended: Five, 14-in.
Length: 166 in.; Width: 82 in.; Height: 86 in.; Weight: 9060 lbs.
Turning Radius: 17 ft.
Motor: Le Roi, 4½x6, vertical, valve-in-head, 6 cylinders, cast in pairs.
Lubrication: Force feed and splash.
Carburetor: Tillotson, 1½-in.
Ignition System: High tension magneto.
Starting & Lighting Equipment: Bosch.
Cooling System: Tubular radiator, centrifugal pump and Automotive fan.
Bearings: Hyatt and Timken in transmission.
Transmission: Sliding gear; 2.4 to 3.2 m.p.h. forward; 2.1 m.p.h. reverse.
Final Drive: Enclosed spur gear.
Belt Pulley: 17½x8; 600 r.p.m. and 4249 feet per minute at normal engine speed.

LAUSON 25-45
John Lauson Mfg. Co., New Holstein, Wis.

MONARCH TRACTORS CORP.
(Subsidiary to Allis-Chalmers Manufacturing Co.)
Springfield, Illinois

Monarch "50"
Monarch "75"

1928
1928

Traction Wheels: One crawler on each side, 13-inch face.
Length: 118 in.; Width: 75½ in.; Height: 63¾ in.
Motor: Stearns, 5⅛x6½, valve-in-head, 4 cylinders, cast en bloc.
Lubrication: Force feed.
Carburetor: Zenith, 1¾ in.
Ignition System: American Bosch ZR4 magneto.
Starting & Lighting Equipment: Auto-Lite.
Cooling System: Centrifugal pump and chain driven fan.
Transmission: Selective sliding gear; 1.81 to 3.96 m.p.h. forward; 3.17 m.p.h. reverse
Final Drive: Chain
Belt Pulley: 12x9½; 950 r.p.m. and 3,000 feet per minute at normal engine speed.

MONARCH "50"
Monarch Tractors Corp., Springfield, Ill.
Subsidiary to Allis-Chalmers Mfg. Co.

MONARCH "75"

Monarch Tractors Corp., Springfield, Ill.
Subsidiary of Allis-Chalmers Mfg. Co.

Traction Wheels: One crawler on each side; 16-inch face.
Length: 150 in.; **Width:** 96 in.; **Height:** 77 in.
Motor: Le Roi, 6½x7, valve-in-head, 4 cylinders, cast in pairs.
Lubrication: Force feed.
Carburetor: Zenith, 1¾-in.
Ignition System: American Bosch magneto.
Starting & Lighting Equipment: Auto-Lite.
Cooling System: Centrifugal pump and chain driven fan.
Transmission: Selective, sliding gear, 1.5 to 3.5 m.p.h. forward; 2.5 m.p.h. reverse
Final Drive: Chain
Belt Pulley: 14x11; 420-713-960 r.p.m. and 1540-3620-3500 feet per minute at normal engine speed.

W. A. RIDDELL CO.

Bucyrus, Ohio

E	1928
HM	1928
KM	1928
Road Hog	1928

WARCO ALWATRACS

THE MODEL KM

The largest of the WARCO family of Alwatracs. Attached to the 15-30 International Tractor. Has 16″ pressed steel semi-flat treads to which lugs can be bolted when required. A pulling unit with power to burn.

THE Models KM and HM Alwatracs can easily be attached to your International Tractor, or the outfit may be bought complete with tractor installed.

These tracks are supplied with tread plates giving sufficient bearing surface that they will not mark the softest asphalt and yet will give ample traction in the most adverse soil conditions. For extreme conditions they can be equipped with our standard lugs or with extra-width treads.

There is a separate clutch in each track, making it possible to turn the tractor under all conditions with a capacity load. It will turn in its own length. The clutches are simple, powerful, and effective, and the control is automatic.

On the 10-20 the bearing pressure per square inch of area is 4.1 lbs.; on the 15-30 it is 5 lbs.

The tractor equipped with these tracks will pull at least 50 per cent more than the standard wheeled tractor, and in many cases will be able to operate where the ordinary wheeled machine could not be used.

W. A. RIDDELL COMPANY
Bucyrus, Ohio

THE MODEL HM

Built for the 10-20 International Tractor. Has 12″ semi-flat treads with provision for lugs. The Model KM'S little brother —and not so little, at that!

WARCO ONE-MAN GRADERS

THE ROAD HOG

Illustration shows "ROAD HOG" Grader, Model 15, powered by the 15-30 International, and equipped with rubber tired wheels. The ROAD HOG is furnished also with Rigid Rail Tracks and in a smaller model powered by 10-20 International Tractor.

THE WARCO line of power graders offers the road worker a machine suited in size, design, and price to meet any requirement he may impose. These sturdy graders are daily making themselves more popular in every kind of work for which it is possible to use a power grader.

In the design of WARCO Graders are embodied all the most modern and practical developments resulting from years of careful study and experiment in grader construction. The frames are heavy steel "I" beam, thoroughly reinforced, sturdy and vibrationless. The blades are extra heavy high carbon steel, double-edged, and reversible. The moldboards are heavily reinforced at the back. The leaning wheel attachment for tilting the front wheels when doing ditch work is supplied on any machine when requested.

Other WARCO features:

The head type steering gear which facilitates steering, the worm-and-gear type lifting gear which makes easy the lifting and lowering of the scarifier, the spring-counterbalance which makes for easy regulation and operation of the blade, and the complete adjustability of all working parts.

W. A. RIDDELL COMPANY
Bucyrus, Ohio

THE MODEL E

Center Control Grader powered by 10-20 International, equipped with Tracks or rubber tired wheels as desired. May also be had in the rear control type.

ROCK ISLAND PLOW CO.
Rock Island, Illinois

Rock Island "F" 18-35   1928-1936

ROCK ISLAND "F" 18-35
Rock Island Plow Co., Rock Island, Ill.

Traction Wheels: Four wheels; two traction in rear, 48x12 and two non-drive in front, 30x6.

No. of Plows Recommended: Three to four, 14-in.

Length: 124 in.; **Width:** 70 in.; **Height:** 65 in.; **Weight:** 4,700 lbs.

Turning Radius: 10 ft.; **Acres Plowed In 10-hr. Day:** 15 to 18.

Motor: Buda, 4½x6, vertical, 4 cylinders, cast en bloc.

Lubrication: Full force.

Carburetor: Stromberg, 1½ in.

Ignition System: Splitdorf magneto.

Starting & Lighting Equipment: Electrical; extra.

Cooling System: Tubular radiator and pump.

Bearings: Ball and roller.

Transmission: Spur gear; 3 to 4½ m.p.h. forward; 2 m.p.h. reverse.

Final Drive: Live axle, fully enclosed.

Belt Pulley: 18x7½; 660 r.p.m. and 3,000 feet per minute at normal engine speed.

POWERFUL *Light* Durable

ROCK ISLAND

Model "F" 18-35 h.p.
Weight 4700 lbs.

Model "G" 15-25 h.p.
Weight 4200 lbs.

─ROCK ISLAND TRACTOR TOOLS─

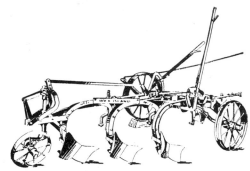

Rock Island Tractor Plows with Famous Rock Island plow bottoms and quick detachable shares.

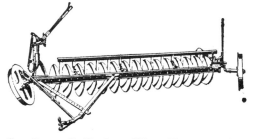

Sanders Cylinder Disc Plows with special electric heat-treated discs

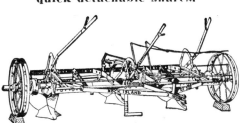

Rock Island 3 or 2 row No. 302 Lister

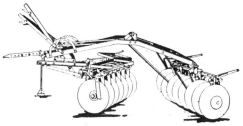

Rock Island No. 37 Tractor Disc Harrow

Rock Island Plow Company

Rock Island, Illinois

**Indianapolis, Minneapolis, East St. Louis, Sioux Falls, Omaha, Kansas City
Denver, Oklahoma City, Dallas**

48

1928

LONG

IN THE production of Long radiators, the thought uppermost in the minds of our entire organization is QUALITY—first, last and always.

LONG MANUFACTURING CO.
DETROIT   MICHIGAN

LONG PRODUCTS—Automotive Clutches & Radiators

1929

The 1929 list contains 34 models of 14 makes not previously included.

In 1929, Allis-Chalmers Manufacturing Co. bought the La Crosse Plow Works. Minneapolis-Moline Power Implement Co. was formed by a merger of Minneapolis Steel & Machinery Co. and Minneapolis Threshing Machine Co., with headquarters established at Hopkins, Minnesota. The Oliver Farm Equipment Co. was formed by a merger of Oliver Chilled Plow Works, Nichols & Shepard and Hart-Parr Co.

Discontinuing tractor production in the United States was Ford Motor Co., which was in the process of moving the Fordson factory to Cork, Ireland. Also disappearing from 1928 lists are Connors Hoe & Tool Co., Emerson Brantingham, Nichols & Shepard, Tioga Tractor Co. and Townsend Tractor Co., mostly because of mergers and acquisitions within the industry.

While 1929 is remembered for the stock market crash and the beginning of the great depression, it was a period of limited recovery for the agricultural community and farm equipment industry, both of which had suffered from hard times for most of the decade. Eighty-nine models of 41 makes were listed for sale in the 1929 *Cooperative Tractor Catalog*.

J. I. CASE CO.

Racine, Wisconsin

The introduction of the Case Model L marked the beginning of a new era for the J. I. Case Co. It was the first tractor introduced by the new regime with the "unit frame" design. This was a departure from the cross-mounted engine design formerly used. The "unit frame" design, first introduced by the Wallis Tractor Co. of Racine, Wisconsin, was rapidly becoming the standard in the industry.

Case Model A 12-20	1929
Case Model L	1929-1930
Case Model T 25-45	1929-1930

Traction Wheels: Four wheels, two drive wheels in rear, 42 x 12.

No. of Plows Recommended: Two to three 14-in.

Length: 109 in.; **Width:** 61 in.; **Height:** 55½ in.

Turning Radius: 12 ft. **Acres Plowed In 10-hr. Day:** 7 to 10.

Motor: Own; 4⅛ x 5, vertical valve-in-head, 4 cylinders, cast en bloc.

Lubrication: Pressure feed through drilled crank shaft.

Carburetor: Kingston, 1¼-in.

Ignition System: High tension magneto with impulse starter.

Cooling System: Pump, fan and radiator.

Bearings: Hyatt roller in transmission and rear axle.

Transmission: Sliding gear, 2.2 to 3 m.p.h. forward.

Final Drive: Enclosed spur gears.

Belt Pulley: 14¼ x 6⅜; 1050 r.p.m.

CASE MODEL A 12-20
J. I. Case Co., Racine, Wis.

Traction Wheels: Two traction wheels in rear, 48x12.

No. of Plows Recommended: Three, four or five, 14-in.

Length: 120 in.; **Width:** 67 in.; **Height:** 57 in.

Turning Radius: 13 ft.

Motor: Own, 4⅝x6, valve-in-head, 4 cylinders, cast en bloc.

Lubrication: Force feed through drilled crankshaft.

Carburetor: Kingston, 1½ in.

Ignition System: High tension magneto with impulse coupling.

Cooling System: Fan, pump and radiator.

Bearings: Bronze babbitt lined in motor.

Transmission: Sliding gear, 2½, 3¼ and 4 m.p.h. forward.

Final Drive: Chain.

Belt Pulley: 13x8¼; 780 r.p.m. and 2650 feet per minute at normal engine speed.

CASE MODEL L
J. I. Case Co., Racine, Wis.

CASE MODEL L
J. I. Case Co., Racine, Wis.

CASE MODEL T 25-45
J. I. Case Co., Racine, Wis.

Traction Wheels: Four wheels with two drive wheels, 56 x 16, in rear.

No. of Plows Recommended: Four to five 14 in.

Length: 153 in.; **Width:** 82½ in.; **Height:** 90 in.

Turning Radius: 20¼ ft.;

Motor: Own, vertical, 5½ x 6¾, 4 cylinders, cast in pairs.

Lubrication: Force feed through drilled crankshaft. Madison-Kipp force feed auxiliary oiler for cylinders.

Carburetor: Kingston, 2 in.

Ignition System: High tension magneto with impulse starter.

Cooling System: Pump, radiator and fan.

Bearing: Hyatt roller, Timken roller and New Departure ball.

Transmission: Selective sliding gear, 2.2 to 3.2 m. p. h. forward; 2.04 m. h. p. reverse.

Final Drive: Spur gear, enclosed.

Belt Pulley: 16½x8½; 850 r.p.m.

CATERPILLAR TRACTOR CO.

Peoria, Illinois and San Leandro, California

Caterpillar Ten	1929-1931
Caterpillar Fifteen	1929-1933
Caterpillar Thirty	1929-1931
Caterpillar Sixty	1929-1931

Traction: Two crawlers, 8x51 1-16.

Length: 99 13-16 in.; **Width:** 52 11-16 in.; **Height:** 51 1-16 in.; **Weight:** 4330 lbs.; **Price:** $1125 f.o.b. factory.

Turning Radius: 5 1-6 ft.

Motor: Own, 3⅜x4, L-head, 4 cylinders, cast en bloc.

Lubrication: Pressure feed.

Carburetor: Ensign, 1-in.

Ignition System: High tension magneto.

Lighting Equipment: Robert Bosch generator.

Cooling System: Water, pump circulation, belt driven fan.

Bearings: Babbitt.

Transmission: Sliding gear, 2-2.6-3.5 m.p.h. forward; 2 m.p.h. reverse.

Final Drive: Spur gears.

Belt Pulley: 9½x6½; 1050 r.p.m. and 2610 feet per minute at normal engine speed.

"CATERPILLAR" TEN
Caterpillar Tractor Co.,
Peoria, Ill., and San Leandro, Calif.

"CATERPILLAR" FIFTEEN
Caterpillar Tractor Co., Peoria, Ill.

Traction Wheels: Two crawlers, 10x54½.
Length: 104⅛ in.; **Width:** 57¾ in.;
Height: 58 in.; **Weight:** 5873 lbs.; **Price:** $1450 f.o.b. Peoria, Ill.
Turning Radius (Outside): 5⅔ ft.
Engine: Own, 3¾x5, L-head, 4 cylinders, cast en bloc.
Lubrication: Pressure feed.
Carburetor: Ensign, 1-in.
Ignition System: High tension magneto.
Lighting Equipment: Robert Bosch generator.
Cooling System: Water, pump circulation, V-belt driven fan.
Bearings: Largely anti-friction ball and roller.
Transmission: Sliding gear, 2-2.6-3.6 m.p.h. forward; 2.1 m.p.h. reverse.
Final Drive: Spur gears.
Belt Pulley: 10½x6½; 950 r.p.m. and 2610 feet per minute at normal engine speed.

"CATERPILLAR" THIRTY
Caterpillar Tractor Co., Peoria, Ill.

Traction Wheels: Two crawlers, 13x61⅛.
No. of Plows Recommended: Four or five 14-in.
Length: 129¼ in ; **Width:** 65⅜ in.; **Height:** 65⅛ in.; **Weight,** 9947 lbs.; **Price:** $2,375, f.o.b. Peoria, Ill.
Turning Radius (Outside): 9 ft.
Engine: Own, 4¾x6½, vertical, 4 cylinders, cast singly.
Lubrication: Force feed.
Carburetor: Ensign.
Ignition System: Eisemann.
Lighting Equipment: Robert Bosch, extra.
Cooling System: Pump.
Bearings: Largely ball and roller, anti-friction.
Transmission: Sliding gear, 1.7-2.6-3.6 m.p.h. forward; 2 m.p.h reverse.
Final Drive: Machine cut gears enclosed in oil bath.
Belt Pulley: 12x8½; 850 r.p.m. and 2670 feet per minute at normal engine speed.

Traction Wheels: Two crawlers, each 79½x16.

No. of Plows Recommended: Eight to ten 14-in.

Length: 158 in.; **Width:** 94⅝ in.; **Height:** 158 in.; **Weight:** 19,500 lbs.; **Price:** $4,175, f.o.b. Peoria, Ill.

Turning Radius (Outside): 15 ft.

Engine: Own, 6½x8½ vertical, 4 cylinders, cast singly.

Lubrication: Force feed.

Carburetor: Ensign.

Ignition System: Eisemann magneto.

Lighting Equipment: Robert Bosch, extra.

Cooling System: Pump.

Bearings: Largely ball or roller anti-friction.

Transmission: Sliding gear, 1.9-2.6-3.7 m.p.h. forward and 1.4 m.p.h. reverse.

Final Drive: Machine cut gears, enclosed in oil bath.

Belt Pulley: 15x11; 650 r.p.m. and 2580 feet per minute at normal engine speed.

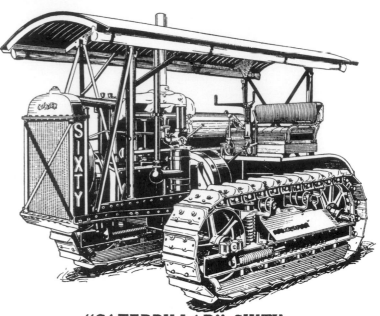

"CATERPILLAR" SIXTY
Caterpillar Tractor Co., Peoria, Ill.

DEERE & CO.
Moline, Illinois

John Deere Model "D"	1929-1937
John Deere General Purpose Wide Tread	1929-1934

Traction Wheels: Four wheels with two traction members, 46x12, in rear.

No. of Plows Recommended: Three to four 14-in.

Length: 117¼ in.; **Width:** 65 in.; **Height:** 56 in.; **Weight:** 4403 lbs.

Turning Radius: 14 ft.; **Acres Plowed in 10-hr. Day:** 12 to 16.

Motor: Own, 6¾x7; horizontal, 2 cylinders, cast en bloc.

Lubrication: Force feed; gear pump; drilled crankshaft and connecting rods.

Carburetor: Schebler, 1½-in.

Ignition System: Splitdorf high tension magneto.

Starting and Lighting Equipment: Electric lights.

Cooling System: Thermo-syphon.

Bearings: Hyatt roller in differential; Timken roller on axles; ball on spline shaft.

Transmission: Sliding gears 2½ to 3¼ m. p. h. forward; 2 m. p. h. reverse.

Final Drive: Double roller chain.

Belt Pulley: 15x7½; 800 r.p.m. and 3200 ft. per minute.

JOHN DEERE MODEL "D" 15-27
Deere & Co., Moline, Ill.

JOHN DEERE "D"
Deere & Co., Moline, Ill.

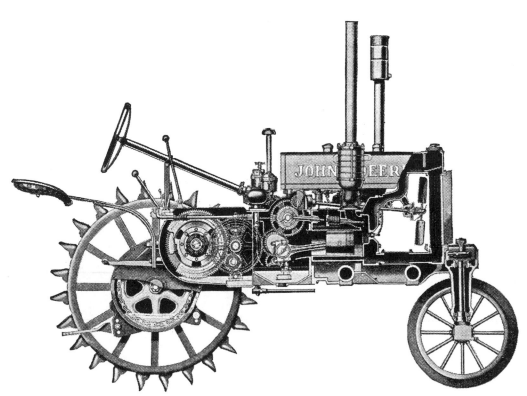

JOHN DEERE "GENERAL PURPOSE" WIDE TREAD
Deere & Co., Moline, Ill.

EAGLE MANUFACTURING CO.

Appleton, Wisconsin

Eagle E, 20-35
Eagle H, 20-40 Special

1929-1935
1929-1938

EAGLE, E, 20-35
Eagle Mfg. Co., Appleton, Wis.

Traction Wheels: Four wheels, two rear, 48x14, affording traction.

No. of Plows Recommended: Three to four 14-in.

Length: 139 in.; **Width:** 73 in.; **Height:** 72 in.; **Weight:** 7,500 lbs.

Turning Radius: 14 ft.

Motor: Own; 8 x 9, valve-in-head, 2 cylinders, cast en bloc.

Lubrication: Madison-Kipp force feed.

Carburetor: Schebler.

Ignition System: Splitdorf high tension magneto with impulse starter.

Cooling System: Tubular radiator, circulating pump and fan.

Bearings: Hyatt and Timken roller in transmission and Hyatt roller on drive axle.

Transmission: Sliding gear. 2 to 3 m.p.h forward; 1¾ m.p.h. reverse.

Final Drive: Enclosed spur gear through semi-floating axle.

Belt Pulley: 24 x 10; 425 to 450 r.p.m. and 2,800 feet per minute at normal engine speed.

Traction Wheels: Four wheel type; two traction in rear, 52x18.

Length: 147 in.; **Width:** 77 in.; **Height:** 80 in.; **Weight:** 7,840 lbs.

Turning Radius: 16 ft.

Motor: Own, 8x10, horizontal, 2 cylinders, cast en bloc.

Lubrication: Madison-Kipp force feed.

Carburetor: Schebler, 1¾-in.

Ignition System: Splitdorf high tension magneto with impulse starter.

Cooling System: Water, Automotive fan, tubular radiator and centrifugal pump.

Bearings: Hyatt roller in transmission; plain babbitt in rear axle.

Transmission: Sliding gear; 2 to 3 m. p. h. forward; 1¾ m. p. h. reverse.

Final Drive: Enclosed spur gear direct to wheels.

Belt Pulley: 24x10; 450 r.p.m. and 2800 feet per minute at normal engine speed.

EAGLE H, 20-40 SPECIAL
Eagle Manufacturing Co., Appleton, Wis.

FOOTE BROS. GEAR & MACHINE CO.

Chicago, Illinois

The Foote Bros. Gear & Machine Co. bought Bates Manufacturing Co. of Joliet, Illinois. They continued to manufacture the Bates Industrial 40 and introduced three new models ready for production.

Bates Steel Mule, Model F, 18-25	1929-1935
Bates Industrial 30	1929
Bates Industrial 40	1929
Bates Industrial 80	1929-1931

Traction Wheels: One crawler on each side, 58x10.

No. of Plows Recommended: Three 14-in.

Length: 105 in.; **Width:** 62 in.; **Height:** 58 in., **Weight:** 5250 lbs.

Turning Radius: 7½ ft.; **Acres Plowed in 10-hr. Day:** 10.

Motor: Le Roi; 4¼x6, valve-in-head, 4 cylinders, cast in pairs.

Lubrication: Pressure.

Carburetor: Kingston.

Ignition System: American Bosch high tension magneto.

Cooling System: Pump.

Bearings: Timken roller in transmission.

Transmission: Sliding gear, 2¼ to 4 m.p.h. forward; 2 m.p.h. reverse.

Final Drive: Enclosed gears running in oil.

Belt Pulley: 12x8½; 850 r.p.m. and 2650 feet per minute at normal engine speed.

BATES STEEL MULE, MODEL F, 18-25
Foote Bros. Gear & Machine Co., Chicago, Ill.

BATES INDUSTRIAL 30
Foote Bros. Gear & Machine Co., Chicago, Ill.

Traction Wheels: Two crawlers full length of tractor, 11-in. wide and 78-in. long.

Length: 103 in.; **Width:** 60 in.; **Height:** 58 in; **Weight:** 8750 lbs.

Turning Radius: 6 ft.

Motor: Le Roi, 4¾x6, over-head, 4-cylinders.

Lubrication: Force feed system.

Carburetor: Kingston.

Ignition System: American Bosch high tension magneto.

Cooling System: Pump.

Bearings: Ball and roller.

Transmission: Sliding gear; 1.75 to 4.3 m.p.h. forward; 2 m.p.h. reverse.

Final Drive: Spur gear, enclosed and running in oil.

Traction Wheels: Two crawlers, 12 inches wide and 92 inches long.
Length: 122 in.; Width: 66 in.; Height: 66 in.; Weight: 12,500 lbs.
Turning Radius: 7 ft.
Motor: Waukesha, 5x6¼, Ricardo-head, 4-cylinders, cast in pairs.
Lubrication: Force feed.
Carburetor: Kingston.
Ignition System: American Bosch high tension magneto.
Cooling System: Pump.
Bearings: Ball and roller.
Transmission: Sliding gear; 1.4 to 4½ m. p.h. forward; 3¼ m.p.h. reverse.
Final Drive: Spur gear, enclosed and running in oil.

BATES INDUSTRIAL 40
Foote Bros. Gear & Machine Co., Chicago, Ill.

Traction Wheels: Two crawlers, 120x18, 3744 sq. in. on ground.
Length: 146 in.; Width: 97 in.; Height: 84 in.; Weight: 22500 lbs.
Turning Radius Outside: 8 ft.
Motor: Waukesha, 6½x7, Ricardo-head, 4 cylinders, 4 cycle, 900 r.p.m.
Lubrication: Force Feed.
Ignition System: American Bosch high tension magneto.
Cooling System: Fan, circulating pump and radiator.
Bearings: Ball and roller.
Transmission: Sliding gear; 1.5 to 3.75 m.p.h. forward; 1.25 m.p.h. reverse.
Final Drive: Spur gear, enclosed and running in oil.

BATES INDUSTRIAL 80
Foote Bros. Gear & Machine Co., Chicago, Ill.

FOUR DRIVE TRACTOR CO.
Big Rapids, Michigan

The Cat 15-30   1929
Fitch Four Drive 20-35   1929-1930

THE CAT 15-30
Four Drive Tractor Co., Big Rapids, Mich.

Traction Wheels: Four Wheel Drive, each 40x12.

No. of Plows Recommended: Three to four, 14-in.

Length: 106 in.; **Width,** 70 in.; **Height:** 61 in.; **Weight:** 5800 lbs.; **Price:** $1495 f. o. b. factory.

Turning Radius: 13 ft.; **Acres plowed in 10-hr. day:** Ten.

Motor: Waukesha C-R, 4⅜x5¾, 4 cylinders, cast in pairs.

Lubrication: Pump.

Carburetor: Kingston, 1¼ in.

Ignition System: Eisemann.

Cooling System: Fan, pump and radiator.

Bearings: Timken.

Transmission: Gear; 3 m.p.h. forward, 1 m.p.h. reverse.

Final Drive: Bevel Gear.

Belt Pulley: 12x8; 1000 r.p.m.

Traction Wheels: Drives on all four wheels, front, 36 x 12, and rear, 42 x 12.

No. of Plows Recommended: Four 14-in.

Length: 120 in.; **Width:** 69 in.; **Height:** 73 in.; **Weight:** 6,000 lbs.; **Price:** $2,650.

Turning Radius: 7½ ft.; **Acres Plowed In 10-hr. Day:** 12.

Motor: Climax; 5x6½; 4 cylinders, cast in pairs.

Lubrication: Force feed.

Carburetor: Kingston or Ensign.

Ignition System: Eisemann high tension magneto.

Cooling System: Circulating pump, Modine tubular radiator and Oakes fan.

Bearings: Timken roller throughout.

Transmission: Cotta sliding gear up to 4 m.p.h. forward; 1 m.p.h. reverse.

Final Drive: Worm on rear axle, bevel gears in front.

Belt Pulley: 14x8; 850 r.p.m. and 3,115 feet per minute at normal engine speed.

FITCH FOUR DRIVE 20-35
Four Drive Tractor Co., Big Rapids, Mich.

ALL
FOUR
WHEELS
PULLING

ALL
WEIGHT
ON
TRACTION

Model E 15-30 Horse Power Tractor Pulling One Way Plow

Just four wheels delivering power. Last a lifetime. Every part thoroughly housed in, removed from dust. Plenty of weight in front holds it down. Gives full pull. Steering so easy that the ladies drive them. Every feature making the Four Drive better fully **patented.** Four Drive Tractors will do the work **better** and **cheaper.** Demand forcing twice doubling the capacity in 1929.

**Your Contract may be open
Write or wire for Information**

EXPORT OFFICE
15 MOORE ST.
NEW YORK, N. Y.

Four Drive Tractor Company

Big Rapids, Mich.

60

1929

HUBER MANUFACTURING CO.

Marion, Ohio

Huber Super 4 21-39   1929-1930
Huber Super Four 32-43   1929-1930
Huber Super Four 40-62   1929-1940

HUBER SUPER 4 21-39
Huber Mfg. Co., Marion, O.

Traction Wheels: Four wheel type; two traction in rear, 56x14.

No. of Plows Recommended: Three to four 14-in.

Length: 158 in.; **Width:** 76 in.; **Height:** 62 in.; **Weight:** 7,200 lbs.

Turning Radius: 14 ft.; **Acres Plowed In 10-hr. Day:** 10 to 12.

Motor: Stearns, 4¾x6½, overhead valves, 4 cylinders, cast en bloc.

Lubrication: Force feed.

Carburetor: Kingston, 1½-in.

Ignition System: Eisemann high tension magneto.

Cooling System: Young radiator.

Bearings: Hyatt and Timken.

Transmission: Selective gears, 2.2 to 3 8 m.p.h. forward; 2 m.p.h. reverse.

Final Drive: Enclosed spur gear; live axle.

Belt Pulley: 15½x8; 700 r.p.m. and 2840 feet per minute at normal engine speed.

Traction Wheels: Four wheel type; two traction in rear, 56x18.

No. of Plows Recommended: Four 14-in.

Length: 160 in.; **Width:** 84 in.; **Height:** 62 in.; **Weight:** 8,900 lbs.

Turning Radius: 14 ft.; **Acres Plowed In 10-hr. Day:** 15.

Motor: Stearns. 5⅛x6½, overhead valves, 4 cylinders, cast en bloc.

Lubrication: Force feed.

Carburetor: Kingston, 1½-in.

Ignition System: Eisemann high tension magneto with impulse starter.

Cooling System: Young radiator.

Bearings: Hyatt and Timken.

Transmission: Selective gears; 2.4 to 3.2 m.p.h. forward; 2 m.p.h. reverse.

Final Drive: Enclosed spur gear, live axle.

Belt Pulley: 15½x8; 666 r.p.m. and 2,677 feet per minute at normal engine speed.

HUBER SUPER FOUR 32-43
Huber Manufacturing Co., Marion. O.

HUBER SUPER FOUR 40-62
Huber Manufacturing Co., Marion, O.

Traction Wheels: Four wheel type; two traction in rear, 56x20.

No. of Plows Recommended: Four to six 14-in.

Length: 160 in.; **Width:** 88 in.; **Height:** 62 in.; **Weight:** 9,200 lbs.

Turning Radius: 14 ft.; **Acres Plowed in 10-hr. Day:** 15 to 20.

Motor: Stearns, 5½x6½, overhead valves, 4 cylinders, cast en bloc.

Lubrication: Force feed.

Carburetor: Kingston, 1¾-in.

Ignition System: Eisemann high tension magneto with impulse starter.

Cooling System: Young radiator.

Bearings: Hyatt and Timken.

Transmission: Selective gears; 2.4 to 3.2 m.p.h. forward; 2 m.p.h. reverse.

Final Drive: Enclosed spur gear, live axle.

Belt Pulley: 15½x8; 666 r.p.m. and 2,677 feet per minute at normal engine speed.

KECK-GONNERMAN CO.

Mt. Vernon, Indiana

Kay Gee 18-35	1929-1935
Kay Gee 25-50	1929-1930
Kay Gee 30-60	1929-1935

Traction Wheels: Four-wheel type; two traction in rear, 50x12.

No. of Plows Recommended: Three to four, 14-in.

Length: 132 in.; **Width:** 70 in.; **Height:** 67 in.; **Weight:** 5,250 lbs; **Price:** $1,600 f.o.b. factory.

Turning Radius: 14 ft. outside; **Acres Plowed in 10-Hr. Day:** 15.

Engine: Buda, 4¾x6, vertical, L-head, 4 cylinders, cast en bloc.

Lubrication: Force feed.

Carburetor: Zenith, 1½-in.

Ignition System: Eisemann magneto with impulse starter.

Starting and Lighting Equipment: Electrical (Leece-Neville) extra.

Cooling System: Modine removable core radiator in cast iron housing.

Bearings: Hyatt, Timken and S. K. F.

Transmission: Selective gears; 2½ to 4 m.p.h. forward; 2 m.p.h. reverse.

Final Drive: Enclosed spur gear, live axle.

Belt Pulley: 16½x8½; 585 r.p.m. and 2,600 feet per minute at normal engine speed.

KAY GEE 18-35
Keck-Gonnerman Co., Mt. Vernon, Ind.

Traction Wheels: Four wheels; two in rear, 56x14 to 24, giving traction.

No. of Plows Recommended: Four, 14-in.

Length: 162 in.; **Width:** 86 in.; **Height:** 69 in.; **Weight:** 9,800 lbs; **Price:** $2,850 f.o.b. factory.

Turning Radius: 15 ft.; **Acres Plowed in 10-Hr. Day:** 18 to 20.

Motor: Le Roi, 5¼x7, valve-in-head, 4 cylinders, cast in pairs.

Lubrication: Force feed.

Carburetor: Ensign, 1½-in.

Ignition System: Eisemann high tension magneto with impulse starter.

Starting and Lighting Equipment: Electric, Leece-Neville (extra).

Cooling System: Modine removable core radiator in cast iron housing.

Bearings: Hyatt, Timken and S. K. F.

Transmission: Selective gears; 2.4 to 3.2 m.p.h. forward; 2 m.p.h. reverse.

Final Drive: Enclosed spur gear; live axle.

Belt Pulley: 15½x9½; 666 r.p.m. and 2,677 feet per minute at normal engine speed.

KAY GEE 25-50

Keck-Gonnerman Co., Mt. Vernon, Ind.

KAY GEE 30-60

Keck-Gonnerman Co., Mt. Vernon, Ind.

Traction Wheels: Four-wheel type; two traction in rear, 56x14 to 24.

No. of Plows Recommended: Four to six, 14-in.

Length: 162 in.; **Width:** 90 in.; **Height:** 69 in.; **Weight:** 10,500 lbs.; **Price:** $3,000 f.o.b. factory.

Turning Radius: 15 ft.; **Acres Plowed in 10-Hr. Day:** 20 to 23.

Motor: Le Roi, 5½x7, valve-in-head, 4 cylinders, cast in pairs.

Lubrication: Force feed.

Carburetor: Ensign, 1¾-in.

Ignition System: Eisemann high tension magneto with impulse starter.

Starting and Lighting Equipment: Electric, Leece-Neville (extra).

Cooling System: Modine removable core radiator in cast iron housing.

Bearings: Hyatt, Timken and S. K. F.

Transmission: Selective gears, 2.4 to 3.2 m.p.h. forward; 2 m.p.h. reverse.

Final Drive: Enclosed spur gear; live axle.

Belt Pulley: 15½x9½; 666 r.p.m. and 2,677 feet per minute at normal engine speed.

MASSEY-HARRIS CO.
Racine, Wisconsin

1929 marks the entrance of Massey-Harris into the tractor field after purchasing the J. I. Case Plow Works in Racine, Wisconsin.

Wallis "Certified" 12-20   1929-1931
Wallis "Certified" Orchard   1929-1930

WALLIS "CERTIFIED" 12-20
Massey-Harris Co., Racine, Wis.

Traction Wheels: Four wheels, with two rear drivers, 44x10 and two non-drive in front, 28x5.

No. of Plows Recommended: Two, 14-in.

Wheelbase: 78 in.; **Width:** 55 in.; **Height:** 51 in.; **Weight:** 3,455 lbs.; **Price,** $945.

Turning Radius: 11½ ft.

Motor: Own, 3⅞x5¼, vertical, 4 cylinders, cast en bloc.

Lubrication: Geared force pump and splash.

Carburetor: Kingston, 1⅛-in.

Ignition System: American Bosch high tension magneto.

Cooling System: Fan, pump and radiator.

Bearings: Three ball bearings on crankshaft.

Transmission: Selective sliding gear, 2⅓-3⅓ to 4⅓ m.p.h. forward; 2⅓ m.p.h. revers.

Final Drive: Spur gear.

Belt Pulley: 17x6; 540 r.p.m. and 2,400 feet per minute at normal engine speed.

Traction Wheels: Four wheels; two in rear, 42x12, giving traction, and two in front, 28x6¼.

No. of Plows Recommended: Three 14-in.

Length: 127 in.; **Width:** 56 in.; **Height:** 50 in.; **Weight,** 4000 lbs.

Turning Radius: 13 ft.

Motor: Own; 4⅜x5¾, valve-in-head, 4 cylinders, cast en bloc.

Lubrication: Circulating splash and geared pump.

Carburetor: Kingston.

Ignition System: American Bosch high tension magneto with Wallis impulse starter.

Cooling System: Modine tubular radiator, centrifugal pump and fan.

Bearings: New Departure and Timken throughout.

Transmission: Selective sliding gear; 2.4 to 3.5 m.p.h. forward; 2.4 m.p.h. reverse.

Final Drive: Spur gear.

WALLIS "CERTIFIED" ORCHARD
Massey-Harris Co., Racine, Wis.

MINNEAPOLIS-MOLINE POWER IMPLEMENT CO.

Minneapolis, Minnesota

Minneapolis 17-30 Type A   1929-1934

Traction Wheels: Four wheels with two drive wheels in rear, 53x12.

Length: 133 in.; Width: 76½ in.; Height: 72 in.; Weight 6100 lbs.

Turning Radius: 13¾ ft.

Motor: Own, 4¾x7, vertical, 4 cylinders, cast en bloc.

Lubrication: Mechanical oil pump and splash.

Carburetor: 1½ in.

Ignition System: High tension magneto.

Cooling System: Radiator, centrifugal pump and fan.

Bearings: Roller and ball.

Transmission: Sliding spur gear, enclosed; approximate 2.35 to 3.09 m.p.h. forward; 2.26 m.p.h. reverse.

Final Drive: Internal gear and pinion.

Belt Pulley: 15½x7½; 825 r.p.m.

MINNEAPOLIS 17-30 TYPE A

MINNEAPOLIS STEEL & MACHINERY CO.

Minneapolis, Minnesota

Minneapolis 17-30 Type A	1929
Minneapolis 17-30 Type B	1929
Twin City 21-32	1929

Traction Wheels: Four wheels with two drive wheels in rear, 53x12.

Length: 133 in.; Width: 76½ in.; Height: 72 in.; Weight 6100 lbs.

Turning Radius: 13¾ ft.

Motor: Own, 4¾x7, vertical, 4 cylinders, cast en bloc.

Lubrication: Mechanical oil pump and splash.

Carburetor: 1½ in.

Ignition System: High tension magneto.

Cooling System: Radiator, centrifugal pump and fan.

Bearings: Roller and ball.

Transmission: Sliding spur gear, enclosed; approximate 2.35 to 3.09 m.p.h. forward; 2.26 m.p.h. reverse.

Final Drive: Internal gear and pinion.

Belt Pulley: 15½x7½; 825 r.p.m.

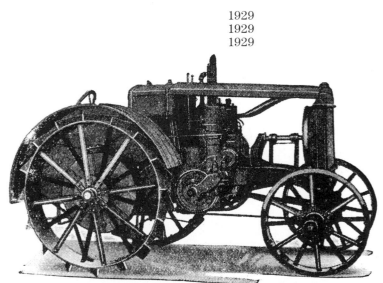

MINNEAPOLIS 17-30 TYPE A

MINNEAPOLIS 17-30 TYPE B

Traction Wheels: Four wheels with two in rear, 53x12, giving traction.

Length: 143 in.; **Width:** 76½ in.; **Height:** 72 in.; **Weight:** 6800 lbs.

Turning Radius: 16 ft.

Motor: Own, 4⅞x7, vertical, 4 cylinders, cast en bloc.

Lubrication: Mechanical oil pump and splash.

Carburetor: 1½ in.

Ignition System: High tension magneto.

Cooling System: Tubular radiator, centrifugal pump and fan.

Bearings: Roller and ball.

Transmission: Sliding spur gear, enclosed, approximate 2.35 to 3.09 m.p.h forward; 2.26 m.p.h. reverse.

Final Drive: Internal gear and pinion.

Belt Pulley: 15½x7½; 825 r.p.m.

Traction Wheels: Four wheels, two in rear, 50x12, giving traction.

No. of Plows Recommended: Three to four, 14-in.

Length: 137 in.; **Width:** 66 in.; **Height:** 66 in.; **Weight:** 5,880 lbs.

Turning Radius: 14 ft.

Motor: Own, 4½x6, vertical, with removable cylinder blocks, 4 cylinders.

Lubrication: Pressure.

Carburetor: Stromberg, 1½-in.

Ignition System: American Bosch magneto with impulse coupling.

Starting and Lighting Equipment: Gas and electric; no battery.

Cooling System: Modine radiator, centrifugal pump and fan.

Bearings: Timken and ball.

Transmission: Sliding gear; 2.36-3.17-4.45 m.p.h. forward; 1.74 m.p.h. reverse.

Final Drive: Enclosed spur gear.

Belt Pulley: 16x7½; 650 r.p.m. and 2720 feet per minute at normal engine speed.

TWIN CITY 21-32
Minneapolis Steel & Machinery Co., Minneapolis, Minn

TWIN CITY 21-32

OLIVER FARM EQUIPMENT CO.
Hart-Parr Tractor Division
Charles City, Iowa

1929 marks the entrance of the "Oliver" name into the tractor field, although the Hart-Parr name and tractors were not new.

Hart-Parr 12-24	1929-1932
Hart-Parr 18-36	1929-1932
Hart-Parr 28-50	1929-1932

Traction Wheels: Four wheels; two traction in rear, 46x10.

No. of Plows Recommended: Two to three 14-in.

Length: 121 in.; **Width:** 66 in. **Height:** 56 in.; **Weight:** 4,805 lbs.

Turning Radius: 11 ft.; **Acres Plowed in 10-hr. Day:** 10 to 12.

Engine: Own, 5¾x6½, horizontal, 2 cylinders, cast en bloc.

Lubrication: Madison-Kipp, force feed.

Carburetor: Schebler, 1½-in.

Ignition System: Robert Bosch high tension magneto with impulse starter.

Cooling System: Radiator, centrifugal pump and fan.

Bearings: Roller and ball in transmission. Own make on axles.

Transmission: Selective, sliding spur gear, three speed, 2⅔, 3⅓ and 4¼ m.p.h. forward, 2⅔ m.p.h. reverse.

Final Drive: External gear, enclosed.

Belt Pulley: 13x8; 850 r.p.m. and 2,890 feet per minute at normal engine speed.

HART-PARR 12-24
Oliver Farm Equipment Sales Co.
Hart-Parr Tractor Div., Charles City, Ia.

HART-PARR 18-36
Oliver Farm Equipment Sales Co.
Hart-Parr Tractor Div., Charles City, Ia.

Traction Wheels: Four-wheel tractor, with two drive members, 51⅛x12, in rear.

No. of Plows Recommended: Three or four 14 to 16-in.

Length: 132 in.; **Width:** 73 in.; **Height:** 61 in.; **Weight:** 6,382 lbs.

Turning Radius: 16 ft.; **Acres Plowed in 10-hr. Day:** 15 to 18.

Engine: Own; 6¾x7; horizontal, 2 cylinders, cast en bloc.

Lubrication: Madison-Kipp force feed lubricator.

Carburetor: Schebler, 1½-in.

Ignition System: Robert Bosch high tension magneto with impulse starter.

Lighting Equipment: To order.

Cooling System: Radiator, centrifugal pump and fan.

Bearings: Roller and ball in transmission and own on drive axle.

Transmission: Selective, sliding spur gear, 2¼, 3¼ and 4⅛ m.p.h. forward; 2¼ m.p.h. reverse.

Final Drive: External gear, enclosed.

Belt Pulley: 14x9; 800 r.p.m. and 2,930 feet per minute at normal engine speed.

Traction Wheels: Four wheels; two in front, 28x7; two traction in rear, 51⅛x14.

No. of Plows Recommended: Five 14 or 16 in.

Length: 141 in.; Width: 88 in.; Height: 64½ in.; Weight: 8,322 lbs.

Engine: Own, 5¾x6½; horizontal, 4 cylinder, cast in pairs.

Lubrication: Madison-Kipp force feed.

Carburetor: Schebler, 1½ in.

Ignition System: Robert Bosch high tension magneto with impulse starter.

Cooling System: Centrifugal pump, fan and radiator.

Bearings: Roller and ball in transmission and own on drive axle.

Transmission: Selective, sliding spur gear, 2¼ to 3¼ m.p.h. forward; 2⅔ m.p.h. reverse.

Final Drive: Internal gear and master pinions.

Belt Pulley: 14x9; 850 r.p.m. and 3,170 feet per minute at normal engine speed.

HART-PARR 28-50
Oliver Farm Equipment Sales Co.
Hart-Parr Tractor Div., Charles City, Ia.

ROCK ISLAND PLOW CO.

Rock Island, Illinois

Rock Island G-2, 15-25   1929-1936

Traction Wheels: Four wheel type; two traction in rear 46x11.

No. of Plows Recommended: Two to three, 14-in.

Length: 118 in.; Width, 66 in.; Height: 62 in.; Weight: 4200 lbs.

Turning Radius (Outside): 9½ ft.; Acres Plowed in 10-Hr. Day: 12 to 15.

Engine: Waukesha, 4¼x5¾, vertical, 4 cylinders, cast in pairs.

Lubrication: Force Feed.

Carburetor: Stromberg, 1¼-in.

Ignition System: High tension magneto.

Starting and Lighting Equipment: Extra.

Cooling System: Fan, pump and radiator.

Bearings: Ball and roller.

Transmission: Spur gear; 2¾ to 4 m.p.h. forward; 1¾ m.p.h. reverse.

Final Drive: Live axle, fully enclosed.

Belt Pulley: 16x6½; 675 r.p.m. and 2840 feet per minute at normal engine speed.

ROCK ISLAND G-2 15-25
Rock Island Plow Co., Rock Island, Ill.

UNITED TRACTOR & EQUIPMENT CO.
Chicago, Illinois

United   1929

Traction Wheels: Four-wheel type, two traction in rear, 42x11⅛.

No. of Plows Recommended: Three, 14-in.

Length: 119 in.; **Width,** 63⅛ in.; **Height:** 53¾ in.; **Weight:** 3900 lbs.; **Price:** $895 f.o.b. factory.

Turning Radius: 12 feet.

Motor: Continental, 4¼x5, L-Head, 4 cylinders, cast en bloc.

Lubrication: Pressure, gear driven oil pump.

Carburetor: Kingston, 1¼-in.

Ignition System: American Bosch magneto.

Cooling System: Fan, pump and radiator.

Bearings: Ball and roller.

Transmission: Automotive, 4-speed; 2⅓ to 10 m.p.h. forward; 2.69 m.p.h. reverse.

Final Drive: Enclosed spur gear.

Belt Pulley: 10x6½; 1095 r.p.m. and 2870 feet per minute at normal engine speed.

UNITED
United Tractor & Equipment Corp., Chicago, Ill.

1930

1930 lists 25 models of 11 makes not included in 1929 and earlier. Sales of farm equipment in 1930 show a slight drop from 1929 but are still good. J. I. Case Co. introduced the Oil Bath Air Cleaner about this time, greatly improving engine life in the normally dusty conditions under which the tractors operate. Previous air cleaners were centrifugal dry types, water bath air cleaners or oiled wick cleaners. Thirty-five tractor manufacturers listed 90 models available in 1930.

ALLIS-CHALMERS MANUFACTURING CO.

Milwaukee, Wisconsin

The Allis-Chalmers Manufacturing Co. designed and built a tractor to be sold by an independent group called United Tractor & Equipment Co., however the group folded and defaulted on their contract. Allis-Chalmers offered the surplus tractors to its dealer organization as the Allis-Chalmers United, then next year incorporated them into their line as the Model U. Also included in the line was the crawler tractor, Monarch 35, the first fruits of their acquisition of the Monarch Tractor Corporation of Springfield, Illinois.

Allis-Chalmers (United)	1930
Allis-Chalmers 20-35 Model "E"	1930-1936
Monarch "35"	1930

Traction Wheels: Four wheel type; two traction in rear, 42x11⅛.
No. of Plows Recommended: Three, 14-in.
Length: 118½ in.; **Width:** 63⅛ in.; **Height:** 53½ in; **Weight:** 4125 lbs.
Turning Radius (Outside): 12 ft.
Engine: Continental, 4¼x5, L-head, 4 cylinders, cast en bloc.
Lubrication: Pressure.
Carburetor: Kingston, 1¼ in.
Ignition System: Magneto.
Cooling System: Fan, pump and radiator.
Bearings: Ball and roller.
Transmission: Automotive; 1½ to 10 m.p.h. forward; 2.69 m.p.h. reverse.
Final Drive: Enclosed spur gear.
Belt Pulley: 10½x7½; 1095 r.p.m. and 3010 feet per minute at normal engine speed.

ALLIS-CHALMERS (UNITED)

Allis-Chalmers Mfg. Co., Milwaukee, Wis.

ALLIS-CHALMERS MODEL "U"
Allis-Chalmers Mfg. Co., Milwaukee, Wis.

ALLIS-CHALMERS 20-35 MODEL "E"

Allis-Chalmers Mfg. Co., Milwaukee, Wis.

Traction Wheels: Four-wheel type; two traction in rear, 50x12.

No. of Plows Recommended: Four 14-in.

Length: 152 in.; **Width:** 76 in.; **Height:** 65 in.; **Weight:** 6000 lbs.

Turning Radius (Outside): 15½ ft.

Engine: Own, 4¾x6½, V-head, 4 cylinders, cast en bloc; Removable sleeves.

Lubrication: Pressure.

Carburetor: Kingston, 1½ in.

Ignition System: Eisemann magneto.

Cooling System: Fan, centrifugal pump and radiator.

Bearings: Plain, ball and roller.

Transmission: Selective gear, 2½ to 3¼ m.p.h. forward and 3¼ m.p.h. reverse.

Final Drive: Spur pinion and internal gear.

Belt Pulley: 13x8½; 930 r.p.m. and 3,160 feet per minute at normal engine speed.

ALLIS-CHALMERS MODEL "E"
Allis-Chalmers Mfg. Co., Milwaukee, Wis.

Perfex Radiators Chosen for both Allis-Chalmers and Monarch Tractors

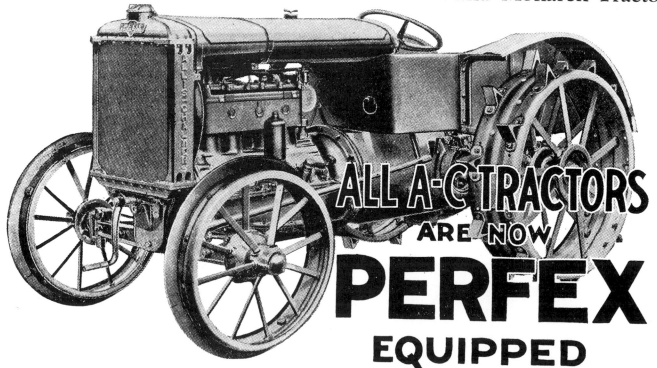

ALL A-C TRACTORS ARE NOW **PERFEX** EQUIPPED

GOOD COOLING—CLEAR AIR PASSAGES—FOR TRACTORS AND COMBINES

PERFEX CORPORATION

Milwaukee   *Eastern and Export Office:*   *Engineering Sales Distributors, Ltd.,*   **Wisconsin**
44 Whitehall St., New York, N. Y.   *7 Front Street, San Francisco, Calif.*

For Over Twenty Years Builders of Heavy-Duty Radiators

Traction Wheels: One crawler on each side, 67x13.

No. of Plows Recommended: Four 14 in.

Length: 119 in.; **Width:** 66 in.; **Height:** 66 in.; **Weight:** 10,500 lbs.; **Price:** $2,450.

Engine: Own, 4¾x6½, vertical, 4 cylinders, cast en bloc.

Lubrication: Full force feed.

Carburetor: Zenith, 1½ in.

Ignition System: Eisemann magneto.

Starting & Lighting Equipment: Electric Auto-Lite.

Cooling System: Fan, pump and radiator.

Transmission: Selective sliding gear; three speeds forward; 1.84 to 4.01 m.p.h. forward; 2.12 m.p.h. reverse.

Final Drive: Gear.

Belt Pulley: 12x8¾; 930 r.p.m. and 2,922 feet per minute at normal engine speed.

MONARCH "35"

Allis-Chalmers Mfg. Co., Monarch Div., Springfield, Ill.

J. I. CASE CO.

Racine, Wisconsin

Case Model C	1930-1938
Case Model CC	1930-1938

Traction Wheels: Two traction wheels in rear, 42x12.

No. of Plows Recommended: Two to three, 14-in.

Length: 114½ in.; **Width:** 61½ in.; **Height:** 53¼ in.

Turning Radius (Outside): 10 ft.

Engine: Own, 3⅞x5½, vertical, 4 cylinders, cast singly.

Lubrication: Force feed through drilled crankshaft.

Carburetor: 1¼-in.

Ignition System: High tension magneto with impulse coupling.

Cooling System: Fan, pump and radiator.

Bearings: Bronze, babbitt lined in motor.

Transmission: Sliding gear; 2⅓, 3⅓ and 4½ m.p.h. forward.

Final Drive: Chain, enclosed in oil.

Belt Pulley: 10¼x6½; 973 r.p.m. and 2,600 feet per minute at normal engine speed.

CASE MODEL C

J. I. Case Co., Racine, Wis.

CASE MODEL CC
J. I. Case Co., Racine, Wis.

Traction Wheels: Two traction in rear, 48x8.

No. of Plows Recommended: Two, 14-in.

Length: 137 in.; **Width:** Variable, 48-84-in. tread; **Height:** 56½ in.

Turning Radius (Outside): Pivots on rear wheel.

Engine: Own, 3⅞x5½, vertical, 4 cylinders, cast singly.

Lubrication: Force feed through drilled crankshaft.

Carburetor: 1¼-in.

Ignition System: High tension magneto with impulse coupling.

Cooling System: Fan, pump and radiator.

Bearings: Bronze babbitt lined in motor.

Transmission: Sliding gear; 2.63, 3.75 and 5.14 m.p.h. forward.

Final Drive: Chain, enclosed in oil.

Belt Pulley: 10¼x6¼; 973 r.p.m. and 2600 feet per minute at normal engine speed.

CLEVELAND TRACTOR CO.

Cleveland, Ohio

Cletrac (80-60)   1930-1931

CLETRAC (80-60)
Cleveland Tractor Co., Cleveland, O.

Traction Wheels: Two crawlers, 75x17.

Length: 156 in.; **Width:** 96 in.; **Height:** 82 in.; **Weight:** 20,250 lbs.; **Price:** $5250.

Turning Radius (Outside): 15 ft.

Engine: Wisconsin, 5½x6½, 6 cylinders, cast in pairs.

Lubrication: Force feed.

Carburetor: Schebler (2).

Ignition System: Delco Remy.

Starting and Lighting Equipment: Delco Remy.

Cooling System: Fan, pump and radiator.

Bearings: Ball and roller.

Transmission: Selective gear, 1¾ to 3.6 m.p.h. forward; 2.1 m.p.h. reverse.

Final Drive: Enclosed, planetary pinion.

Belt Pulley: 24x15; 455 r.p.m. and 2980 feet per minute at normal engine speed.

DEERE & CO.
Moline, Illinois

John Deere General Purpose Standard

1930-1934

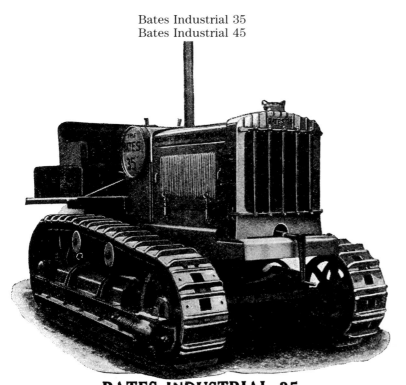

JOHN DEERE GENERAL PURPOSE STANDARD
Deere & Co., Moline, Ill.

Traction Wheels: Four wheels; two traction in rear, 43¾x8.
No. of Plows Recommended: Two, 14-in.
Length: 114¾ in.; **Width:** 60½ in.; **Height:** 55½ in.; **Weight:** 3600 lbs.
Turning Radius: 8 ft.
Motor: Own, 5¾x6, horizontal, 2 cylinders, cast en bloc.
Lubrication: Pressure; drilled crankshaft.
Carburetor: Schebler, 1½-in.
Ignition System: High tension magneto.
Starting and Lighting Equipment: K-W lighting generator.
Cooling System: Thermo-syphon.
Bearings: Timken and ball.
Transmission: Sliding gear; 2⅓, 3⅛ and 4⅓ m.p.h. forward; 2 m.p.h. reverse.
Final Drive: Chains.
Belt Pulley: 13⅛x6 $\frac{7}{16}$; 950 r.p.m. and 3200 feet per minute at normal engine speed.

FOOTE BROS. GEAR & MACHINE CO.
Chicago, Illinois

Bates Industrial 35
Bates Industrial 45

1930-1931
1930-1931

BATES INDUSTRIAL 35
Foote Bros. Gear & Machine Co., Chicago, Ill.

Traction Wheels: Two crawlers full length of tractor, 12-in. wide and 78-in. long.
Length: 120 in.; **Width:** 72 in.; **Height:** 70 in.; **Weight:** 10,800 lbs.
Turning Radius (Outside): 6 ft.
Engine: Waukesha, 4¾x6¼, Ricardo head, 4-cylinders, 975 r.p.m.
Lubrication: Force feed system.
Carburetor: Stromberg.
Ignition System: American Bosch high tension magneto.
Cooling System: Pump.
Bearings: Ball and roller.
Transmission: Sliding gear; 1.75 to 3.75 m.p.h. forward; 1.75 m.p.h. reverse.
Final Drive: Spur gear, enclosed and running in oil.

JOHN LAUSON MANUFACTURING CO.

New Holstein, Wisconsin

Lauson 20-35   1930-1937
Lauson 25-45   1930-1937
Lauson 65 22-35   1930-1937

Traction Wheels: Four wheels; two in rear, 54x12, giving traction.

No. of Plows Recommended: Four 14-in.

Length: 126 in.; **Width:** 64 in.; **Height:** 66 in.; **Weight:** 7,650 lbs.

Turning Radius: 14 ft.

Motor: Beaver, vertical, 4 cylinders, cast en bloc.

Lubrication: Splash and force feed.

Carburetor: Kingston, 1½-in.

Ignition System: Splitdorf high tension magneto.

Lighting Equipment: Bosch.

Cooling System: Perfex radiator, centrifugal pump and Automotive fan.

Transmission: Sliding gear; 2½ to 3½ m.p.h. forward; 2 m.p.h. reverse.

Final Drive: Spur gear.

Belt Pulley: 17½x8; 600 r.p.m.

LAUSON 20-35
John Lauson Mfg. Co., New Holstein, Wis.

LAUSON 25-45
Lauson Corp., New Holstein, Wis.

Traction Wheels: Four wheel type; two drivers in rear, 54x16; 20-inch optional; non-drives, 36x6.

No. of Plows Recommended: Five, 14-in.

Length: 166 in.; **Width:** 82 in.; **Height:** 86 in.; **Weight:** 9060 lbs.

Turning Radius (Outside): 17 ft.

Engine: Le Roi, 4½x6, vertical, valve-in-head, 6 cylinders, cast in pairs.

Lubrication: Force feed and splash.

Carburetor: Tillotson, 1½-in.

Ignition System: High tension magneto.

Starting & Lighting Equipment: Bosch.

Cooling System: Tubular radiator, centrifugal pump and Automotive fan.

Bearings: Hyatt and Timken in transmission.

Transmission: Sliding gear; 2.4 to 3.2 m.p.h. forward; 2.1 m.p.h. reverse.

Final Drive: Enclosed spur gear.

Belt Pulley: 17½x8; 600 r.p.m. and 4249 feet per minute at normal engine speed.

Traction Wheels: Four wheel type; two drivers in rear 48x12 and two non-drive in front, 32x6.

No. of Plows Recommended: Three to four, 14-in.

Length: 145 in.; **Width:** 72 in.; **Height:** 62 in.

Turning Radius (Outside): 15 ft.

Engine: Wisconsin, 3⅞x5, valve-in-head, 6 cylinders, cast en bloc.

Lubrication: Force feed.

Carburetor: Tillotson, 1¼-in.

Ignition System: American Bosch high tension magneto.

Cooling System: Tubular radiator, centrifugal pump and fan.

Bearings: Hyatt and Gurney in transmission.

Transmission: Selective gear; 2¼ to 3½ m.p.h. forward; 2¼ m.p.h. reverse.

Final Drive: Spur gear, heat treated steel.

Belt Pulley: 16x8; 700 r.p.m. and 2930 feet per minute at normal engine speed.

LAUSON 65 22-35
Lauson Corp., New Holstein, Wis.

MINNEAPOLIS-MOLINE POWER IMPLEMENT CO.

Minneapolis, Minnesota

The sale of tractors formerly manufactured by Minneapolis Steel & Machinery Co. and Minneapolis Threshing Machine Co. are combined under the new corporate management, but new models await consolidation of engineering and manufacturing facilities.

Minneapolis 17-30 Type B	1930-1934
Minneapolis 27-42	1930-1934
Twin City KT	1930-1934
Twin City 17-28	1930 1934
Twin City 21-32	1930-1934
Twin City 27-44	1930-1934

MINNEAPOLIS 17-30 TYPE B

Traction Wheels: Four wheels with two in rear, 53x12, giving traction.

Length: 143 in.; **Width:** 76½ in.; **Height:** 72 in.; **Weight:** 6800 lbs.

Turning Radius: 16 ft.

Motor: Own, 4⅞x7, vertical, 4 cylinders, cast en bloc.

Lubrication: Mechanical oil pump and splash.

Carburetor: 1½ in.

Ignition System: High tension magneto.

Cooling System: Tubular radiator, centrifugal pump and fan.

Bearings: Roller and ball.

Transmission: Sliding spur gear, enclosed, approximate 2.35 to 3.09 m.p.h forward; 2.26 m.p.h. reverse.

Final Drive: Internal gear and pinion.

Belt Pulley: 15½x7½; 825 r.p.m.

MINNEAPOLIS 27-42
Minneapolis-Moline Power Impl. Co.
Minneapolis, Minn.

Traction Wheels: Four wheels; two traction in rear, 53x12; spade lugs standard equipment. Cleats can be furnished.

No. of Plows Recommended: Four, 14-in.

Length: 143 in.; **Width:** 76½ in.; **Height:** 72 in.; **Weight:** 6800 lbs.

Turning Radius (Outside): 16 ft.

Engine: Own, 4⅞x7, 4 cycle, sleeve-valve in head, 4 cylinders.

Lubrication: Force feed and splash.

Carburetor: Optional, 1½-in.

Ignition System: High tension magneto.

Cooling System: Fan, pump and radiator

Bearings: Roller and bronze.

Transmission: Selective, enclosed, full spur gear; 2.69 to 3.42 m.p.h. forward; 2.52 m.p.h. reverse.

Final Drive: Internal spur gear.

Belt Pulley: 15½x8¼; 925 r.p.m. and 3753 feet per minute at normal engine speed.

Traction Wheels: Four wheels; two traction in rear, 42x10; twenty 4-in. high, two-bolt lugs per wheel.

No. of Plows Recommended: Two to three. 14-in.

Length: 131 in.; **Width:** 59 in.; **Height:** 60½ in.; **Weight:** 4300 lbs.

Turning Radius (Outside): 8 ft.

Engine: Own, 4¼x5, vertical, 4 cylinders, cast en bloc.

Lubrication: Pressure.

Carburetor: Stromberg, 1-in.

Ignition System: Magneto.
Lighting Equipment: Can be furnished.

Cooling System: Pump.

Bearings: Ball, roller and tapered roller.

Transmission: Sliding gear; 2.1, 3⅛ to 4.15 m.p.h. forward; 1.8 m.p.h. reverse.

Final Drive: Spur gear.

Belt Pulley: 14x7; 715 r.p.m. and 2620 feet per minute at normal engine speed.

TWIN CITY KT
Minneapolis-Moline Power Impl. Co.,
Minneapolis, Minn.

Traction Wheels: Four wheels, two in rear, 50x12, giving traction.

No. of Plows Recommended: Three 14-in.

Length: 139 in.; **Width:** 66 in.; **Height:** 66 in.; **Weight:** 5,350 lbs.

Turning Radius (Outside): 14 ft.

Engine: Own make, 4 cylinder, 4¼x6. vertical, cast en bloc, removable sleeve.

Lubrication: Pressure feed.

Carburetor: Schebler, 1¼-in.

Ignition System: American Bosch magneto with impulse coupling.

Cooling System: Modine radiator, centrifugal pump and fan.

Bearings: Hyatt in transmission; Timken in fan and front wheels.

Transmission: Sliding gear; 2.2 and 3 m.p.h. forward.

Final Drive: Enclosed spur gear.

Belt Pulley: 16x7½; 650 r.p.m. and 2720 f.p.m. at normal engine speed.

TWIN CITY 17-28
Minneapolis-Moline Power Impl. Co., Minneapolis, Minn.

TWIN CITY 17-28
Minneapolis-Moline Power Implement Co., Minneapolis, Minn.

Traction Wheels: Four wheels, two in rear, 50x12, giving traction.
No. of Plows Recommended: Three to four, 14-in.
Length: 137 in.; Width: 66 in.; Height: 66 in.; Weight: 5,880 lbs.
Turning Radius (Outside): 14 ft.
Engine: Own, 4½x6, vertical, with removable cylinder blocks, 4 cylinders.
Lubrication: Pressure.
Carburetor: Stromberg, 1¼-in.
Ignition System: American Bosch magneto with impulse coupling.
Lighting Equipment: Gas and electric, with battery or no battery generator.
Cooling System: Modine radiator, centrifugal pump and fan.
Bearings: Timken and ball.
Transmission: Sliding gear; 2.36-3.17-4.05 m.p.h. forward; 1.74 m.p.h. reverse.
Final Drive: Enclosed spur gear.
Belt Pulley: 16x7½; 650 r.p.m. and 2720 feet per minute at normal engine speed.

TWIN CITY 21-32
**Minneapolis-Moline Power Impl. Co.,
Minneapolis, Minn.**

Traction Wheels: Four wheels; two drivers in rear, 60x20.
No. of Plows Recommended: Five to six, 14-in.
Length: 152 in.; Width: 88 in.; Height: 73 in.; Weight: 9,200 lbs.
Turning Radius (Outside): 15 ft.
Engine: Own, 5½x6¾, vertical, valve-in-head, 4 cylinders, cast en bloc, removable sleeve.
Lubrication: Pressure feed.
Carburetor: Schebler 1½ in.
Ignition System: American Bosch magneto with impulse starter.
Cooling System: Modine tubular radiator, centrifugal pump and fan.
Bearings: Hyatt throughout.
Transmission: Sliding gear, 2.2 and 2.9 m.p.h. forward; 1.85 m.p.h. reverse.
Final Drive: Enclosed spur gear.
Belt Pulley: 21x8½; 466 r.p.m. and 2560 feet per minute at normal engine speed.

TWIN CITY 27-44
**Minneapolis-Moline Power Impl. Co.,
Minneapolis, Minn.**

MONARCH TRACTORS CORP.
(Subsidiary to Allis-Chalmers Manufacturing Co.)
Springfield, Illinois

Monarch "50"	1930-1931
Monarch "75"	1930-1931

MONARCH "50"
Allis-Chalmers Mfg. Co., Monarch Div.,
Springfield, Ill.

Traction Wheels: One crawler on each side, 13-inch face.

No. of Plows Recommended: Six, 14-in.

Length: 128 in.; **Width:** 75½ in.; **Height:** 85¼ in.; **Weight:** 14,000 lbs.; **Price:** $3,540.

Engine: Stearns, 5⅛x6½, valve-in-head, 4 cylinders, cast en bloc.

Lubrication: Force feed.

Carburetor: Zenith, 1½-in.

Ignition System: Eisemann magneto.

Starting & Lighting Equipment: Electric Auto-Lite.

Cooling System: Centrifugal pump and fan.

Transmission: Selective sliding gear; 1.81 to 3.96 m.p.h. forward; 2.07 m.p.h. reverse.

Final Drive: Roller chain.

Belt Pulley: 12x9½; 950 r.p.m. and 3,000 feet per minute at normal engine speed.

Traction Wheels: One crawler on each side; 16-inch face.

No. of Plows Recommended: Ten, 14-in.

Length: 159 in.; **Width:** 96⅞ in.; **Height:** 102 in.; **Weight:** 23,600 lbs.; **Price:** $5,350.

Engine: Le Roi, 6½x7, valve-in-head, 4 cylinders, cast in pairs.

Lubrication: Force feed.

Carburetor: Zenith, 1½-in.

Ignition System: Eisemann magneto.

Starting & Lighting Equipment: Electric Auto-Lite.

Cooling System: Centrifugal pump and gear driven fan.

Transmission: Selective, sliding gear, 1.55 to 3.56 m.p.h. forward; 2.64 m.p.h. reverse.

Final Drive: Roller chain.

Belt Pulley: 14x11; 960 r.p.m. and 3500 feet per minute at normal engine speed.

MONARCH "75"
Allis-Chalmers Mfg. Co., Monarch Div.,
Springfield, Ill.

OLIVER FARM EQUIPMENT SALES CO.
Hart-Parr Tractor Division

Charles City, Iowa

1930 marks the first appearance of the Oliver name on a farm tractor but the Charles City plant continued to be known as the Hart-Parr Tractor Division and continued to build the tractor.

Oliver Hart-Parr Row Crop	1930-1937
Oliver Hart-Parr 2-3	1930
Oliver Hart-Parr 3-5	1930

Traction Wheels: Two traction in rear, 59½ by $\frac{9}{16}$ in. face; centers adjust from 60 in., to 74 in. Lug equipment for all soil conditions.

No. of Plows Recommended: Two to three, 14-in.

Length: 125 in.; **Width:** 80 in.; **Height:** 64 in.; **Weight:** 3500 lbs.

Turning Radius: (Outside) 12 ft.

Engine: Own, 4⅛x5¼, vertical valve-in-head; 4 cylinders; removable sleeves.

Lubrication: Pressure.

Carburetor: Ensign, 1¼-in.

Ignition System: High tension magneto.

Cooling System: Fan, pump and radiator.

Bearings: Crank shaft bearings bronze back, babbitt lined.

Transmission. Selective, sliding spur gear, 2.62, 3.23 and 4.15 m.p.h. forward; 2.90 m.p.h. reverse.

Final Drive: Spur gear.

Belt Pulley: 14½x7½; 700 r.p.m. and 2610 feet per minute at normal engine speed.

OLIVER HART-PARR ROW CROP
Oliver Farm Equipment Sales Co.
Hart-Parr Tractor Div., Charles City, Ia.

OLIVER ROW CROP
Oliver Farm Equipment Sales Co., Hart-Parr Tractor Div., Charles City, Ia.

OLIVER HART-PARR 2-3
Oliver Farm Equipment Sales Co.
Hart-Parr Tractor Div., Charles City, Ia.

Traction Wheels: Two traction in rear, 44x10; two non-drive in front, 28x5.

No. of Plows Recommended: Two to three, 14-in.

Length: 112 in.; **Width:** 61 in.; **Height:** 53½ in.; **Weight:** 3825 lbs.

Turning Radius: (Outside) 13½ ft.

Engine: Own, 4⅛x5¼, vertical valve-in-head, 4 cylinders; removable sleeves.

Lubrication: Pressure.

Carburetor: Ensign, 1¼-in.

Ignition System: High tension magneto.

Cooling System: Fan, pump and radiator.

Bearings: Crank shaft bearings bronze back, babbitt lined.

Transmission: Selective, sliding spur gear; 2.62, 3.23 and 4.15 m.p.h. forward; 2.90 m.p.h. reverse.

Final Drive: Spur gear.

Belt Pulley: 14½x7½; 726 r.p.m. and 2709 feet per minute at normal engine speed.

Traction Wheels: Two in rear, 46x12, giving traction and two non-drive in front, 29x6.

No. of Plows Recommended: Three to five, 14-in.

Length: 125¾ in.; **Width:** 65 in.; **Height:** 59½ in.; **Weight:** 5500 lbs.

Turning Radius: (Outside) 14 ft.

Engine: Own, 4¾x6¼, vertical valve-in-head, 4 cylinders; removable sleeves.

Lubrication: Pressure.

Carburetor: Ensign, 1½-in.

Ignition System: High tension magneto.

Cooling System: Fan, pump and radiator.

Bearings: Crank shaft bearings bronze backed, babbitt lined.

Transmission: Selective, sliding spur gear; 2.23, 3.30 and 4.33 m.p.h. forward; 2.63 m.p.h. reverse.

Final Drive: Spur gear.

Belt Pulley: 16¾x8¼; 596 r.p.m. and 2600 feet per minute at normal engine speed.

OLIVER HART-PARR 3-5
Oliver Farm Equipment Sales Co.
Hart-Parr Tractor Div., Charles City, Ia.

OLIVER

HART PARR

POWER

1931

In 1931, the weeding out of tractor manufacturers continued, with 30 manufacturers listing 92 models for sale. Included were 17 models of ten makes not listed in 1930.

The tractor division of Allis-Chalmers Manufacturing Co. purchased the Advance-Rumely Thresher Co. of La Porte, Indiana, with the purchase completed in late May. Caterpillar started production of a diesel tractor.

ADVANCE-RUMELY THRESHER CO., INC.

La Porte, Indiana

Doall   1931
Rumely "Six"   1931

Traction Wheels: Four wheels with two in rear, 42x7, giving traction and two non-drive in front, 26x5.

No. of Plows Recommended: Two, 14-in.

Length: 108 in.; **Width:** 46 to 85 in.; **Height:** 64 in.; **Weight:** 3,000 lbs.

Turning Radius (Outside): 10 ft.; **Acres Plowed in 10-hr. day:** 6.

Engine: Waukesha, 3½x4½, vertical, L-head, 4 cylinders, cast en bloc.

Lubrication: Pressure.

Carburetor: Zenith, 1-in.

Ignition System: High tension magneto with impulse starter.

Cooling System: Thermo-syphon.

Bearings: Three bearings 2 inches in diameter and 7 inches long.

Transmission: Sliding gear; 2⅝ to 3¾ m.p.h. forward; 2⅞ m.p.h. reverse.

Final Drive: Enclosed spur gear.

Belt Pulley: 10x6½; 1,200 r.p.m. and 3,146 feet per minute at normal engine speed.

DOALL
Convertible and Non-Convertible Types

Advance-Rumely Thresher Co., Inc., La Porte, Ind.

RUMELY "SIX"

Advance-Rumely Thresher Co., Inc., La Porte, Ind.

Traction Wheels: Four wheels with two in rear, 48x12, giving traction and two non-drive in front, 30x6.

No. of Plows Recommended: Four, 14-in.

Length: 163 in.; **Width:** 70 in.; **Height:** 74 in.; **Weight:** 5,510 lbs.

Turning Radius (Outside): 15¾ ft:

Engine: Own, 4¼x4¾, L-head, 6 cylinders, cast en bloc.

Lubrication: Pressure

Carburetor: Zenith, 1½-in.

Ignition System: High tension magneto with impulse starter.

Starting and Lighting Equipment: Special attachment.

Cooling System: Fan, centrifugal pump and radiator.

Bearings: New Departure, Timken and bronze.

Transmission: Spur gear; 2.5 to 4.75 m. p.h. forward; 3 to 3.5 m.p.h. reverse.

Final Drive: Spur gear, enclosed in transmission.

Belt Pulley: 13x8; 785 or 892 r.p.m.

ALLIS-CHALMERS MANUFACTURING CO.

Milwaukee, Wisconsin

Allis-Chalmers Models "U" and "UC" are introduced, based on the "United" tractor engineered earlier on a contract basis.

Allis-Chalmers Model "U"   1931-1945
Allis-Chalmers Model "UC"   1931-1945

ALLIS-CHALMERS MODEL "U"

Allis-Chalmers Mfg. Co., Milwaukee, Wis.

Traction Wheels: Four wheel type; two traction in rear, 42x11⅛.

No. of Plows Recommended: Three, 14-in.

Length: 118½ in.; **Width:** 63⅛ in.; **Height:** 53½ in; **Weight:** 4125 lbs.

Turning Radius (Outside): 12 ft.

Engine: Continental, 4¼x5, L-head, 4 cylinders, cast en bloc.

Lubrication: Pressure.

Carburetor: Kingston, 1¼ in.

Ignition System: Magneto.

Cooling System: Fan, pump and radiator.

Bearings: Ball and roller.

Transmission: Automotive; 1½ to 10 m.p.h. forward; 2.69 m.p.h. reverse.

Final Drive: Enclosed spur gear.

Belt Pulley: 10½x7½; 1095 r.p.m. and 3010 feet per minute at normal engine speed.

Traction Wheels: Open type, 2 in. face.
No. of Plows Recommended: Three 14-in.
Length: 138 in.; **Width:** 81$\frac{1}{16}$ in.; **Height:** 67⅝ in.
Turning Radius (Outside): 9 ft.
Engine: Continental, 4¼x5; 4 cylinders.
Lubrication: Force feed by pump.
Carburetor: Kingston, 1¼ in.
Ignition System: Eisemann.
Cooling System: Water, circulated by pump.
Bearings: Ball and roller.
Transmission: Sliding gear; 2⅓ to 3⅓ m.p.h. forward; 2⅓ m.p.h. reverse.
Final Drive: Spur gear.
Belt Pulley: 10½x7½; 1095 r.p.m.

ALLIS-CHALMERS MODEL "UC"
Allis-Chalmers Manufacturing Co., Milwaukee, Wis.

J. I. CASE CO.

Racine, Wisconsin

Case "CO"	1931-1939
Case "L"	1931-1940

Traction Wheels: Four wheels; two traction in rear, 42x12; two non-drive in front, 28x6.
No. of Plows Recommended: Two to three, 14 in.
Length: 112 in.; **Width:** 62 in.; **Height:** 52 in.
Turning Radius (Outside): 10 ft.
Engine: Own, 3⅞x5½, vertical, 4 cylinders, cast singly.
Lubrication: Own make, force feed.
Ignition System: High tension magneto.
Lighting Equipment: Electric.
Cooling System: Fan, pump and radiator.
Transmission: Sliding gear; 2⅓ to 4½ m.p.h. forward.
Final Drive: Chain.
Belt Pulley: 10¼x6¼; 973 r.p.m. and 2600 feet per minute at normal engine speed.

CASE "CO"
J. I. Case Co., Racine, Wis.

CASE "L"

J. I. Case Co., Racine, Wis.

Traction Wheels: Two traction wheels in rear, 48x12.

No. of Plows Recommended: Three or four, 14-in.

Length: 130 in.; **Width:** 67 in.; **Height:** 57 in.

Turning Radius (Outside): 13 ft.

Engine: Own, 4⅝x6, valve-in-head, 4 cylinders, cast singly.

Lubrication: Force feed through drilled crankshaft.

Carburetor: 1½ in.

Ignition System: High tension magneto with impulse coupling.

Cooling System: Fan, pump and radiator.

Bearings: Bronze babbitt lined in motor.

Transmission: Sliding gear, 2½, 3¼ and 4 m.p.h. forward.

Final Drive: Chain, enclosed in oil.

Belt Pulley: 13x8¼; 780 r.p.m. and 2650 feet per minute at normal engine speed.

New CASE Tractors

MODEL "L"

Four cylinder, vertical, valve-in-head engine. Renewable cylinder sleeves. Heavy three-bearing crankshaft drilled for pressure lubrication. 4⅝-inch bore, 6-inch stroke. Turning radius 13-ft. Weight, slightly heavier than three draft horses. Speeds, 2½, 3¼ and 4 miles per hour. Pulls 3-4 fourteen-inch plows.

MODEL "C"

Practically the same tractor as the Model "L," except in size. 3⅞-inch bore, 5½-inch stroke. Turns in 10-ft. radius. Weighs about the same as two horses. Speeds, 2 1/3, 3 1/3 and 4½ miles per hour. Pulls 2-3 fourteen-inch plows.

MODEL "CC"

Does all power jobs equally well, including planting and cultivating row crops. Adjustable rear wheels. Standard tread, 48 inches. Widest spread, 84 inches. Pulls 2 or 4 row planters or cultivators, two bottom fourteen-inch plows or similar loads. Full line of implements available.

MODEL "CO"

For orchard work. Low and light. Only 48 inches high. Does not pack the soil. Deep spade lugs actually loosen it. No protruding parts.

Write the J. I. Case Co., Racine, Wis., for detailed information on these tractors or any other machine in which you may be interested.

CLEVELAND TRACTOR CO.
Cleveland, Ohio

Cletrac 15   1931-1932
Cletrac 40-30   1931

CLETRAC 15
Cleveland Tractor Co., Cleveland, O.

Traction Wheels: Crawlers; each track driven through cast steel drive sprocket meshing with rollers in track.
No. of Plows Recommended: Three, 14-in.
Length: 93½ in.; **Width:** 50½ in.; **Height:** 52½ in.; **Weight:** 5,170 lbs.; **Price:** $1,245.
Turning Radius (outside): 8 ft.; **Acres Plowed in 10-hr. Day:** 11.
Engine: Hercules, 4x4½, L Head, 4 cylinders, cast en bloc.
Lubrication: Force feed to crank, connecting rods and timing gears.
Carburetor: Tillotson, 1-in.
Ignition System: Eisemann high tension magneto with impulse starter.
Cooling System: Tubular radiator with four blade fan.
Bearings: New Departure ball bearings.
Transmission: Selective type sliding gear; 1.95 to 4.37 m.p.h. forward; 2.2 m.p.h. reverse.
Final Drive: Through differential and bull gear on drive sprocket shaft.
Belt Pulley: 10½x6½; 1,040 r.p.m. and 2,860 feet per minute at normal engine speed.

CLETRAC "15"
Cleveland Tractor Co., Cleveland, O.

CLETRAC 40-30
Cleveland Tractor Co., Cleveland, O.

Traction Wheels: Crawlers; each track driven through cast steel drive sprocket meshing with rollers in track.
No. of Plows Recommended: Five 14-in.
Length: 117 in.; **Width:** 61½ in.; **Height,** 63 in.; **Weight:** 9400 lbs.; **Price:** $2475.
Turning Radius (Outside): 8½ ft.; **Acres Plowed in 10-hr. Day:** 18.
Engine: Hercules, 4¼x4½, L-head, 6 cylinders, block removable.
Lubrication: Force feed to crank, connecting rods and timing gears.
Carburetor: Tillotson, 1½-in.
Ignition System: Eisemann high tension or battery; starter and generator.
Starting and Lighting Equipment: Delco-Remy.
Cooling System: Tubular radiator and four blade fan.
Bearings: Ball, New Departure.
Transmission: Selective type sliding gear 2.06 to 4.42 m.p.h. Forward; 2.28 m.p.h. Reverse.
Final Drive: Through differential and bull gear on drive sprocket shaft.
Belt Pulley: 13x8½; 943 r.p.m. and 3200 feet per minute at normal engine speed.

EAGLE MANUFACTURING CO.

Appleton, Wisconsin

Eagle "6A"   1931-1938

EAGLE "6A"
Eagle Mfg. Co., Appleton, Wis.

Traction Wheels: Four wheels; two in rear, 48x12, giving traction.
No. of Plows Recommended: Three to four, 14-in.
Length: 134 in.; **Width:** 70 in.; **Height:** 61 in.; **Weight:** 5000 lbs.
Turning Radius (Outside): 15 ft.
Engine: Waukesha, 4x4¾, L Head, 6 cylinders, cast en bloc.
Lubrication: Force feed, pump.
Carburetor: Zenith, 1¼-in.
Ignition System: Splitdorf, (H.T.), with automatic impulse.
Cooling System: Fan, pump and radiator.
Bearings: Hyatt, Timken and S. K. F.
Transmission: Selective, sliding spur gear; 4½ to 2½ m.p.h. forward; 2½ m.p.h. reverse.
Final Drive: Enclosed spur gear through live axle.
Belt Pulley: 16x8; 625 r.p.m. and 2600 ft. per minute at normal engine speed.

HUBER MANUFACTURING CO.
Marion, Ohio

Huber Super Four 32-45
Modern Farmer 30

1931-1938
1931-1933

HUBER SUPER FOUR 32-45
Huber Manufacturing Co., Marion. O.

Traction Wheels: Four wheel type; two traction in rear, 56x18.

No. of Plows Recommended: Four 14-in.

Length: 160 in.; **Width:** 84 in.; **Height:** 62 in.; **Weight:** 8,900 lbs.

Turning Radius (Outside): 14 ft. Acres Plowed in 10-hr. **Day:** 15.

Engine: Stearns, 5⅛x6½, overhead valves, 4 cylinders, cast en bloc.

Lubrication: Force feed.

Carburetor: Zenith.

Ignition System: Eisemann high tension magneto with impulse starter.

Cooling System: Young radiator.

Bearings: Hyatt and Timken.

Transmission: Selective gears; 2.4 to 3.2 m.p.h. forward; 2 m.p.h. reverse.

Final Drive: Enclosed spur gear, live axle.

Belt Pulley: 15½x8; 666 r.p.m. and 2,677 feet per minute at normal engine speed.

HUBER "SUPER FOUR"
Huber Mfg. Co., Marion, O.

MODERN FARMER 30
Huber Mfg. Co., Marion, O.

Traction Wheels: Four wheels; two traction in rear, 42x10.
No. of Plows Recommended: Three, 14 in.
Length: 115 in.; **Width:** 68 in.; **Height:** 61 in.; **Weight:** 3700 lbs.
Turning Radius (outside): 12 ft.
Engine: Waukesha, 4¼x5; L-head, 4 cylinders, cast en bloc.
Lubrication: Force feed.
Carburetor: Zenith, 1¼ in.
Ignition System: United Bosch; U-4, high tension magneto.
Cooling System: Young radiator, own fan.
Bearings: Hyatt and Timken.
Transmission: Selective gear; 2.4 to 6.4 m.p.h. forward.
Final Drive: Bull gear.
Belt Pulley: 14x6; 705 r.p.m. and 2600 ft. per minute at normal engine speed.

INTERNATIONAL HARVESTER CO. OF AMERICA
Chicago, Illinois

International Harvester celebrated the McCormick Reaper Centennial in 1931 by introducing a new line of industrial tractors.

McCormick-Deering Fairway	1931-1933
McCormick-Deering Industrial 30	1931-1932
McCormick-Deering 10-20 Orchard	1931-1933

McCORMICK-DEERING FAIRWAY
International Harvester Co. of America, Chicago, Ill.

Traction Wheels: Four wheel type; two traction in rear, 40x16; two non-traction in front, 25x8.
Length: 140 in.; **Width:** 73 in.; **Height:** 76 in.; **Weight:** 3,650 lbs.
Turning Radius (Outside): 8 ft.
Engine: Own, 3¾x5, vertical, valve-in-head, 4 cylinders, removable cylinders.
Lubrication: Circulating splash.
Carburetor: Own, 1¼ in.
Ignition System: Own high tension magneto with automatic impulse starter.
Cooling System: Thermo-syphon.
Bearings: New Departure on crankshaft, in transmission and differential.
Transmission: Selective; 2, 3 and 4 m.p.h. forward; 2½ m.p.h. reverse.
Final Drive: Spur gear.
Belt Pulley: 14x6½; 693 r.p.m. and 2,540 feet per minute.

McCORMICK-DEERING INDUSTRIAL 30
International Harvester Co. of America, Chicago, Ill.

Traction Wheels: Four rubber-tired wheels; dual pneumatic traction in rear, 42x9; two non-traction in front, 32x6.

Length: 129 in.; **Width:** 66 in.; **Height:** 70 in.; **Weight:** 9,750 lbs.

Turning Radius (Outside): 16½ ft.

Engine: Own, 4¾x6, valve-in-head, 4 cylinders; removable cylinders.

Lubrication: Circulating splash.

Carburetor: Own.

Ignition System: Own high tension with automatic impulse starter.

Cooling System: Impeller pump; thermostatic control.

Bearings: New Departure on crankshaft; own make roller in transmission, wheels and rear axle.

Transmission: 2.5, 4.2, 6.8 m.p.h. forward; 3.2 m.p.h. reverse.

Final Drive: Spur gear, live axle.

Belt Pulley: 16¾x9; 593 r.p.m. and 2,600 feet per minute.

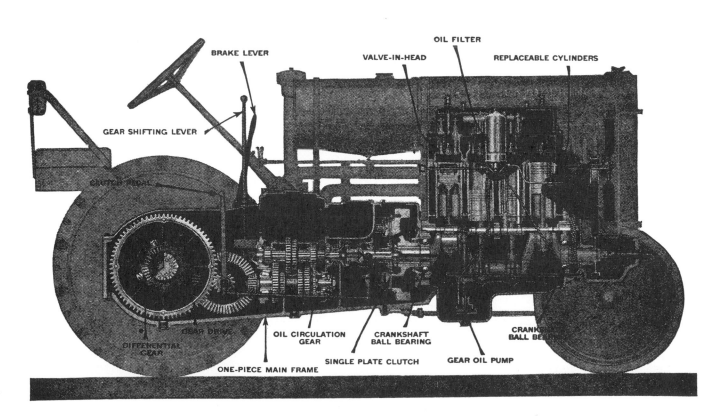

McCORMICK-DEERING "INDUSTRIAL"
International Harvester Co. of Am., Chicago, Ill.

McCORMICK-DEERING 10-20 ORCHARD
International Harvester Co. of America, Chicago, Ill.

Traction Wheels: Four wheels; two traction in rear, 36x12; two non-traction in front, 26x4½.
No. of Plows Recommended: Two, 11 in.
Length: 118 in.; **Width:** 62 in.; **Height:** 55 in.; **Weight:** 4,335 lbs.
Turning Radius (Outside): 14½ ft.
Engine: Own, 4¼x5, vertical, valve-in-head, 4 cylinders, removable cylinders.
Lubrication: Circulating splash.
Carburetor: Own, 1¼ in.
Ignition System: Own high tension magneto with automatic impulse starter.
Cooling System: Thermo-syphon.
Bearings: Own make roller in transmission and rear axle; New Departure on crankshaft.
Transmission: Selective; 1¾, 2½, 3½ m.p.h. forward; 2¼ m.p.h. reverse.
Final Drive: Spur gear.
Belt Pulley: 15¼x7; 645 r.p.m. and 2,575 feet per minute.

OLIVER FARM EQUIPMENT SALES CO.
Hart-Parr Tractor Division
Charles City, Iowa

Oliver Hart-Parr 18-28   1931-1937
Oliver Hart-Parr 28-44   1931-1937

Traction Wheels: Two traction in rear, 44x10; two non-drive in front, 28x5.
No. of Plows Recommended: Two to three, 14-in.
Length: 112 in.; **Width:** 61 in.; **Height:** 53½ in.; **Weight:** 4000 lbs.
Turning Radius: (Outside) 13½ ft.
Engine: Own, 4⅛x5¼, vertical valve-in-head, 4 cylinders; removable sleeves.
Lubrication: Pressure.
Carburetor: Ensign, 1¼-in.
Ignition System: High tension magneto.
Cooling System: Fan, pump and radiator.
Bearings: Crank shaft bearings bronze back, babbitt lined.
Transmission: Selective, sliding spur gear; 2.62, 3.23 and 4.15 m.p.h. forward; 2.90 m.p.h. reverse.
Final Drive: Spur gear.
Belt Pulley: 14½x7½; 726 r.p.m. and 2709 feet per minute at normal engine speed.

OLIVER HART-PARR 18-28
**Oliver Farm Equipment Sales Co.
Hart-Parr Tractor Div., Charles City, Ia.**

OLIVER HART-PARR 18-28
Oliver Farm Equipment Sales Co., Hart-Parr Tractor Div., Charles City, Ia.

OLIVER HART-PARR 28-44
Oliver Farm Equipment Sales Co.
Hart-Parr Tractor Div., Charles City, Ia.

Traction Wheels: Two in rear, 46x12, giving traction and two non-drive in front, 29x6.

No. of Plows Recommended: Three to five, 14-in.

Length: 125¾ in.; **Width:** 65 in.; **Height:** 59½ in.; **Weight:** 5575 lbs.

Turning Radius: (Outside) 14 ft.

Engine: Own, 4¾x6¼, vertical valve-in-head, 4 cylinders; removable sleeves.

Lubrication: Pressure.

Carburetor: Ensign, 1½-in.

Ignition System: High tension magneto.

Cooling System: Fan, pump and radiator.

Bearings: Crank shaft bearings bronze backed, babbitt lined.

Transmission: Selective, sliding spur gear; 2.23, 3.30 and 4.33 m.p.h. forward; 2.63 m.p.h. reverse.

Final Drive: Spur gear.

Belt Pulley: 16¾x8¼; 596 r.p.m. and 2600 feet per minute at normal engine speed.

OLIVER HART-PARR 28-44
Oliver Farm Equipment Sales Co., Hart-Parr Tractor Div., Charles City, Ia.

Many prominent manufacturers equip their machines with Twin Disc clutches.

When Steady Performance Counts

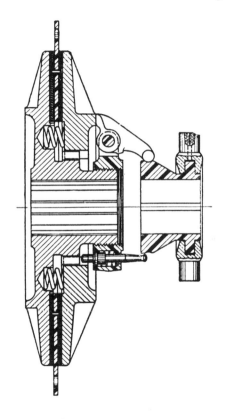

A popular Twin Disc clutch used in tractors and combines. A driving plate of tempered steel, smooth and true on both sides, bolts firmly to engine flywheel. The dark lines on both sides of driving plate show the large contact areas. Lock pin and threaded yoke for adjustment, and the simple, effective method of applying clamping pressure gradually are clearly shown.

TRACTORS and combines, built and sold to reduce crop production costs, must keep going—sometimes for weeks at a time.

A Twin Disc clutch eliminates all the expensive and annoying delays that can be caused by clutches. Tractor and combine operators prefer this dependable, smooth working clutch because it requires little attention, is easy to adjust, and carries them through emergencies.

Twin Disc clutches have been developed and improved by twelve years of tractor and combine field work. They are made in a large variety of sizes and styles and are standard equipment on many of the most popular tractors and combines. Write for information on clutch care and operation.

TWIN DISC CLUTCH COMPANY
RACINE   WISCONSIN

1932

Eighty-eight models of 32 makes of tractors were shown in the 1932 *Cooperative Tractor Catalog*, including 29 models of eleven makes not offered in 1931. This year was generally marked as the beginning of the dust bowl. Such things are hard to pinpoint because they are not uniform. By 1936 there was little doubt we had a dust bowl.

In 1932, Allis-Chalmers Manufacturing Co. introduced farm tractors equipped with rubber tires and many farmers were as skeptical about the tires as they were about the possibility of rain. Users questioned the ability of the tires to last and their ability to provide traction in the field, but everyone was surprised by the fuel savings they received.

ALLIS-CHALMERS MANUFACTURING CO.

Milwaukee, Wisconsin

Allis-Chalmers Rumely Doall	1932-1933
Allis-Chalmers Rumely "6"	1932-1933
Allis-Chalmers Rumely Oilpull "Y" 30-50	1932-1935
Allis-Chalmers "35"	1932-1933
Allis-Chalmers "50"	1932-1933
Allis-Chalmers Model "L"	1932-1944
Monarch "75"	1932

Traction Wheels: Four wheels with two in rear, 42x7, giving traction and two non-drive in front, 26x5.

No. of Plows Recommended: Two, 14-in.

Length: 108 in.; **Width:** 46 to 85 in.; **Height:** 64 in.; **Weight:** 3,000 lbs.

Turning Radius (Outside): 10 ft.; **Acres Plowed in 10-hr. day:** 6.

Engine: Waukesha, 3½x4½, vertical, L-head, 4 cylinders, cast en bloc.

Lubrication: Pressure.

Carburetor: Zenith, 1-in.

Ignition System: High tension magneto with impulse starter.

Cooling System: Thermo-syphon.

Bearings: Three bearings 2 inches in diameter and 7 inches long.

Transmission: Sliding gear; 2⅝ to 3¾ m.p.h. forward; 2⅞ m.p.h. reverse.

Final Drive: Enclosed spur gear.

Belt Pulley: 10x6½; 1,200 r.p.m. and 3,146 feet per minute at normal engine speed.

ALLIS-CHALMERS RUMELY DOALL
Allis-Chalmers Mfg. Co., Milwaukee, Wis.

ALLIS-CHALMERS RUMELY "6"
Allis-Chalmers Mfg. Co., Milwaukee, Wis.

Traction Wheels: Four wheels with two in rear, 48x12, giving traction and two non-drive in front, 30x6.

No. of Plows Recommended: Four, 14-in.

Length: 163 in.; **Width:** 70 in.; **Height:** 74 in.; **Weight:** 5,510 lbs.

Turning Radius (Outside): 15¾ ft:

Engine: Own, 4¼x4¾, L-head, 6 cylinders, cast en bloc.

Lubrication: Pressure

Carburetor: Zenith, 1½-in.

Ignition System: High tension magneto with impulse starter.

Starting and Lighting Equipment: Special attachment.

Cooling System: Fan, centrifugal pump and radiator.

Bearings: New Departure, Timken and bronze.

Transmission: Spur gear; 2.5 to 4.75 m. p. h. forward; 3 to 3.5 m.p.h. reverse.

Final Drive: Spur gear, enclosed in transmission.

Belt Pulley: 13x8; 785 or 892 r.p.m.

Traction Wheels: Four wheels with two in rear, 57½x18, giving traction and two non-drive in front, 38½x8.

No. of Plows Recommended: Five to six 14-in.

Length: 167 in.; **Width:** 82 in.; **Height:** 98½ in.

Turning Radius (Outside): 19 ft.

Engine: Own, 7⅛x9½, horizontal, valve-in-head, 2 cylinders, removable sleeve.

Lubrication: Mechanical oiler and splash.

Carburetor: Own, 2⅜ in.

Ignition System: High tension.

Cooling System: Pump circulation; oil in system.

Bearings: New Departure, Timken roller and bronze.

Transmission: Spur gear; 2.3, 2.9 and 3.5 m. p. h. forward; 2.9 m. p. h. reverse.

Final Drive: Spur gear enclosed in transmission.

Belt Pulley: 21¾x10; 610 to 635 r.p.m. and 3400 feet per minute at 610 r.p.m.

ALLIS-CHALMERS RUMELY OILPULL "Y" 30-50
Allis-Chalmers Mfg. Co., Milwaukee, Wis.

ALLIS-CHALMERS "35"
Allis-Chalmers Mfg. Co., Milwaukee, Wis.

Traction Wheels: One crawler on each side, 67x13.

No. of Plows Recommended: Four 14 in.

Length: 119 in.; **Width:** 66 in.; **Height:** 66 in.; **Weight:** 10,500 lbs.; **Price:** $2,450.

Engine: Own, 4¾x6½, vertical, 4 cylinders, cast en bloc. Removable cylinder liners.

Lubrication: Full force feed.

Carburetor: Zenith, 1½ in.

Ignition System: Eisemann magneto.

Starting & Lighting Equipment: Electric Auto-Lite.

Cooling System: Fan, pump and radiator.

Transmission: Selective sliding gear; three speeds forward; 1.84 to 4.01 m.p.h. forward; 2.12 m.p.h. reverse.

Final Drive: Gear.

Belt Pulley: 12x8¾; 930 r.p.m. and 2,922 feet per minute at normal engine speed.

ALLIS-CHALMERS "35"
Allis-Chalmers Mfg. Co., Milwaukee, Wis.

Traction Wheels: One crawler on each side, 13-inch face.

No. of Plows Recommended: Six, 14-in.

Length: 128 in.; **Width:** 75½ in.; **Height:** 85¼ in.; **Weight:** 14,000 lbs.; **Price:** $3,540.

Engine: Own, 5¼x6½, valve-in-head, 4 cylinders, cast en bloc. Removable cylinder liners.

Lubrication: Force feed.

Carburetor: Zenith, 1½-in.

Ignition System: Eisemann magneto.

Starting & Lighting Equipment: Electric Auto-Lite.

Cooling System: Fan, pump and radiator.

Transmission: Selective sliding gear; 1.81 to 3.96 m.p.h. forward; 2.07 m.p.h. reverse.

Final Drive: Roller chain.

Belt Pulley: 12x9½; 950 r.p.m. and 3,000 feet per minute at normal engine speed.

ALLLIS-CHALMERS "50"
Allis-Chalmers Mfg. Co., Milwaukee, Wis.

Traction Wheels: One crawler on each side.

No. of Plows Recommended: Ten, 14-in.

Length: 153¼ in.; **Width:** 93 in.; **Height:** 103$\frac{13}{16}$ in.; **Weight:** 22,000 lbs.

Engine: Own, 5¼x6½, vertical, 6 cylinders, cast en bloc.

Lubrication: Pressure.

Carburetor: Zenith, 2—1½-in.

Ignition System: Eisemann magneto.

Starting and Lighting Equipment: Extra.

Cooling System: Fan, pump and radiator.

Bearings: 2¾-in. Diam., rear 4¾-in. long, front and Int. 4-in. long.

Transmission: Own type, 1.94 to 4.10 m.p.h. forward; 1.45-3.07 m.p.h. reverse.

Final Drive: Nickel steel gear.

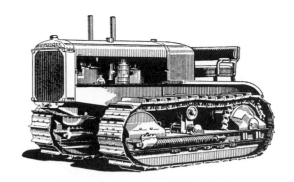

ALLIS-CHALMERS MODEL "L"
Allis-Chalmers Mfg. Co., Milwaukee, Wis.

ALLIS-CHALMERS MODEL "L"
Allis-Chalmers Mfg. Co., Milwaukee, Wis.

MONARCH "75"
Allis-Chalmers Mfg. Co., Milwaukee, Wis.

Traction Wheels: One crawler on each side; 16-inch face.

No. of Plows Recommended: Ten, 14-in.

Length: 159 in.; **Width:** 96⅞ in.; **Height:** 102 in.; **Weight:** 23,600 lbs.; **Price:** $5,350.

Engine: Le Roi, 6¾x7, valve-in-head, 4 cylinders, cast in pairs.

Lubrication: Force feed.

Carburetor: Zenith, 1½-in.

Ignition System: Eisemann magneto.

Starting & Lighting Equipment: Electric Auto-Lite.

Cooling System: Centrifugal pump and gear driven fan.

Transmission: Selective, sliding gear, 1.55 to 3.56 m.p.h. forward; 2.64 m.p.h. reverse.

Final Drive: Roller chain.

Belt Pulley: 14x11; 960 r.p.m. and 3500 feet per minute at normal engine speed.

CATERPILLAR TRACTOR CO.
Peoria, Illinois

Caterpillar Twenty-Five	1932-1933
Caterpillar Thirty-Five 37-41	1932
Caterpillar Fifty 50-55	1932
Caterpillar Sixty-Five 68-79	1932
Caterpillar Diesel 68-79	1932

Traction Wheels: Two self-laying tracks; 56⅞ in. ground contact; 11 in. wide.

No. of Plows Recommended: Four 14-in.

Length: 115.5 in.; **Width:** 61.5 in.; **Height:** 60⅝ in.; **Weight:** 7,670 lbs.; **Price:** $1900, f.o.b. Peoria, Ill.

Turning Radius (Outside): 68½ in.

Engine: Own, 4x5½, vertical, 4 cylinders, cast singly.

Lubrication: Pressure oiling system.

Carburetor: Ensign, 1¼ in.

Ignition System: Eisemann high tension magneto.

Lighting Equipment: Robert Bosch generator.

Cooling System: Water pump and gear driven fan.

Bearings: Largely anti-friction ball and roller.

Transmission: Sliding gear; 1.8-2.6-3.6 m.p.h. forward; 2 m.p.h. reverse.

Final Drive: Spur gears, completely enclosed.

Belt Pulley: 11⅞x6½; 835 r.p.m. and 2600 feet per minute at governed engine speed.

"CATERPILLAR" TWENTY-FIVE
Caterpillar Tractor Co., Peoria, Ill.

Traction Wheels: Two self-laying tracks, 14x71⅜ in.

Length: 139⅜ in.; Width: 72⅛ in.; Height: 69¼ in.; Weight: 12,280 lbs.; Price: $2400 f.o.b. factory.

Turning Radius (Outside): 7.2 ft.

Engine: Own, 4⅞x6½, vertical, 4 cylinders, cast singly.

Lubrication: Pressure oiling system.

Carburetor: Ensign, 1½ in.

Ignition System: Eisemann high tension magneto.

Lighting Equipment: Robert Bosch generator.

Cooling System: Water, pump circulation, gear driven fan.

Bearings: Largely anti-friction ball and roller.

Transmission: Sliding gear; 1.7, 2.5, 3.2 and 4.6 m.p.h. forward; 1.9 m.p.h. reverse.

Final Drive: Spur gears, completely enclosed.

Belt Pulley: 12x8½; 850 r.p.m. and 2670 feet per minute at normal engine speed.

"CATERPILLAR" THIRTY-FIVE 37-41
Caterpillar Tractor Co., Peoria, Ill.

"CATERPILLAR" FIFTY 50-55
Caterpillar Tractor Co., Peoria, Ill.

Traction Wheels: Two self-laying tracks, 15x81⅞ in.

Length: 146¼ in.; Width: 78⅞ in.; height: 75¾ in.; Weight: 17,190 lbs.; Price: $3675 f.o.b. factory.

Turning Radius (outside): 7½ ft.

Engine: Own, 5½x6½, vertical, 4 cylinders, cast singly.

Lubrication: Pressure oiling system.

Carburetor: Ensign, 1½ in.

Ignition System: Eisemann high tension magneto.

Lighting Equipment: Robert Bosch generator.

Cooling System: Water, pump circulation, gear driven fan.

Bearings: Largely anti-friction ball and roller.

Transmission: Sliding gear, 1.6, 2.4, 3.4 and 4.7 m.p.h. forward; 1.9 m.p.h. reverse.

Final Drive: Spur gears, completely enclosed.

Belt Pulley: 13⅜x10; 752 r.p.m. and 2630 feet per minute at governed engine speed.

Traction Wheels: Two self-laying tracks, 16x83½.

Length: 159⅛ in.; Width: 101 in.; Height: 87½ in.; Weight: 23,007 lbs.; Price: $4350, f.o.b. factory.

Engine: Own, 7x8½, vertical, 4 cylinders, cast singly.

Lubrication: Pressure oiling system.

Carburetor: Ensign, 1¾ in.

Ignition System: Eisemann high tension magneto.

Lighting Equipment: Robert Bosch generator.

Cooling System: Water, pump circulation, gear driven fan.

Bearings: Largely anti-friction ball and roller.

Transmission: Sliding gear; 1.9, 2.6 and 4.4 m.p.h. forward; 1.4 m.p.h. reverse.

Final Drive: Spur gears, completely enclosed.

Belt Pulley: 15x11; 650 r.p.m. and 2555 feet per minute at normal engine speed.

"CATERPILLAR" SIXTY-FIVE 68-79
Caterpillar Tractor Co., Peoria, Ill.

"CATERPILLAR" DIESEL 68-79
Caterpillar Tractor Co., Peoria, Ill.

Traction Wheels: Two self-laying tracks, 16x83½.
Length: 161¼ in.; **Width:** 101 in.; **Height:** 86⅝ in.; **Weight:** 24,390 lbs.; **Price:** $6500 f.o.b. factory.
Engine: Own, 6⅛x9¼, vertical, 4 cylinders, cast en bloc, with seperate cylinder liners.
Lubrication: Pressure oiling system.
Ignition System:
Starting Equipment: Auxiliary gasoline engine.
Lighting Equipment: Bosch generator.
Cooling System: Water, pump circulation, belt driven pump and fan.
Bearings: Largely anti-friction ball and roller.
Transmission: Sliding gear; 2.1, 2.8 and 4.7 m.p.h. forward; 1.5 m.p.h. reverse.
Final Drive: Spur gear, completely enclosed.
Belt Pulley: 15x11; 700 r.p.m. and 2750 feet per minute at normal engine speed.

CENTAUR TRACTOR CORP.

Greenwich, Ohio

Centaur 6-10

1932-1934

Traction Wheels: Steel, 28x4.
No. of Plows Recommended: One 12-in.
Length: 113 in.; **Width:** 30½ in.; **Height:** 45 in.; **Weight:** 1,590 lbs.; **Price:** $548.
Turning Radius: 7 ft. inside.
Engine: Le Roi, 3⅜x4¼, vertical, 2 cylinders, cast en bloc.
Lubrication: Splash and force.
Carburetor: Le Roi.
Ignition System: Eisemann, high tension magneto.
Cooling System: Thermo syphon.
Bearings: Bronze and roller.
Transmission: Own, 1 to 3½ m. p. h. forward and ½ m. p. h. reverse.
Final Drive: Chain.
Belt Pulley: 5x4½; 800 to 1,600 r.p.m.

CENTAUR 6-10
The Centaur Tractor Corp., Greenwich, Ohio

CLEVELAND TRACTOR CO.
Cleveland, Ohio

Cletrac "25"	1932-1935
Cletrac "35"	1932-1935
Cletrac "55"	1932-1935
Cletrac (80)	1932-1935

Traction: Crawlers; each track driven through cast steel drive sprocket meshing with rollers in track.

No. of Plows Recommended: Four to five, 14-in.

Length: 105 in.; **Width:** 57½ in.; **Height:** 55¼ in.; **Weight:** 7000 lbs., approximately; **Price** $1850.

Turning Radius (outside); 8½ ft.

Engine: Hercules, 3¾x4¼, L-head, 6 cylinders, cast en bloc.

Lubrication: Force feed to crank, connecting rods and timing gears.

Carburetor: Tillotson, 1¼-in.

Ignition System: Battery, starter and generator or Eisemann magneto.

Cooling System: Tubular radiator with fan. Pump circulation.

Bearings: New Departure ball.

Transmission: Selective type sliding gear; 1.95 to 4 m.p.h. forward; 1.8 m.p.h. reverse.

Final Drive: Through differential and bull gear on drive sprocket shaft.

Belt Pulley: 12x6½; 2950 feet per minute at normal engine speed.

Power Reduction: 542 r.p.m.

CLETRAC "25"
Cleveland Tractor Co., Cleveland, O.

CLETRAC "35"
Cleveland Tractor Co., Cleveland, O.

Traction Wheels: Crawlers; each track driven through cast steel drive sprocket meshing with rollers in track.

No. of Plows Recommended: Five to seven, 14-in.

Length: 117 in.; **Width:** 61½ in.; **Height,** 63 in.; **Weight:** 10,400 lbs., approximately; **Price:** $2475.

Turning Radius (outside): 8½ ft.

Engine: Hercules, 4¼x4½, L-head, 6 cylinders, block removable.

Lubrication: Force feed to crank, connecting rods and timing gears.

Carburetor: Tillotson, 1½-in.

Ignition System: Eisemann high tension or battery; starter and generator.

Starting and Lighting Equipment: Delco-Remy.

Cooling System: Tubular radiator and four blade fan. Pump circulation.

Bearings: Ball, New Departure.

Transmission: Selective type sliding gear. 1.87 to 4.42 m.p.h. forward; 2.28 m.p.h. reverse.

Final Drive: Through differential and bull gear on drive sprocket shaft.

Belt Pulley: 13x8½; 943 r.p.m. and 3200 feet per minute at normal engine speed.

Power Reduction: 545 r.p.m.

CLETRAC "35"
Cleveland Tractor Co., Cleveland, O.

Traction Wheels: One crawler on each side, 80x14.

No. of Plow Recommended: Six to eight, 14-in.

Length: 132 in.; **Width:** 69 in.; **Height:** 63 in.; **Weight:** 12,000 lbs., approximately; **Price:** $3685.

Turning Radius (Outside): 11 ft.

Engine: Wisconsin, 4½x5, valve-in-head, 6 cylinders, cast en bloc.

Lubrication: Force feed to crankshaft, connecting rods and valve rockers.

Carburetor: Schebler, 1¾ in.

Ignition System: Battery, coil and distributor, or magneto.

Starting and Lighting Equipment: Delco Remy.

Cooling System: Water with pump circulation.

Bearings: Bronze backed, babbitt lined.

Transmission: Selective, sliding gear; 2 to 4.6 m.p.h. forward; 2 m.p.h. reverse.

Final Drive: Through differential and bull gear on drive sprocket shaft.

Belt Pulley: 15x13; 855 r.p.m. and 3,300 feet per minute at normal engine speed.

Power Take-Off: 850 r.p.m.

CLETRAC "55"
Cleveland Tractor Co., Cleveland, O.

CLETRAC (80)
Cleveland Tractor Co., Cleveland, O.

Traction Wheels: Two crawlers, 96x17.

No. of Plows Recommended: Twelve to fourteen, 14-in.

Length: 161 in.; **Width:** 96 in.; **Height:** 82 in.; **Weight:** 21,900 lbs., approximately; **Price:** $4975.

Turning Radius (Outside): 15 ft.

Engine: Wisconsin, 5¾x6½, 6 cylinders, cast in pairs.

Lubrication: Force feed.

Carburetor: Schebler (2).

Ignition System: Delco Remy.

Starting and Lighting Equipment: Delco Remy.

Cooling System: Fan, pump and radiator.

Bearings: Ball and roller.

Transmission: Selective gear, 1¾ to **3.6** m.p.h. forward; 2.1 m.p.h. reverse.

Final Drive: Enclosed, planetary pinion.

Belt Pulley: ·24x15; 477 r.p.m. and 2980 feet per minute at normal engine speed.

FOOTE BROS. GEAR & MACHINE CO.

Chicago, Illinois

Bates Steel Mule Model 35	1932-1935
Bates Steel Mule Model 45	1932
Bates Steel Mule Model 80	1932-1935

BATES STEEL MULE MODEL 35
Foote Bros. Gear & Machine Co., Chicago, Ill.

Traction Wheels: Two crawlers, 12-in. wide and 70-in. long.

Length: 120 in.; **Width:** 72 in.; **Height:** 70 in.; **Weight:** 10,750 lbs.

Turning Radius (Outside): 6 ft.

Engine: Waukesha, 4¼x4¾, Ricardo head, 6 cylinders, 1500 r.p.m.

Lubrication: Force feed system.

Carburetor: Schebler.

Ignition System: Bosch high tension magneto.

Cooling System: Pump.

Bearings: Ball and roller.

Transmission: Sliding gear; 1.75 to 3.75 m.p.h. forward; 1.75 m.p.h. reverse.

Final Drive: Spur gear, enclosed and running in oil.

Belt Pulley: 12x8¾; 858 r.p.m. and 2695 f.p.m. at normal engine speed.

Traction Wheels: Two crawlers, 14 inches wide and 82 inches long.
Length: 128 in.; Width: 74 in.; Height: 72 in.; Weight: 14,000 lbs.
Turning Radius (Outside): 7 ft.
Engine: Waukesha, 4⅝x5⅛, Ricardo-head, 6 cylinders, cast in pairs, 1400 r.p.m.
Lubrication: Force feed.
Carburetor: Schebler.
Ignition System: Bosch high tension magneto.
Cooling System: Pump.
Bearings: Ball and roller.
Transmission: Sliding gear; 1¾ to 3¾ m.p.h. forward; 1¾ m.p.h. reverse.
Final Drive: Spur gear, enclosed and running in oil.
Belt Pulley: 12x8¾; 858 r.p.m. and 2695 f.p.m. at normal engine speed.

BATES STEEL MULE MODEL 45
Foote Bros. Gear & Machine Co., Chicago, Ill

BATES STEEL MULE MODEL 80
Foote Bros. Gear & Machine Co., Chicago, Ill.

Traction Wheels: Two crawlers, 104x18, 3744 sq. in. on ground.
Length: 146 in.; Width: 97 in.; Height: 84 in.; Weight: 22500 lbs.
Turning Radius (Outside): 8 ft.
Engine: Waukesha, 6½x7, Ricardo-head, 4 cylinders, 4 cycle, 900 r.p.m.
Carburetor: Stromberg.
Lubrication: Force feed.
Ignition System: Bosch high tension magneto.
Cooling System: Fan, circulating pump and radiator.
Bearings: Ball and roller.
Transmission: Sliding gear; 1.5 to 3.75 m.p.h. forward; 1.25 m.p.h. reverse.
Final Drive: Spur gear, enclosed and running in oil.
Belt Pulley: 16x10½; 650 r.p.m. and 2700 f.p.m. at normal engine speed.

INTERNATIONAL HARVESTER CO. OF AMERICA

Chicago, Illinois

McCormick-Deering Farmall 30	1932-1940
McCormick-Deering T-20 Tractractor	1932-1939

Traction Wheels: Four wheel type; two traction in rear, 42x12; two non-drive in front, 25x4.

No. of Plows Recommended: Three, 14-in.

Length: 147 in.; **Width:** 89¼ in.; **Height:** 81 in.; **Weight:** 5300 lbs., approximately.

Turning Radius (outside): 8⅔ ft.

Engine: Own, 4¼x5, vertical, valve-in-head, 4 cylinders, removable cylinders.

Lubrication: Circulating splash.

Carburetor: Zenith, 1¼-in.

Ignition System: Own, high-tension, with impulse starter.

Cooling System: Pump; thermostatic control.

Bearings: Ball and roller.

Transmission: Own, selective; 2, 2¾ and 3¾ m.p.h. forward; 2½ m.p.h. reverse.

Final Drive: Spur gear.

Belt Pulley: 14⅝x7; 682 r.p.m. and 2612 feet per minute at normal engine speed.

McCORMICK-DEERING FARMALL 30
International Harvester Co. of America, Chicago, Ill.

McCORMICK-DEERING T-20 TRACTRACTOR
International Harvester Co. of America, Chicago, Ill.

Traction Wheels: One crawler on each side, 10x52½.

No. of Plows Recommended: Three, 14-in.

Length: 112½ in.; **Width:** 54¾ in.; **Height:** 55½ in.; **Weight:** 6250 lbs.

Turning Radius (outside): 6 ft.

Engine: Own, 3¾x5, vertical, valve-in-head, 4 cylinders, removable cylinders.

Lubrication:. Circulating splash; transmission oil gauge also.

Carburetor: Zenith, 1¼-in.

Ignition System: Own high tension magneto with automatic impulse starter.

Cooling System: Impeller pump; thermostatic control.

Bearings: New Departure roller on crankshaft, transmission, final drive and sprocket bearings.

Transmission: Selective; 1¾, 2¾ and 3¾ m.p.h. forward; 3 m.p.h. reverse.

Final Drive: Machine-cut gears running in oil bath.

*Belt Pulley: 15¼x7; 645 r.p.m. and 2575 feet per minute at normal engine speed.

*Supplied on special order.

LA CROSSE BOILER CO.

La Crosse, Wisconsin

La Crosse Oil 12-25	1932-1937
La Crosse Oil 20-40	1932-1937

LA CROSSE OIL 12-25
LaCrosse Boiler Co., LaCrosse, Wis.

Traction Wheels: Four wheel type; two traction in rear, 45x10.

No. of Plows Recommended: Two to three, 14-in.

Length: 117 in.; **Width:** 56 in.; **Height:** 60 in.; **Weight:** 4000 lbs.

Turning Radius (outside): 12 ft.; **Acres Plowed in 10-hr. day:** 6 to 10.

Engine: Own, 6x8, horizontal, 2 cylinders, cast en bloc.

Lubrication: Force feed pump direct to cylinders and bearings.

Carburetor: Own, 1½-in.

Ignition System: High tension magneto.

Starting and Lighting Equipment: Optional.

Cooling System: Radiator.

Bearings: Babbitt lined.

Transmission: Spur gear, 2 to 3 m.p.h. forward; 1½ to 2 m.p.h. reverse.

Final Drive: Spur gear.

Belt Pulley: 14x7; 450-600 r.p.m.

Traction Wheels: Four wheels; two traction in rear, 56x18.

No. of Plows Recommended: Four to six, 14-in.

Length: 140 in.; **Width:** 78 in.; **Height:** 83 in.; **Weight:** 7200 lbs.

Turning Radius (outside): 18 ft.; **Acres Plowed in 10-hr. Day:** 9 to 16.

Engine: Own, 7½x9, horizontal, 2 cylinders, cast en bloc.

Lubrication: Force feed pump direct to cylinders and bearings.

Carburetor: Own, 2-in.

Ignition System: High tension magneto.

Starting and Lighting Equipment: Optional.

Cooling System: Radiator.

Bearings: Babbitt lined.

Transmission: Spur gear, 2 to 2¾ m.p.h. forward; 1½ to 2 m.p.h. reverse.

Final Drive: Spur gear.

Belt Pulley: 20x8; 400-480 r.p.m.

LA CROSSE OIL 20-40
LaCrosse Boiler Co., LaCrosse, Wis.

MASSEY-HARRIS CO.

Racine, Wisconsin

Massey-Harris General Purpose 15-22	1932-1935
Massey-Harris 12-20	1932-1933
Massey-Harris Orchard 12-20	1932-1933
Massey-Harris 20-30	1932-1933

Traction Wheels: Four wheel drive, each 38x8.

No. of Plows Recommended: Two, 14-in.

Length: 119 in.; **Width:** 58$\frac{15}{16}$ in.; **Height:** 54$\frac{13}{16}$ in.; **Weight:** 3861 lbs.

Turning Radius (outside): 10 ft.

Engine: Hercules, 4x4½, vertical, 4 cylinders, cast en bloc.

Lubrication: Force feed by gear pump and dip pan splash; oil filtering device.

Carburetor: Zenth, 1-in.

Ignition System: Bosch.

Cooling System: Centrifugal pump; tubular radiator, four gallons capacity.

Bearings: Timken and ball.

Transmission: Selective sliding gear, 2.2 to 4 m.p.h. forward; 2½ m.p.h. reverse.

Final Drive: Spur gear.

Belt Pulley: 12⅛x6½; 802 r.p.m. and 2546 feet per minute at normal engine speed.

MASSEY-HARRIS GENERAL PURPOSE 15-22
Massey-Harris Co., Racine, Wis.

Traction Wheels: Four wheels, with two rear drivers, 44x10 and two non-drive in front, 28x5.

No. of Plows Recommended: Two, 14-in.

Wheelbase: 78 in.; **Width:** 55 in.; **Height:** 51 in.; **Weight:** 3544 lbs.

Turning Radius (Outside): 11½ ft.

Engine: Own, 3⅞x5¼, vertical, 4 cylinders, cast en bloc.

Lubrication: Geared force pump and splash.

Carburetor: Kingston, 1⅛-in.

Ignition System: American Bosch high tension magneto.

Cooling System: Fan, pump and radiator.

Bearings: Ball and Timken bearings throughout.

Transmission: Selective sliding gear, 2⅓-3⅓ to 4⅓ m.p.h. forward; 2⅓ m.p.h. reverse.

Final Drive: Spur gear.

Belt Pulley: 17x6 5/16; 540½ r.p.m. and 2406 ft. per minute at normal engine speed.

MASSEY-HARRIS 12-20
Massey-Harris Co., Racine, Wis.

MASSEY-HARRIS ORCHARD 12-20

Massey-Harris Co., Racine, Wis.

Traction Wheels: Four wheels; two traction in rear, 44x10.

No. of Plows Recommended: Two, 14-in.

Turning Radius (Outside): 11½ ft.

Engine: Own, 3⅞x5¼, vertical, 4 cylinders, cast en bloc.

Lubrication: Pressure and splash.

Carburetor: Kingston, 1⅛-in.

Ignition System: American Bosch high tension magneto.

Cooling System: Modine radiator, fan and pump.

Bearings: Timken roller in differential; Timken and ball in transmission.

Transmission: Selective, sliding gear; 2⅓, 3⅓ to 4⅓ m.p.h. forward; 2⅓ m.p.h. reverse.

Final Drive: Spur gear.

Belt Pulley: 17x6 5/16; 540½ r.p.m. and 2406 feet per minute at normal engine speed.

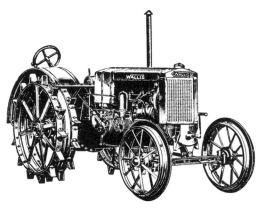

MASSEY-HARRIS 20-30
Massey-Harris Co., Racine, Wis.

Traction Wheels: Four wheels; two traction in rear, 48x12.

No. of Plows Recommended: Three, 14-in.

Weight: 4383 lbs.

Turning Radius (Outside): 14 ft.

Engine: Own, 4⅜x5¾, vertical, 4 cylinders, cast en bloc.

Lubrication: Pressure and splash.

Carburetor: Kingston, 1¼-in.

Ignition System: American Bosch high tension magneto.

Cooling System: Modine radiator, fan and pump.

Bearings: Timken roller in differential; Timken and ball in transmission.

Transmission: Selective, sliding gear; 2¾ to 3⅓ m.p.h. forward.

Final Drive: Spur gear.

Belt Pulley: 19x7⅛; 500 r.p.m. and 2487 feet per minute at normal engine speed.

THE MASSEY-HARRIS GENERAL PURPOSE FOUR WHEEL DRIVE TRACTOR . . . .

GET MORE BUSINESS
with the MASSEY-HARRIS COMPLETE LINE . . .

The Massey-Harris General Purpose Four Wheel Drive Tractor is the only tractor that has four drive wheels and three-point suspension that keeps all four wheels on the ground. No other tractor of equal weight has as much traction . . . as much drawbar pull per pound of weight. It will work land too tough for horses . . . land too steep, rough or soft for ordinary tractors. It will pull the tools now on the farm or can be equipped with easy-connecting Massey-Harris attachments for every type of field work.

Massey-Harris two-wheel drive tractors, 12-20 and larger size, have the famous boiler-plate steel "U" frame, and many other outstanding advantages that result in longer life and superior performance.

And we haven't overlooked the 14,000,000 farm horses in the United States. The Massey-Harris line includes every type of farm tool for either horse or tractor operation.

Our franchise allows ample territory for a good profit and an abundance of advertising and sales help. Manufacturing plants, branches, sub-branches, service stocks and dealers throughout the United States, Canada and in foreign countries.

Write today for information on any tool you may need, or particulars of our complete dealer plan.

THE MASSEY-HARRIS CO.

General Offices : Racine, Wisconsin

Factories : - **Racine, Wis.** - **Batavia, N. Y.**

TILLAGE

Tractor Plows, Riding Plows
Walking Plows, Disc Harrows
Tractor Harrows
8½ ft. Power Lift Discs
Spring-Tooth Harrows
Spike-Tooth Harrows
Rotary Hoes, Soil Pulverizers

PLANTING AND SEEDING

Corn Planters and Drills
Cotton Planters
Cotton Planters, Corn Listers
Potato Planters, Transplanters
Grain Drills
Fertilizer Drills
2 and 3 Row Tractor Listers

CULTIVATING

Walking Cultivators
Shovel Cultivators
Disc Cultivators
Two-Row Cultivators
Listed Corn, 2 and 3-row types
Field Cultivators

HAYING

Mowers, Rakes, Tedders
Side Rakes and Tedders
Loaders
Sweep Rakes, Stackers

HARVESTING

Reaper-Threshers, Binders
Tractor Binders
Headers, Reapers
Windrow Harvesters
Corn Binders
Ensilage Cutters

MISCELLANEOUS FARM EQUIPMENT

Pulverator—Plow Combine
Manure Spreaders
Farm Wagons and Trucks
Cream Separators
Stalk Cutters. Tractor Hitches
Potato Sprayers
Hammer Type Feed Mills
Orchard and Vineyard Tools

TRACTORS

Two Wheel Drive
General Purpose
Four Wheel Drive

MINNEAPOLIS-MOLINE POWER IMPLEMENT CO.
Minneapolis, Minnesota

Twin City Universal 13-25   1932-1934

TWIN CITY UNIVERSAL 13-25
Minneapolis-Moline Power Impl. Co.,
Minneapolis, Minn.

Traction Wheels: Four wheel type; two traction in rear, 42x10.
No. of Plows Recommended: Two to three, 14-in.
Length: 143 in.; **Width:** 93 in.; **Height:** 64½ in.; **Weight:** 4860 lbs.
Turning Radius (outside): 8½ ft.
Engine: Own, 4¼x5, overhead, 4 cylinders, cast en bloc.
Lubrication: Full pressure.
Carburetor: Schebler, 1-in.
Ignition System: Magneto.
Starting and Lighting Equipment: Optional.
Cooling System: Fan, pump and radiator.
Bearings: Bronze backed babbitt.
Transmission: Spur and bevel, 2.1 to 4.15 m.p.h. forward; 1.8 m.p.h. reverse.
Final Drive: Spur gear.
Belt Pulley: 14x7; 715 r.p.m. and 2620 feet per minute at normal engine speed.

1933

In 1933, 16 models of five makes not included in 1932 were added.

ALLIS-CHALMERS MANUFACTURING CO.

Milwaukee, Wisconsin

Allis-Chalmers "M" 27-34   1933

Traction Wheels: One crawler on each side, 12-inch face.

No. of Plows Recommended: Three to four 14-in.

Length: 101⅜ in.; **Width:** 57¼ in.; **Height:** 56 3/16 in.; **Weight:** 6,200 lbs.

Turning Radius (Outside): 5¼ ft.; **Acres Plowed in 10-Hour Day:** 15-25.

Engine: Own, 4⅜x5, vertical, 4 cylinders, cast en bloc.

Lubrication: Full pressure.

Carburetor: Zenith, 1¼-in.

Ignition System: Magneto with impulse coupling.

Starting and Lighting Equipment: Optional.

Cooling System: Radiator, fan and pump.

Transmission: Selective, sliding gear; 2.23 to 5.82 m.p.h. forward; 2.55 m. p.h. reverse.

Final Drive: Cut nickel steel gears.

Belt Pulley: 12x8¾; 960 r.p.m. and 3,016 feet per minute at normal engine speed.

ALLIS-CHALMERS "M" 27-34
Allis-Chalmers Mfg. Co., Milwaukee, Wis.

CATERPILLAR TRACTOR CO.

Peoria, Illinois

Caterpillar Thirty-Five	1933-1934
Caterpillar Fifty	1933-1937
Caterpillar Diesel Fifty	1933-1935
Caterpillar Seventy	1933-1936
Caterpillar Diesel Seventy	1933-1935
Caterpillar Diesel Seventy-Five	1933-1935

Traction Wheels: Two self-laying tracks, 16x71⅜ in.

Tread Width: Std., 53; Spl., 74. Adjustment: None.

Length: 139⅜ in.; **Width:** 72½ in.; **Height:** 69¼ in.; **Weight:** 12,597 lbs.; **Price:** $2400 f.o.b. factory.

Turning Radius (Outside): 7.2 ft.

Engine: Own, 4⅞x6½, vertical, 4 cylinders, cast singly.

Lubrication: Pressure oiling system.

Carburetor: Ensign, 1½ in.

Ignition System: Eisemann high tension magneto.

Lighting Equipment: Robert Bosch generator.

Cooling System: Water, pump circulation, gear driven fan.

Bearings: Largely anti-friction ball and roller.

Transmission: Sliding gear; 1.7, 2.5, 3.2 and 4.6 m.p.h. forward; 1.9 m.p.h. reverse.

Final Drive: Spur gears, completely enclosed.

Belt Pulley: 11¹⁵⁄₁₆x8½; 850 r.p.m. and 2660 feet per minute at normal engine speed.

"CATERPILLAR" THIRTY-FIVE
Caterpillar Tractor Co., Peoria, Ill.

"CATERPILLAR" FIFTY
Caterpillar Tractor Co., Peoria, Ill.

Traction Wheels: Two self-laying tracks, 18x81⅞ in.

Tread Width: Std. 60, Spl. 74. Adjustment: None.

Length: 146¼ in.; **Width:** 81⅝ in.; **Height:** 75¾ in.; **Weight:** 18,080 lbs.; **Price:** $3,400 f.o.b. factory.

Turning Radius (Outside): 90¾ in.

Engine: Own, 5½x6½, vertical, 4 cylinders, cast singly.

Lubrication: Pressure oiling system.

Carburetor: Ensign, 1½ in.

Ignition System: Eisemann high tension magneto.

Lighting Equipment: Robert Bosch generator.

Cooling System: Water, pump circulation, gear driven fan.

Bearings: Largely anti-friction ball and roller.

Transmission: Sliding gear, 1.6, 2.4, 3.4 and 4.7 m.p.h. forward; 1.9 m.p.h. reverse.

Final Drive: Spur gears, completely enclosed.

Belt Pulley: 13⅜x10; 753 r.p.m. and 2,630 feet per minute at governed engine speed.

Traction Wheels: Two self-laying tracks, 18x81⅞ inches.

Tread Width: Std. 60, Spl. 74. Adjustment: None.

Length: 150¼ in.; **Width:** 81⅝ in.; **Height:** 81⅝ in.; **Weight:** 20,250 lbs.; **Price:** $4,500 f.o.b. factory.

Turning Radius (Outside): 90¾ in.

Engine: Own, 5¼x8 vertical, 4 cylinders, cast en bloc.

Lubrication: Pressure oiling system.

Lighting Equipment: Robert Bosch generator.

Cooling System: Water, pump circulation, gear driven fan.

Bearings: Largely anti-friction ball and roller.

Transmission: Sliding gears, 1.6, 2.4, 3.4 and 4.7 m.p.h. forward; 1.9 m.p.h. reverse.

Final Drive: Spur gears, completely enclosed.

Belt Pulley: 13⅜x10; 753 r.p.m. and 2,630 feet per minute at governed engine speed.

"CATERPILLAR" DIESEL FIFTY
Caterpillar Tractor Co., Peoria, Ill.

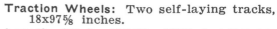

"CATERPILLAR" SEVENTY
Caterpillar Tractor Co., Peoria, Ill.

Traction Wheels: Two self-laying tracks, 18x97⅝ inches.
Length: 175 in.; **Width:** 103¾ in.; **Height:** 87⅞ in.; **Weight:** 29,500 lbs.; **Price:** $4,750 f.o.b. factory.
Engine: Own, 7x8½, vertical, 4 cylinders, cast singly.
Lubrication: Pressure oiling system.
Carburetor: Ensign, 1¾ in.
Ignition System: Eisemann high tension magneto.
Lighting Equipment: Robert Bosch generator.
Cooling System: Water, pump circulation, gear-driven fan.
Bearings: Largely anti-friction ball and roller.
Transmission: Sliding gears, 1.7, 2.3, 2.7, 3.1, 3.7 and 5.0 m.p.h. forward; 1.7, 2.7 m.p.h. reverse.
Final Drive: Spur gears, completely enclosed.
Belt Pulley: 15x11; 700 r.p.m. and 2,750 feet per minute at normal engine speed.

Traction Wheels: Two self-laying tracks, 18x97⅝ inches.
Length: 175 in.; **Width:** 103¾ in.; **Height:** 87⅞ in.; **Weight:** 30,800 lbs.; **Price:** $6,250 f. o. b. factory.
Engine: Own, 6⅛x9¼, vertical, 4 cylinders, cast en bloc.
Lubrication: Pressure oiling system.
Lighting Equipment: Robert Bosch generator.
Cooling System: Water, pump circulation, gear-driven fan.
Bearings: Largely anti-friction ball and roller.
Transmission: Sliding gear, 1.7, 2.3, 2.7, 3.1, 3.7 and 5.0 m.p.h. forward; 1.7, 2.7 m.p.h. reverse.
Final Drive: Spur gears, completely enclosed.
Belt Pulley: 15x11; 694 r.p.m. and 2,730 feet per minute at normal engine speed.

"CATERPILLAR" DIESEL SEVENTY
Caterpillar Tractor Co., Peoria, Ill.

Traction Wheels: Two self-laying tracks, 18x97⅝ inches.
Length: 183 in.; **Width:** 103¾ in.; **Height:** 84⅛ in.; **Weight:** 30,550 lbs.; **Price:** $6,500 f.o.b. factory.
Engine: Own, 5¼x8, vertical, 6 cylinders, cast en bloc.
Lubrication: Pressure oiling system.
Lighting Equipment: Robert Bosch generator.
Cooling System: Water, pump circulation, gear-driven fan.
Bearings: Largely anti-friction ball and roller.
Transmission: Sliding gear, 1.7, 2.3, 2.7, 3.1, 3.7 and 5.0 m.p.h. forward; 1.7, 2.7 m.p.h. reverse.
Final Drive: Spur gears, completely enclosed.
Belt Pulley: 15x11; 694 r.p.m. and 2,730 feet per minute at normal engine speed.

"CATERPILLAR" DIESEL SEVENTY-FIVE
Caterpillar Tractor Co., Peoria, Ill.

CLEVELAND TRACTOR CO.
Cleveland, Ohio

Cletrac 20

CLETRAC 20
Cleveland Tractor Co., Cleveland, O.

Traction Wheels: One crawler on each side, 56x11; each track driven through cast steel drive sprocket meshing with rollers in track.
Tread Width: 40. **Adjustment:** None.
No. of Plows Recommended: Three, 14-in.
Length: 106 in.; **Width:** 53½ in.; **Height:** 55 in.; **Weight:** 6,000 lbs. approximately.
Turning Radius (Outside): 6½ ft.
Engine: Hercules, 4x4½, L Head, 4 cylinders, cast en bloc.
Lubrication: Force feed to crank, connecting rods and timing gears.
Carburetor: Tillotson, 1⅛ in.
Ignition System: Bosch high tension magneto with impulse starter.
Cooling System: Tubular radiator with four blade fan. Pump circulation.
Bearings: New Departure ball bearings.
Transmission: Selective type sliding gear; 1.95, 2.8 and 4 m.p.h. forward; 1.8 m.p.h. reverse.
Final Drive: Through controlled differential and bull gear on drive sprocket shaft.
Belt Pulley: 10½x6½; 1,040 r.p.m. and 2,860 feet per minute at normal engine speed.
Power Reduction: 550 r.p.m.
Power Take-Off: 833 r.p.m.

FOOTE BROS. GEAR & MACHINE CO.
Chicago, Illinois

Bates Steel Mule Model 50

BATES STEEL MULE MODEL 50
Foote Bros. Gear & Machine Co., Chicago, Ill
(Bates Mfg. Co. Div.)

Traction Wheels: Two crawlers, 14 inches wide and 82 inches long.
Tread Width: 53¼ in.; **Adjustment:** None.
Length: 128 in.; **Width:** 74 in.; **Height:** 72 in.; **Weight:** 14,000 lbs.
Turning Radius (Outside): 7 ft.
Engine: Waukesha, 4⅝x5⅛, Ricardo-head 6 cylinders, cast in pairs, 1400 r.p.m.
Lubrication: Force feed.
Carburetor: Schebler.
Ignition System: Bosch high tension magneto.
Cooling System: Pump.
Bearings: Ball and roller.
Transmission: Sliding gear; 1¾ to 3¾ m.p.h. forward; 1¾ m.p.h. reverse.
Final Drive: Spur gear, enclosed and running in oil.
Belt Pulley: 12x8¾; 858 r.p.m. and 2695 f.p.m. at normal engine speed.

INTERNATIONAL HARVESTER CO. OF AMERICA
Chicago, Illinois

INTERNATIONAL INDUSTRIAL 20
International Harvester Co., Chicago, Ill.

Traction Wheels: Four rubber tirea wheels; two traction in rear, 40x10; two non-traction in front, 29x5. Rubber tires optional types.

Length: 123 in.; **Width:** 64½ in.; **Height:** 62 in.; **Weight:** 7,400 lbs.

Turning Radius (Outside): 14½ ft.

Engine: Own; 4¼x5, valve-in-head, 4 replaceable cylinders.

Lubrication: Circulating splash.

Carburetor: Zenith.

Ignition System: Own high tension with automatic impulse starter.

Cooling System: Thermo-syphon.

Bearings: New Departure on crankshaft; own make roller in transmission, wheels and rear axle.

Transmission: 2¼, 4, 7 and 10 m.p.h. forward; 3 m.p.h. reverse.

Final Drive: Spur gear, live axle.

Belt Pulley: 15¼x7; 645 r.p.m. and 2575 feet per minute. (Extra equipment.)

INTERNATIONAL INDUSTRIAL I-30
International Harvester Co., Chicago, Ill.

Traction Wheels: Four wheels; two traction in rear, 40x8, dual pneumatic. Two non-drive in front, 20x5½. Rubber tires optional.

Length: 121 in.; **Width:** 85 in.; **Height:** 62 in.; **Weight:** 7,550 lbs.

Turning Radius (Outside): 14½ ft.

Engine: Own, vertical, 4¼x5, valve-in-head, 4 replaceable cylidners.

Lubrication: Circulating splash.

Carburetor: Zenith, 1¼-in.

Ignition System: Own high tension magneto with automatic impulse starter.

Starting and Lighting Equipment: Special.

Cooling System: Impeller pump and thermostatic control.

Bearings: Ball and roller.

Transmission: Selective gears, 2½ to 12¼ m. p. h. forward.

Final Drive: Enclosed spur gear.

Belt Pulley: 15¼x7; 719 r. p. m. and 2,870 feet per minute at normal engine speed. Extra equipment.

McCORMICK-DEERING FARMALL F12
International Harvester Co. of America, Chicago, Ill.

Traction Wheels: Two drive wheels in rear, 54x6; one non-drive in front, 23x6.
No. of Plows Recommended: One 16-in. or two 12-in.
Length: 125½ in.; **Width:** 44 to 79 in. tread; **Height:** 62½ in.; **Weight:** Approximately 2,500 lbs.; **Price:** $525 f.o.b. factory.
Turning Radius (Outside): 7 ft.
Engine: Waukesha FL, 3x4, L head, 4 cylinders, cast en bloc.
Lubrication: Force feed with oil filter.
Carburetor: Zenith 93½W, 1 in.
Ignition System: High tension magneto.
Cooling System: Thermo-syphon.
Bearings Bronze backed, babbitt lined mains; ball in transmission and differential.
Transmission: Three speed, ball bearing, 2¼ to 3¾ m.p.h. forward; 2¼ m.p.h. reverse.
Final Drive: Enclosed machine cut gears in oil bath.
Belt Pulley: 12⅜x5; 800 r.p.m. and 2,591 feet per minute at normal engine speed.

Traction Wheels: Four wheels; two traction in rear, 40x8, dual pneumatic. Two non-drive in front, 20x5½.
Length: 123 in.; **Width:** 85 in.; **Height:** 62 in.; **Weight:** 7,550 lbs.
Turning Radius (Outside): 14½ ft.
Engine: Own, vertical, 4¼x5, valve-in-head, 4 cylinders, cast removable cylinders.
Lubrication: Circulating splash.
Carburetor: Zenith, 1¼-in.
Ignition System: Own high tension magneto.
Starting and Lighting Equipment: Special.
Cooling System: Fan, pump and Modine radiator.
Bearings: New Departure ball in transmission. Own roller in differential.
Transmission: Selective gears, 2½ to 10 m. p. h. forward.
Final Drive: Enclosed spur gear.
Belt Pulley: 15¼x7; 719 r. p. m. and 2,870 feet per minute at normal engine speed.

McCORMICK-DEERING INDUSTRIAL I-30
International Harvester Co. of America, Chicago, Ill.

McCORMICK-D. TRACTRACTOR DIESEL 40
International Harvester Co. of America, Chicago, Ill.

Traction Members: One crawler on each side, 16x70.
No. of Plows Recommended: Six to eight, 14 in.
Length: 140 in.; **Width:** 63¾ in.; **Height:** 65½ in.; **Weight:** 12,000 lbs.
Turning Radius (Outside): 7 ft.
Engine: Own, 4¾x6½, Diesel, 4 cylinders, cast removable sleeves.
Lubrication: Full pressure.
Carburetor: Diesel pump.
Starting and Lighting Equipment: Own starting; special lighting system.
Cooling System: Fan and radiator, water circulating pump.
Bearings: Precision mains, ball in transmission and final drive.
Transmission: Selective; five speeds forward; 1¾ to 4 m.p.h. forward; 2.25 m.p.h. reverse.
Final Drive: Gear type, enclosed.
Belt Pulley: 16¾x9; 591 r.p.m. and 2,593 feet per minute at normal engine speed.

McCORMICK-DEERING TRACTRACTOR T40
International Harvester Co. of America, Chicago, Ill.

Traction Members: One crawler on each side, 16x70.
No. of Plows Recommended: Six to eight 14 in.
Length: 141 in.; **Width:** 61¾ in.; **Height:** 65½ in.; **Weight:** 10,600 lbs.
Turning Radius (Outside): 7 ft.
Engine: Own, 3⅝x4½, vertical, valve-in-head, 6 replaceable cylinders.
Lubrication: Pressure, gear-type oil pump.
Carburetor: Zenith, 1¼ in.
Ignition System: High tension with automatic impulse starter.
Starting and Lighting Equipment: Special.
Cooling System: Impeller pump, thermostat control.
Bearings: Precision type main, ball in transmission and final drive.
Transmission: Selective; five speeds forward and one reverse, 1¾ to 4 m.p.h. forward; 2¼ m.p h. reverse.
Final Drive: Enclosed machine cut gears in oil bath.
Belt Pulley: Special; 16¾x9; 604 r.p.m. and 2,650 feet per minute at normal engine speed.

McCORMICK-DEERING
Triple-Power Tractors

THE great advantages in tractor power are all available in McCormick-Deering Tractors, built by the world's largest tractor builder. Users tell us of the satisfaction derived from these dependable power plants; of their flexibility in tackling one job after another; and of their ability to dispose of all farm power work economically.

Exceptional performance is the result of developing tractors to meet actual farming conditions. The all-purpose Farmall is available in three sizes, ranging in capacity from one 16-inch plow to three 14-inch plows. Standard wheel-type McCormick-Deering tractors are built in two popular sizes. TracTracTors are available in three types, one of which is powered with a Diesel engine.

Unequaled engineering skill, rigidly maintained manufacturing standards, and McCormick-Deering after-sale service combine to make these tractors the outstanding values in their fields. The McCormick-Deering owner can expect low-cost, reliable service from his tractor for years to come.

The new all-purpose Farmall 12 pulls one 16-inch or two 10-inch plow bottoms.

The Farmall 30 is a powerful 3-plow tractor. There is also the original Farmall, a 2-plow unit.

The regular McCormick-Deering 15-30 and 10-20—known as standard farm power plants the world around.

The McCormick-Deering T-20 TracTracTor shown here is a popular model for orchard, grove, and open-field work in sections where crawler-type tractors are required. For heavier work there is the big, powerful, 6-cylinder, Model T-40 with power to pull from 6 to 8 plow bottoms. There is also a 4-cylinder Diesel-type Model T-40.

INTERNATIONAL HARVESTER COMPANY
OF AMERICA
(INCORPORATED)

606 So. Michigan Ave.   CHICAGO, ILL.

The Quality in

QUALITY
Piston Rings

Built this Plant

MORE than one hundred fifty leading manufacturers specify Quality Brand rings for original installation.

Used the world over for replacement, they have set a standard for piston ring performance and long life.

There is a Quality Brand ring for every purpose and to solve every piston ring problem.

QUALITY—Plain compression rings.

DRAINOIL—Slotted oil controlling rings.

NO-LEAK-O—Grooved oil-sealing rings.

The Piston Ring Company
Muskegon Michigan
U.S.A.

1934

In 1934, 24 tractors of 12 makes not included in 1933 were added. John Deere introduced the Model "A" and in 1935 the "B", both of which went through a style change in 1938 but continued to be built until 1952.

ALLIS-CHALMERS MANUFACTURING CO.

Milwaukee, Wisconsin

Allis-Chalmers Rumely "6A"	1934-1935
Allis-Chalmers Model "K"	1934-1944
Allis-Chalmers Model "M"	1934-1945
Allis-Chalmers Model "WC"	1934-1948

Traction Wheels: Four wheels with two in rear, 48x12, giving traction and two non-drive in front, 30x6.

No. of Plows Recommended: Four, 14-in.

Length: 163 in.; **Width:** 70 in.; **Height:** 74 in.; **Weight:** 5,510 lbs.

Turning Radius (Outside): 15¾ ft:

Engine: Own, 4¼x4¾, L-head, 6 cylinders, cast en bloc.

Lubrication: Pressure

Carburetor: Zenith, 1½-in.

Ignition System: High tension magneto with impulse starter.

Starting and Lighting Equipment: Special attachment.

Cooling System: Fan, centrifugal pump and radiator.

Bearings: New Departure, Timken and bronze.

Transmission: Spur gear; 2.5 to 4.75 m.p.h. forward; 3 to 3.5 m.p.h. reverse.

Final Drive: Spur gear, enclosed in transmission.

Belt Pulley: 13x8; 785 or 892 r.p.m.

ALLIS-CHALMERS RUMELY "6A"
Allis-Chalmers Mfg. Co., Milwaukee, Wis.

Traction Wheels: One crawler on each side, 67x13.

No. of Plows Recommended: Four to five, 14-in.

Length: 119 in.; **Width:** 66 in.; **Height:** 66 in.; **Weight:** 11,500 lbs.

Engine: Own, 5x6½, vertical, 4 cylinders. Removable cylinder liners.

Lubrication: Full force feed.

Carburetor: Zenith, 1½ in.

Ignition System: Bendix magneto.

Starting & Lighting Equipment: Electric Auto-Lite.

Cooling System: Fan, pump and radiator.

Transmission: Selective sliding gear; three speeds forward; 2.08 to 4.50 m.p.h. forward; 2.39 m.p.h. reverse.

Final Drive: Gear.

Belt Pulley: 12x8¾; 1050 r.p.m.

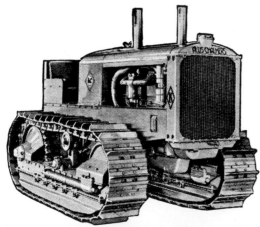

ALLIS-CHALMERS MODEL "K"
Allis-Chalmers Mfg. Co., Milwaukee, Wis.

ALLIS-CHALMERS MODEL "M"
Allis-Chalmers Mfg. Co., Milwaukee, Wis.

Traction Wheels: One crawler on each side, 12-inch face.
No. of Plows Recommended: Three to four 14-in.
Length: 101⅜ in.; **Width:** 57¼ in.; **Height:** 56⅞ in.; **Weight:** 6,200 lbs.
Turning Radius (Outside): 5¼ ft.; **Acres Plowed in 10-Hour Day:** 15-25.
Engine: Own, 4⅜x5, vertical, 4 cylinders, removable sleeves.
Lubrication: Full pressure.
Carburetor: Zenith, 1¼-in.
Ignition System: Magneto with impulse coupling.
Starting and Lighting Equipment: Optional.
Cooling System: Radiator, fan and pump.
Transmission: Selective, sliding gear; 2.23 to 5.82 m.p.h. forward; 2.55 m.p.h. reverse.
Final Drive: Cut nickel steel gears.
Belt Pulley: 12x8¾; 960 r.p.m. and 3,016 feet per minute at normal engine speed.

Traction Wheels: Four wheels; rear, 40x6 steel wheels or 11.25-24, 6-ply low pressure air tires; front, 24x4 steel wheels or 5.25-17, 4-ply low pressure air tires.
No. of Plows Recommended: Two, 14-in.
Length: 136-in.; **Width:** 71 and 82-in.; **Height:** 63-in.; **Tread Width:** 65 and 76-in.
Weight: 2700 lbs. with steel wheels, or 3300 lbs. with air tires.
Turning Radius (Outside): 8 ft.; **Acres Plowed in 10-Hr. Day:** 6 to 10.
Engine: Own, 4x4, vertical, valve-in-head, 1300 r.p.m.
Lubrication: Pressure.
Carburetor: Zenith.
Ignition System: High tension magneto with impulse starter.
Cooling System: Water, circulated by pump and cooled by air from belt driven fan.
Bearings: Mainly ball and roller.
Transmission: Sliding gear, 4-speeds forward, 2½, 3½, 4¾ and 9½ m.p.h. Reverse: 2 m.p.h.
Final Drive: Enclosed spur gear.
Belt Pulley: 9x6½; 1170 r.p.m. and 2760 feet per minute at normal engine speed.

ALLIS-CHALMERS MODEL "WC"
Allis-Chalmers Mfg. Co., Milwaukee, Wis.

CATERPILLAR TRACTOR CO.

Peoria, Illinois

Caterpillar Twenty-Two	1934-1938
Caterpillar Twenty-Eight	1934-1935
Caterpillar Diesel Thirty-Five	1934

"CATERPILLAR" TWENTY-TWO
Caterpillar Tractor Co., Peoria, Ill.

Traction Wheels: Two self-laying tracks; 56⅞ in. ground contact; 11 in. wide.
Tread Width: Std. 42, Spl. 55. Adjustment: None.
Length: 116⅛ in.; **Width:** 61½ in.; **Height:** 60⅝ in.; **Weight:** 7,870 lbs.; **Price:** $1900, f.o.b. Peoria, Ill.
Turning Radius (Outside): 68½ in.
Engine: Own, 4³⁄₁₆x5½, vertical, 4 cylinders, cast singly.
Lubrication: Pressure oiling system.
Carburetor: Ensign, 1¼ in.
Ignition System: Eisemann high tension magneto.
Lighting Equipment: Robert Bosch generator.
Cooling System: Water pump and gear driven fan.
Bearings: Largely anti-friction ball and roller.
Transmission: Sliding gear; 1.8-2.6-3.6 m.p.h. forward; 2 m.p.h. reverse.
Final Drive: Spur gears, completely enclosed.
Belt Pulley: 11¾x6½; 835 r.p.m. and 2580 feet per minute at governed engine speed.

Traction Wheels: Two self-laying tracks, 10x54½.
Tread Width: Std. 40, Spl. 50. Adjustment: None.
Length: 108 in.; **Width:** 57¾ in.; **Height:** 56⅛ in.; **Weight:** 6,200 lbs., **Price:** $1450 f.o.b. Peoria, Ill.
Turning Radius (Outside): 61½ in.
Engine: Own, 4x5, 4 cylinders, cast in pairs.
Lubrication: Pressure feed.
Carburetor: Zenith, 1-in.
Ignition System: Eisemann high tension magneto.
Lighting Equipment: Robert Bosch generator.
Cooling System: Water, pump circulation, V-belt driven fan.
Bearings: Largely anti-friction ball and roller.
Transmission: Sliding gear, 2-2.6-3.6 m.p.h. forward; 2.1 m.p.h. reverse.
Final Drive: Spur gears, completely enclosed.
Belt Pulley: 10½x6½; 950 r.p.m. and 2,610 feet per minute at governed engine speed.

"CATERPILLAR" TWENTY-EIGHT
Caterpillar Tractor Co., Peoria, Ill.

"CATERPILLAR" DIESEL THIRTY-FIVE
Caterpillar Tractor Co., Peoria, Ill.

Traction Wheels: Two self-laying tracks, 16x71⅜.
Tread Width: Std., 56; Spl., 74. Adjustment: None.
Length: 128⅜ in.; **Width:** 75 in.; **Height:** 70⁹⁄₁₆ in.; **Weight:** 14,271 lbs.; **Price:** $3,150 f.o.b. factory.
Turning Radius (Outside): 7 ft.
Engine: Own, 5¼x8, vertical, 3 cylinders, cast en bloc.
Lubrication: Pressure oiling system.
Carburetor: None.
Starting Equipment: Own two-cylinder gasoline engine starter, Robert Bosch magneto.
Cooling System: Water, pump circulation, gear driven fan.
Bearings: Largely anti-friction ball and roller.
Transmission: Sliding gears, 1.7 to 4.6 m.p.h. forward; 1.9 m.p.h. reverse.
Final Drive: Spur gear, completely enclosed.
Belt Pulley: 11¹¹⁄₁₆x8½; 850 r.p.m. and 2,670 feet per minute at normal engine speed.

CLEVELAND TRACTOR CO.
Cleveland, Ohio

Cletrac 80 Diesel   1934-1935

CLETRAC 80 DIESEL
Cleveland Tractor Co., Cleveland, O.

Traction Wheels: Two crawlers, 96x17.
Tread Width: 67-in. **Adjustment:** None.
No. of Plows Recommended: Twelve to fourteen, 14-in.
Length: 168 in.; **Width,** 94½ in.; **Height:** 83¾ in.; **Weight:** Approximately 24,-000 lbs.
Turning Radius (Outside): 9 ft.
Engine: Hercules, 5x6, 6 cylinders, cast in two pairs of three.
Lubrication: Force feed.
Starting & Lighting Equipment: Leece-Neville.
Cooling System: Fan, pump and radiator.
Bearings: Ball and roller.
Transmission: Selective gear, 1.75, 2.75 and 4.25 m.p.h. forward; 2.1 m.p.h. reverse.
Final Drive: Enclosed planetary pinion.
Belt Pulley: 24x15; 535 r.p.m. and 3,350 feet per minute at normal engine speed.

DEERE & CO.
Moline, Illinois

John Deere General Purpose Model "A"   1934-1937

JOHN DEERE GEN'L PURPOSE MODEL "A"
Deere & Co., Moline, Ill.

Traction Wheels: Four wheels; two traction in rear, 50x6.
No. of Plows Recommended: Two, 14-in.
Length: 125 $\frac{13}{16}$ in.; **Width:** 56 to 80 in. center to center; **Weight:** 3496 lbs.
Turning Radius (Outside): 8 ft.
Engine: Own, 5½x6½, horizontal, 2 cylinders, cast en bloc.
Lubrication: Force feed; gear pump; drilled crankshaft.
Carburetor: Schebler.
Ignition System: High tension magneto.
Starting & Lighting Equipment: K-W lighting generator.
Cooling System: Thermo-syphon.
Bearings: Timken, Hyatt and ball.
Transmission: Sliding gear; 2⅓, 3⅓, 4¾, 6¾ m.p.h. forward; 3⅓ m.p.h. reverse.
Final Drive: Gear.
Belt Pulley: 13x7½; 975 r.p.m. and 3270 feet per minute at normal engine speed.

FATE-ROOT-HEATH CO.
Plymouth, Ohio

Plymouth 10-20   1934

Traction Wheels: Steel or low-pressure tires.

Tread Width: 38 in. Adjustment: None.

No. of Plows Recommended: One, 14-in.

Length: 97 in.; **Width:** 48 in.; **Height:** 49 in.; **Weight** 2170 lbs.

Turning Radius (Outside): 9 ft.; Acres Plowed in 10-hr. Day: 5.

Engine: Hercules, IXA; 3x4, horizontal, 4 cylinders.

Lubrication: Full force feed.

Carburetor: Zenith, ⅞-in.

Ignition System: Fairbanks-Morse.

Starting & Lighting Equipment: Auto-Lite.

Cooling System: Thermo-Syphon.

Bearings: Timken and New Departure.

Transmission: Standard automotive, 1 to 25 m.p.h. forward; 1.5 m.p.h. reverse.

Final Drive: Direct.

Belt Pulley: 6x6; 1400 r.p.m.

PLYMOUTH 10-20
Fate-Root Heath Co., Plymouth, O.

HUBER MANUFACTURING CO.
Marion, Ohio

Modern Farmer   1934-1935

Traction Wheels: Four wheels; two traction in rear, 42x10.

Tread Width: 50 in. Adjustment None.

No. of Plows Recommended: Three, 14 in.

Length: 123½ in.; **Width:** 60 in.; **Height:** 57½ in.; **Weight:** 3700 lbs.

Turning Radius (outside): 12 ft.

Engine: Waukesha, 4¼x5; L-head, 4 cylinders, cast en bloc.

Lubrication: Force feed.

Carburetor: Zenith, 1¼ in.

Ignition System: United Bosch; U-4, high tension magneto.

Cooling System: Young radiator, own fan.

Bearings: Hyatt and Timken.

Transmission: Selective gear; 2.4 to 6.4 m.p.h. forward.

Final Drive: Bull gear.

Belt Pulley: 14x6; 705 r.p.m. and 2600 ft. per minute at normal engine speed.

MODERN FARMER
Huber Mfg. Co., Marion, O.

INTERNATIONAL HARVESTER CO. OF AMERICA
Chicago, Illinois

International Model I-12	1934-1937
McCormick-Deering Farmall 20	1934-1940
McCormick-Deering O-12	1934-1937
McCormick-Deering W-12	1934-1937

Traction Wheels: Four wheel type; two traction in rear and two non-traction in front. Rubber tires regular on I-12 and O-12; Special on W-12 and Fairway 12.

No. of Plows Recommended: One, 16-in. (Models O-12 and W-12).

Length: 103 in.; **Width:** 50, 50½, 63½ in.; **Weight:** 2900, 3000, 3200 lbs.

Turning Radius (Outside): 8½, 9 ft.

Engine: Own, 3x4, vertical, 4 cylinders, replaceable, cast en bloc.

Lubrication: Pressure.

Carburetor: Own, 1-in.

Ignition System: Own high tension magneto with automatic impulse starter.

Starting & Lighting Equipment: Special.

Cooling System: Thermo-Syphon.

Bearings: Precision type.

Transmission: Selective, W-2 to 3½; I., O. & F.-2 to 10⅜ m.p.h. forward; W.-2¼, I., O. & F.-2½ to 3½ m.p.h. reverse.

Final Drive: Gear.

Belt Pulley: Special; 13¼x6¼; 748 r.p.m. and 2593 feet per minute at normal engine speed.

(Illustration is I-12 and O-12. W-12 and Fairway-12 equipped with steel wheels.)

INTERNATIONAL MODEL I-12
International Harvester Co., Chicago, Ill.

Traction Wheels: Four wheel type; two traction in rear, 40x6.

Tread Width: Regular, 74⅜ and 83-in.; narrow, 57 and 77-in.

No. of Plows Recommended: Two, 14-in.

Length: 140 in.; **Width:** 86 in.; **Height:** 76 in.; **Weight:** 3950 (approximately) lbs.

Turning Radius (Outside): 8 ft.; **Acres Plowed in 10-Hr. Day:** 7 to 9.

Engine: Own, 3¾x5, vertical, valve-in-head, 4 cylinders, removable.

Lubrication: Circulating pump and splash.

Carburetor: Own, 1¼-in.

Ignition System: Own, high tension magneto; automatic impulse starter.

Starting & Lighting Equipment: Special.

Cooling System: Thermo-Syphon.

Bearings: Ball and roller.

Transmission: Selective, 2¼, 2¾, 3¼, 3¾ m.p.h. forward; 2¾ m.p.h. reverse.

Final Drive: Spur gear.

Belt Pulley: 14x6½; 654 r.p.m. and 2395 feet per minute at normal engine speed.

McCORMICK-DEERING FARMALL 20
International Harvester Co. of America, Chicago, Ill.

McCORMICK-DEERING O-12
International Harvester Co., Chicago, Ill.

Wheels: Pneumatic tires regular; front 6.00-16; rear 11.25-24.
Length: 104½ in.; **Width:** 54¾ in.; **Weight:** 3,200 lbs.
Turning Radius (Outside): 9¼ ft.; **Acres Plowed in 10-hr. Day:** 4 to 7.
Engine: Own, 3x4, vertical, 4 cylinders, replaceable, cast en bloc; Speed, 1,400 to 2,000 r.p.m.; Fuel, regular gasoline; kerosene-distillate equipment available.
Lubrication: Pressure.
Carburetor: Own, 1-in.
Ignition System: Own high tension magneto with automatic impulse coupling.
A.S.A.E. and S.A.E. Rated Power: (at 1,400 r.p.m.) approximately 10.5 h.p. drawbar; 14 h.p. belt.
Cooling System: Thermo-syphon.
Bearings: Precision type.
Speeds: (maximum) 3⅝, 6⅛ and 10⅝ m.p.h. forward; 3⅝ m.p.h. reverse.
Belt Pulley: Special, 13¼x6¼; 748 r.p.m. and 2,593 feet per minute with engine speed at 1,400 r.p.m.
Power Take-off: Regular, 538 r.p.m. with engine at 1,400 r.p.m.

McCORMICK-DEERING W-12
International Harvester Co., Chicago, Ill.

Wheels: Regular steel; rear 42x8; front 22½x3½.
Length: 103 in.; **Width:** 50 in.; **Weight:** 2,900 lbs.
Turning Radius (Outside): 9 ft.; **Acres Plowed in 10-hr. Day:** 4 to 7.
Engine: Own, 3x4 vertical, 4 cylinders, replaceable, cast en bloc; Speed, 1,700 r.p.m.; Fuel, regular gasoline; kerosene-distillate equipment available.
Lubrication: Pressure.
Carburetor: Own, 1-in.
Ignition System: Own high tension magneto with automatic impulse coupling.
A.S.A.E. and S.A.E. Rated Power: Drawbar 10.46; belt 16.07.
Cooling System: Thermo-syphon.
Bearings: Precision type.
Speeds: 2⅛, 2¾ and 3⅝ m.p.h. forward; 2⅛ m.p.h. reverse.
Belt Pulley: Special; 13¼x6¼; 787 r.p.m. and 2,730 feet per minute.
Power Take-off: Regular, 566 r.p.m.

LA CROSSE BOILER CO.

La Crosse, Wisconsin

La Crosse Oil 30-60

LA CROSSE OIL 30-60
La Crosse Boiler Co., La Crosse, Wis.

1934-1937

Traction Wheels: Four wheels; two traction in rear, 60x22, and two non-drive in front, 36x12.
No. of Plows Recommended: Eight to twelve, 14-in.
Turning Radius (Outside): 20 ft.
Engine: Own make, 9½x12, horizontal, 2 cylinders, cast en bolc.
Lubrication: Madison-Kipp force feed.
Carburetor: Own, 2½-in.
Ignition System: High tension magneto.
Starting & Lighting Equipment: Optional.
Cooling System: Radiator.
Bearings: Own, babbitt lined.
Transmission: Spur gear, 2 to 2¼ m.p.h. forward.
Final Drive: Spur gear.
Belt Pulley: 22x10; 375-450 r.p.m.

MASSEY-HARRIS CO.

Racine, Wisconsin

Massey-Harris Model GP, 4-Wheel Drive Industrial	1934-1938
Massey-Harris Model "12" (12-20)	1934-1935
Massey-Harris Model "12" Industrial	1934-1935
Massey-Harris Orchard Model "12" (12-20)	1934-1935
Massey-Harris Model "25" Industrial	1934-1940
Massey-Harris Model "25" 26-41	1934-1941

MASSEY-HARRIS MODEL GP, 4-WHEEL DRIVE INDUSTRIAL

Massey-Harris Co., Racine, Wis.

Traction Wheels: Four wheel drive; 38x7 pneumatic tires (Other tires and sizes available.)
Tread Width: 50-in.; **Adjustment:** None.
Length: 111¼ in.; **Width:** 58$\frac{15}{16}$ in.; **Height:** 55¼ in.; **Weight:** 4000 to 6700 lbs.
Turning Radius (Outside): 10 ft.
Engine: Hercules "OOC", 4x4½ L-head, 4 cylinders, cast en bloc.
Lubrication: Force feed by gear pump and dip pan splash.
Carburetor: Zenith, 1-in.
Ignition System: Bosch high tension magneto.
Starting & Lighting Equipment: Special.
Cooling System: Fan, pump and radiator.
Bearings: Ball and Timken tapered roller bearings throughout.
Transmission: Selective, sliding gear, 2¾ to 9 m.p.h. forward; 3¼ m.p.h. reverse.
Final Drive: Spur gear.
Belt Pulley: 12⅛x6½; 802 r.p.m. and 2546 feet per minute at normal engine speed.

MASSEY-HARRIS MODEL "12" (12-20)

Massey-Harris Co., Racine, Wis.

Traction Wheels: Four wheels, with two rear drivers, 44x10 and two non-drive in front, 28x5.
Tread Width: 45¼-in.; **Adjustment:** None.
No. of Plows Recommended: Two, 14-in.
Wheelbase: 78 in.; **Width:** 55¼ in.; **Height:** 51 in.; **Weight:** 3544 lbs.
Turning Radius (Outside): 11½ ft.
Engine: Own, 3⅞x5¼, vertical, valve-in-head, 4 cylinders, removable cylinder sleeves.
Lubrication: Geared force pump and splash.
Carburetor: Kingston, 1⅛-in.
Ignition System: American Bosch high tension magneto.
Cooling System: Fan, pump and radiator.
Bearings: Ball and Timken bearings throughout.
Transmission: Selective sliding gear, 2⅓-3⅓ to 4⅓ m.p.h. forward; 2⅓ m.p.h. reverse.
Final Drive: Spur gear.
Belt Pulley: 17x6$\frac{5}{8}$; 540½ r.p.m. and 2406 ft. per minute at normal engine speed.

Traction Wheels: Four wheels; 40x6, single solid rubber rear tires and 29x5 single solid front tires. (Other tires and sizes available.)

Tread Width: 44-in.; Adjustment: None.

Length: 112¾ in.; Width: 53 1/16 in.; Height: 51 in.

Weight: 5140 lbs.

Turning Radius (Outside): 10 ft.

Engine: Own, 3⅞x5¼, vertical, valve-in-head, 4 cylinders, removable cylinder sleeves.

Lubrication: Force feed by gear pump and dip pan splash.

Carburetor: Kingston, 1⅛-in.

Ignition System: Bosch high tension magneto.

Starting & Lighting Equipment: Special.

Cooling System: Fan, pump and radiator.

Bearings: Ball and Timken tapered roller bearings throughout.

Transmission: Selective, sliding gear, 2.3 to 10 m.p.h. forward; 2.3 m.p.h. reverse.

Final Drive: Spur gear.

Belt Pulley: 17x6 5/16; 450.5 r.p.m. and 2406 feet per minute at normal engine speed.

MASSEY-HARRIS MODEL "12" INDUSTRIAL
Massey-Harris Co., Racine, Wis.

MASSEY-HARRIS ORCHARD MODEL "12" (12-20)
Massey-Harris Co., Racine, Wis.

Traction Wheels: Four wheels; two traction in rear, 44x10, and two non-drivers in front, 28x5.

Tread Width: 45¼-in.; Adustment: None.

No. of Plows Recommended: Two, 14-in.

Turning Radius (Outside): 11½ ft.

Engine: Own, 3⅞x5¼, vertical, valve-in-head, 4 cylinders, removable cylinder sleeves.

Lubrication: Pressure and splash.

Carburetor: Kingston, 1⅛-in.

Ignition System: American Bosch high tension magneto.

Cooling System: Modine radiator, fan and pump.

Bearings: Timken roller and ball bearings throughout.

Transmission: Selective, sliding gear; 2⅓, 3⅓ to 4⅓ m.p.h. forward; 2⅓ m.p.h. reverse.

Final Drive: Spur gear.

Belt Pulley: 17x6 5/16; 540½ r.p.m. and 2406 feet per minute at normal engine speed.

MASSEY-HARRIS MODEL "25" INDUSTRIAL
Massey-Harris Co., Racine, Wis.

Traction Wheels: Four wheels; 42x9, dual pneumatic rear tires and 32x6 single pneumatic front tires. (Other tires and sizes available.)

Tread Width: 66⅛-in.; Adjustment: None.

Length: 125 in.; Width: 90⅞ in.; Height: 55½ in.; Weight: 8125 lbs.

Turning Radius (Outside): 13 ft.

Engine: Own, 4⅜x5¾, vertical, valve-in-head, 4 cylinders, removable cylinder sleeves.

Lubrication: Force feed by gear pump and dip pan splash.

Carburetor: Kingston, 1½-in.

Ignition System: Bosch high tension magneto.

Starting & Lighting Equipment: Special.

Cooling System: Fan, pump and radiator.

Bearings: Ball and Timken tapered roller bearings throughout.

Transmisison: Selective, sliding gear, 2.5 to 10.5 m.p.h forward; 2.5 m.p.h. reverse.

Final Drive: Spur gear.

Belt Pulley: 19x7⅛; 525 r.p.m. and 2612 feet per minute at normal engine speed.

Traction Wheels: Four wheels; two drivers in rear, 48x12, and two non-drive in front, 30x6.

Tread Width: 53½-in.; Adjustment: None.

No. of Plows Recommended: Three to four, 14-in.

Length: 135 in.; Width: 65½ in.; Height: 57 in.; Weight: 4917 lbs.

Turning Radius (Outside): 13 ft.

Engine: Own, 4⅜x5¾, vertical, valve-in-head, 4 cylinders, removable cylinder sleeves.

Lubrication: Force feed by gear pump and dip pan splash.

Carburetor: Kingston, 1½ in.

Ignition System: Bosch high tension magneto.

Cooling System: Fan, pump and radiator.

Bearings: Ball and Timken tapered roller bearings throughout.

Transmission: Selective, sliding gear, 2.5 to 4 m.p.h. forward; 2.5 m.p.h. reverse.

Final Drive: Spur gear.

Belt Pulley: 19x7⅛; 525 r.p.m. and 2612 feet per minute at normal engine speed.

MASSEY-HARRIS MODEL "25" 26-41
Massey-Harris Co., Racine, Wis.

1935

In 1935, 21 models of 13 makes not included in 1934 were added. The Badley Tractor Co. of Portland, Oregon, made a brief appearance and Fate-Root-Heath changed their Plymouth's name to Silver King.

BADLEY TRACTOR CO., INC.

Portland, Oregon

Angleworm 10   1935-1936

ANGLEWORM 10
Badley Tractor Co., Inc., 2860 N. W. Front Ave.,
Portland, Ore.

Traction Wheels. Track layer—crawler.
Tread Width: Adjustment: Spring and screw take up.
No. of Plows Recommended: Two, 14-in.
Length: 90 in.; **Width:** 58 in., standard; 43, narrow; 58, row crop; 49, narrow row crop; **Height:** 37 in.; **Weight:** 2600 lbs.; **Price:** $947, f. o. b. factory.
Turning Radius (Outside): 6 ft.; **Acres Plowed in 10-hr. Day:** 8.
Engine: Continental, 3⅜x4; 4 cylinders, cast en bloc.
Lubrication: Force feed, pump.
Carburetor: Marvel, Model AC, ⅞-in.
Ignition System: Battery — distributor. Automatic spark control.
Starting & Lighting Equipment: Starting standard; lighting optional at extra cost.
Cooling System: Pump.
Bearings: Bi-metal—Inter.
Transmission: Synchro mesh type; 3 speeds forward, 1 reverse. 2.0, 3.5 to 5.7 m.p.h. forward; 1.7 m.p.h. reverse.
Final Drive: Sprocket to track.
Belt Pulley: 9½x6½; 1,050 r.p.m. and 2,550 feet per minute at normal engine speed.

Proven in the Field

The ANGLE-WORM pulling a 6½-foot cover crop disc with 22-inch blades weighted to the spools.

Offering ... A BRAND NEW FIELD FOR TRACTOR PROFITS!

The ANGLEWORM 10 horsepower, track type tractor offers you a fast selling, popular type, year around machine which assures a real volume of sales with unusual profits. The ANGLEWORM is a power unit of proven ability, stamina and sales appeal; sensibly designed and ruggedly built to meet every conceivable farm requirement—a power unit that is making tractor history in the 10 H.P. field.

The ANGLEWORM is a sure-fire dealer opportunity. Powered by a sturdy, four cylinder motor, and equipped with ANGLEWORM suregrip grousers, its performance under all conditions is a revelation to even the most seasoned tractor operator. ANGLEWORM operation costs set a new standard of economy. Priced at less than $1,000.00, and backed by a program of national advertising. Full specifications will be found elsewhere in this catalogue.

Dealers and distributors seeking a tractor which will enable them to secure a large volume of highly profitable business are invited to write the BADLEY TRACTOR COMPANY, Portland, Oregon, for franchise particulars.

ANGLEWORM

TRADE MARK REG.

J. I. CASE CO.
Racine, Wisconsin

Case Industrial, Model LI

1935-1940

CASE INDUSTRIAL, MODEL LI
J. I. Case Co., Racine, Wis.

Traction Wheels: Two traction wheels in rear, 42x9 pneumatic tires; two non-drive in front, 30x5 pneumatic tires.
Length: 118 in.; **Width:** 67 in.; **Height:** 58 in.
Turning Radius (Outside): 13 ft.
Engine: Own, 4⅝x6, vertical, 4 cylinders, cast en bloc with removable sleeves.
Lubrication: Force feed through drilled crankshaft.
Carburetor: 1½-in.
Ignition System: High tension magneto with impulse coupling.
Cooling System: Fan, pump and radiator.
Bearings: Bronze backed babbitt.
Transmission: Sliding gear, 2.39, 3.52 and 9 m.p.h. forward; 2.68 m.p.h. reverse.
Final Drive: Chain, enclosed and runs in oil.
Belt Pulley: 13x8½; 780 r.p.m. and 2,650 feet per minute at normal engine speed.

CATERPILLAR TRACTOR CO.
Peoria, Illinois

Caterpillar Forty
Caterpillar Diesel Forty

1935-1936
1935

"CATERPILLAR" FORTY
Caterpillar Tractor Co., Peoria, Ill.

Traction Wheels: Two self-laying tracks, 16x74¾ in.
Tread Width: Std., 56; Spl., 74. Adjustment: None.
Length: 139⅜ in.; **Width:** 75 in.; **Height:** 70 in.; **Weight:** 13,140 lbs.; **Price:** $2575.00 f.o.b. factory.
Turning Radius (Outside): 7.2 ft.
Engine: Own, 5⅛x6½, vertical, 4 cylinders, cast in pairs.
Lubrication: Pressure oiling system.
Carburetor: Ensign, 1½ in.
Ignition System: Eisemann high tension magneto.
Lighting Equipment: Robert Bosch generator.
Cooling System: Water, pump circulation, gear driven fan.
Bearings: Largely anti-friction ball and roller.
Transmission: Sliding gear; 1.7, 2.5, 3.2 and 4.6 m.p.h. forward; 1.9 m.p.h. reverse.
Final Drive: Spur gears, completely enclosed.
Belt Pulley: 12x8½; 850 r.p.m. and 2,670 feet per minute at normal engine speed.

Traction Wheels: Two self-laying tracks, 16x74¾.

Tread Width: Std., 56; Spl., 74. Adjustment: None.

Length: 128⅜ in.; Width: 75 in.; Height: 72¹⁄₁₆ in.; Weight: 14,700 lbs., Price: $3,325 f.o.b. factory.

Turning Radius (Outside): 6 ft., 8½ in.

Engine: Own, 5¼x8, vertical, 3 cylinders, cast en bloc.

Lubrication: Pressure oiling system.

Carburetor: None.

Starting Equipment: Own two-cylinder gasoline engine starter.

Lighting: Robert Bosch magneto.

Cooling System: Water, pump circulation, gear driven fan.

Bearings: Largely anti-friction ball and roller.

Transmission: Sliding gears, 1.7, 2.5, 3.2 and 4.6 m.p.h. forward; 1.9 m.p.h. reverse.

Final Drive: Spur gear, completely enclosed.

Belt Pulley: 12x8½; 850 r.p.m. and 2,670 feet per minute at normal engine speed.

"CATERPILLAR" DIESEL FORTY
Caterpillar Tractor Co., Peoria, Ill

The CENTAUR TRACTOR CORP.

Greenwich, Ohio

Centaur 6-10 "G"   1935-1937
Centaur, Model KV, 22   1935-1939

CENTAUR 6-10 "G"
The Centaur Tractor Corp., Greenwich, Ohio

Traction Wheels: Steel, 28x4 with 28-in. extension bands with 6-in. face.

No. of Plows Recommended: One 12-in.

Length: 108 in.; Width: 30 in.; Height: 44 in.; Weight: 1,590 lbs.; Price: $515.

Turning Radius: 7 ft. outside. Acres Plowed in 10-Hour Day: 2½.

Engine: Le Roi, 3⅜x4¼, vertical, 2 cylinders, cast en bloc.

Lubrication: Splash and pump.

Carburetor: Zenith.

Ignition System: Eisemann, high tension magneto.

Cooling System: Thermo syphon.

Bearings: Timken and Bower.

Transmission: Own, 1¾ to 3¾ m.p.h forward and 1¾ m.p.h. reverse.

Final Drive: Chain.

Belt Pulley: 5x4½; 800 to 1,600 r.p.m. and 1,333 feet per minute at normal engine speed.

Traction Wheels: Steel or low pressure tires.
Tread Width: 36 in.; Adjustment: None.
No. of Plows Recommended: One, 14-in.
Length: 112 in.; Width: 45 in.; Height: 45.; Weight: 2,200 lbs.; Price: $745.00.
Turning Radius (Outside): 9 ft.; Acres Plowed in 10-hr. Day: 4 to 5.
Engine: Le Roi, 4 cycle, 4 cylinders, cast en bloc.
Lubrication: Full force feed.
Carburetor: Zenith, 7/8-in.
Ignition System: Eisemann, with impulse starter.
Starting & Lighting Equipment: Auto-Lite.
Cooling System: Thermo-syphon.
Bearings: Timken and New Departure.
Transmission: Standard automotive, 1 to 20 m.p.h. forward; 2 m.p.h. reverse.
Final Drive: Chains, enclosed, running in oil.
Belt Pulley: 6x6; 1,400 r.p.m. and 2,500 feet per minute at normal engine speed.

CENTAUR, MODEL KV, 22
Centaur Tractor Corp., Greenwich, O.

CLEVELAND TRACTOR CO.

Cleveland, Ohio

Cletrac Model E	1935-1939
Cletrac Model EN	1935
Cletrac "40" Diesel 46-60	1935

Traction Wheels: One crawler on each side, 56x8.
No. of Plows Recommended: Two to three, 14-in.
Length: 105½ in.; Width: 75½ in.; Height: 55½ in.; Weight: 4,950 lbs.
Turning Radius (Outside): 8 ft.
Engine: Hercules, 4x4½, L-head, 4 cylinders, cast en bloc.
Lubrication: Force feed.
Carburetor: Tillotson, 1⅛ in.
Ignition System: Bosch.
Cooling System: Water, belt driven fan, centrifugal pump, tubular radiator.
Transmission: Selective, 2 to 4.2 m.p.h. forward; 1.9 m.p.h. reverse.
Final Drive: Spur gear.
Belt Pulley: 10½x6½; 1,040 r.p.m. and 2,859 feet per minute at normal engine speed.

CLETRAC MODEL E
Cleveland Tractor Co., Cleveland, O.

Traction Wheels: One crawler on each side 56x8.
No. of Plows Recommended: Two to three 14-in.
Length: 105½ in.; Width: 41¼ in.; Height: 55½ in.; Weight: 4,870 lbs.
Turning Radius (Outside): 4½ ft.
Engine: Hercules, 4x4½, L-head, 4 cylinders, cast en bloc.
Lubrication: Force feed.
Carburetor: Tillotson, ·1⅛-in.
Ignition System: Bosch.
Cooling System: Water, belt driven fan, centrifugal pump, tubular radiator.
Transmission: Selective, 2 to 4.2 m.p.h. forward; 1.9 m.p.h reverse .
Final Drive: Spur gear.
Belt Pulley: 10½x6½; 1,040 r.p.m. and 2,859 feet per minute at normal engine speed.

CLETRAC MODEL EN
Cleveland Tractor Co., Cleveland, O.

CLETRAC "40" DIESEL 46-60
Cleveland Tractor Co., Cleveland, O.

Traction Wheels: One crawler on each side, 75x15.
Tread Width: 48. Adjustment: None.
No. of Plows Recommended: Six to seven, 14-in.
Length: 132 in.; Width: 65½ in.; Height: 64¾ in.; Weight: 11,500 lbs., approximately.
Turning Radius (Outside): 9-ft. 2-in.
Engine: Hercules Diesel, 4⅜x5¼, 6 cylinders, cast en bloc.
Lubrication: Force feed.
Starting & Lighting Equipment: Leece-Neville.
Cooling System: Tubular radiator, four blade fan, pump circulation.
Bearings: New Departure ball.
Transmission: Selective type sliding gear; 1.8, 3.0 and 4.3 m.p.h. forward; 2.2 m.p.h. reverse.
Final Drive: Through controlled differential and bull gear on drive sprocket shaft.
Belt Pulley: 13x8½; 884 r.p.m. and 3,000 feet per minute at normal engine speed.

DEERE & CO.

Moline, Illinois

John Deere AR	1935-1937
John Deere General Purpose Model "B"	1935-1937

JOHN DEERE AR

Deere & Co., Moline, Ill.

Traction Wheels: Four wheels; two traction in rear, 42¾x10.
No. of Plows Recommended: Two, 14-in.
Length: 124 in.; **Width:** 60 in.; **Height:** 55½ in.
Engine: Own, 5½x6½, valve-in-head, 2 cylinders, cast en bloc.
Lubrication: Pressure.
Carburetor: Schebler.
Ignition System: Fairbanks-Morse.
Starting & Lighting Equipment: K-W electric.
Cooling System: Thermo-syphon.
Bearings: Main—bronze back babbitt. Connecting rods—spun babbitt.
Transmission: Sliding gear, 2 to 6⅓ m.p.h. forward; 3⅛ m.p.h. reverse.
Final Drive: Gear.
Belt Pulley: 12¾x7⅜; 975 r.p.m. and 3,270 feet per minute at normal engine speed.

JOHN DEERE GEN'L PURPOSE MODEL "B," MODEL "BN" SINGLE FRONT WHEEL, MODEL "BW" ADJUSTABLE FRONT WHEEL TREAD.

Deere & Co., Moline, Ill.

Traction Wheels: Two traction in rear, 48x5¼. Rubber tires available.
Tread Width: Adjustable 56 to 84 in.
No. of Plows Recommended: One 16-in. or two 10-in.
Length: 120½-in.; **Width:** 85 in.; **Height to Radiator Cap:** 56 in.; **Weight:** 2763 lbs.
Turning Radius (Outside): 8 ft.
Engine: Own, 4¼x5¼, valve-in-head, 2 cylinders, cast en bloc.
Lubrication: Full force feed pressure with oil filter.
Carburetor: Schebler.
Ignition System: Fairbanks-Morse.
Lighting Equipment: K-W.
Cooling System: Thermo-syphon with gear and shaft driven fan.
Bearings: 2 main, bronze backed babbitt lined. Removable. Connecting rod bearings, babbitt centrifugally spun in rods.
Transmission: Selective type spur gears forged cut and heat treated. 2⅓, 3, 4¾ and 6¼ m.p.h. forward; 3½ m.p.h. reverse.
Final Drive: Spur gear, completely enclosed, running in oil.
Belt Pulley: 10⅝x6; 1,150 r.p.m. and 3,200 feet per minute at normal engine speed.

FATE-ROOT-HEATH CO.

Plymouth, Ohio

Silver King Model R38	1935-1936
Silver King Model R66	1935-1939

3 Wheel Type

SILVER KING

4 Wheel Type

What a Tractor — AND HOW IT SELLS!

FOR SPECIFICATIONS, PRICES AND COMPLETE DETAILS CONCERNING TERRITORIES AND DEALER PROFITS, WRITE

FARMERS, orchardists, gardeners are all finding the Silver King the very tractor they've always wanted. Ample power, modern design, variable speeds up to 25 m. p. h., rugged construction, low cost operation . . . these are but a few of its features. It's just the thing for small farms and an ideal auxiliary to the larger tractor on large farms. Every farm is a prospect. You'll like the Silver King's compactness, light weight, easily steering and easy riding. And remember, it plows, discs, plants, cultivates, mows, saws wood, pulls a trailer, replaces trucks.

THE FATE-ROOT-HEATH CO., *Plymouth, Ohio*

Traction Wheels: Steel or low-pressure tires.

Tread Width: 38 in. Adjustment: None.

No. of Plows Recommended: One, 14-in.

Length: 97 in.; Width: 48 in.; Height: 49 in.; Weight 2170 lbs.

Turning Radius (Outside): 9 ft.; Acres Plowed in 10-hr. Day: 5.

Engine: Hercules, IXA; 3x4, vertical, 4 cylinders.

Lubrication: Full force feed.

Carburetor: Zenith, ⅞-in.

Ignition System: Fairbanks-Morse.

Starting & Lighting Equipment: Auto-Lite.

Cooling System: Thermo-Syphon.

Bearings: Timken and New Departure.

Transmission: Standard automotive, 1 to 25 m.p.h. forward; 1.5 m.p.h. reverse.

Final Drive: Direct.

Belt Pulley: 6x6; 1400 r.p.m.

SILVER KING MODEL R38
Fate-Root-Heath Co., Plymouth, O.

SILVER KING MODEL R66
Fate-Root-Heath Co., Plymouth, O.

Traction Wheels: Steel or low pressure.

Tread Width: 66. Adjustment: 66-70.

No. of Plows Recommended: One, 14-in.

Length: 128 in.; Width: 75-79 in.; Height: 64 in.; Weight: 2,400 lbs.

Turning Radius (Outside): 7 ft.; Acres Plowed in 10-hr. Day: 5.

Engine: Hercules, 3x4, vertical, L-head, 4 cylinders, cast en bloc.

Lubrication: Full force feed.

Carburetor: Zenith, ⅞-in.

Ignition System: High tension magneto.

Starting & Lighting Equipment: Auto-Lite.

Cooling System: Thermo-syphon.

Bearings: Timken and New Departure.

Transmission: Automotive, 1 to 25 m.p.h. forward; 1.5 m.p.h. reverse.

Final Drive: Direct.

Belt Pulley: 6x6; 1,400 r.p.m. and 2,200 feet per minute at normal engine speed.

HUBER MANUFACTURING CO.

Marion, Ohio

Huber "HK" 32-45	1935-1940
Modern Farmer "SC"	1935

HUBER "HK" 32-45
Huber Mfg. Co., Marion, O.

Traction Wheels: Four wheel type; two drivers in rear, 50x12.

Tread Width: 61. Adjustment: None.

No. of Plows Recommended: Four to five, 14-in.

Length: 135 in.; Width: 77 in.; Height: 61 in.; Weight: Approx. 6,000 lbs.

Turning Radius (Outside): 15 ft.

Engine: Waukesha, 5⅛x6¼, overhead valve, 4 cylinders, cast en bloc, removable sleeves.

Lubrication: Force feed.

Carburetor: Zenith, 1½-in.

Ignition System: Bosch.

Starting & Lighting Equipment: On special order.

Cooling System: Fan, pump and radiator.

Bearings: Roller throughout.

Transmission: Automotive, 2.32 to 5.5 m.p.h. forward; 1.8 m.p.h. reverse.

Final Drive: Spur gear

Belt Pulley: 17x8½; 616 r.p.m. and 2,740 feet per minute at normal engine speed.

MODERN FARMER "SC"
Huber Mfg. Co., Marion, O.

Traction Wheels: Four wheel type; two drivers in rear.

Tread Width: 73½. Adjustment: None.

No. of Plows Recommended: Two to three, 14-in.

Length: 127⅝ in.; Width: 82½ in.; Height: 57 in.; Weight: 4,000 lbs.

Turning Radius (Outside): 9¼ ft.

Engine: Waukesha, 4⅛x5¼, overhead valve, 4 cylinders, cast en bloc, removable sleeves.

Lubrication: Force feed.

Carburetor: Zenith, 155, 1¼-in.

Ignition System: Bosch high tension.

Starting & Lighting Equipment: On special order.

Cooling System: Fan, pump and radiator.

Bearings: Ball and roller; no plain bearings.

Transmission: Automotive, 2.4 to 4.6 m.p.h. forward; 1.8 m.p.h. reverse.

Final Drive: Spur gear.

Belt Pulley: 14x6⅜; 705 r.p.m. and 2,600 feet per minute at normal engine speed.

INTERNATIONAL HARVESTER CO.
Chicago, Illinois

McCormick-D. Tractractor TD-40 Diesel   1935-1936

McCORMICK-D. TRACTRACTOR TD-40 DIESEL

International Harvester Co., Chicago, Ill.

Traction Members: Crawler track on each side, 16x70.
No. of Plows Recommended: Six to eight, 14 in.
Length: 140 in.; **Width:** 63¾ in.; **Height:** 63¾ in.; **Weight:** 12,000 lbs.
Turning Radius (Outside): 7 ft.
Engine: Own, 4¾x6½, Diesel, 4 replaceable cylinders.
Lubrication: Pressure.
Carburetor: Diesel pump.
Starting and Lighting Equipment: Own starting; special lighting system.
Cooling System: Impeller pump, thermostatic control.
Bearings: Precision mains, ball in transmission and final drive.
Transmission: Selective; five speeds forward; 1¾ to 4 m.p.h. forward; 2.25 m.p.h. reverse.
Final Drive: Gear type, enclosed.
Belt Pulley: 16¾x9; 591 r.p.m. and 2,593 feet per minute at 1100 engine speed. Special equipment.

MINNEAPOLIS-MOLINE POWER IMPLEMENT CO.

Minneapolis, Minnesota

M-M Twin City 27-44	1935-1937
M-M Twin City 21-32 FT-A	1935-1937
M-M Twin City KT-A	1935-1939
M-M Twin City Universal M	1935-1939
M-M Universal J	1935-1938

M-M TWIN CITY 27-44

Minneapolis-Moline Power Impl. Co., Minneapolis, Minn.

Traction Wheels: Four wheels; two drivers in rear, 60x20.
Tread Width: 68-in.; **Adjustment:** None.
No. of Plows Recommended: Five to six, 14-in.
Length: 152 in.; **Width:** 88 in.; **Height:** 73 in.; **Weight:** 9,200 lbs.
Turning Radius (Outside): 15 ft.
Engine: Own, 5½x6¾, vertical, valve-in-head, 4 cylinders, cast en bloc, removable sleeve.
Lubrication: Pressure feed.
Carburetor: Schebler 1½ in.
Ignition System: American Bosch magneto with impulse starter.
Cooling System: Modine tubular radiator, centrifugal pump and fan.
Bearings: Hyatt throughout.
Transmission: Sliding gear, 2.2 and 3 m.p.h. forward; 1.85 m.p.h. reverse.
Final Drive: Enclosed spur gear.
Belt Pulley: 21x8½; 466 r.p.m. and 2560 feet per minute at normal engine speed.

Traction Wheels: Four wheels, two in rear, 50x12, giving traction. Rubber tires available.
Tread Width: 42-in.; Adjustment: None.
No. of Plows Recommended: Three to four, 14-in.
Length: 137 in.; Width: 66 in.; Height: Rad. Cap, 66 in.; Weight: 6,070 lbs.
Turning Radius (Outside): 14 ft.
Engine: Own, 4⅝x6, vertical, with removable cylinder blocks, 4 cylinders.
Lubrication: Pressure.
Carburetor: Schebler, 1¼-in.
Ignition System: American Bosch magneto with impulse coupling.
Lighting Equipment: Electric, with battery or no battery generator. Optional.
Cooling System: Modine radiator, centrifugal pump and fan.
Bearings: Timken and ball.
Transmission: Sliding gear; 2.36-3.17-4.05 m.p.h. forward; 1.74 m.p.h. reverse.
Final Drive: Enclosed spur gear.
Belt Pulley: 16x7½; 650 r.p.m. and 2720 feet per minute at normal engine speed.

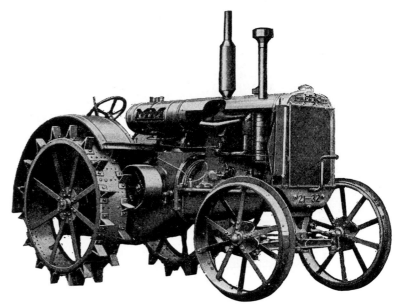

M-M TWIN CITY 21-32 FT-A
**Minneapolis-Moline Power Impl. Co.,
Minneapolis, Minn.**

M-M TWIN CITY KT-A
**Minneapolis-Moline Power Impl. Co.,
Minneapolis, Minn.**

Traction Wheels: Four wheels; two traction in rear, 42x10; twenty 4-in. high, two-bolt lugs per wheel. Rubber tires available.
Tread Width: 49-in.; Adjustment: None.
No. of Plows Recommended: Three, 14-in.
Length: 131 in.; Width: 59 in.; Height: Rad. Cap, 64½ in.; Weight: 4,300 lbs.
Turning Radius (Outside): 8 ft.
Engine: Own, 4¼x5, vertical, 4 cylinders, cast en bloc.
Lubrication: Pressure.
Carburetor: Schebler, 1¼-in.
Ignition System: Magneto.
Lighting Equipment: Can be furnished.
Cooling System: Pump.
Bearings: Ball, roller and tapered roller.
Transmission: Sliding gear; 2.1, 3⅛ to 4.15 m.p.h. forward; 1.8 m.p.h. reverse.
Final Drive: Spur gear.
Belt Pulley: 14x7; 822 r.p.m. and 3000 feet per minute at normal engine speed.

Traction Wheels: Four wheel type; two traction in rear, 42x10.
Tread Width: 75-in.; Adjustment: None.
No. of Plows Recommended: Three, 14-in.
Length: 143 in.; Width: 93 in.; Height: 64½ in.; Weight: 4860 lbs.
Turning Radius (outside): 8½ ft.
Engine: Own, 4¼x5, overhead, 4 cylinders, cast en bloc.
Lubrication: Full pressure.
Carburetor: Schebler, 1¼-in.
Ignition System: Magneto.
Starting and Lighting Equipment: Optional.
Cooling System: Fan, pump and radiator.
Bearings: Ball, roller and tapered roller.
Transmission: Spur and bevel, 2.1, 3⅛ to 4.15 m.p.h. forward; 1.8 m.p.h. reverse.
Final Drive: Spur gear.
Belt Pulley: 14x7; 822 r.p.m. and 3000 feet per minute at normal engine speed.

M-M TWIN CITY UNIVERSAL M
Minneapolis-Moline Power Impl. Co., Minneapolis, Minn.

Traction Wheels: Four-wheel type, two-traction in rear, 50x8; two non-drive in front, 25x4½.
Tread Adjustment: 54-76.
No. of Plows Recommended: Three, 14-in.
Length: 115½ in.; Width: 79 in.; Height: 56 in.; Weight: 3450 lbs.
Turning Radius (Outside): 7 ft.
Engine: Own, 3⅝x4¾, vertical, 4 cylinders, cast en bloc.
Lubrication: Pressure to crankshaft bearings, camshaft bearings, connecting rod bearings, piston pins, timing gears and valves.
Carburetor: Zenith, 1¼-in.
Ignition System: High tension magneto.
Starting & Lighting Equipment: Electric, generator type; no battery. Optional.
Cooling System: Radiator, pump and fan.
Bearings: Bronze backed babbitt lined shells.
Transmission: Sliding gear, with five forward speeds, 2.2 to 12.2 m.p.h. forward; 1.2 m.p.h. reverse.
Final Drive: Spur gear.
Belt Pulley: 15⅝x6½; 730 r.p.m. and 3,000 feet per minute at normal engine speed.

M-M UNIVERSAL J
Minneapolis-Moline Power Impl. Co., Minneapolis, Minn.

PARRETT TRACTORS

Benton Harbor, Michigan

Parrett Model 6   1935-1937

Traction Wheels: Three wheels; two traction, 11.25-24 air tires.

Tread Width: 48-in.; Adjustment: 44 min., 76 max.

No. of Plows Recommended: Two, 14-in.

Length: 117 in.; Width: 60 in.; Height: 48 in.; Weight: 2600 lbs.

Turning Radius: (Outside) 8 ft.; Acres Plowed in 10-Hr. Day: 6-10.

Engine: Hercules IXB, 3¼x4, vertical, 4 cylinders, cast en bloc.

Lubrication: Full pressure by gear pump through drilled crankshaft.

Carburetor: Zenith, ¾-in.

Ignition System: Distributor, storage battery and generator.

Starting and Lighting Equipment: Electric, two head lamps.

Cooling System: Tubular radiator, V-belt driven fan, thermo-syphon.

Bearings: Ball bearings in transmission; Timkens on final drive and wheels.

Transmission: Selective, sliding gear; three speeds forward, one reverse, standard shift; 1½ to 20 m.p.h. Forward; 3 m.p.h. Reverse.

Final Drive: Spiral bevel gears, alloy steel forgings, heat treated.

Belt Pulley: 12x6½; 830 r.p.m. and 2600 feet per minute at normal engine speed.

PARRETT MODEL 6
Parrett Tractors, Benton Harbor, Mich.

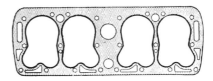
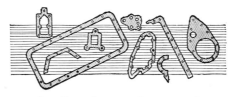

1936

In 1936, 45 models of 15 makes not included in 1935 were added and Ford Motor Co. resumed selling the Fordson through their marketing organization. More than half of the new tractors sold were equipped with rubber tires.

BATES MANUFACTURING CO.

Joliet, Illinois

Bates "40" Diesel	1936-1937
Bates Steel Mule, Model F, 18-25	1936-1937
Bates Steel Mule Model 35	1936-1937
Bates Steel Mule Model 50	1936-1937
Bates Steel Mule Model 80	1936-1937

BATES "40" DIESEL
Bates Mfg. Co., Joliet, Ill.

Traction: Crawlers.
Tread Width: 14 in; **Adjustment:** None.
No. of Plows Recommended: Five to six, 14-in.
Length: 120 in.; **Width:** 72 in.; **Height:** 70 in.; **Weight:** 11,000 lbs.; **Price:** $3100 f.o.b. factory.
Engine: Waukesha-Hesselman, 4½x5¼, overhead valves, 4 cylinders, wet sleeves.
Lubrication: Force feed.
Carburetor: None.
Ignition System: High tension magneto.
Starting & Lighting Equipment: Optional as extra.
Cooling System: Fan, pump and radiator.
Bearings: Removable shell type.
Transmission: Selective sliding gears; 1¾ to 4 m.p.h. forward; 1¾ m.p.h. reverse.
Final Drive: Enclosed gear.
Belt Pulley: 12x8¾; 920 r.p.m. and 2,800 feet per minute at normal engine speed.

Traction Wheels: One crawler on each side, 58x10. Rubber tires optional on front wheels.

Tread Width: 36-in.; **Adjustment:** None.

No. of Plows Recommended: Three 14-in.

Length: 105 in.; **Width:** 62 in.; **Height:** 58 in.; **Weight:** 5250 lbs.

Turning Radius (Outside): 7½ ft.; **Acres Plowed in 10-hr. Day:** 10.

Engine: Le Roi; 4¼x6, valve-in-head, 4 cylinders, cast in pairs.

Lubrication: Pressure.

Carburetor: Kingston.

Ignition System: American Bosch high tension magneto.

Cooling System: Pump.

Bearings: Timken roller in transmission.

Transmission: Sliding gear, 2¼ to 4 m.p.h. forward; 2 m.p.h. reverse.

Final Drive: Enclosed gears running in oil.

Belt Pulley: 12x8½; 850 r.p.m. and 2650 feet per minute at normal engine speed.

BATES STEEL MULE, MODEL F, 18-25
Bates Mfg. Co., Joliet, Ill.

BATES STEEL MULE MODEL 35
Bates Mfg. Co., Joliet, Ill.

Traction Wheels: Two crawlers, 12-in. wide and 70-in. long.

Tread Width: 53¼ in.; **Adjustment:** None.

Length: 120 in.; **Width:** 72 in.; **Height:** 70 in.; **Weight:** 10,750 lbs.

Turning Radius (Outside): 6 ft.

Engine: Waukesha, 4¼x4¾, Ricardo head, 6 cylinders, 1500 r.p.m.

Lubrication: Force feed system.

Carburetor: Schebler.

Ignition System: Bosch high tension magneto.

Cooling System: Pump.

Bearings: Ball and roller.

Transmission: Sliding gear; 1.75 to 3.75 m.p.h. forward; 1.75 m.p.h. reverse.

Final Drive: Spur gear, enclosed and running in oil.

Belt Pulley: 12x8¾; 858 r.p.m. and 2695 f.p.m. at normal engine speed.

Traction Wheels: Two crawlers, 14 inches wide and 82 inches long.

Tread Width: 53¼ in.; **Adjustment:** None.

Length: 128 in.; **Width:** 74 in.; **Height:** 72 in.; **Weight:** 14,000 lbs.

Turning Radius (Outside): 7 ft.

Engine: Waukesha, 4⅝x5⅛, Ricardo-head 6 cylinders, cast in pairs, 1400 r.p.m.

Lubrication: Force feed.

Carburetor: Schebler.

Ignition System: Bosch high tension magneto.

Cooling System: Pump.

Bearings: Ball and roller.

Transmission: Sliding gear; 1¾ to 3¾ m.p.h. forward; 1¾ m.p.h. reverse.

Final Drive: Spur gear, enclosed and running in oil.

Belt Pulley: 12x8¾; 858 r.p.m. and 2695 f.p.m. at normal engine speed.

BATES STEEL MULE MODEL 50
Bates Mfg. Co., Joliet, Ill.

BATES STEEL MULE MODEL 80

Bates Mfg. Co., Joliet, Ill.

Traction Wheels: Two crawlers, 104x18, 3744 sq. in. on ground.

Tread Width: 72 in.; **Adjustment:** None.

Length: 146 in.; **Width:** 97 in.; **Height:** 84 in.; **Weight:** 22500 lbs.

Turning Radius (Outside): 8 ft.

Engine: Waukesha, 6½x7, Ricardo-head, 4 cylinders, 4 cycle, 900 r.p.m.

Carburetor: Stromberg.

Lubrication: Force reed.

Ignition System: Bosch high tension magneto.

Cooling System: Fan, circulating pump and radiator.

Bearings: Ball and roller.

Transmission: Sliding gear; 1.5 to 3.75 m.p.h. forward; 1.25 m.p.h. reverse.

Final Drive: Spur gear, enclosed and running in oil.

Belt Pulley: 16x10½; 650 r.p.m. and 2700 f.p.m. at normal engine speed.

J. I. CASE CO.

Racine, Wisconsin

Case Industrial, Model CI   1936-1939
Case Model RC   1936-1940

CASE INDUSTRIAL, MODEL CI

J. I. Case Co., Racine, Wis.

Traction Wheels: Two traction wheels in rear, 40x8 pneumatic tires; two non-drive wheels in front, 30x5 pneumatic tires. (Other sizes and types of tires available.)

Length: 104 in.; **Width:** 61 in.; **Height:** 49 in.

Turning Radius (Outside): 10 ft.

Engine: Own, 3⅞x5½, vertical, valve-in-head, 4 cylinders, cast en bloc with removable sleeves.

Lubrication: Force feed through drilled crankshaft.

Carburetor: 1¼-in.

Ignition System: High tension magneto with impulse coupling.

Cooling System: Fan, pump and radiator.

Bearings: Bronze backed babbitt in motor.

Transmission: Sliding gear, 2.83, 4.02 and 11.10 m.p.h. forward; 3.15 m.p.h. reverse.

Final Drive: Chain, enclosed and runs in oil.

Belt Pulley: 10¼x6¼; 973 r.p.m. and 2,600 feet per minute at normal engine speed.

Traction Wheels: Two traction in rear; rubber tires available as extra; **Tread Adjustment:** 44-80.
No. of Plows Recommended: One, 16-in.
Length: 124 in.; **Width:** Variable, 44-80 in.; **Height:** 61 in.
Turning Radius (Outside): Pivots on rear wheel.
Engine: Waukesha, 3¼x4, vertical, L-head, 4 cylinders, cast en bloc.
Lubrication: Force feed through drilled crankshaft.
Ignition System: High tension magneto with impulse coupling.
Transmission: Sliding gear; 2⅛, 3⅓ and 4½ m.p.h. forward.
Final Drive: Chain, enclosed and running in oil.
Belt Pulley: 10⅛x6¼; 991 r.p.m. and 2600 feet per minute at normal engine speed.

CASE MODEL RC
J. I. Case Co., Racine, Wis.

CATERPILLAR TRACTOR CO.

Peoria, Illinois

Caterpillar Thirty	1936-1937
Caterpillar Diesel RD4	1936-1937
Caterpillar Diesel RD6	1936-1937
Caterpillar Diesel RD7	1936-1937
Caterpillar Diesel RD8	1936-1937

Traction: Two self-laying tracks; 61⅛ in. ground contact; 13 in. wide.
Tread Width: 60 and 44-in.; **Adjustment:** None.
Length: 10 ft., 9 in.; **Width:** 6 ft., 6 in. and 5 ft., 2 in.; **Height:** 5 ft., ⅝-in.; **Weight:** 9280 and 9010 lbs.; **Price:** $2235 and $2100 f. o. b. factory.
Turning Radius (Outside): 6 ft., 10 in. and 6 ft., 7 in.
Engine: Own, 4¼x5½, vertical, 4 cylinders, cast en bloc.
Lubrication: Pressure oiling system.
Carburetor: Zenith, 1¼-in.
Ignition System: Eisemann high tension magneto.
Cooling System: Belt driven water pump and fan.
Bearings: Largely anti-friction ball and roller.
Transmission: Sliding gear; 1.7, 2.4, 3.0, 3.7 and 5.4 m.p.h. forward; 1.9 m.p.h. reverse.
Final Drive: Spur gears completely enclosed.
Belt Pulley: 12x8½; 840 r.p.m. and 2640 feet per minute at normal engine speed.

"CATERPILLAR" THIRTY
Caterpillar Tractor Co., Peoria, Ill.

"CATERPILLAR" DIESEL RD4

Caterpillar Tractor Co., Peoria, Ill.

Traction: Two self-laying tracks; $61\frac{1}{8}$ in. ground contact; 13 in. wide.
Tread Width: 60 and 44 in. **Adjustment:** None.
Length: 10 ft., $1\frac{3}{16}$ in.; **Width:** 6 ft. 6 in. and 5 ft., 2 in.; **Height:** 5 ft., $\frac{5}{8}$-in.; **Weight:** 9740 and 9470 lbs.; **Price:** \$2585 and \$2450 f. o. b. factory.
Turning Radius (Outside): 6 ft., $8\frac{1}{2}$ in. and 6 ft.
Engine: Own, $4\frac{1}{4}$x$5\frac{1}{2}$, vertical, 4 cylinders, cast en bloc.
Lubrication: Pressure oiling system.
Starting Equipment: Own two-cylinder gasoline starting engine.
Cooling System: Belt driven water pump and fan.
Bearings: Largely anti-friction ball and roller.
Transmission: Sliding gear, 1.7, 2.4, 3.0, 3.7 and 5.4 m.p.h forward; 1.9 m.p.h reverse.
Final Drive: Spur gears completely enclosed.
Belt Pulley: 12x$8\frac{1}{2}$; 840 r.p.m. and 2640 feet per minute at normal engine speed.

"CATERPILLAR" DIESEL RD6

Caterpillar Tractor Co., Peoria, Ill

Traction Wheels: Two self-laying tracks, 16x$74\frac{3}{4}$.
Tread Width: 74 and 56-in.; **Adjustment:** None.
Length: $138\frac{3}{8}$ in.; **Width:** 93 and 75 in.; **Height:** $72\frac{1}{16}$ in.; **Weight:** 15,560 and 14,820 lbs.; **Price:** \$3575 and \$3375 f.o.b. factory.
Turning Radius (Outside): $8\frac{1}{3}$ and 7 ft.
Engine: Own, $5\frac{3}{4}$x8, vertical, 3 cylinders, cast en bloc.
Lubrication: Pressure oiling system.
Starting Equipment: Own two-cylinder gasoline starting engine.
Lighting: Robert Bosch magneto.
Cooling System: Water, pump circulation, gear driven fan.
Bearings: Largely anti-friction ball and roller.
Transmission: Sliding gears, 1.7, 2.5, 3.2 and 4.6 m.p.h. forward; 1.9 m.p.h. reverse.
Final Drive: Spur gear, completely enclosed.
Belt Pulley: 12x$10\frac{3}{4}$; 850 r.p.m. and 2,670 feet per minute at normal engine speed.

"CATERPILLAR" DIESEL RD7

Caterpillar Tractor Co., Peoria, Ill.

Traction Wheels: Two self-laying tracks, 18x$81\frac{7}{8}$ inches.
Tread Width: 74 and 60 in.; **Adjustment:** None.
Length: $150\frac{1}{4}$ in.; **Width:** 7 ft., $11\frac{5}{8}$ in. and 6 ft., $9\frac{5}{8}$ in.; **Height:** $81\frac{5}{8}$ in.; **Weight:** 21,130 and 20,410 lbs.; **Price:** \$4850 and \$4600 f.o.b. factory.
Turning Radius (Outside): $8\frac{2}{3}$ ft. and $7\frac{2}{3}$ ft.
Engine: Own, $5\frac{3}{4}$x8 vertical, 4 cylinders, cast en bloc.
Lubrication: Pressure oiling system.
Starting Equipment: Own two-cylinder gasoline starting engine.
Lighting Equipment: Bosch generator.
Cooling System: Water, pump circulation, gear driven fan.
Bearings: Largely anti-friction ball and roller.
Transmission: **Sliding gears, 1.6, 2.4, 3.4** and 4.7 m.p.h. forward; 1.9 m.p.h. reverse.
Final Drive: Spur gears, completely enclosed.
Belt Pulley: $13\frac{3}{8}$x13; 753 r.p.m. and 2,630 feet per minute at governed engine speed.

Traction Wheels: Two self-laying tracks, 20x97⅝ inches.

Tread Width: 78. Adjustment: None.

Length: 183 in.; **Width:** 103¾ in.; **Height:** 90 in.; **Weight:** 32,790 lbs.; **Price:** $6650 f.o.b. factory.

Turning Radius (Outside): 9 ft., 5 in.

Engine: Own, 5¾x8, vertical, 6 cylinders, cast en bloc.

Lubrication: Pressure oiling system.

Starting Equipment: Own, two-cylinder gasoline starting engine.

Lighting Equipment: Bosch generator.

Cooling System: Water, pump circulation, gear-driven fan.

Bearings: Largely anti-friction ball and roller.

Transmission: Sliding gear, 1.7, 2.4, 2.8, 3.2, 3.9 and 5.3 m.p.h. forward; 1.7, 2.8 m.p.h. reverse

Final Drive: Spur gears, completely enclosed.

Belt Pulley: 14⁷⁄₁₆x15; 721 r.p.m. and 2,690 feet per minute at normal engine speed.

"CATERPILLAR" DIESEL RD8
Caterpillar Tractor Co., Peoria, Ill.

CLEVELAND TRACTOR CO.

Cleveland, Ohio

Cletrac "AG"	1936-1944
Cletrac "BD"	1936-1944
Cletrac "BG"	1936-1944
Cletrac "CG"	1936-1943
Cletrac "DD"	1936-1944
Cletrac "FD"	1936-1944
Cletrac "FG"	1936-1943

Traction: One crawler on each side, 62x12; crawler centers, 42-in. No adjustment.

No. of Plows Recommended: Three, 14-in.

Length: 106 in.; **Width:** 57¼ in.; **Height:** 55 in; **Weight:** 6,800 lbs.

Engine: Hercules, 4x4½, L-head, 4 cylinders.

Lubrication: Force feed.

Carburetor: Tillotson, 1⅛-in.

Ignition System: Bosch high tension magneto with impulse starter.

Cooling System: Tubular radiator with 4-blade fan. Pump circulation.

Bearings: New Departure ball—Hyatt.

Transmission: Selective type sliding gear; 1¾, 2⅝ and 3¾ m.p.h. forward; 1⅝ m.p.h. reverse.

Final Drive: Through controlled differential and bull gear on sprocket drive shaft, completely enclosed.

Belt Pulley: 10½x8½; 3,500 f.p.m. at 1,275 r.p.m.; **Power Reduction:** 680 r.p.m.; **Power Take Off:** 1,020 r.p.m.

CLETRAC "AG"
Cleveland Tractor Co., Cleveland, O.

Traction: One crawler on each side, 63x14; crawler centers, Std., 44 in.; Spec. 52 in. No adjustments.

No. of Plows Recommended: Four to five, 14-in.

Length: 116½ in.; Width: Std., 60⅛; Spec., 68⅛ in.; Height: 59 in.; Weight: 8,800 lbs.

Engine: Hercules Diesel, 3½x4½, 6 cylinders.

Lubrication: Force feed.

Starting System: Battery starting, using Leece Neville equipment.

Cooling System: Tubular radiator with 6-blade fan. Pump circulation.

Bearings: New Departure ball.

Transmission: Selective type sliding gear; 1.8, 2⅝ and 3½ m.p.h. forward; 1.7 m.p.h. reverse

Final Drive: Through controlled differential and bull gear on sprocket drive shaft, completely enclosed

Belt Pulley: 12x8½; 3,300 f.p.m. at 1,045 r.p.m.; Power Reduction: 600 r.p.m.; Power Take Off: 1,045 r.p.m.

CLETRAC "BD"
Cleveland Tractor Co., Cleveland, O.

Traction: One crawler on each side, 63x14; crawler centers, Std., 49 in.; Spec., 52 in.; no adjustment.

No. of Plows Recommended: Four to five, 14-in.

Length: 116½ in.; Width: Std., 60⅛, Spec., 68⅛ in.; Height: 59 in.; Weight: 8,350 lbs.

Engine: Hercules, 3¾x4¼, L-head, 6 cylinders.

Lubrication: Force feed.

Carburetor: Tillotson, 1¼-in.

Ignition System: Std. battery starting with generator Delco-Remy, Bosch high tension magneto with impulse starter optional.

Cooling System: Tubular radiator with 6-blade fan. Pump circulation.

Bearings: New Departure ball.

Transmission: Selective type sliding gear; 1.8, 2⅝ and 3½ m.p.h. forward; 1.7 m.p.h. reverse

Final Drive: Through controlled differential and bull gear on sprocket drive shaft, completely enclosed

Belt Pulley: 12x8½; 3,300 f.p.m at 1,045 r.p.m.; Power Reduction: 600 r.p.m.; Power Take Off: 1045 r.p.m.

CLETRAC "BG"
Cleveland Tractor Co., Cleveland, O.

Traction: One crawler on each side, 74¾x 13; crawler centers; Std., 48-in. Spec., 61-in. No adjustment.

No. of Plows Recommended: Five to seven, 14-in.

Length:. 127 in.; Width: Std., 67¼, Spec., 80¼ in.; Height: 63⅞ in.; Weight: 11,500 lbs.

Engine: Hercules, 4¼x4½, L-head, 6 cylinders.

Lubrication: Force feed.

Carburetor: Tillotson, 1½-in.

Ignition System: Standard battery starting with generator, Delco-Remy; Bosch high tension magneto with impulse starter optional.

Cooling System: Tubular radiator with 4-blade fan. Pump circulation.

Bearings: New Departure ball.

Transmission: Selective type sliding gear; 1.87, 3.05 and 4.44 m.p.h. forward; 2.28 m.p.h. reverse.

Final Drive: Through controlled differential and bull gear on sprocket drive shaft, completely enclosed.

Belt Pulley: 13x11; 3,400 f.p.m. at 1,000 r.p.m.; Power Reduction: 640 r.p.m.; Power Take Off: 1,000 r.p.m.

CLETRAC "CG"
Cleveland Tractor Co., Cleveland, O.

CLETRAC "DD"
Cleveland Tractor Co., Cleveland, O.

Traction: One crawler on each side, 74¾ x 15; crawler centers; Std., 48-in., Spec., 61-in. No adjustment.
No. of Plows Recommended: Six to seven, 14-in.
Length: 132 in.; **Width:** Std. 67¼, Spec. 80¼ in.; **Height:** 65 in.; **Weight:** 12,700 lbs.
Engine: Hercules Diesel, 4⅜x5¼, 6 Cylinders.
Lubrication: Force feed.
Starting System: Battery starting, using Leece Neville equipment.
Cooling System: Tubular radiator with 4-blade fan. Pump circulation.
Bearings: New Departure ball.
Transmission: Selective type sliding gear; 1.8, 2.7, and 4.3 m.p.h. forward; 1.8 m.p.h. reverse.
Final Drive: Through controlled differential and bull gear on sprocket drive shaft, completely enclosed.
Belt Pulley: 13x11; 3000 f.p.m. at 884 r.p.m.
Power Production: 510 r.p.m.
Power Take-Off: 884 r.p.m.

Traction: One crawler on each side. 96x20; crawler centers; 67-in. No adjustment.
No. of Plows Recommended: Twelve to fourteen, 14-in.
Length: 173 in.; **Width:** 94½ in.; **Height:** 84 in.; **Weight:** 25,800 lbs.
Engine: Hercules, Diesel, 5x6, 6 cylinders, cast in two pairs of three.
Lubrication: Force feed.
Starting System: Battery starting, using Leece Neville equipment.
Cooling System: Tubular radiator with 4-blade fan. Pump circulation.
Bearings:. Timken roller, New Departure ball and Hyatt roller.
Transmission: Selective type sliding gear; 1.75, 2.75 and 4.25 m.p.h. forward; 2.1 m.p.h. reverse.
Final Drive: Through controlled differential, to gear reduction and planetary drive on sprocket shaft, completely enclosed.
Belt Pulley: 24½x15; 3350 f.p.m. at 535 r.p.m.
Power Reduction: 320 r.p.m.
Power Take-Off: 930 r.p.m.

CLETRAC "FD"
Cleveland Tractor Co., Cleveland, O.

Traction: One crawler on each side. 96x20; crawler centers; 67-in. No adjustment.
No. of Plows Recommended: Twelve to fourteen, 14-in.
Length: 173 in.; **Width:** 94½ in.; **Height:** 84 in.; **Weight:** 25,000 lbs.
Engine: Hercules, 5¾x6, L-head, 6 cylinders, cast in two pairs of three.
Lubrication: Force feed.
Carburetor:. Tillotson, 2-in.
Ignition System: Bosch high tension magneto with impulse starter.
Starting Equipment: Electric starter.
Cooling System: Tubular radiator with 4-blade fan. Pump circulation.
Bearings: Timken roller, New Departure ball and Hyatt roller.
Transmission: Selective type sliding gear; 1.75, 2.5 and 4.3 m.p.h. forward; 2.1 m.p.h. reverse.
Final Drive: Through controlled differential, to gear reduction and planetary drive on sprocket shaft, completely enclosed.
Belt Pulley: 24½x15; 3200 f.p.m. at 510 r.p.m.
Power Reduction: 308 r.p.m.
Power Take-Off: 800 r.p.m.

CLETRAC "FG"
Cleveland Tractor Co., Cleveland, O.

![Cletrac Crawler Tractors logo] **Cletrac** Crawler Tractors
REG. U.S. PAT. OFF.

★ **4 Models with Diesel Motors**

★ **11 Models with Gasoline or Tractor Fuel Motors**

★ **22 — 94 Horsepower**

Cletrac Answers Every Agricultural and Industrial Need...

FOR MORE than twenty years Cletrac has specialized in the manufacture of crawler type tractors exclusively. Each year has seen new features, originated by Cletrac and incorporated in the Cletrac line, become time-tested and finally adopted by others.

Today Cletrac offers a complete line with a model for every agricultural and industrial need—streamlined with modern design and many improvements that add to Cletrac's famous efficiency.

Five widths in Model E meet any row crop requirement. Attachments for this model, specially designed for Cletrac—are available for any farming operation. Each is a complete unit—easily attached—easily detached—and easily stored.

All models have Cletrac's exclusive controlled differential steering. Gasoline or tractor fuel power in the smaller sizes and gasoline or Diesel power from 35 horsepower and up answer the demand for choice of fuel.

More than ever the most adaptable and salable line of crawler tractors for both agriculture and industry, Cletrac offers a money-making opportunity to alert dealers.

The Cleveland Tractor Co., Euclid Avenue, Cleveland, Ohio

DEERE & CO.
Moline, Illinois

John Deere AN	1936-1937
John Deere AO	1936
John Deere AW	1936-1937
John Deere BN	1936-1937
John Deere BO	1936-1937
John Deere BR	1936-1937
John Deere BW	1936-1937
John Deere DI	1936-1937

Traction Wheels: Two traction in rear, 50x6. Rubber tires available.
Tread Width: Adjustable 56 to 84 in.
No. of Plows Recommended: Two, 14-in.
Length: 130 in.; **Width:** 86 in.; **Height to Radiator Cap:** 61½ in.; **Weight:** 3697 lbs.
Turning Radius (Outside): 8 ft.
Engine: Own, 5½x6½, horizontal, 2 cylinders, valve-in-head, cast en bloc.
Lubrication: Full force feed pressure with oil filter.
Carburetor: Schebler.
Ignition System: Fairbanks Morse.
Lighting Equipment: K-W.
Cooling System: Thermo-syphon with gear and shaft driven fan.
Bearings: 2 main, bronze backed babbitt lined. Removable. Connecting rod bearings babbitt centrifugally spun in rod.
Transmission: Selective type spur gears forged cut and heat treated; 2½, 3, 4¾ and 6¼ m.p.h. forward; 3½ m.p.h. reverse.
Final Drive: Spur gear, completely enclosed, running in oil.
Belt Pulley: 12¾x7⅜; 975 r.p.m. and 3270 feet per minute at normal engine speed.

JOHN DEERE GEN'L PURPOSE MODEL "A", MODEL AN, SINGLE FRONT WHEEL, MODEL AW, ADJUSTABLE FRONT WHEEL TREAD

Deere & Co., Moline, Ill.

JOHN DEERE AR STANDARD TREAD, MODEL AO FOR GROVE, ORCHARD AND VINEYARD

Deere & Co., Moline, Ill.

Traction Wheels: Two traction in rear, 42¾x10. Rubber tires available.
Tread Width: 54-in.
No. of Plows Recommended: Two, 14-in.
Length: 124 in.; **Width:** 64⅛ in.; **Height to Radiator Cap:** 55 in; **Weight:** 4010 lbs.
Turning Radius (Outside): 13 ft.
Engine: Own, 5½x6½, valve-in-head, 2 cylinders, cast en bloc.
Lubrication: Full force feed pressure with oil filter.
Carburetor: Schebler.
Ignition System: Fairbanks-Morse.
Lighting Equipment: K-W.
Cooling System: Thermo-syphon with gear and shaft driven fan.
Bearings: 2 Main, bronze back and babbitt lined, removable. Connecting rod bearings babbitt centrifugally spun in rod.
Transmission: Selective type spur gear forged cut and heat treated. 2, 3, 4 and 6¾ m.p.h. forward; 3 m.p.h. reverse.
Final Drive: Spur gears, completely enclosed, running in oil.
Belt Pulley: 12¾x7¼, 975 r.p.m. and 3270 feet per minute at normal engine speed.

Traction Wheels: Two traction in rear, 48x5¼. Rubber tires available.

Tread Width: Adjustable 56 to 84 in.

No. of Plows Recommended: One 16-in. or two 10-in.

Length: 120½-in.; Width: 85 in.; Height to Radiator Cap: 56 in.; Weight: 2763 lbs.

Turning Radius (Outside): 8 ft.

Engine: Own, 4¼x5¼, valve-in-head, 2 cylinders, cast en bloc.

Lubrication: Full force feed pressure with oil filter.

Carburetor: Schebler.

Ignition System: Fairbanks-Morse.

Lighting Equipment: K-W.

Cooling System: Thermo-syphon with gear and shaft driven fan.

Bearings: 2 main, bronze backed babbitt lined. Removable. Connecting rod bearings, babbitt centrifugally spun in rods.

Transmission: Selective type spur gears forged cut and heat treated. 2⅓, 3, 4¾ and 6¼ m.p.h. forward; 3½ m.p.h. reverse.

Final Drive: Spur gear, completely enclosed, running in oil.

Belt Pulley: 10⅝x6; 1,150 r.p.m. and 3,200 feet per minute at normal engine speed.

JOHN DEERE MODEL B GEN'L PURPOSE, MODEL BN — SINGLE FRONT WHEEL, MODEL BW—ADJUSTABLE FRONT WHEEL TREAD.

Deere & Co., Moline, Ill.

Traction Wheels: Two in rear, 40x8. Rubber tires available.

Tread Width: 44¼ in.

No. of Plows Recommended: One 16 or two 10 in.

Length: 117¾ in.; Width: 52¼ in.; Height to Radiator Cap: 50½ in.; Weight: 2889 lbs.

Turning Radius (Outside): 11⅔ ft.

Engine: Own, 4¼x5¼, valve-in-head, 2 cylinders, cast en bloc.

Lubrication: Full force feed pressure.

Carburetor: Schebler.

Ignition System: Fairbanks Morse.

Lighting Equipment: K-W.

Cooling System: Thermos-syphon with gear and shaft driven fan.

Bearings: 2 main, bronze backed babbitt lined. Removable. Connecting rod bearings, babbitt centrifugally spun in rod.

Transmission: Selective type spur gears forged, cut and heat treated; 2, 3, 4 and 6¼ m.p.h. forward; 3 m.p.h. reverse.

Final Drive: Spur gears, completely enclosed, running in oil.

Belt Pulley: 10⅝x5½; 1150 r.p.m. and 3200 feet per minute at normal engine speed.

JOHN DEERE STANDARD TREAD MODEL BR, MODEL BO FOR GROVE, ORCHARD AND VINEYARD

Deere & Co., Moline, Ill.

Traction Wheels: Two L. P. rubber tires on rear, 12.75x28, standard equipment.
Tread Width: 53½ in.
Length: 117 in.; **Width:** 56 in.; **Height to Radiator Cap:** 57 in.; **Weight:** 6250 lbs.
Turning Radius (Outside) 13½ ft.
Engine: 6¾x7, valve-in-head, 2 cylinders, cast en bloc.
Lubrication: Full force feed pressure with oil filter.
Carburetor: Schebler.
Ignition System: Edison Splitdorf.
Lighting Equipment: K-W.
Cooling System: Thermos-syphon with gear and shaft driven fan.
Bearings: 2 main, bronze backed babbitt lined, removable. Connecting rod bearings, bronze backed, babbitt lined, removable.
Transmission: Selective type spur gears, forged cut and heat treated, 4, 5 and 7½ m.p.h. forward; 3 m.p.h. reverse. Lower speeds can be furnished, 2½, 3¼ and 4½ m.p.h. forward; 3 m.p.h. reverse.
Final Drive: Hardened steel chains, running in oil.
Belt Pulley: 13¼x8½; 900 r.p.m. and 3122 feet per minute at normal engine speed.

JOHN DEERE MODEL DI INDUSTRIAL
Deere & Co., Moline, Ill.

FORD MOTOR CO.
Dearborn, Michigan

Fordson

1936-1940

FORDSON
Ford Motor Co., Dearborn, Mich.

Traction Wheels: Four wheels; two traction in rear, 42 or 54 inches in diameter with steel lugs. Rubber tires optional.
Tread Width: 51; **Adjustment:** 33 to 88.
No. of Plows Recommended: Two, 14-in.
Length 103½ in.; **Width:** 63 in.; **Height:** 57 in.; **Weight:** 3310 lbs.
Turning Radius (Outside): 10½ ft.; **Acres Plowed in 10-hr. Day:** 6.
Engine: Own, 4⅛x5, L-head, 4 cylinders, cast en bloc.
Lubrication: Circulating splash.
Carburetor: Zenith or Kingston, 1¼-in.
Ignition System: High tension magneto.
Starting & Lighting Equipment: Optional.
Cooling System: Pump.
Bearings: Babbitt.
Transmission Constant mesh gear with internal clutches for each speed; 2.2 to 4.3 m.p.h. forward; 1.67 m.p.h. reverse.
Final Drive Worm.
Belt Pulley: 9½x6½; 1100 r.p.m. and 2730 feet per minute at normal engine speed.

HUBER MANUFACTURING CO.

Marion, Ohio

Modern Farmer "L"   1936-1944
Modern Farmer "LC"   1936-1944
Huber "HS" 27-42   1936-1940

Traction Wheels: Four wheel type; two drivers in rear, 42x10. Rubber tires optional.
Tread Width: 50 in. Adjustment None.
No. of Plows Recommended: Three, 14-in.
Length: 123½ in.; **Width:** 60 in.; **Height:** 57½ in.; **Weight:** 3,700 lbs.
Turning Radius (outside): 12 ft.
Engine: Waukesha: 4½x5¼, valve-in-head, 4 cylinders, removable sleeves.
Lubrication: Force feed.
Carburetor: Zenith, 1¼-in.
Ignition System: Bosch high tension magneto.
Starting & Lighting Equipment: Optional.
Cooling System: Fan, pump and radiator.
Bearings: Roller and ball.
Transmission: Sliding gear; 2.4 to 8.7 m.p.h. forward; 1.8 m.p.h. reverse.
Final Drive: Spur gear.
Belt Pulley: 14x7⅜; 705 r.p.m. and 2600 feet per minute at normal engine speed.

MODERN FARMER "L"
Huber Mfg. Co., Marion, O.

MODERN FARMER "LC"
Huber Mfg. Co., Marion, O.

Traction Wheels: Four wheels with two traction in rear; 42-in. diameter. Rubber tires optional.
Tread Width: 73-in. Adjustment None.
No. of Plows Recommended: Three, 14-in.
Length: 130 in.; **Width:** 81½ in.; **Height** 57 in.; **Weight:** 3900 lbs.
Turning Radius (outside); 9¼ ft.
Engine: Waukesha, 4½x5¼, valve-in-head, 4 cylinders, removable sleeves.
Lubrication: Force feed.
Carburetor: Zenith, 1¼-in.
Ignition System: Bosch high tension magneto.
Starting & Lighting Equipment: Optional.
Cooling System: Fan, pump and radiator.
Bearings: Ball and roller.
Transmission: Sliding gear; 2.4 to 8.7 m.p.h. forward; 1.8 m.p.h. reverse
Final Drive: Spur gear.
Belt Pulley: 14x7⅜; 705 r.p.m. and 2600 f.p.m. at normal engine speed.

Traction Wheels: Four wheels, with two drivers in rear, 50x12. Rubber tires available.

No. of Plows Recommended: Three to four, 14 in.

Length: 137 in.; Width: 73½ in.; Height: 61 in.; Weight: 5,700 lbs.

Turning Radius (Outside): 15 ft.; Acres Plowed in 10-Hour Day: 10 to 15.

Engine: Waukesha, 4¾x6¼, overhead valves. 4 cylinders, removable sleeves.

Lubrication: Force feed.

Carburetor: Zenith, 1¼-in.

Ignition System: American Bosch high tension magneto.

Cooling System: Young radiator, pump and Automotive fan.

Bearings: Hyatt and Timken.

Transmission: Selective gear; 2 to 8.6 m.p.h. forward; 1.83 m.p.h. reverse.

Final Drive: Gear.

Belt Pulley: 17x8; 616 r.p.m. and 2,700 feet per minute at normal engine speed.

HUBER "HS" 27-42
Huber Mfg. Co., Marion, O.

INTERNATIONAL HARVESTER CO.

Chicago, Illinois

McCormick-Deering T-A 40 Tractractor	1936
McCormick-Deering W-30	1936-1940
McCormick-Deering WD-40	1936-1940
McCormick-Deering WK-40	1936

McCORMICK-DEERING T-A 40 TRACTRACTOR
International Harvester Co., Chicago, Ill.

Traction Members: One crawler on each side, 16x70.

No. of Plows Recommended: Six to eight, 14-in.

Length: 140 in.; Width: 63¾ in.; Height: 63⅜ in.; Weight: 11,400 lbs.

Turning Radius (Outside): 7 ft.

Engine: Own, 3⅝x4½, vertical, valve-in-head, 6 replaceable cylinder.

Lubrication: Pressure, gear-type oil pump.

Carburetor: Zenith, 1¼ in.

Ignition System: High tension with automatic impulse starter.

Starting and Lighting Equipment: Special.

Cooling System: Impeller pump, thermostat control.

Bearings: Precision type main, ball in transmission and final drive.

Transmission: Selective; five speeds forward and one reverse, 1¾ to 4 m.p.h. forward; 2¼ m.p.h. reverse.

Final Drive: Enclosed machine cut gears in oil bath.

Belt Pulley: Special; 16¾x9; 604 r.p.m. and 2,650 feet per minute at normal engine speed.

Traction Wheels: Four wheels, two traction in rear, 42x12.
No. of Plows Recommended: Two to three, 14-in.
Length: 121¾ in.; Width: 66¼ in.; Height: 60 in.; Weight: 4820 lbs.
Turning Radius (Outside): 13½ ft.
Engine: Own, vertical, valve-in-head, 4 replaceable cylinders, 4¼x5.
Lubrication: Circulating pump and splash.
Carburetor: Zenith, 1¼-in.
Ignition System: Own high tension magneto with automatic impulse starter.
Cooling System: Impeller pump, thermostatic control.
Bearings: Ball and roller.
Transmission: Selective, 2½, 3¼ and 3¾ m.p.h. forward; 2¾ m.p.h. reverse.
Final Drive: Spur gear.
Belt Pulley: 15¼x7; 675 r.p.m. and 2695 feet per minute at normal engine speed.

McCORMICK-DEERING W-30
International Harvester Co., Chicago, Ill.

McCORMICK-DEERING WD-40
International Harvester Co., Chicago, Ill.

Traction Wheels: Four wheels, two traction in rear, 50x12.
No. of Plows Recommended: Four, 14-in.
Length: 141½ in.; Width: 65½ in.; Height: 66¾ in.; Weight: 7550 lbs.
Turning Radius (Outside): 17 ft.
Engine: Own, Diesel, 4¾x6½, vertical, valve-in-head, 4 replaceable cylinders.
Lubrication: Full pressure.
Carburetor: Own, Diesel injection pump.
Starting and Lighting Equipment: Own starting; lighting equipment special.
Cooling System: Impeller pump, thermostatic control.
Bearings: Precision mains, ball in transmission and final drive.
Transmission: Selective, 2½, 3½ and 4 m.p.h. forward; 2½ m.p.h. reverse.
Final Drive: Spur gear.
Belt Pulley: 16¾x9; 588 r.p.m. and 2580 feet per minute at normal engine speed.

McCORMICK-DEERING WK-40
International Harvester Co., Chicago, Ill.

Traction Wheels: Four wheels, two traction in rear, 50x12.
No. of Plows Recommended: Four, 14-in.
Length: 141½ in.; Width: 65¼; Height: 66¾ in.; Weight: 6100 lbs.
Turning Radius (Outside): 17 ft.
Engine: Own, 3¾x4½, vertical, valve-in-head, 6 replaceable cylinders.
Lubrication: Full pressure.
Carburetor: Zenith.
Ignition System: Own high tension magneto with automatic impulse starter.
Cooling System: Impeller pump; thermostatic control.
Bearings: Ball and roller.
Transmission: Selective, 2½, 3 and 3½ m.p.h. forward; 2¼ m.p.h. reverse.
Final Drive: Spur gear.
Belt Pulley: 16¾x9; 599 r.p.m. and 2627 feet per minute at normal engine speed.

KAYWOOD CORP.
Benton Harbor, Michigan

Kaywood Model D
1936-1937

KAYWOOD MODEL D
Kaywood Corp., Benton Harbor, Mich.

Traction Wheels: Four wheel type; two traction in rear and two non-traction in front.
Tread Width: 44-68; **Adjustment:** Additional adjustment by spacers.
Length: 114 in.; **Width:** 61 in.; **Height:** 54 in.; **Weight:** 3000 lbs.
Turning Radius (outside): 9 ft.
Engine: Hercules IXB, 3¼x4, vertical; 4 cylinders.
Lubrication: Forced feed.
Carburetor: Zenith, 1-in.
Ignition System: Autolite generator; distributor coil.
Starting & Lighting Equipment: Autolite.
Cooling System: Thermo-syphon.
Transmission: Automotive, 1½ to 16½ m.p.h. forward; 2½ m.p.h. reverse.
Final Drive: Direct.
Belt Pulley: 12-in.; 550 r.p.m. and 2600 f.p.m. at normal engine speed.

KECK-GONNERMAN CO.
Mt. Vernon, Indiana

Kay Gee 30-60 Model N
Kay Gee 18-35 Model ZW

1936-1937
1936-1937

KAY GEE 30-60 MODEL N
Keck-Gonnerman Co., Mt. Vernon, Ind.

Traction Wheels: Four-wheel type; two traction in rear, 56x14 to 24.
No. of Plows Recommended: Four to six, 14-in.
Length: 162 in.; **Width:** 90 in.; **Height:** 69 in.; **Weight:** 10,500 lbs.; **Price:** $3,000 f.o.b. factory.
Turning Radius (Outside): 15 ft.; **Acres Plowed in 10-Hr. Day:** 20 to 23.
Engine: Le Roi, 5½x7, valve-in-head, 4 cylinders, cast in pairs.
Lubrication: Force feed.
Carburetor: Ensign, 1¾-in.
Ignition System: Eisemann high tension magneto with impulse starter.
Starting and Lighting Equipment: Electric, Leece-Neville (extra).
Cooling System: Modine removable core radiator in cast iron housing.
Bearings: Hyatt, Timken and S. K. F.
Transmission: Selective gears, 2.4 to 3.2 m.p.h. forward; 2 m.p.h. reverse.
Final Drive: Enclosed spur gear; live axle.
Belt Pulley: 15x9½; 666 r.p.m. and 2,677 feet per minute at normal engine speed.

Traction Wheels: Four-wheel type; two traction in rear, 50x12. Rubber tires optional.

No. of Plows Recommended: Three to four, 14-in.

Length: 132 in.; Width: 70 in.; Height: 67 in.; Weight: 5,250 lbs; Price: $1,600 f.o.b. factory.

Turning Radius: 14 ft. outside; Acres Plowed in 10-Hr. Day: 15.

Engine: Waukesha, $5\frac{1}{8}$x$6\frac{1}{4}$, valve-in-head, 4 cylinders, cast en bloc.

Lubrication: Force feed.

Carburetor: Zenith, $1\frac{1}{2}$-in.

Ignition System: American Bosch magneto with impulse starter.

Cooling System: Young removable core radiator in cast iron housing.

Bearings: Hyatt, Timken and S. K. F.

Transmission: Selective gears; $2\frac{1}{2}$ to 4 m.p.h. forward; 2 m.p.h. reverse.

Final Drive: Enclosed spur gear, live axle.

Belt Pulley: 16x$8\frac{1}{2}$; 590 r.p.m. and 2,600 feet per minute at normal engine speed.

KAY GEE 18-35 MODEL ZW
Keck-Gonnerman Co., Mt. Vernon, Ind.

MASSEY-HARRIS CO.

Racine, Wisconsin

Massey-Harris 4-Wheel Drive General Purpose	1936-1938
Massey-Harris Challenger	1936-1941
Massey-Harris (Orchard) Pacemaker	1936-1941
Massey-Harris "Pacemaker"	1936-1941

MASSEY-HARRIS 4-WHEEL DRIVE GENERAL PURPOSE
Massey-Harris Co., Racine, Wis.

Traction Wheels: Four wheel drive, each 38x8. Rubber tires available.

Tread Width: 40, 48, 56, 60, 66 and 76 in.

No. of Plows Recommended: Two, 14-in.

Length: 119 in.; Width: $50\frac{9}{16}$, $58\frac{9}{16}$, $66\frac{9}{16}$, $70\frac{9}{16}$, $76\frac{9}{16}$ and $86\frac{9}{16}$ in.; Height: $54\frac{11}{16}$ in.

Turning Radius (outside): 10 ft.

Engine: Hercules, 4x$4\frac{1}{2}$, vertical, valve-in-head, 4 cylinders, removable cylinder sleeves.

Lubrication: Force feed by gear pump and dip pan splash; oil filtering device.

Carburetor: Kingston.

Ignition System: Bosch.

Cooling System: Centrifugal pump; tubular radiator, four gallons capacity.

Bearings: Timken and ball.

Transmission: Selective sliding gear, 2.2, 3.2 to 4 m.p.h. forward; $2\frac{1}{2}$ m.p.h. reverse.

Final Drive: Spur gear.

Belt Pulley: $12\frac{1}{8}$x$6\frac{1}{2}$; 802 r.p.m. and 2546 feet per minute at normal engine speed.

Traction Wheels: Four wheels, with two traction in rear, 52x8, and two non-drive in front, 24x4½. Rubber tires available.
Tread Width: Adjustable 52 to 80.
No. of Plows Recommended: Two, 14 in.
Width: 56 in.; Height: 53½ in.; Weight: 3860 lbs.
Turning Radius (outside); pivots on either rear wheel.
Engine: Own, 3⅞x5¼, vertical, valve-in-head, 4 Cylinders, removable cylinder sleeves.
Lubrication: Geared force pump and splash.
Carbureator: Kingston, 1¼ in.
Ignition System: American Bosch high tension magneto.
Cooling System: Fan, pump and radiator.
Bearings: Ball and Timken bearings throughout.
Transmission: Selective sliding gear, 2.4. 3.3, 4.1 and 8.5 m.p.h. forward; 3 m.p.h. reverse.
Final Drive: Spur gear.
Belt Pulley: 12x6¼; 831 r.p.m. and 2610 feet per minute at normal engine speed.

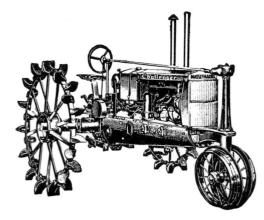

MASSEY-HARRIS CHALLENGER
Massey-Harris Co., Racine, Wis.

MASSEY-HARRIS (ORCHARD) PACEMAKER
VINEYARD MODEL PA
(Tread Width 40 in. Belt Pulley None)
Massey-Harris Co., Racine, Wis.

Traction Wheels: Four wheels; two traction in rear, 44x10, and two non-drivers in front, 28x5. Rubber tires available.
Tread Width: 46-in.; Adjustment: None.
No. of Plows Recommended: Two, 14-in.
Turning Radius (Outside): 11½ ft.
Engine: Own, 3⅞x5¼, vertical, valve-in-head, 4 cylinders, removable cylinder sleeves.
Lubrication: Pressure and splash.
Carburetor: Kingston, 1¼-in.
Ignition System: American Bosch high tension magneto.
Cooling System: Modine radiator, fan and pump.
Bearings: Timken roller and ball bearings throughout.
Transmission: Selective, sliding gear; 2.4, 3.3, 4.1 and 8.5 m.p.h. forward; 3 m.p.h. reverse.
Final Drive: Spur gear.
Belt Pulley: 12x6¼; 831 r.p.m. and 2610 feet per minute at normal engine speed.

Traction Wheels: Four wheels, with two rear drivers, 44x10 and two non-drive in front, 28x5. Rubber tires available.
Tread Width: 46-in.; Adjustment: None.
No. of Plows Recommended: Two, 14-in.
Wheelbase: 78 in.; Width: 56 in.; Height: 53½ in.; Weight: 3695 lbs.
Turning Radius (Outside): 11½ ft.
Engine: Own, 3⅞x5¼, vertical, valve-in-head, 4 cylinders, removable cylinder sleeves.
Lubrication: Geared force pump and splash.
Carburetor: Kingston, 1¼ in.
Ignition System: American Bosch high tension magneto.
Cooling System: Fan, pump and radiator.
Bearings: Ball and Timken bearings throughout.
Transmission: Selective sliding gear, 2.4, 3.3, 4.1 and 8.5 m.p.h. forward; 3 m.p.h. reverse.
Final Drive: Spur gear.
Belt Pulley: 12x6¼; 831 r.p.m. and 2610 ft. per minute at normal engine speed.

MASSEY-HARRIS "PACEMAKER"
Massey-Harris Co., Racine, Wis.

MINNEAPOLIS-MOLINE POWER IMPLEMENT CO.
Minneapolis, Minnesota

M-M Twin City Standard J

1936-1938

M-M TWIN CITY STANDARD J
Minneapolis-Moline Power Impl. Co.,
Minneapolis, Minn.

Traction Wheels; Four wheel type, two traction in rear, 50x8, two non-drive in front, 25x4½.

Tread Width: 48 in.; Adjustment: None.

No. of Plows Recommended: Two to three 14-in.

Length: 124½ in.; Width: 57¼ in.; Height: 56 in.; **Weight: 3115 lbs.**

Turning Radius (outside): 7½ ft.

Engine: Own, 3⅝x4¾, vertical, 4 cylinders, cast en bloc.

Lubrication: Pressure to crankshaft bearings, camshaft bearings, connecting rod bearings, piston pins, timing gears and valves.

Carberutor: Zenith, 1¼-in.

Ignition System: High tension magneto.

Starting and Lighting Equipment: Electric generator type; no battery; optional.

Cooling System: Raditor, pump and fan.

Bearings: Bronze backed battitt lined shells.

Transmission: Sliding gear with five speeds forward; 2.2 to 12.2 m.p.h. forward, 1.2 m.p.h. reverse.

Final Drive: Spur gear.

Belt Pulley: 15⅝x6½; 730 r.p.m. and 3000 feet per minute at normal engine speed.

OLIVER FARM EQUIPMENT SALES CO.
Hart-Parr Tractor Division

Charles City, Iowa

Oliver Row Crop 70 HC
Oliver Row Crop 70 KD

1936-1937
1936-1937

OLIVER ROW CROP 70 HC
Oliver Farm Equipment Co.,
Hart-Parr Tractor Div., Charles City, Ia.

Traction Wheels: Two rear, 55x⁹⁄₁₆-in. face. Rubber tires available.

Tread Adjustment: 60 to 72.

No. of Plows Recommended: Two, 14-in.

Length: 133¾ in.; Width: 80½ in.; Height: 58 in.; Weight: Approx. 3000 lbs.

Turning Radius (outside): 8 ft.; Acres Plowed in 10-hr. Day: 8 to 10

Engine: Own, 3⅛x4⅜, vertical, 6 cylinders, removable sleeves.

Lubrication: Pressure.

Carburetor: Zenith, 1¼-in.

Ignition System: Bosch high tension magneto.

Starting and Lighting Equipment: Electric, Delco-Remy.

Cooling System: Fan, pump and radiator.

Bearings: Ball, roller and Timken.

Transmission: Selective sliding spur gear, 2.44, 3.32, 4.33 and 5.88 m.p.h. forward; 2.44 m.p.h. reverse.

Final Drive: Spur gear

Belt Pulley: 12¾x7¼; 778 r.p.m. and 2600 feet per minute at normal engine cpeed.

Traction Wheels: Two in rear, 55x9/16-in. face. Rubber tires available.
Tread Adjustment: 60 to 72.
No. of Plows Recommended: Two, 14-in.
Length: 133¾ in.; Width: 80½ in.; Height: 58 in.; Weight: Approx. 3025 lbs.
Turning Radius (outside): 8 ft..
Engine: Own, 3⅛x4⅜, vertical, 6 cylinders, removable sleeves.
Lubrication: Pressure.
Carburetor: Zenith, 1¼-in.
Ignition System: Bosch high tension magneto.
Starting and Lighting Equipment: Electric; Delco-Remy.
Cooling System: Fan, pump and radiator.
Bearings: Ball, roller and Timken.
Transmission: Selective sliding spur gear, 2.44, 3.32, 4.33 and 5.88 m.p.h. forward; 2.44 m.p.h. reverse.
Final Drive: Spur gear.
Belt Pulley: 12¾x7¼; 778 r.p.m. and 2600 feet per minute at normal engine speed.

OLIVER ROW CROP 70 KD

Oliver Farm Equipment Co.,
Hart-Parr Tractor Div., Charles City, Ia.

FARMERS ALL OVER NATION PROVE SAVINGS OF MOBILOIL

MOBILOIL SAVES YOU MONEY whether it's used in car or tractor. It lasts—won't gum valves. You don't suffer costly delays in busy seasons—or have breakdowns and expensive repairs.

Made by the famous Socony-Vacuum Clearosol Process Mobiloil is freed of gum and carbon-forming elements. Use Mobiloil in your engine. And, to give gears equal protection use Mobiloil Gear Oil.

Get these famous money-saving lubricants. Ask your local Mobiloil agent or dealer about them.

SOCONY-VACUUM OIL COMPANY, INCORPORATED

READ WHAT USERS FIND WITH NEW MOBILOIL

"Farm work is hard on engines. I use Mobiloil in my car, because Mobiloil keeps the engine running clean and saves on oil and repair bills as much as 25%." J. P. CURRIE.

"My tractor is 7 years old—I've used it for all types of farm work and I've never had any repair on my motor. The only oil I've ever used is Mobiloil." CHARLES SINAY.

1937

In 1937, 28 models of 13 makes not previously included were added to the list, including the Fordson Allaround which was a tricycle.

ALLIS-CHALMERS MANUFACTURING CO.

Milwaukee, Wisconsin

Allis-Chalmers Model "A"	1937-1944
Allis-Chalmers Model "K-O"	1937-1939
Allis-Chalmers Model "L-O"	1937-1939
Allis-Chalmers Model "S-O"	1937-1939

Wheels: Four wheel type, two traction in rear, 48x12⅛ steel.
Rubber Tires: Yes.
Tread Width: 61½.
No. of Plows Recommended: Four, 14-in.
Length: 140 in.; **Width,** 63 in ; **Height:** 66 in.; **Weight,** 7,175 lbs.
Turning Radius (Outside): 15 ft.
Engine: Own, 4¾x6½, overhead valves, 4 cylinders, removable sleeves.
Lubrication: Pressure.
Carburetor: Zenith, 1½-in.
Ignition System: Fairbanks-Morse magneto.
Starting and Lighting Equipment: Electric, special equipment.
Cooling System: Fan, pump and radiator.
Bearings: Ball and roller.
Transmission: Automotive, 2⅝ to 9½ m.p.h. forward; 3 m.p.h reverse.
Final Drive: Differential.
elt **Pulley:** 13x8½; 1,000 r.p.m. and 3,160 feet per minute at normal engine speed.

ALLIS-CHALMERS MODEL "A"
Allis-Chalmers Mfg. Co., Milwaukee, Wis.

Traction: One crawler on each side; 15-inch face, standard shoe.
Tread Width: 48, std; **Adjustment:** 63, wide tread model.
No. of Plows Recommended: Four to five, 14-in.
Length: 118$\frac{9}{16}$ in.; **Width:** 65$\frac{7}{8}$ in.; **Height:** 64 in.; **Weight:** 11,012 lbs.
Turning Radius (Outside): 7 ft.
Engine: Own, 5¼x6½, vertical, 4 cylinders, cast en bloc.
Lubrication: Force feed.
Injection Pump: Deco.
Ignition System: Scintilla magneto.
Starting and Lighting Equipment: Extra.
Cooling System: Fan, pump, radiator and thermostat.
Transmission: Selective, sliding gear, 1.72 to 5.92 m.p.h. forward; 2.10 m.p.h. reverse.
Final Drive: Gear.
Belt Pulley: 12x8¾; 1,050 r.p.m. and 3,300 feet per minute at normal engine speed.

ALLIS-CHALMERS MODEL "K-O"
Allis-Chalmers Mfg. Co., Milwaukee, Wis.

ALLIS-CHALMERS MODEL "L-O"
Allis-Chalmers Mfg. Co., Milwaukee, Wis.

Traction: One crawler on each side, 20-inch face, standard shoe.
Tread Width: 68 in.
No. of Plows Recommended: Ten, 14-in.
Length: 153¼ in.; **Width:** 93 in.; **Height:** 81¼ in.; **Weight:** 23,000 lbs.
Turning Radius (Outside): 9 ft.
Engine: Own, 5¼x6½, vertical, 6 cylinders, cast en bloc.
Lubrication: Force feed.
Injection Pump: Deco.
Ignition System: Mallory.
Starting and Lighting Equipment: Starting, standard; lights, extra.
Cooling System: Thermostat, pump, fan and radiator.
Transmission: Selective, sliding gear, 4.8 to 6.41 m.p.h. forward; 2.25-1.72 m.p.h. reverse.
Final Drive: Gear.
Belt Pulley: 20x15; 444-580 r.p.m and 2,330-3,040 feet per minute at normal engine speed.

ALLIS-CHALMERS MODEL "S-O"
Allis-Chalmers Mfg. Co., Milwaukee, Wis.

Traction: One crawler on each side, 18-inch face, standard shoe.
Tread Width: 74.
No. of Plows Recommended: Six to eight, 14-in.
Length: 146 in.; **Width:** 96⅝ in.; **Height:** 74$\frac{3}{16}$ in.; **Weight:** 19,500 lbs.
Turning Radius (Outside): 9 ft.
Engine: Own, 5¾x6½, vertical, 4 cylinders, cast en bloc.
Lubrication: Force feed.
Injection Pump: Deco.
Ignition System: Mallory.
Starting and Lighting Equipment: Standard starting; lighting, extra.
Cooling System: Thermostat, fan, pump and radiator.
Transmission: Selective, sliding gear, 1.52 to 6.37 m.p.h. forward; 1.76 m.p.h. reverse.
Final Drive: Gear.
Belt Pulley: 13⅜x10; 770 r.p.m. and 2,700 feet per minute at normal engine speed.

J. I. CASE CO.
Racine, Wisconsin

Case Industrial, Model LI—4-speed

1937-1940

CASE INDUSTRIAL, MODEL LI—4-Speed
J. I. Case Co., Racine, Wis.

Wheels: Two traction wheels in rear, 42x9 pneumatic tires; two non-drive in front, 32x6 pneumatic tires. (Other types and sizes of tires available.)
Length: 118 in.; **Width:** 67 in.; **Height:** 58 in.
Turning Radius (Outside): 13 ft.
Engine: Own, 4⅝x6, vertical, 4 cylinders, cast en bloc with removable sleeves.
Carburetor: 1½-in.
Ignition System: High tension magneto with impulse coupling.
Cooling System: Fan, pump and radiator.
Bearings: Bronze backed babbitt in motor.
Transmission: Sliding gear; 2.28, 4.45, 6.63 and 11.37 m.p.h. forward; 2.85 m.p.h. reverse.
Final Drive: Chain, enclosed and running in oil.
Belt Pulley: 13x8¼; 780 r.p.m and 2,650 feet per minute at normal engine speed.

CLEVELAND TRACTOR CO.
Cleveland, Ohio

Cletrac "DG"

1937-1944

Traction: One crawler on each side, 74¾x 15; crawler centers; Std., 48-in., Spec., 61-in. No adjustment.
No. of Plows Recommended: Six to seven. 14-in.
Length: 132 in.; **Width:** Std. 67¼, Spec. 80¼ in.; **Height:** 65 in.; **Weight:** 12,000 lbs.
Engine: Hercules, 4⅝x5¼, L-head, 6 Cylinders.
Lubrication: Force feed.
Carburetor: Schebler, 1¾-in.
Ignition System: Delco-Remy magneto optional.
Starting & Lighting Equipment: 12-volt battery.
Cooling System: Tubular radiator with 4-blade fan.
Bearings: New Departure ball.
Transmission: Selective type sliding gear; 1.95, 2.9 and 4.6 m.p.h. forward; 1.9 m.p.h. reverse.
Final Drive: Through controlled differential, and bull gear on sprocket drive shaft, completely enclosed.
Belt Pulley: 13x11; 960 r.p.m. and 3,250 feet per minute at normal engine speed.
Power Reduction: 550 r.p.m.
Power Take-Off: 960 r.p.m.

CLETRAC "DG"
Cleveland Tractor Co., Cleveland, O.

DEERE & CO.
Moline, Illinois

John Deere Model "AI" Industrial	1937
John Deere Model "AO"	1937
John Deere Model "BI" Industrial	1937
John Deere Model "L"	1937-1945

JOHN DEERE MODEL "AI" INDUSTRIAL
Deere & Co., Moline, Ill.

Traction Wheels: Two low pressure rubber tires on rear, 11.25x24, standard equipment.
Tread Width: 52 in.
Length: 119½ in.; **Width:** 64½ in.; **Height to Radiator Cap:** 54½ in.; **Weight,** 4,680 lbs.
Turning Radius (Outside): 12⅔ ft.
Engine: Own, 5½x6½, valve-in-head, 2 cylinders, cast en bloc.
Lubrication: Full force feed pressure with oil filter.
Carburetor: Schebler.
Ignition System: Fairbanks-Morse.
Lighting Equipment: K-W.
Cooling System: Thermo syphon with gear and shaft driven fan.
Bearings: Two main, bronze backed, babbitt lined, removable. Connecting rod bearings babbitt, centrifugally spun in rod.
Transmission: Selective type spur gears, forged, cut and heat treated; 2, 3, 4 and 6¼ m.p.h. forward; 3 m.p.h. reverse.
Final Drive: Spur gear, completely enclosed, running in oil.
Belt Pulley: 12¾x7¼; 975 r.p.m. and 3,270 feet per minute at normal engine speed.

JOHN DEERE MODEL "AO" FOR GROVE, ORCHARD AND VINEYARD
Deere & Co., Moline, Ill.

Traction Wheels: Two traction in rear, 42¾x10. Rubber tires available.
Tread Width: 45¼.
No. of Plows Recommended: Two, 14-in.
Length: 124¼ in.; **Width:** 55¾ in.; **Height to Radiator Cap:** 52¼ in.; **Weight:** 4,093 lbs.
Turning Radius (Outside): 13⅓ ft.
Engine: Own, 5½x6½, valve-in-head, 2 cylinders, cast en bloc.
Lubrication: Full force feed pressure with oil filter.
Carburetor: Schebler.
Ignition System: Fairbanks-Morse.
Cooling System: Thermo syphon with gear and shaft driven fan.
Bearings: Two main, bronze back and babbitt lined, removable. Connecting rod bearings babbitt, centrifugally spun in rod.
Transmission: Selective type spur gear, forged, cut and heat treated; 2, 3, 4 and 6¼ m.p.h. forward; 3 m.p.h. reverse.
Final Drive: Spur gears, completely enclosed, running in oil.
Belt Pulley: 12¾x6¼; 975 r.p.m. and 3,270 feet per minute at normal engine speed.

Traction Wheels: Two low pressure rubber tires on rear, 9.00x28, standard equipment.
Tread Width: 44.
Length: 115 in.; Width: 53¾ In.; Height to Radiator Cap: 51¾ in.; Weight: 3,620 lbs.
Turning Radius (Outside): 11¼ ft.
Engine: Own, 4¼x5¼, valve-in-head, 2 cylinders, cast en bloc.
Lubrication: Full force feed pressure with oil filter.
Carburetor: Schebler.
Ignition System: Fairbanks-Morse.
Lighting Equipment: K-W.
Cooling System: Thermo syphon with gear and shaft driven fan.
Bearings: Two main, bronze backed, babbitt lined, removable. Connecting rod bearings babbitt, centrifugally spun in rod.
Transmission: Selective spur gears, forged, cut and heat treated; 2, 3¼, 4¼ and 6¾ m.p.h. forward; 3½ m.p.h. reverse.
Final Drive: Spur gears, completely enclosed, running in oil.
Belt Pulley: 10⅝x5½; 1,150 r.p.m. and 3,200 feet per minute at normal engine speed.

JOHN DEERE MODEL "BI" INDUSTRIAL
Deere & Co., Moline, Ill.

Air Cleaner: United, oil bath.
Caburetor: Marvel-Schebler, ⅞ in.
Clutch: Thelander, dry, single plate.
Governor: Handy, centrifugal, variable speed.
Ignition: Edison-Splitdorf, high tension magneto.
Lighting: _____
Oil Filter: _____
Radiator: Modine, tubular.
Radiator Cover: _____
Spark Plugs: No. 1 Commercial Champion, ⅞ in.
Starting: _____
Data: H.P.—Neb. Test No. 313; Max. Belt 10.42; Max. D.B. 9.06; Max. lbs. pull 1,235 at 2.55 m.p.h. Weight as tested (with operator) 2,180 lbs. Number of plows recommended: One, 14 in.
Engine: John Deere-Hercules, "L"; 3¼ x 4, 1,550 r.p.m., 2 cylinders, vertical, cast en bloc; removable sleeves, no.
Pulley: 6¾x4½, 1,480 r.p.m. and 2,615 f.p.m. at normal engine speed.
Speeds: M.P.H. forward 6.5, and 2½ reverse.

JOHN DEERE MODEL "L"
Deere & Co., Moline, Ill.

DUPLEX MACHINERY CO.
(Cooperative Manufacturing Co.)
Battle Creek, Michigan

Co-op No. 1

1937-1938

CO-OP No. 1
Duplex Machinery Co., Battle Creek, Mich.

Wheels: Three wheels; two traction in rear; 10.00x28 pneumatic tires.

Tread Width: 56 in.; **Adjustment:** 44 to 80.

No. of Plows Recommended: One, 14-in.

Length: 123.87 in.; **Width:** 74.75 in.; **Height:** 55 in.; **Weight:** 3,380 lbs.

Turning Radius (Outside): 8 ft.

Engine: Waukesha, 3¼x4, vertical, 4 cylinders, cast en bloc.

Lubrication: Pressure feed.

Carburetor: Zenith, ⅞-in.

Ignition System: Battery.

Starting and Lighting Equipment: Standard equipment.

Cooling System: Fan, pump and radiator.

Bearings: Steel backed babbitt lined.

Transmission: Selective, 1.4 to 22.8 m.p.h. forward; 2.25 m.p.h. reverse.

Final Drive: Full floating rear axle.

Belt Pulley: 16x7; 620 r.p.m. and 2,600 feet per minute at normal engine speed.

FARMERS UNION CENTRAL EXCHANGE, INC.

St. Paul, Minnesota

Co-op No. 2   1937-1944
Co-op No. 3   1937-1944

CO-OP No. 2

Wheels: Four wheels; two traction in rear; 11.25x28 pneumatic tires.

Tread Width: 60 in.; **Adjustment:** 48 to 76.

No. of Plows Recommended: Two, 14-in.

Length: 124¾ in.; **Width:** 76½ in.; **Height:** 57½ in.; **Weight:** 4,050 lbs.

Turning Radius (Outside): 13 ft.

Engine: Chrysler Industrial, 3⅛x4⅜, vertical, 6 cylinders, cast en bloc.

Lubrication: Pressure feed.

Carburetor: Zenith, 1-in.

Ignition System: Battery.

Starting and Lighting Equipment: Standard equipment.

Cooling System: Fan, pump and radiator.

Bearings: Steel backed babbitt.

Transmission: Selective (constant mesh and sliding), 1½ to 28 m.p.h. forward; 2.52 m.p.h. reverse.

Final Drive: Full floating rear axle.

Belt Pulley: 14x8¾; 754 r.p.m. and 2,600 feet per minute at normal engine speed.

Wheels: Four wheels; two traction in rear; 12.75x28 pneumatic tires.

Tread Width: 64-in.; **Adjustment:** 52 to 80.

No. of Plows Recommended: Three, 14-in.

Length: 132¼ in.; **Width:** 76½ in.; **Height:** 62 in.; **Weight:** 4,500 lbs.

Turning Radius (Outside): 14¼ ft.

Engine: Chrysler Industrial, 3⅜x4½, vertical, 6 cylinders, cast en bloc.

Lubrication: Pressure feed.

Carburetor: Zenith, 1¼-in.

Ignition System: Battery.

Starting and Lighting Equipment: Standard equipment.

Cooling System: Fan, pump and radiator.

Bearings: Steel backed babbitt.

Transmission: Selective (constant mesh and sliding), 1.3 to 25 m.p.h. forward; 2.16 m.p.h. reverse.

Final Drive: Full floating rear axle.

Belt Pulley: 14x8¾; 754 r.p.m. and 2,600 feet per minute at normal engine speed.

CO-OP No. 3

FATE-ROOT-HEATH CO.

Plymouth, Ohio

Silver King Model SR38   1937-1939
Silver King Model R44   1937-1939

SILVER KING MODEL SR38 AND R44
Fate-Root-Heath Co., Plymouth, O.

Traction Wheels: Steel or low-pressure tires.

Tread Width: 38 and 44 in.; **Adjustment:** None.

No. of Plows Recommended: One, 14-in.

Length: 97 in.; **Width:** 48 in.; **Height:** 49 in.; **Weight** 2170 lbs.

Turning Radius (Outside): 9 ft.; **Acres Plowed in 10-hr. Day:** 5.

Engine: Hercules, IXB; 3¼x4, vertical, 4 cylinders.

Lubrication: Full force feed.

Carburetor: Zenith, 1-in.

Ignition System. Am. Bosch.

Starting & Lighting Equipment: Auto-Lite.

Cooling System: Thermo-Syphon.

Bearings: Timken and New Departure.

Transmission: Standard automotive, 1 to 25 m.p.h. forward; 1.5 m.p.h. reverse.

Final Drive: Direct.

Belt Pulley: 6x6; 1400 r.p.m.

FOUR WHEEL DRIVE AUTO CO.
Eagle Division
Appleton, Wisconsin

Eagle "6B" Universal   1937-1946
Eagle "6C" Utility   1937-1946

Wheels; Four wheels, rubber tires; two drivers in rear, 40 inches in diameter.
Tread Width: 68 in.; **Adjustment:** 11 to 79 in.
No. of Plows Recommended: Two to three, 14-in.
Length: 130 in.; **Width:** 80 in.; **Height:** 60 in.; **Weight:** 3,250 lbs.
Turning Radius (Outside): 7¾ ft.
Engine: Hercules, 3¼x4⅛, vertical, 6 cylinders, cast en bloc.
Lubricatjon: Full presure—pump.
Carburetor: Zenith, 1¼-in.
Ignition System: Edison-Splitdorf H.T. with I.S.
Starting and Lighting Equipment: Electric—Auto-Lite.
Cooling System: Fan, pump and radiator.
Bearings: Hyatt, Timken, New Departure, Cleveland and Bantam.
Transmission: Selective, helical and sliding spur. 1.8 to 13.0 m.p.h. forward; 1.5 m.p.h. reverse.
Final Drive: Enclosed spur gear.
Belt Pulley: 8½x7; 1,180 r.p.m. and 2,625 feet per minute at normal engine speed.

EAGLE "6B" UNIVERSAL

EAGLE "6C" UTILITY

Wheels: Four wheels, rubber tires; two drivers in rear, 40 inches in diameter.
Tread Width: 48; **Adjustment:** 11 to 59 in.
No. of Plows Recommended: Two to three, 14-in.
Length: 110 in.; **Width:** 60 in.; **Height:** 57 in.; **Weight:** 3,250 lbs.
Turning Radius (Outside): 11 ft.
Engine: Hercules, 3¼x4⅛, vertical, 6 cylinders, cast en bloc.
Lubrication: Full pressure—pump.
Carburetor: Zenith, 1¼-in.
Ignition System: Edison-Splitdorf H.T. with I.S.
Starting and Lighting Equipment: Electric "Auto-Lite."
Cooling System: Fan, pump and radiator.
Bearings: Hyatt, Timken, New Departure, Cleveland and Bantam.
Transmission: Selective, helical and sliding spur. 1.8 to 13.0 m.p.h. forward; 1.5 m.p.h. reverse.
Final Drive: Enclosed spur gear.
Belt Pulley: 8½x7; 1,180 r.p.m. and 2,625 feet per minute at normal engine speed.

FORD MOTOR CO.
Dearborn, Michigan

Fordson Allaround

1937-1940

FORDSON ALLAROUND
Ford Motor Co., Dearborn, Mich.

Wheels: Four wheels; two traction in rear, 50 inches in diameter.
Tread Width: 52; **Adjustment:** 52 to 88.
No. of Plows Recommended: Two, 14-in.
Length: 130 in.; **Width:** 62 in.; **Height,** 63 ins.; **Weight:** 3,700 lbs.
Turning Radius (Outside): 9 1/6 ft.; **Acres Plowed in 10-hr. Day:** 10.
Engine: Own, 4⅛x5, vertical, 4 cylinders, cast en bloc.
Lubrication: Splash.
Carburetor: Zenith, 1¼-in.
Ignition System: High tension magneto with impulse coupler.
Cooling System: Fan, pump and radiator.
Bearings: Babbitt.
Transmission: Selective; constant mesh; three speeds 1.92 to 5.13 m.p.h. forward; 1.65 m.p.h. reverse.
Final Drive: Worm and worm wheel.
Belt Pulley: 9½x6½; 1,100 r.p.m. and 2,728 feet per minute at normal engine speed.

HUBER MANUFACTURING CO.
Marion, Ohio

Huber "B" 30

1937-1938

HUBER "B" 30
Huber Mfg. Co., Marion, O.

Wheels: Four wheels; two traction in rear, 50x8.
Tread Width: 50; **Adjustment:** 50-76.
No. of Plows Recommended: Two, 14-in.
Length: 127½ in.; **Height:** 54⅝ in.
Turning Radius (Outside); 7 7/12 ft.
Engine: Buda, 3¹³⁄₁₆x4½, vertical, 4 cylinders, cast en bloc.
Lubrication: Full force feed.
Carburetor: Zenith, 1-in.
Ignition System: Bosch.
Starting and Lighting Equipment: Delco Remy.
Cooling System: Young radiator.
Bearings: Timken and Rollway.
Transmission: Automotive, 2.3 to 10 m.p.h. forward; 1.8 m.p.h. reverse.
Final Drive: Gears.
Belt Pulley: 10x6⅜; 990 r.p.m. and 2,617 feet per minute at normal engine speed.

INTERNATIONAL HARVESTER CO.
Chicago, Illinois

International I-40   1937-1940
International ID-40   1937-1939
McCormick-Deering T-35   1937-1939
McCormick-Deering TD-35   1937-1939
McCormick-Deering T-40 Tractractor   1937-1939
McCormick-Deering TD-40 Diesel Tractractor   1937-1939
McCormick-Deering W-40   1937-1940

INTERNATIONAL I-40
International Harvester Co., Chicago, Ill.

Wheels: Dual pneumatic tires on rear.
Tread Width: Front 54, rear (between dual pneumatic tires) 69.
Weight: 8,000 lbs.
Engine: Own, 3¾x4½, vertical, 6 cylinders, 1,750 r.p.h.
Carburetor: Zenith.
Speeds: 2¼, 3⅜ and 6⅝ m.p.h. forward; 2⅛ m.p.h. reverse.
Belt Pulley: Special, 16¾x9; 645 r.p.m.
Power Take-off: 553 r.p.m.

Wheels: Dual pneumatic tires on rear.
Tread Width: Front, 54; rear (between dual pneumatic tires) 69.
Weight: Approx. 10,550 lbs.
Engine: Own deisel, 4¾x6½, vertical, valve-in-head, 4 cylinders, 1,100 r.p.m. Own injection pump.
Speeds: 2¼, 3⅜ and 6⅝ m.p.h. forward; 2⅛ m.p.h. reverse.
Belt Pulley: Special, 16¾x9; 588 r.p.m.
Power Take-off: 559 r.p.m.

INTERNATIONAL ID-40
International Harvester Co., Chicago, Ill.

McCORMICK-DEERING T-35
International Harvester Co., Chicago, Ill.

Traction: One crawler on each side.
Tread Width: 45 in.
Weight: (Standard tread) 10,050 lbs.
Acres Plowed in 10-hr. Day: 15 to 25.
Engine: Own, $3\frac{5}{8}$x$4\frac{1}{2}$, vertical, 6 cylinders.
Carburetor: Zenith.
Speeds: $1\frac{3}{4}$, $2\frac{1}{8}$, $2\frac{3}{4}$, $3\frac{1}{8}$ and 4 m.p.h. forward; $2\frac{1}{4}$ m.p.h. reverse.
Belt Pulley: Special, $16\frac{3}{4}$x9; 619 r.p.m.
Power Take-off: 560 r.p.m.

Traction: One crawler on each side.
Tread Width: 45 in.
Weight: Regular tread, 10,550 lbs.
Acres Plowed in 10-hr. Day: 15 to 25.
Engine: Own, diesel, vertical, valve-in-head, $4\frac{1}{2}$x$6\frac{1}{2}$, 1,100 r.p.m., 4 cylinders, own injection pump.
Speeds: $1\frac{3}{4}$, $2\frac{1}{4}$, $2\frac{3}{4}$, $3\frac{1}{4}$, and 4 m.p.h. forward; $2\frac{1}{4}$ m.p.h. reverse.
Belt Pulley: Special; $16\frac{3}{4}$x9; 591 r.p.m.
Power Take-off: 560 r.p.m.

McCORMICK-DEERING TD-35
International Harvester Co., Chicago, Ill.

McCORMICK-DEERING T-40 TRACTRACTOR
International Harvester Co., Chicago, Ill.

Tracks: Length of ground contact 70; shoe face 16.
Length: 140 in.; **Width:** $63\frac{3}{4}$ in.; **Weight:** 11,705 lbs.
Turning Radius (Outside): 7 ft.; **Acres Plowed in 10-hr. Day:** 20 to 30.
Engine: Own, $3\frac{3}{4}$x$4\frac{1}{2}$, vertical, 6 cylinders, replaceable, cast en bloc; Speed, 1,750 r.p.m.; Fuel, gasoline, kerosene or No. 1 distillate.
Lubrication: Pressure.
Carburetor: Zenith, $1\frac{1}{2}$-in.
Ignition System: Own high tension magneto with automatic impulse coupling.
Cooling System: Pump—thermostatic control.
Bearings: Precision type.
Speeds: $1\frac{3}{4}$, $2\frac{1}{4}$, $2\frac{3}{4}$, $3\frac{1}{8}$ and 4 m.p.h. forward; $2\frac{1}{4}$ m.p.h. reverse.
Belt Pulley: Special, $16\frac{3}{4}$x9; 619 r.p.m. and 2,715 feet per minute.
Power-Take-off: Regular, 560 r.p.m.

Tracks: Length of ground contact 70; shoe face 16.

Length: 140 in.; Width: 63¾ in.; Weight: 12,218 lbs.

Turning Radius (Outside): 7 ft.; Acres Plowed in 10-hr. Day: 20 to 30.

Engine: Own, diesel, 4¾x6½, vertical, 4 cylinders, replaceable, cast en bloc; Speed, 1,100 r.p.m.; Fuel, diesel; injection pump own make.

Lubrication: Pressure.

Rated Power: Drawbar 33.51; belt 43.12.

Cooling System: Pump—thermostatic control.

Bearings: Precision type.

Speeds: 1¾, 2¼, 2¾, 3⅛ and 4 m.p.h. forward; 2¼ m.p.h. reverse.

Belt Pulley: Special, 16¾x9; 591 r.p.m. and 2,593 feet per minute.

Power Take-off: Regular, 535 r.p.m.

McCORMICK-DEERING TD-40 DIESEL TRACTRACTOR
International Harvester Co., Chicago, Ill.

Wheels: Regular, steel; rear 50x12; front 34x6.

Length: 141½ in.; Width: 65¾ in.; Weight: 6,630 lbs.

Turning Radius (Outside): 17 ft.; Acres Plowed in 10-hr. Day: 15 to 20.

Engine: Own, 3¾x4½, vertical, 6 cylinders, replaceable, cast en bloc; Speed, 1,750 r.p.m.; Fuel, gasoline or No. 1 distillate.

Lubrication: Pressure.

Carburetor: Zenith, 1½-in.

Ignition System: Own high tension magneto with automatic impulse coupling.

A.S.A.E. and S.A.E. Rated Power: Drawbar 28.34; belt 44.80.

Cooling System: Pump—thermostatic control.

Bearings: Precision type.

Speeds: 2⅜, 3⅛ and 3⅝ m.p.h. forward; 2¼ m.p.h. reverse.

Belt Pulley: 15¹¹⁄₁₆x9; 645 r.p.m. and 2,648 feet per minute.

Power Take-off: Special, 552 r.p.m.

McCORMICK-DEERING W-40
International Harvester Co., Chicago, Ill.

OLIVER FARM EQUIPMENT CO.
Hart-Parr Tractor Division

Charles City, Iowa

Oliver Standard "70"	1937
Oliver Orchard "70"	1937
Oliver Special High Compression	1937

Wheels: Four wheels; two traction in rear, 42x10.

Rubber Tires: 9.00-24 rear; 5.50-16 front. Special 11.25-24 and 6.00-16.

Tread Width: 40 or 48; **Adjustment:** None.

No. of Plows Recommended: Two, 14-in.

Length: 120½ in.; **Width:** 40 to 53½; 48 to 61½ in.; **Height:** 51 in.; **Weight:** Approx. 3,000 lbs. on steel; 3,300 lbs. on rubber.

Turning Radius (Outside): 11½ ft.; **Acres Plowed in 10-hr. Day:** 8 to 10.

Engine: Own, 3⅛x4⅜, vertical, 6 cylinders, removable sleeves.

Lubrication: Pressure; gear type pump.

Carburetor: Zenith, 1¼-in.

Ignition System: American Bosch high tension magneto.

Starting and Lighting Equipment: Electric; Delco-Remy.

Cooling System: Fan, pump and radiator.

Bearings: Ball, roller and Timkens.

Transmission: Selective sliding spur gears; 2.44, 3.32, 4.33 and 5.88 m.p.h. forward; 2.44 m.p.h. reverse.

Final Drive: Spur gear.

Belt Pulley: 12¾x7¼; 778 r.p.m. and 2,600 feet per minute at normal engine speed.

OLIVER STANDARD "70"
**Oliver Farm Equipment Co.,
Hart-Parr Tractor Div., Charles City, Ia.**

OLIVER STANDARD "70"
Oliver Farm Equipment Co., Hart-Parr Tractor Div., Charles City, Ia.

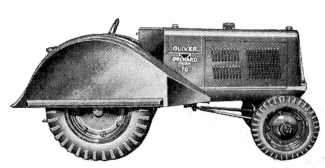

OLIVER ORCHARD "70"
**Oliver Farm Equipment Co.,
Hart-Parr Tractor Div., Charles City, Ia.**

Wheels: Four wheels; two traction in rear, 42x10.

Rubber Tires: 9.00-24, rear; 5.50-16, front. Special 11.25-24 and 6.00-16.

Tread Width: 40 or 48; **Adjustment:** None.

No. of Plows Recommended: Two, 14-in.

Length: 120½ in.; **Width:** 40-53½; 48-61½ in.; **Height:** 51 in.; **Weight:** Approx. 3,000 lbs. on steel; 3,300 on rubber.

Turning Radius (Outside): 11½ ft.; **Acres Plowed in 10-hr. Day:** 8 to 10.

Engine: Own, 3⅛x4⅜, vertical, 6 cylinders, removable sleeves.

Lubrication: Pressure; gear type oil pump.

Carburetor: Zenith, 1¼-in.

Ignition System: American Bosch high tension magneto.

Starting and Lighting Equipment: Delco-Remy electric.

Cooling System: Fan, pump and radiator.

Bearings: Ball, roller and Timkens.

Transmission: Selective sliding spur gear, 2.44, 3.32, 4.33 and 5.88 m.p.h. forward; 2.44 m.p.h. reverse.

Final Drive: Spur gear.

Belt Pulley: 12¾x6½; 778 r.p.m. and 2,600 feet per minute at normal engine speed.

Wheels: Four wheels; two traction in rear, 46x12.

Rubber Tires: 13.50-28.

Tread Width: 52.

No. of Plows Recommended: Five to seven, 14-in.

Length: 125¾ in.; **Width:** 65 in.; **Height:** 59½ in.; **Weight:** 6,343 lbs. on steel; 6,936 on rubber.

Turning Radius (Outside): 14 ft.

Engine: Own, 4¾x6¼, vertical, valve-in-head, 4 cylinders, removable sleeves.

Lubrication: Full pressure.

Carburetor: Ensign, 1½-in.

Ignition System: High tension magneto.

Cooling System: Fan, pump and radiator.

Bearings: Ball, cylindrical roller and tapered roller.

Transmission: Selective sliding spur gear; 2.23, 3.32, 4.32 and 5.55 m.p.h. forward; 2.90 m.p.h. reverse on steel wheels; 2.45, 3.64, 4.75 and 6.14 m.p.h. forward; 3.56 m.p.h. reverse on rubber tires.

Final Drive: Spur gear.

Belt Pulley: 16¾x8¼; 596 r.p.m. and 2,600 feet per minute at normal engine speed.

OLIVER SPECIAL HIGH COMPRESSION
Oliver Farm Equipment Co.,
Hart-Parr Tractor Div., Charles City, Ia.

Ride with Oliver and Go Places

THE LINE
Row Crop "70"
Standard "70"
Orchard "70"
Standard Row Crop
18-28   28-44
Special Tractors

Sell the tractors and power farming tools whose demonstration clinches all selling argument. Ride with the Oliver line of proved tool leadership —with the line that enjoys the well-earned and deep-seated faith of farmers everywhere. You'll go far on the road to better business and better profits.

With the sensational new 6-Cylinder "70" to lead off, the Oliver franchise presents a selling opportunity that is unequaled in the farm implement business today. Find out about it now. A letter to the nearest Oliver branch will bring you full details quickly.

OLIVER 70
ROW-CROP
STANDARD·ORCHARD
IT'S THE "6"

OLIVER FARM EQUIPMENT SALES COMPANY
400 West Madison Street, Chicago
BRANCHES

Amarillo, Texas	Houston, Texas	Oakland, Calif.	Springfield, Mo.
Atlanta, Ga.	Indianapolis, Ind.	Ocala, Fla.	Springfield, Ohio
Battle Creek, Mich.	Kansas City, Mo.	Oklahoma City, Okla.	St. Louis, Mo.
Billings, Mont.	Lansing, Mich.	Omaha, Nebr.	Waukesha, Wis.
Charles City, Iowa	Lincoln, Nebr.	Peoria, Ill.	Wichita, Kans.
Columbus, Ohio	Los Angeles, Calif.	Richmond, Va.	
Dallas, Texas	Louisville, Ky.	Rochester, N. Y.	**Oliver Limited**
Denver, Colo.	Memphis, Tenn.	Saginaw, Mich.	Calgary, Alta.
Des Moines, Iowa	Minneapolis, Minn.	Shreveport, La.	Edmonton, Alta.
Fargo, N. D.	Minot, N. D.	Sidney, Nebr.	Regina, Sask.
Great Falls, Mont.	Montgomery, Ala.	Sioux Falls, S. D.	Saskatoon, Sask.
Harrisburg, Pa.	Nashville, Tenn.	South Bend, Ind.	Winnipeg, Man.

1938

In 1938, 51 models of nine makes not previously included were added. Allis-Chalmers Manufacturing Co. introduced Model "B" and most John Deere tractors went through a restyling.

ALLIS-CHALMERS MANUFACTURING CO.

Milwaukee, Wisconsin

Allis-Chalmers Model "B"   1938-1958
Allis-Chalmers Model "WF"   1938-1947

Air Cleaner: Donaldson, oil bath.
Carburetor: Zenith, ⅞ in.
Clutch: Rockford, single dry plate.
Governor: Own, centrifugal.
Ignition: Fairbanks-Morse, high tension magneto.
Lighting: None.
Oil Filter: Own.
Radiator: McCord, fin tube.
Radiator Cover: Postrum.
Spark Plugs: AC 47.
Starting: _____
Data: H.P.—Neb. Test No. 302; Max. Belt 15.68; Max. D.B. 13.17; Max. lbs. pull 1,473 at 3.30 m.p.h. Weight as tested (with operator) 2,620 lbs. Number of plows recommended: One, 16 in.
Engine: Own "B"; 3¼x3½, 1,400 r.p.m., 4 cylinders, vertical, valve-in-head, cast en bloc; removable sleeves, yes.
Pulley: 8x5½, 1,050 r.p.m.
Speeds: M.P.H. forward, 2½, 4, 7½ and 3 reverse.

ALLIS-CHALMERS MODEL "B"
Allis-Chalmers Mfg. Co., Milwaukee, Wis.

ALLIS-CHALMERS MODEL "WF"
Allis-Chalmers Mfg. Co., Milwaukee, Wis.

Air Cleaner: United, oil.
Carburetor: Zenith, ⅞ in.
Clutch: Rockford, single dry plate.
Governor: Own, centrifugal.
Ignition: Fairbanks-Morse, high tension magneto.
Lighting: Guide-Lamp or Delco-Remy.
Oil Filter: Own.
Radiator: Perfex, fin tube.
Radiator Cover: Postrum.
Spark Plugs: AC 47.
Starting: Delco-Remy.
Data: H.P.—Neb. Test No. (not tested). Number of plows recommended: Two, 14 in.
Engine: Own "W"; 4x4, 1,300 r.p.m., 4 cylinders, vertical, valve-in-head, cast en bloc; removable sleeves, yes.
Pulley: 9x6½, 1,170 r.p.m. and 2,760 f.p. m. at normal engine speed.
Speeds: M.P.H. forward, 2½, 3¾, 5, 9¾ and 2¼ reverse.

AVERY FARM MACHINERY CO.

Peoria, Illinois

Ro-Trak   1938-1941

Air Cleaner: United, oil bath.
Carburetor: Zenith, 1¼ in.
Clutch: Borg & Beck, single disc, spring loaded.
Governor: Handy, flyball.
Ignition: Delco-Remy, battery.
Lighting: Guide; head lamps optional.
Oil Filter: Fram.
Radiator: Modine, tube and fin.
Radiator Cover: Own.
Spark Plugs: Regular, ⅞ in.
Starting: Delco-Remy.
Data: H.P.—Neb. Test No. (not tested). Number of plows recommended: Two to three, 14 in.
Engine: Hercules, QXB5; 3¼x4⅛, 1,000-2,000 r.p.m., 6 cylinders, L-head, cast en bloc; removable sleeves, no.
Pulley: 12x7½, 827 r.p.m. and 2,600 f. p.m. at normal engine speed.
Speeds: M.P.H. forward 3.69, 5.62, 16.55, and 2.89 reverse.

RO-TRAK
Avery Farm Machinery Co., Peoria, Ill.

CATERPILLAR TRACTOR CO.

Peoria, Illinois

Caterpillar Diesel D2	1938-1958
Caterpillar Diesel D4	1938-1958
Caterpillar Diesel D6	1938-1958
Caterpillar Diesel D7	1938-1958
Caterpillar Diesel D8	1938-1958
Caterpillar R4	1938-1941
Caterpillar R5	1938-1940

Air Cleaner. Donaldson, oil bath.

Clutch: Own, over center.

Diesel: Own, injection pump.

Governor: Own, centrifugal.

Ignition: Compression.

Lighting: Optional, electric.

Oil Filter: Own.

Radiator: Modine, tube and fin.

Radiator Cover: Optional.

Starting: Own, gasoline engine.

Data: H.P.—Neb. Test No. 322; Max. Belt 29.98; Max. D.B. 25.15; Max. lbs. pull 5903 at 1.60 m.p.h. Weight as tested (with operator) 7,420 lbs. Number of plows recommended: Three to four, 14 in.

Engine: Own, D2; 3¾x5, 1,525 r.p.m., 4 cylinders, 4-cycle, vertical, cast en bloc; removable sleeves, yes.

Pulley: 12x7½, 835 r.p.m. and 2,625 f.p.m. at normal engine speed.

Speeds: M.P.H. forward 1.7, 2.5, 3.0, 3.6, 5.1, and 2.1 reverse.

"CATERPILLAR" DIESEL D2
Caterpillar Tractor Co., Peoria, Ill.

Caterpillar Diesel "D2"

"CATERPILLAR" DIESEL D4
Caterpillar Tractor Co., Peoria, Ill.

Air Cleaner: Donaldson, oil bath.
Clutch: Own, over center.
Diesel: Own, injection pump.
Governor: Own, centrifugal.
Ignition: Compression.
Lighting: Optional, electric.
Oil Filter: Own.
Radiator: Modine, tube and fin.
Radiator Cover: Optional.
Starting: Own, gasoline engine.
Data: H.P.—Neb. Test No. 273; Max. Belt 39.82; Max. D.B. 35.36; Max. lbs. pull 7,852 at 1.60 m.p.h. Weight as tested (with operator) 10,100 lbs. Number of plows recommended: Four to six, 14 in.
Engine: Own, D4; 4¼x5½, 1,400 r.p.m., 4 cylinders, 4-cycle, vertical, cast en bloc; removable sleeves, yes.
Pulley: 12x8½, 648 or 840 r.p.m. and 2,040 or 2,640 f.p.m. at normal engine speed.
Speeds: M.P.H. forward 1.7, 2.4, 3.0, 3.7, 5.4, and 1.9 reverse.

Caterpillar Diesel "D4"
Caterpillar Tractor Co., Peoria, Ill.

"CATERPILLAR" DIESEL D6
Caterpillar Tractor Co., Peoria, Ill.

Air Cleaner: Donaldson, oil bath.
Clutch: Own, over center.
Diesel: Own, injection pump.
Governor: Own, centrifugal.
Ignition: Compression.
Lighting: Optional, electric.
Oil Filter: Purolator.
Radiator: Modine, tube and fin.
Radiator Cover: Optional.
Starting: Own, gasoline engine.
Data: H.P.—Neb. Test No. 243; Max. Belt 48.60; Max. D.B. 42.82; Max. lbs. pull 9,692 at 1.66 m.p.h. Weight as tested (with operator) 15,642 lbs. Number of plows recommended: Six to eight, 14 in.
Engine: Own, D6; 5¾x8, 850 r.p.m., 3 cylinders, 4-cycle, vertical, cast en bloc; removable sleeves, yes.
Pulley: 12x10¾, 850 r.p.m. and 2,670 f.p.m. at normal engine speed.
Speeds: M.P.H. forward 1.7, 2.5, 3.2. 4.6, and 1.9 reverse.

Caterpillar Diesel "D6"

Air Cleaner: Donaldson, oil bath.

Clutch: Own, over center.

Diesel: Own, injection pump.

Governor: Own, centrifugal.

Ignition: Compression.

Lighting: Optional, electric.

Oil Filter: Own.

Radiator: Modine, tube and fin.

Radiator Cover: Optional.

Starting: Own, gasoline engine.

Data: H.P.—Neb. Test No. (present "D7" not tested).

Engine: Own, D7; 5¾x8, 1,000 r.p.m., 4 cylinders, 4-cycle, vertical, cast en bloc; removable sleeves, yes.

Pulley: 17⅝x15, 692 r.p.m. and 3,190 f.p.m. at normal engine speed.

Speeds: M.P.H. forward 1.4 2.2, 3.2, 4.6, 6.0, and 1.6, 2.6, 3.8, 5.4 reverse.

"CATERPILLAR" DIESEL D7
Caterpillar Tractor Co., Peoria, Ill.

Caterpillar Diesel "D7"
Caterpillar Tractor Co., Peoria, Ill.

"CATERPILLAR" DIESEL D8
Caterpillar Tractor Co., Peoria, Ill.

Air Cleaner: Donaldson, oil bath
Clutch: Own, over center.
Diesel: Own, injection pump.
Governor: Own, centrifugal.
Ignition: Compression.
Lighting: Optional, electric.
Oil Filter: Purolator.
Radiator: Modine, tube and fin.
Radiator Cover: Optional.
Starting: Own, gasoline engine.
Data: H.P.—Neb. Test No. 314; Max. Belt 109.64; Max. D.B. 96.37; Max. lbs. pull 26,111 at 1.37 m.p.h. Weight as tested (with operator) 32,925 lbs. H.P. Test No. 256 (850 r.p.m); Max. Belt 103.21; Max. D.B. 91.75; Max. lbs. pull 20,485 at 1.68 m.p.h. Weight as tested (with operator) 33,690 lbs. Number of plows recommended: Twelve to twenty, 14 inch.
Engine: Own, D8; 5¾x8, 850 r.p.m., 6 cylinders, 4-cycle, vertical, cast en bloc; removable sleeves, yes.
Pulley: 14x15, 719 r.p.m. and 2,630 f.p.m. at normal engine speed.
Speeds: M.P.H. forward 1.7, 2.4, 2.8, 3.2, 3.9, 5.3, and 1.7, 2.8 reverse.

Caterpillar Diesel "D8"
Caterpillar Tractor Co., Peoria, Ill.

"CATERPILLAR" R4
Caterpillar Tractor Co., Peoria, Ill.

Air Cleaner: Donaldson, oil bath.
Carburetor: Zenith, 1¼ in.
Clutch: Own, over center.
Governor: Own, centrifugal.
Ignition: Eisemann, magneto.
Lighting: Optional, electric.
Oil Filter: Own.
Radiator: Modine, fin and tube.
Radiator Cover: Pines on tractor fuel model.
Spark Plugs: Champion 1 Com.
Starting: Manual or electric.
Data: H.P.—Neb. Test No. 272 (gasoline); Max. Belt 39.15; Max. D.B. 35.05; Max. lbs. pull 7,211 at 1.61 m.p.h. Weight as tested (with operator) 9,950 lbs. H.P. Test No. 271 (distillate); Max. Belt 36.37; Max. D.B. 30.88; Max. lbs. pull 6,120 at 1.64 m.p.h. Weight as tested (with operator) 9,975 lbs. Number of plows recommended: Four to six, 14 in.
Engine: Own, R4; 4¼x5½, 1,400 r.p.m., 4 cylinders, 4-cycle, vertical, cast en bloc; removable sleeves, yes.
Pulley: 12x8½, 648 or 840 r.p.m. and 2,040 or 2,640 f.p.m. at normal engine speed.
Speeds: M.P.H. forward 1.7, 2.4, 3.0, 3.7, 5.4, and 1.9 reverse.

"CATERPILLAR" R5
Caterpillar Tractor Co., Peoria, Ill.

Air Cleaner: Donaldson, oil bath.
Carburetor: Zenith, 1½ in.
Clutch: Own, over center.
Governor: Own, centrifugal.
Ignition: Eisemann, high tension magneto.
Lighting: Optional, electric.
Oil Filter: Optional.
Radiator: Modine, tube and fin.
Radiator Cover: Optional.
Spark Plugs: Champion 1 Com.
Starting: Manual and electric.
Data: H.P.—Neb. Test No. 224; Max. Belt 58.99; Max. D.B. 49.44; Max. lbs. pull 10,384 at 1.77 m.p.h. Weight as tested (with operator) 13,675 lbs. Number of plows recommended: Six to eight, 14 in.
Engine: Own, R5; 5½x6½, 950 r.p.m., 4 cylinders, 4-cycle, vertical, cast in pairs; removable sleeves, no.
Pulley: 12x10¼, 950 r.p.m. and 2,985 f.p.m. at normal engine speed.
Speeds: M.P.H. forward 1.9, 2.8, 3.6, 5.1, and 2.1 reverse.

CLEVELAND TRACTOR CO.
Cleveland, Ohio

Cletrac "AD"   1938-1944
Cletrac "ED$_2$-38"   1938
Cletrac "EHD$_2$-62"   1938-1940
Cletrac "EHD$_2$-68"   1938-1939
Cletrac "EHD$_2$-76"   1938-1939

CLETRAC "AD"
Cleveland Tractor Co., Cleveland, O.

Air Cleaner: Vortox and A-C, oil bath and wire screen.
Clutch: Long, double plate, dry.
Diesel: American Bosch, injection pump.
Governor: Timken, flyball.
Lighting: K. D. Co., 12-volt.
Oil Filter: Purolator.
Radiator: McCord, tube and fin.
Radiator Cover: _____
Starting: Leece-Neville.
Data: H.P.—Neb. Test No. (not tested). Number of plows recommended: Three, 14 in.
Engine: Hercules, DOOC; 4x4½, 1,530 r.p.m., 4 cylinders, valve-in-head, cast en bloc; removable sleeves, yes.
Pulley: 10½x8½, 1,130 r.p.m. and 3,100 f.p.m. at normal engine speed.
Speeds: M.P.H. forward 1.79, 2.62, 3.74, and 1.36 reverse.

Traction: One crawler on each side, 56½x8.
No. of Plows Recommended: Two to three, 14-in.
Length: 105½ in.; **Width:** 48$\frac{5}{16}$-78½-84½-92½ in.; **Height:** 55½ in.; **Weight:** 5,800-5,900 lbs.
Engine: Buda diesel, 3⅝x4¾, 4 cylinders.
Lubrication: Pressure.
Starting and Lighting Equipment: Electric.
Cooling System: Fan, pump and radiator.
Bearings: New Departure ball and Timken roller.
Transmission: Selective sliding gear; 2.3 to 5 m.p.h. forward; 2.5 m.p.h. reverse.
Final Drive: Through controlled differential and bull gear.
Belt Pulley: 10½x8½; 1,275 r.p.m., and 3,500 f.p.m. at normal engine speed.

CLETRAC "ED$_2$-38" "EHD$_2$-62, 68, 76"
Cleveland Tractor Co., Cleveland, O.

DEERE & CO.
Moline, Illinois

John Deere General Purpose Model "A"	1938-1952
John Deere Model "AI" Industrial	1938-1940
John Deere Model "AN"	1938-1952
John Deere Model "AO"	1938-1953
John Deere Model "AR"	1938-1953
John Deere Model "AW"	1938-1952
John Deere General Purpose Model "B"	1938-1952
John Deere Model "BI" Industrial	1938-1941
John Deere Model "BN"	1938-1952
John Deere Model "BO"	1938-1946
John Deere Model "BR"	1938-1946
John Deere Model "BW"	1938-1952
John Deere Model "D"	1938-1953
John Deere Model "DI" Industrial	1938-1941
John Deere General Purpose Model "G"	1938-1944

Air Cleaner: United, oil washed.
Carburetor: Marvel-Schebler, 1½ in.
Clutch: Own, dry disc, hand operated.
Governor: Own, centrifugal, variable speed.
Ignition: Wico, high tension magneto.
Lighting: Delco-Remy, battery.
Oil Filter: Purolator.
Radiator: Modine, fin tube.
Radiator Cover: Pines Winterfront, dash controlled.
Spark Plugs: Regular, 18 mm.
Starting: Delco-Remy.
Data: H.P.—Neb. Test No. 335; Max. Belt 29.59; Max. D.B. 26.20; Max. lbs. pull 4,110 at 2¼ m.p.h. Weight as tested (with operator) 6,410 lbs. Number of plows recommended: Two, 16 in.
Engine: Own "A"; 5½x6¾, 975 r.p.m., 2 cylinders, horizontal, cast en bloc; removable sleeves, no.
Pulley: 12¾x7⅜, 975 r.p.m. and 3,270 f.p.m. at normal engine speed.
Speeds: M.P.H. forward 1-2⅓, 2-3, 3-4, 4-5¼, and 3¾ reverse.

JOHN DEERE GEN'L PURPOSE MODEL "A." MODEL "AN" SINGLE FRONT WHEEL. MODEL "AW" ADJUSTABLE FRONT WHEEL TREAD

Deere & Co., Moline, Ill.

JOHN DEERE MODEL "AI" INDUSTRIAL

Deere & Co., Moline, Ill.

Air Cleaner: Vortox, oil washed.
Carburetor: Marvel-Schebler, 1½ in.
Clutch: Own, dry disc, hand operated.
Governor: Own, centrifugal, variable speed.
Ignition: Wico, high tension magneto.
Lighting: Delco-Remy, battery.
Oil Filter: Purolator.
Radiator: Modine, fine tube.
Radiator Cover: Pines Winterfront, dash controlled.
Spark Plugs: Regular, ⅞ in.
Starting: Delco-Remy.
Data: H.P.—Neb. Test No. (not tested).
Engine: Own "AI"; 5½x6½, 975 r.p.m., 2 cylinders, horizontal, cast en bloc; removable sleeves, no.
Pulley: 12¾x7¼, 975 r.p.m. and 3,270 f.p.m. at normal engine speed.
Speeds: M.P.H. forward 1-2, 2-3, 3-4, 4-6¼, and 3 reverse.

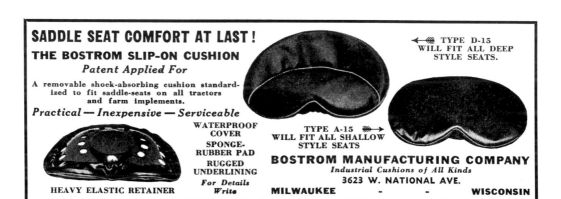

JOHN DEERE MODEL "AO" FOR GROVE, ORCHARD AND VINEYARD

Deere & Co., Moline, Ill.

Air Cleaner: United, oil washed.
Carburetor: Marvel-Schebler, 1½ in.
Clutch: Own, dry disc, hand operated.
Governor: Own, centrifugal, variable speed.
Ignition: Wico, high tension magneto.
Lighting: Delco-Remy, battery.
Oil Filter: Purolator.
Radiator: Modine, fin tube.
Radiator Cover: Pines Winterfront, dash controlled.
Spark Plugs: Regular, ⅞ in.
Starting: Delco-Remy.
Data: H.P.—Neb. Test No. (not tested). Number of plows recommended: Two, 16 in.
Engine: Own "AO"; 5½x6½, 975 r.p.m., 2 cylinders, horizontal, cast en bloc; removable sleeves, no.
Pulley: 12¾x6¼, 975 r.p.m. and 3,270 f.p.m. at normal engine speed.
Speeds: M.P.H. forward 1-2, 2-3, 3-4, 4-6¼, and 3 reverse.

Air Cleaner: Vortox, oil washed.
Carburetor: Marvel-Schebler, 1½ in.
Clutch: Own, dry disc, hand operated.
Governor: Own, centrifugal, variable speed.
Ignition: Wico, high tension magneto.
Lighting: Delco-Remy, battery.
Oil Filter: Purolator.
Radiator: Modine, fin tube.
Radiator Cover: Pines Winterfront, dash controlled.
Spark Plugs: Regular, ⅞ in.
Starting: Delco-Remy.
Data: H.P.—Neb. Test No. (not tested). Number of plows recommended: Two, 16 in.
Engine: Own "AR"; 5½x6½, 975 r.p.m., 2 cylinders, horizontal, cast en bloc; removable sleeves, no.
Pulley: 12¾x7¼, 975 r.p.m. and 3,270 f.p.m. at normal engine speed.
Speeds: M.P.H. forward 1-2, 2-3, 3-4, 4-6¼, and 3 reverse.

JOHN DEERE STANDARD TREAD MODEL "AR"

Deere & Co., Moline, Ill.

Air Cleaner: Donaldson, oil washed.
Carburetor: Marvel-Schebler, 1⅛ in.
Clutch: Own, dry disc, hand operated.
Governor: Own centrifugal, variable speed.
Ignition: Wico, high tension magneto.
Lighting: Delco-Remy, battery.
Oil Filter: Purolator.
Radiator: Modine, fin tube.
Radiator Cover: Pines Winterfront, dash controlled.
Spark Plugs: Champion 2.
Starting: Delco-Remy.
Data: H.P.—Neb. Test No. 305; Max. Belt 18.53; Max. D.B. 16.44 on rubber, 14.03 on steel; Max. lbs. pull 2,690 on rubber at 2.22 m.p.h., 2,088 on steel at 2.52 m.p.h. Weight as tested (with operator) 3,390 with steel wheels, 4,360 on rubber. Number of plows recommended: Two, 14 in.
Engine: Own "B"; 4½x5½, 1,150 r.p.m., 2 cylinders, horizontal, cast en bloc; removable sleeves, no.
Pulley: 10⅝x6, 1,150 r.p.m. and 3,200 f.p.m. at normal engine speed.
Speeds: M.P.H. forward 1-2⅓, 2-3, 3-4, 4-5¼, and 3¾ reverse.

JOHN DEERE, GEN'L PURPOSE MODEL "B," MODEL "BN" SINGLE FRONT WHEEL, MODEL "BW" ADJUSTABLE FRONT WHEEL TREAD

Deere & Co., Moline, Ill.

JOHN DEERE MODEL "BI" INDUSTRIAL
Deere & Co., Moline, Ill.

Air Cleaner: Donaldson, oil washed.
Carburetor: Marvel-Schebler, 1⅛ in.
Clutch: Own, dry disc, hand operated.
Governor: Own, centrifugal, variable speed.
Ignition: Wico, high tension magneto.
Lighting: Delco-Remy, battery.
Oil Filter: Purolator.
Radiator: Modine, fin tube.
Radiator Cover: Pines Winterfront, dash controlled.
Spark Plugs: Regular, ⅞ in.
Starting: Delco-Remy.
Data: H.P.—Neb. Test No. (not tested).
Engine: Own "BI"; 4½x5½, 1,150 r.p.m., 2 cylinders, horizontal, cast en bloc; removable sleeves, no.
Pulley: 10⅝x5½, 1,150 r.p.m. and 3,200 f.p.m. at normal engine speed.
Speeds: M.P.H. forward 1-2, 2-3, 3-4, 4-6¼, and 3 reverse.

JOHN DEERE STANDARD TREAD MODEL "BR," MODEL "BO" FOR GROVE, ORCHARD AND VINEYARD
Deere & Co., Moline, Ill.

Air Cleaner: Donaldson, oil washed.
Carburetor: Marvel-Schebler, 1⅛ in.
Clutch: Own, dry disc, hand operated.
Governor: Own, centrifugal, variable speed.
Ignition: Wico, high tension magneto.
Lighting: Delco-Remy, battery.
Oil Filter: Purolator.
Radiator: Modine, fin tube.
Radiator Cover: Pines Winterfront, dash controlled.
Spark Plugs: Regular, ⅞ in.
Starting: Delco-Remy.
Data: H.P.—Neb. Test No. (not tested). Number of plows recommended: Two, 14 in.
Engine: Own "BR-BO"; 4½x5½, 1,050 r.p.m., 2 cylinders, horizontal, cast en bloc; removable sleeves, no.
Pulley: 10⅝x5½, 1,150 r.p.m. and 3,200 f.p.m. at normal engine speed.
Speeds: M.P.H. forward 1-2, 2-3, 3-4, 4-6¼, and 3 reverse.

JOHN DEERE MODEL "D"

Deere & Co., Moline, Ill.

Air Cleaner: Donaldson, oil washed.
Carburetor: Marvel-Schebler, 1½ in.
Clutch: Own, dry disc, hand operated.
Governor: Own, centrifugal, variable speed.
Ignition: Edison-Splitdorf, high tension magneto.
Lighting: Delco-Remy, battery.
Oil Filter: Purolator.
Radiator: Modine, fin tube.
Radiator Cover: Pines Winterfront, dash controlled.
Spark Plugs: Regular, ⅞ in.
Starting: Delco-Remy.
Data: H.P.—Neb. Test No. 236; Max. Belt 41.59; Max. D.B. 30.74; Max. lbs. pull 4,037 at 2.86 m.p.h. Weight as tested (with operator) 5,690 lbs. Number of plows recommended: Three to four, 14 in.
Engine: Own "D"; 6¾x7, 900 r.p.m., 2 cylinders, horizontal, cast en bloc; removable sleeves, no.
Pulley: 13¼x8½, 900 r.p.m. and 3,122 f.p.m. at normal engine speed.
Speeds: M.P.H. forward 1-2¼, 2-3¼, 3-4, and 1½ reverse.

JOHN DEERE MODEL "DI" INDUSTRIAL

Deere & Co., Moline, Ill.

Air Cleaner: Donaldson, oil washed.
Carburetor: Marvel-Schebler, 1½ in.
Clutch: Own, dry disc, hand operated.
Governor: Own, centrifugal, variable speed.
Ignition: Edison-Splitdorf, high tension magneto.
Lighting: Delco-Remy, battery.
Oil Filter: Purolator.
Radiator: Modine, fin tube.
Radiator Cover: Pines Winterfront, dash controlled.
Spark Plugs: Regular, ⅞ in.
Starting: Delco-Remy.
Data: H.P.—Neb. Test No. (not tested).
Engine: Own "DI"; 6¾x7, 900 r.p.m., 2 cylinders, horizontal, cast en bloc; removable sleeves, no.
Pulley: 13¼x8½, 900 r.p.m. and 3,122 f.p.m. at normal engine speed.
Speeds: M.P.H. forward 1-3⅔, 2-5¼, 3-7½ (2¼, 3¼ and 4 available), and 2½ reverse (1½ available).

Air Cleaner: Donaldson, oil washed.
Carburetor: Marvel-Schebler, 1⅝.
Clutch: Own, dry disc, hand operated.
Governor: Own, centrifugal, variable speed.
Ignition: Edison-Splitdorf, high tension magneto.
Lighting: K. W., generator.
Oil Filter: Purolator.
Radiator: Modine, fin tube.
Radiator Cover: Pines Winterfront, dash controlled.
Spark Plugs: Regular, ⅞ in.
Starting: _____
Data: H.P.—Neb. Test No. 295; Max. Belt 35.91; Max. D.B. 27.63; Max. lbs. pull 4,085 at 2.37 m.p.h. Weight as tested (with operator) 5,160 lbs. Number of plows recommended: Three, 14 in.
Engine: Own "G"; 6⅛x7, 975 r.p.m., 2 cylinders, horizontal, cast en bloc; removable sleeves, no.
Pulley: 12¾x8½, 975 r.p.m. and 3,270 f.p.m. at normal engine speed.
Speeds: M.P.H. forward 1-2¼, 2-3¼, 3-4¼, 4-6, and 3 reverse.

JOHN DEERE GENERAL PURPOSE MODEL "G"

Deere & Co., Moline, Ill.

GRAHAM-PAIGE MOTORS CORP.

Detroit, Michigan

Graham-Bradley 32 H.P.   1938-1939

GRAHAM-BRADLEY 32 H.P.
Graham-Paige Motors Corp., Detroit, Mich.

Air Cleaner: Donaldson, oil.
Carburetor: Schebler, 1 in.
Clutch: Long, double disc.
Governor: Handy, flyball.
Ignition: Delco-Remy, battery.
Lighting: Delco-Remy.
Oil Filter: _____
Radiator: McCord, tubular.
Radiator Cover: _____
Spark Plugs: Champion C-7.
Starting: Delco-Remy.
Data: H.P.—Neb. Test No. 296; Max. Belt 30.38; Max. D.B. 25.20; Max. lbs. pull 3,013 at 2.38 m.p.h. Weight as tested (with operator) 4,955 lbs. Number of plows recommended: Two, 14 in.
Engine: Own "103"; 3¼x4⅜; 1,500 r.p.m., 6 cylinders, vertical, L-head, cast en bloc.
Pulley: 15x7¼, 714 r.p.m. and 2,800 f.p.m. at normal engine speed.
Speeds: M.P.H. forward 2.77 to 19.8, and 2.03 reverse.

INTERNATIONAL HARVESTER CO.
Chicago, Illinois

International Model I-14   1938-1940
McCormick-Deering Farmall 14   1938-1940
McCormick-Deering O-14   1938-1940
McCormick-Deering W-14   1938-1940

Air Cleaner: Own, oil.
Carburetor: Own, 1 in.
Clutch: Rockford, special.
Governor: Handy.
Ignition: Own, high tension magneto.
Lighting: Delco-Remy, special.
Oil Filter: _____
Radiator: Own, tubular.
Radiator Cover: _____
Spark Plugs: AC 75.
Starting: Delco-Remy, special.
Data: H.P.—Neb. Test No. (not tested).
Engine: Own; 3x4, 1,400-2,000 r.p.m., 4 cylinders, vertical, valve-in-head; removable sleeves, yes.
Pulley: 13¼x6¼, 748 r.p.m. and 2,593 f.p.m. at normal engine speed.
Speeds: M.P.H. forward 2 to 10⅜, and 2½ to 3½ reverse.

INTERNATIONAL MODEL I-14
International Harvester Co., Chicago, Ill.

Air Cleaner: Own, oil.
Carburetor: Own, down draft.
Clutch: Rockford, single disc.
Governor: Own, variable speed.
Ignition: Own, high tension magneto.
Lighting: Robert Bosch.
Oil Filter: _____
Radiator: Own, tubular.
Radiator Cover: _____
Spark Plugs: AC 75.
Starting: Special.
Data: H.P.—Neb. Test No. 297; Max. Belt 17.44; Max. D.B. 14.84; Max. lbs. pull 2,369 at 2.10 m.p.h. Weight as tested (with operator) 4,900 lbs. Number of plows recommended: Two, 12 or 14 in.
Engine: Own; 3x4, 1,650 r.p.m., 4 cylinders, vertical, valve-in-head; removable sleeves, yes.
Pulley: 12⅜x6¼, 797 r.p.m. and 2,580 f.p.m. at normal engine speed.
Speeds: M.P.H. forward 2¼, 3, 3⅞ (higher speed optional); 2¼ reverse.

McCORMICK-DEERING FARMALL 14
International Harvester Co., Chicago, Ill.

McCORMICK-DEERING O-14
International Harvester Co., Chicago, Ill.

Air Cleaner: Own, oil.
Carburetor: Own, 1 in.
Clutch: Rockford, single disc.
Governor: Own, variable speed.
Ignition: Own, high tension magneto.
Lighting: Bosch.
Oil Filter: _____
Radiator: Own, tubular.
Radiator Cover: _____
Spark Plugs: AC 75.
Starting: Special.
Data: H.P.—Neb. Test No. (not tested).
Engine: Own; 3x4, 1,400-2,000 r.p.m., 4 cylnders, vertical, valve-in-head; removable sleeves, yes.
Pulley: 13¼ x 6¼, 748 r.p.m. and 2,593 f.p.m. at 1,400 r.p.m. engine speed.
Speeds: M.P.H. forward 3⅝, 6⅛, 10⅝, and 3⅝ reverse.

McCORMICK-DEERING W-14
International Harvester Co., Chicago, Ill.

Air Cleaner: Own, oil.
Carburetor: Own, 1 in.
Clutch: Rockford, single disc.
Governor: Own, variable speed.
Ignition: Own, high tension magneto.
Lighting: Robert Bosch.
Oil Filter: _____
Radiator: Own, tubular.
Radiator Cover: _____
Spark Plugs: AC 75.
Starting: Special.
Data: H.P.—Neb. Test No. (not tested).
Engine: Own; 3x4, 1,650 r.p.m., 4 cylinders, vertical, valve-in-head, cast en bloc; removable sleeves, yes.
Pulley: 13¼ x 6¼, 764 r.p.m. and 2,650 f.p.m. at normal engine speed.
Speeds: M.P.H. forward 2⅛, 2¾, 3½, and 2⅛ reverse.

MASSEY-HARRIS CO.

Racine, Wisconsin

Massey-Harris Twin Power Challenger	1938-1941
Massey-Harris Twin Power Pacemaker	1938-1941
Massey-Harris Twin Power Orchard Pacemaker	1938-1941

Air Cleaner: Donaldson, oil.
Carburetor: Zenith, 1¼ in.
Clutch: Twin Disc, dry.
Governor: Handy, centrifugal.
Ignition: Fairbanks-Morse, magneto.
Oil Filter: H-W.
Radiator: Modine, tubular.
Radiator Cover: _____
Spark Plugs: Champion, 1 com., ⅞ in.
Data: H.P.—Neb. Test No. 293: Max. Belt 34.85 at 1,200 r.p.m. and 40.73 at 1,400 r.p.m.; Max. D.B. 25.52 on steel and 29.83 on rubber; Max. lbs. pull 3,432 at 2.66 m.p.h. on steel and 4,009 at 2.24 m.p.h. on rubber. Weight as tested (with operator) 4,570 on steel and 5,900 on rubber. Number of plows recommended: Three, 14 in.
Engine: Own; 3⅞x5¼, 1,200-1,400 r.p.m., 4 cylinders, cast en bloc; removable sleeves, yes.
Pulley: 12x6¼, 830 r.p.m. and 2,610 f.p.m. at normal engine speed.
Speeds: M.P.H. forward 2.4, 3.3, 4.1, 8.5, and 3 reverse.

MASSEY-HARRIS TWIN POWER CHALLENGER

Massey-Harris Co., Racine, Wis.

MASSEY-HARRIS TWIN POWER PACEMAKER

Massey-Harris Co., Racine, Wis.

Air Cleaner: Donaldson, oil.
Carburetor: Zenith, 1¼ in.
Clutch: Twin Disc, dry.
Governor: Handy, centrifugal.
Ignition: Fairbanks-Morse, magneto.
Lighting: _____
Oil Filter: H-W.
Radiator: Modine, tubular.
Radiator Cover: None.
Spark Plugs: Champion, 1 com., ⅞ in.
Starting: _____
Data: H.P.—Neb. Test No. 294; Max. Belt 36.83 at 1,200 r.p.m. and 42.13 at 1,400 r.p.m.; Max. D.B. 26.26 on steel and 30.58 on rubber; Max. lbs. pull 3,555 at 2.57 m.p.h. on steel and 32.36 at 2.23 m.p.h. on rubber. Weight as tested (with operator) 4,090 lbs. on steel and 5,250 lbs. on rubber. Number of plows recommended: Three, 14 in.
Engine: Own; 3⅞x5¼, 1,200-1,400 r.p.m., 4 cylinders, overhead valves, cast en bloc; removable sleeves, yes.
Pulley: 12x6¼.
Speeds: M.P.H. forward 2.4, 3.3, 4.1, 8.5, and 3 reverse.

TWIN = POWER

MASSEY-HARRIS TWIN POWER ORCHARD PACEMAKER

Massey-Harris Co., Racine, Wis.

Air Cleaner: Donaldson, oil.
Carburetor: Zenith, 1¼ in.
Clutch: Twin Disc, dry.
Governor: Handy, centrifugal.
Ignition: Fairbanks-Morse, magneto.
Lighting: _____
Oil Filter: H-W.
Radiator: Modine, tubular.
Radiator Cover: _____
Spark Plugs: Champion, 1 com., ⅞ in.
Starting: _____
Data: H.P.—Neb. Test No. (not tested). Number of plows recommended: Three, 14 in.
Engine: Own; 3⅞x5¼, 1,200-1,400 r.p. m., 4 cylinders, cast en bloc; removable sleeves, yes.

MINNEAPOLIS-MOLINE POWER IMPLEMENT CO.

Minneapolis, Minnesota

M-M Twin City FT-A	1938-1939
MM Model "ZTS"	1938-1948

M-M TWIN CITY FT-A
Minneapolis-Moline Power Impl. Co., Minneapolis, Minn.

Traction Wheels: Four wheels, two in rear, 50x12, giving traction. Rubber tires available.
Tread Width: 42-in.; **Adjustment:** None.
No. of Plows Recommended: Four to five, 14-in.
Length: 137 in.; **Width:** 66 in.; **Height:** Rad. Cap. 66 in.; **Weight:** 6,070 lbs.
Turning Radius (Outside): 14 ft.
Engine: Own, 4⅝x6, vertical, with removable cylinder blocks, 4 cylinders.
Lubrication: Pressure.
Carburetor: Schebler, 1¼-in.
Ignition System: American Bosch magneto with impulse coupling.
Lighting Equipment: Electric, with battery or no battery generator. Optional.
Cooling System: Modine radiator, centrifugal pump and fan.
Bearings: Timken and ball.
Transmission: Sliding gear; 2.36-3.17-4.05 m.p.h. forward; 1.74 m.p.h. reverse.
Final Drive: Enclosed spur gear.
Belt Pulley: 16x7½; 650 r.p.m. and 2720 feet per minute at normal engine speed.

Air Cleaner: United, oil wash.
Carburetor: Schebler, 1 in.
Clutch: Twin Disc, over center.
Governor: Own, flyball, variable speed.
Ignition: Fairbanks-Morse, magneto.
Lighting: Optional; Delco-Remy, 6-volt.
Oil Filter: H-W, renewable waste type.
Radiator: Modine.
Radiator Cover: _____
Spark Plugs: Champion, J8, 14 mm.
Starting: Optional; Delco-Remy.
Data: H.P.—Neb. Test No. (not tested).
Number of plows recommended:........
Engine: Own, RE; 3⅝x4½, 1,500 r.p.m.,
4 cylinders, vertical, side valve, cast in
removable pairs; removable sleeves, no.
Pulley: 14x7, 786 r.p.m. and 2,880 f.p.m.
at normal engine speed.
Speeds: M.P.H. forward 2.3, 2.8, 3.9, 4.9,
15.3, and 1.2 reverse.

MM MODEL "ZTS"
**Minneapolis-Moline Power Impl. Co.,
Minneapolis, Minn.**

OLIVER FARM EQUIPMENT CO.
Tractor Division

Charles City, Iowa

Oliver Standard "70" HC	1938-1948
Oliver Orchard "70" HC	1938-1948
Oliver Row Crop "70" HC	1938-1948
Oliver Standard "70" KD	1938-1948
Oliver Orchard "70" KD	1938-1948
Oliver Row Crop "70" KD	1938-1948
Oliver Row Crop "80" HC	1938-1948
Oliver Standard "80" HC	1938-1948
Oliver Row Crop "80" KD	1938-1948
Oliver Standard "80" KD	1938-1948

OLIVER STANDARD "70" HC

Oliver Farm Equipment Co.,
Tractor Div., Charles City, Ia.

Air Cleaner: Donaldson, oil wash.
Carburetor: Zenith, 1 in.
Clutch: Borg & Beck, 9", single plate, dry.
Governor: Own, centrifugal, flyball, variable speed.
Ignition: Bosch, high tension magneto.
Lighting: Delco-Remy—Guide L., electric, storage battery.
Oil Filter: Michiana.
Radiator: Modine-Young, tubular-fin.
Radiator Cover: Own.
Spark Plugs: Champion 5 Com.
Starting: Delco-Remy.
Data: H.P.—Neb. Test No. 283: Max. Belt 27.79; Max. D.B. 19.84; Max. lbs. pull 2,493 at 2.43 m.p.h. Weight as tested (with operator) 3,500 lbs. Number of plows recommended: Two, 14 in.
Engine: Own; 3⅛x4⅜, 1,500 r.p.m., 6 cylinders, vertical, cast en bloc; removable sleeves, yes.
Pulley: 12¾x7¼, 774 r.p.m. and 2,600 f.p.m. at normal engine speed.
Speeds: M.P.H. forward 2.44, 3.32, 4.33, 5.88, and 2.44 reverse.

Air Cleaner: Donaldson, oil wash.
Carburetor: Zenith, 1 in.
Clutch: Borg & Beck, 9", single plate, dry.
Governor: Own, centrifugal, flyball, variable speed.
Ignition: Bosch, high tension.
Lighting: Delco-Remy—Guide L., electric, storage battery.
Oil Filter: Michiana.
Radiator: Modine-Young, tubular-fin.
Radiator Cover: Own.
Spark Plugs: Champion 5 Com.
Starting: Delco-Remy.
Data: H.P.—Neb. Test No. (not tested). No. of plows recommended: Two, 14".
Engine: Own; 3⅛x4⅜, 1,500 r.p.m., 6 cylinders, vertical, cast en bloc; removable sleeves, yes.
Pulley: 12¾x6½, 774 r.p.m. and 2,600 f.p.m. at normal engine speed.
Speeds: M.P.H. forward 2.44, 3.32, 4.33, 5.88, and 2.44 reverse.

OLIVER ORCHARD "70" HC

Oliver Farm Equipment Co.,
Tractor Div., Charles City, Ia.

OLIVER ROW CROP 70 HC
**Oliver Farm Equipment Co.,
Tractor Div., Charles City, Ia.**

Air Cleaner: Donaldson, oil wash.
Carburetor: Zenith, 1 in.
Clutch: Borg & Beck, 9", single plate, dry.
Governor: Own, centrifugal, flyball, variable speed.
Ignition: Bosch, high tension.
Lighting: Delco-Remy—Guide L., electric, storage battery.
Oil Filter: Michiana.
Radiator: Modine-Young, tubular-fin.
Radiator Cover: Own.
Spark Plugs: Champion 5 Com.
Starting: Delco-Remy.
Data: H.P.—Neb. Test No. 252: Max. Belt 28.40; Max. D.B. 21.93; Max. lbs. pull 3,120 at 2.17 m.p.h. Weight as tested (with operator) 3,500 lbs. Number of plows recommended: Two, 14 in.
Engine: Own; 3⅛x4⅜, 1,500 r.p.m., 6 cylinders, vertical, cast en bloc; removable sleeves, yes.
Pulley: 12¾x7¼, 774 r.p.m. and 2,600 f.p.m. at normal engine speed.
Speeds: M.P.H. forward 2.44, 3.32, 4.33, 5.88, and 2.44 reverse.

OLIVER STANDARD "70" KD
**Oliver Farm Equipment Co.,
Tractor Div., Charles City, Ia.**

Air Cleaner: Donaldson, oil wash.
Carburetor: Zenith, 1¼ in.
Clutch: Borg & Beck, 9", single plate, dry.
Governor: Own, centrifugal, flyball, variable speed.
Ignition: Bosch, high tension.
Lighting: Delco-Remy—Guide L., electric, storage battery.
Oil Filter: Michiana.
Radiator: Modine-Young, tubular-fin.
Radiator Cover: Own.
Spark Plugs: Champion 6 Com.
Starting: Delco-Remy.
Data: H.P.—Neb. Test No. 284: Max. Belt 26.75; Max. D.B. 19.83; Max. lbs. pull 2,634 at 2.26 m.p.h. Weight as tested (with operator) 3,500 lbs. Number of plows recommended: Two, 14 in.
Engine: Own; 3⅛x4⅜, 1,500 r.p.m., 6 cylinders, vertical, cast en bloc; removable sleeves, yes.
Pulley: 12¾x7¼, 774 r.p.m. and 2,600 f.p.m. at normal engine speed.
Speeds: M.P.H. forward 2.44, 3.32, 4.33, 5.88, and 2.44 reverse.

OLIVER ORCHARD "70" KD

**Oliver Farm Equipment Co.,
Tractor Div., Charles City, Ia.**

Air Cleaner: Donaldson, oil wash.
Carburetor: Zenith, 1¼ in.
Clutch: Borg & Beck, 9", single plate, dry.
Governor: Own, centrifugal, flyball, variable speed.
Ignition: Bosch, high tension.
Lighting: Delco-Remy—Guide L., electric, storage battery.
Oil Filter: Michiana.
Radiator: Modine-Young, tubular-fin.
Radiator Cover: Own.
Spark Plugs: Champion 6 Com.
Starting: Delco-Remy.
Data: H. P.—Neb. Test No. (not tested). No. of plows recommended: Two, 14".
Engine: Own; 3⅛x4⅜, 1,500 r.p.m., 6 cylinders, vertical, cast en bloc; removable sleeves, yes.
Pulley: 12¾x6½, 774 r.p.m. and 2,600 f.p.m. at normal engine speed.
Speeds: M.P.H. forward 2.44, 3.32, 4.33, 5.88, and 2.44 reverse.

Air Cleaner: Donaldson, oil wash.
Carburetor: Zenith, 1¼ in.
Clutch: Borg & Beck, 9", single plate, dry.
Governor: Own, centrifugal, flyball, variable speed.
Ignition: Bosch, high tension.
Lighting: Delco-Remy—Guide L., electric, storage battery.
Oil Filter: Michiana.
Radiator: Modine-Young, tubular-fin.
Radiator Cover: Own.
Spark Plugs: Champion 6 Com.
Starting: Delco-Remy.
Data: H.P.—Neb. Test No. 267: Max. Belt 27.15; Max. D.B. 20.48; Max. lbs. pull 2,523 at 2.23 m.p.h. Weight as tested (with operator) 3,900 lbs. Number of plows recommended: Two, 14 in.
Engine: Own; 3⅛x4⅜, 1,500 r.p.m., 4 cylinders, vertical, cast en bloc; removable sleeves, yes.
Pulley: 12¾x7¼, 774 r.p.m. and 2,600 f.p.m. at normal engine speed.
Speeds: M.P.H. forward 2.44, 3.32, 4.33, 5.88 and 2.44 reverse.

OLIVER ROW CROP 70 KD

**Oliver Farm Equipment Co.,
Tractor Div., Charles City, Ia.**

OLIVER ROW CROP "80" HC
Oliver Farm Equipment Co.,
Tractor Div., Charles City, Ia.

Air Cleaner: Donaldson, oil wash.
Carburetor: Schebler, 1¼ in.
Clutch: Borg & Beck, 12 in., single plate, dry.
Governor: Own, centrifugal, flyball, variable speed.
Ignition: Bosch, high tension.
Lighting: K-W—Guide L., low tension magneto generator, no battery.
Oil Filter: Michiana, H-W.
Radiator: Modine, tubular-fin.
Radiator Cover: Own.
Spark Plugs: Champion 2.
Data: H.P.—Neb. Test No. (not tested). Number of plows recommended: Three, 14 in.
Engine: Own; 4¼x5¼, 1,200 r.p.m., 4 cylinders, vertical, cast en bloc; removable sleeves, yes.
Pulley: 14½x7¼, 731 r.p.m. and 2,750 f.p.m. at normal engine speed.
Speeds: M.P.H. forward 2.52, 3.35, 4.33, 5.82, and 3.08 reverse.

Air Cleaner: Donaldson, oil wash.
Carburetor: Schebler, 1¼ in.
Clutch: Borg & Beck, 12 in., single plate, dry.
Governor: Own, centrifugal, flyball, variable speed.
Ignition: Bosch, high tension.
Lighting: Delco-Remy—Guide L., electric, storage battery.
Oil Filter: Michiana, H-W.
Radiator: Modine, tubular-fin.
Radiator Cover: Own.
Spark Plugs: Champion 2.
Starting: Delco-Remy.
Data: H.P.—Neb. Test No. (not tested). Number of plows recommended: Three, 14 in.
Engine: Own; 4¼x5¼, 1,200 r.p.m., 4 cylinders, vertical, cast en bloc; removable sleeves, yes.
Pulley: 14½x7¼, 731 r.p.m. and 2,750 f.p.m. at normal engine speed.
Speeds: M.P.H. forward 2.42, 3.23, 4.17, 5.60, and 2.96 reverse.

OLIVER STANDARD "80" HC
Oliver Farm Equipment Co.,
Tractor Div., Charles City, Ia.

OLIVER ROW CROP "80" KD
Oliver Farm Equipment Co.,
Tractor Div., Charles City, Ia.

Air Cleaner: Donaldson, oil wash.
Carburetor: Schebler, 1¼ in.
Clutch: Borg & Beck, 12 in., single plate, dry.
Governor: Own, centrifugal, flyball, variable speed.
Ignition: Bosch, high tension.
Lighting: K-W—Guide L., low tension magneto, generator—no battery.
Oil Filter: Michiana H-W.
Radiator: Modine, tubular-fin.
Radiator Cover: Own.
Spark Plugs: Champion 2.
Data: H.P.—Neb. Test No. 300; Max. Belt 38.78; Max. D.B. 29.92; Max. lbs. pull 3,785 at 2.69 m.p.h. Weight as tested (with operator) 4,930 lbs. Number of plows recommended: Three, 14".
Engine: Own; 4½x5¼, 1,200 r.p.m., 4 cylinders, vertical, cast en bloc; removable sleeves, yes.
Pulley: 14½x7¼, 731 r.p.m. and 2,750 f.p.m. at normal engine speed.
Speed: M.P.H. forward 2.52, 3.35, 4.33, 5.82, and 3.08 reverse.

Traction Wheels: Two traction in rear, 44x10; two non-drive in front, 28x5. Rubber tires available.
Tread Width: 50-in.; **Adjustment:** None.
No. of Plows Recommended: Two to three, 14-in.
Length: 112 in.; **Width:** 61 in.; **Height:** 56½ in.; **Weight:** 4,220 lbs.
Turning Radius (Outside): 12½ ft.
Engine: Own, 4½x5¼, vertical valve-in-head, 4 cylinders; removable sleeves.
Lubrication: Pressure.
Carburetor: Schebler, 1¼-in.
Ignition System: High tension magneto.
Starting and Lighting Equipment: Delco-Remy.
Cooling System: Fan, pump and radiator.
Bearings: Ball, roller and Timken.
Transmission: Selective, sliding spur gear; 2.62, 3.22 and 4.18 m.p.h. forward; 2.92 m.p.h. reverse.
Final Drive: Spur gear.
Belt Pulley: 14½x7¼; 731 r.p.m. and 2709 feet per minute at normal engine speed.

OLIVER STANDARD "80" KD
Oliver Farm Equipment Co.,
Tractor Div., Charles City, Ia.

OLIVER FARM EQUIPMENT CO.
Hart-Parr Tractor Division

Charles City, Iowa

Oliver "90" HC	1938
Oliver "90" KD	1938
Oliver "99"	1938

Traction Wheels: Four wheel type; two traction in rear. Rubber tires.
Tread Width: 52 in.; Adjustment: None.
No. of Plows Recommended: Four 14-in.
Length: 125¾ in.; Width: 65 in.; Height: 59½ in.; Weight: 5,700 lbs.
Turning Radius (Outside): 14 ft.
Engine: 4¾x6¼, vertical, 4 cylinders, cast en bloc; removable sleeves.
Lubrication: Pressure.
Carburetor: Ensign, 1½-in.
Ignition System: Bosch high tension.
Starting and Lighting Equipment: Delco-Remy, extra.
Cooling System: Fan, pump and radiator.
Bearings: SKF and Timken. Bronze back babbitt in engine.
Transmission: Selective, sliding spur gear; 2¼ to 5½ m.p.h. forward; 3 m.p.h. reverse.
Final Drive: Spur gear.
Belt Pulley: 16¾x8¼; 596 r.p.m. and 2,600 feet per minute at normal engine speed.

OLIVER "90" HC
Oliver Farm Equipment Co.,
Hart-Parr Tractor Div., Charles City, Ia.

OLIVER "90" KD
Oliver Farm Equipment Co.,
Hart-Parr Tractor Div., Charles City, Ia.

Traction Wheels: Two steel spoke traction in rear, 46x12, with steel spade lugs. Rubber tires special equipment.
Tread Width: 52-in.; Adjustment: None.
No. of Plows Recommended: Four, 14-in.
Length: 125¾ in.; Width: 65 in.; Height: 59½ in.; Weight: 5,700 lbs.
Turning Radius: (Outside) 14 ft.
Engine: Own, 4¾x6¼, vertical, 4 cylinders, cast en bloc; removable sleeves.
Lubrication: Pressure.
Carburetor: Ensign, 1½-in.
Ignition System: Bosch high tension magneto.
Starting and Lighting Equipment: Delco-Remy, extra.
Cooling System: Fan, pump and radiator.
Bearings: SKF and Timken. Bronze back babbitt in engine.
Transmission: Selective, sliding spur gear; 2¼ to 5½ m.p.h. forward; 3 m.p.h. reverse.
Final Drive: Spur gear.
Belt Pulley: 16¾x8¼; 596 r.p.m. and 2600 feet per minute at normal engine speed.

OLIVER "99"

Oliver Farm Equipment Co.,
Hart-Parr Tractor Div., Charles City, Ia.

Wheels: Four wheels; two steel spoke traction in rear, 46x12, with steel spade lugs.

Rubber Tires: Special equipment.

Tread Width: 52; **Adjustment:** None.

No. of Plows Recommended: Five 14-in.

Length: 125¾ in.; **Width:** 65 in.; **Height:** 59½ in.; **Weight:** 5,900 lbs.

Turning Radius (Outside): 14 ft.

Engine: Own, 4¾x6¼, vertical, 4 cylinders, cast en bloc, removable sleeves.

Lubrication: Pressure.

Carburetor: Ensign, 1½-in.

Ignition System: Bosch high tension magneto.

Starting and Lighting Equipment: Delco-Remy, extra.

Cooling System: Fan, pump and radiator.

Bearings: SKF and Timken. Bronze back babbitt in engine.

Transmission: Selective sliding spur gear; 2¼ to 5½ m.p.h. forward; 3 m.p.h. reverse.

Final Drive: Spur gear.

Belt Pulley: 16¾x8¼; 596 r.p.m. and 2,600 feet per minute at normal engine speed.

MODERN WHEEL DESIGN

The experience of French & Hecht in designing and building wheels extends over a period of nearly half a century. During this period French & Hecht engineers have designed over six thousand different types of wheels and have contributed countless improvements in wheel design and construction to the implement industry.

French & Hecht was first in the implement industry to develop wheels for low pressure tires and is now supplying the wheels for most of the pneumatic tire installations on tractors and other farm machines.

French & Hecht specialize in wheel engineering and manufacture for farm implements and tractors, industrial tractors, road machinery, trucks, trailers, wheelbarrows, carts and other wheel equipment.

FRENCH & HECHT, INC., Davenport, Iowa, Springfield, Ohio—Wheel Builders since 1888.

One distinctive feature of French & Hecht wheels is the forging of the spokes in the hub. This is one reason for the added strength and structural superiority of French & Hecht wheels.

FRENCH & HECHT
STEEL WHEELS

1939

In 1939, 51 models of 28 makes not previously listed were added. Cleveland Tractor Co., the crawler manufacturer, introduced the General "GG", which was a wheeled tricycle; and Four Wheel Drive Auto Co. introduced the Eagle "6A", which was not a four-wheel drive.

ALLIS-CHALMERS MANUFACTURING CO.

Milwaukee, Wisconsin

Allis-Chalmers "RC"	1939-1941
Allis-Chalmers "S"	1939-1944

ALLIS-CHALMERS "RC"

Allis-Chalmers Mfg. Co., Milwaukee, Wis.

Air Cleaner: Donaldson, oil.
Carburetor: Zenith, ⅞ in.
Clutch: Rockford, single dry plate.
Governor: Own, centrifugal.
Ignition: Fairbanks-Morse, high tension magneto.
Lighting: Guide-Lamp or Delco-Remy.
Oil Filter: Own.
Radiator: Perfex, fin tube.
Radiator Cover: Postrum.
Spark Plugs: AC 47.
Starting: Delco-Remy.
Data: H.P.—Neb. Test No. 316; Max. Belt 18.21; Max. D.B. 15.25; Max. lbs. pull 2,840 at 1.66 m.p.h. Weight as tested (with operator) 4,005 lbs. Number of plows recommended: Two, 14 in.
Engine: Own "R"; 3⅜x3½, 1,500 r.p.m., 4 cylinders, vertical, valve-in-head, cast en bloc; removable sleeves, yes.
Pulley: 8x5½, 1,350 r.p.m., 2,840 f.p.m. at normal engine speed.
Speeds: M.P.H. forward, 2, 2¾, 4, 7½, and 1¾ reverse.

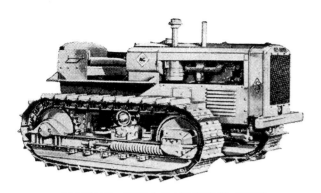

ALLIS-CHALMERS "S"
Allis-Chalmers Mfg. Co., Milwaukee, Wis.

Air Cleaner: United, oil.
Carburetor: Zenith, 1½ in.
Clutch: Rockford, single dry plate-multiple disc.
Governor: Pierce, centrifugal.
Ignition: Delco-Remy, high tension magneto.
Lighting: Auto-Lite or Guide-Lamp.
Oil Filter: Purolator.
Radiator: Perfex, fin tube.
Radiator Cover: Own.
Spark Plugs: AC 75.
Starting: Auto-Lite.
Data: H.P.—Neb. Test No. 337; Max. Belt 34.34; Max. D.B. 68.86; Max. lbs. pull 17,843 at 1.44 m.p.h. Weight as tested (with operator) 20,330. Number of plows recommended: Six to eight, 14 in.
Engine: Own "S"; 5¾x6½, 1,050 r.p.m., 4 cylinders, vertical, valve-in-head, cast en bloc; removable sleeves, yes.
Pulley: 13⅜x10, 770 r.p.m. and 2,700 f.p.m. at normal engine speed.
Speeds: M.P.H. forward 1.52, 2.32, 3.25, 4.55, 6.37, and 1.76 reverse.

J. I. CASE CO.

Racine, Wisconsin

Case Model R	1939-1940
Case Model RI	1939-1940

CASE MODEL R
J. I. Case Co., Racine, Wis.

Air Cleaner: United, oil wash.
Carburetor: Zenith.
Clutch: Twin Disc.
Governor: Flyball.
Ignition: American Bosch, magneto.
Lighting: Electric.
Oil Filter: _ _ _ _ _ _ _ _ _ _ _ _ _ _ _ _ _ _ _
Radiator: Own.
Radiator Cover: _ _ _ _ _ _ _ _ _ _ _ _ _ _
Spark Plugs: AC 75.
Starting: Electric.
Data: H.P.—Neb. Text No. 308; Max. Belt 20.52; Max. D.B. 18.23; Max. lbs. pull 2,574 at 2.27 m.p.h. Weight as tested (with operator) 4,140 lbs. Number of plows recommended: Two, 14 in.
Engine: Waukesha; 3¼x4, 1,425 r.p.m., 4 cylinders, L-head; removable sleeves, yes.
Pulley: 10⅛x6¼, 991 r.p.m. and 2,600 f.p.m. at normal engine speed.
Speeds: M.P.H. forward 2⅓, 3⅓, 4½, 10, and 2½ reverse.

Air Cleaner: United, oil wash.

Carburetor: Zenith.

Clutch: Twin Disc.

Governor: Flyball.

Ignition: American Bosch, magneto.

Lighting: Electric.

Oil Filter: _____

Radiator: Own.

Radiator Cover: _____

Spark Plugs: AC 75.

Starting: Electric.

Data: H.P.—Neb. Test No. (not tested).

Engine: Waukesha; 3 1/4 x4, 1,425 r.p.m., 4 cylinders, L-head; removable sleeves, yes.

Pulley: 10 1/8 x6 1/4, 991 r.p.m. and 2,600 f.p.m. at normal engine speed.

Speeds: M.P.H. forward 2.3, 3.3, 4.5, 9.2, and 2.6 reverse.

CASE MODEL RI
J. I. Case Co., Racine, Wis.

CATERPILLAR TRACTOR CO.

Peoria, Illinois

Caterpillar R2   1939-1941

Air Cleaner: Donaldson, oil bath.

Carburetor: Zenith, 1 1/4 in.

Clutch: Own, over center.

Governor: Own, centrifugal.

Ignition: Eisemann, magneto.

Lighting: Optional, with or without battery.

Oil Filter: Own.

Radiator: Modine, tube and fin.

Radiator Cover: Pines on tractor fuel model.

Spark Plugs: Champion 1 Com.

Starting: Manual or electric.

Data: H.P.—Neb. Test No. 320 (gasoline); Max. Belt 29.31; Max. D.B. 23.84; Max. lbs. pull 5,676 at 1.58 m.p.h. Weight as tested (with operator) 6,835 lbs. H.P. Test No. 321 (distillate); Max. Belt 28.56; Max. D.B. 22.98; Max. lbs. pull 5,379 at 1.57 m.p.h. Weight as tested (with operator) 6,835 lbs. Number of plows recommended: Three to four, 14 in.

Engine: Own, R2; 3 3/4 x5, 1,525 r.p.m., 4 cylinders, 4-cycle, vertical, cast en bloc; removable sleeves, yes.

Pulley: 12x7 1/2, 835 r.p.m. and 2,630 f.p.m. at normal engine speed.

Speeds: M.P.H. forward 1.7, 2.5, 3.0, 3.6, 5.1, and 2.1 reverse.

"CATERPILLAR" R2
Caterpillar Tractor Co., Peoria, Ill.

CLEVELAND TRACTOR CO.
Cleveland, Ohio

Cletrac "AD2"   1939-1940
Cletrac "ED2-42"   1939
Cletrac "EH"   1939
Cletrac "HG"   1939-1944
General "GG"   1939-1942

Traction: One crawler on each side, 62x12.
Tread Width: 42 or 50. **Adjustment:** None.
No. of Plows Recommended: Three to four, 14-in.
Length: 109½ in.; **Width:** 57¼ or 65¼ in.; **Height:** 54 in.; **Weight:** 7471 lbs.
Engine: Buda, 4TD-212, 3⅝x5⅛, vertical, valve-in-head, 4 cylinders, cast en bloc.
Lubrication: Force feed.
Starting and Lighting Equipment: Delco-Remy.
Cooling System: Fan, pump and radiator.
Transmission: Selective gear, 1.78 to 3.74 m.p.h. forward; 1.36 m.p.h. reverse.
Final Drive: Spur gear.
Belt Pulley: 10½x8½; 1130 r.p.m. and 3100 feet per minute at normal engine speed.

CLETRAC "AD2"
Cleveland Tractor Co., Cleveland, O.

CLETRAC "ED2-42"
Cleveland Tractor Co., Cleveland, O.

Traction: One crawler on each side, 56½x8.
Tread Width: 42. **Adjustment:** None.
No. of Plows Recommended: Three to four, 14-in.
Length: 105½ in.; **Width:** 54⅝ in.; **Height:** 55½ in.; **Weight:** 6150 lbs.
Engine: Buda, 4DT-212, 3⅝x5⅛, vertical, valve-in-head, 4 cylinders, cast en bloc.
Lubrication: Force feed.
Starting and Lighting Equipment: Delco-Remy.
Cooling System: Fan, pump and radiator.
Transmission: Selective gear, 2.04 to 4.28 m.p.h. forward; 1.5 m.p.h. reverse.
Final Drive: Spur gear.
Belt Pulley: 10½x8½; 1010 r.p.m. and 2780 feet per minute at normal engine speed.

Traction: One crawler on each side, 56½x8.

Tread Width: 62-68-76. **Adjustment:** None.

No. of Plows Recommended: Three to four, 14-in

Length: 105½ in.; **Width:** 76¾-82¾-90¾ in.; **Height:** 60 in.; **Weight:** 5575 lbs.

Engine: Hercules "OOC," 4x4½, vertical, L-head, 4 cylinders, cast en bloc.

Lubrication: Force feed.

Carburetor: Tillotson, 1⅛-in.

Ignition System: Wico high tension magneto.

Cooling System: Fan, pump and radiator.

Transmission: Selective gear, 2.2 to 4.6 m.p.h. forward; 1.67 m.p.h. reverse.

Final Drive: Spur gear.

Belt Pulley: 12x8½; 860 r.p.m. and 2700 feet per minute at normal engine speed.

CLETRAC "EH"
Cleveland Tractor Co., Cleveland, O.

Traction: One crawler on each side, 51x6; 8 in. wide available.

Tread Width: 42-68. **Adjustment:** None.

No. of Plows Recommended: Two 14-in.

Length: 91 in.; **Width:** 52½-78¼ in.; **Height:** 50 in.; **Weight:** 2950 lbs.

Engine: Hercules, IXA-3, 3x4, 4 cylinders, cast en bloc.

Lubrication: Force feed.

Carburetor: Tillotson, ⅞-in.

Ignition System: Wico high tension magneto.

Cooling System: Fan and radiator.

Bearings: Bronze and babbitt.

Transmission: Selective spur gear, 2 to 5 m.p.h. forward; 2.25 m.p.h. reverse.

Final Drive: Spur pinion and gear totally enclosed.

Belt Pulley: 9½x5½; 1055 r.p.m. and 2625 feet per minute at normal engine speed.

CLETRAC "HG"
Cleveland Tractor Co., Cleveland, O.

Air Cleaner: Vortox, oil bath.

Carburetor: Tillotson, ⅞ in.

Clutch: Long, single plate, dry.

Governor: Hercules-Handy, flyball.

Ignition: Wico, magneto.

Lighting: _____

Oil Filter: Michiana.

Radiator: McCord, tube and fin.

Radiator Cover: _____

Spark Plugs: 1 com., ⅞ in.

Starting: _____

Data: H.P.—Neb. Test No. 323; Max. Belt 19.29; Max. D.B. 14.26; Max. lbs. pull, 1,699 at 1.86 m.p.h. Weight as tested (with operator) 3,115 lbs. Number of plows recommended: One, 14 in.

Engine: Hercules, IXA; 3x4, 1,400 r.p.m., 4 cylinders, L-head, cast en bloc; removable sleeves, no.

Pulley: 8½x6½, 1,280 r.p.m. and 2,850 f.p.m. at 1,700 engine speed.

Speeds: M.P.H. forward 2.25, 3.50, 6.00 and 2.50 reverse.

GENERAL "GG"
Cleveland Tractor Co., Cleveland, O.

"BUILT TO ENDURE"

Like the Cleveland Tractor Company's wheel and crawler types of agricultural tractors they equip, Long semi-centrifugal clutches are "Built to Endure" in the hardest service. Agricultural operation always is severe—a real proving ground of tractor value. That Long clutch-equipped "Cletracs" and "Generals" have won farmers' preference is tribute to their enduring quality.

**LONG MANUFACTURING DIVISION
BORG-WARNER CORP., Detroit and Windsor**

LONG
CLUTCHES AND RADIATORS

DEERE & CO.
Moline, Illinois

John Deere General Purpose "H"

JOHN DEERE GENERAL PURPOSE "H"
(Model "HN" Single Front Wheel)
Deere & Co., Moline, Ill.

1939-1946

Air Cleaner: Donaldson, oil washed.
Carburetor: Marvel-Schebler, 1 in.
Clutch: Own, dry disc, hand operated.
Governor: Own, centrifugal, variable speed.
Ignition: Wico, high tension magneto.
Lighting: K. W., generator.
Oil Filter: Purolator.
Radiator: Modine, fin tube.
Radiator Cover: Pines Winterfront, optional.
Spark Plugs: Regular, 18 mm.
Starting: ----------------------------
Data: H.P.—Neb. Test No. 312; Max. Belt 14.84; Max. D.B. 12.48; Max. lbs. pull 1,839 at 2.38 m.p.h. Weight as tested (with operator) 3,035 lbs. Number of plows recommended: One, 16 in.
Engine: Own "H"; $3\frac{9}{16}$x5, 1,400 r.p.m., 2 cylinders, horizontal, cast en bloc; removable sleeves, no.
Pulley: $12\frac{1}{4}$x$4\frac{1}{2}$, 700 r.p.m. and 2,245 f.p.m. at normal engine speed.
Speeds: M.P.H. forward 1-$2\frac{1}{2}$, 2-$3\frac{1}{2}$, 3-$5\frac{3}{4}$, and $1\frac{3}{4}$ reverse.

FOUR WHEEL DRIVE AUTO CO.
Eagle Division
Appleton, Wisconsin

Eagle "6A"

Air Cleaner: Donaldson, oil.
Carburetor: Zenith, $1\frac{1}{4}$ in.
Clutch: Twin Disc, over center.
Governor: Waukesha, centrifugal.
Ignition: Edison-Splitdorf, magneto.
Lighting: Guide, 6-volt.
Oil Filter: Hall-Winslow.
Radiator: Young, tubular.
Radiator Cover: None.
Spark Plugs: Champion 8 Com.
Starting: Auto-Lite.
Data: H.P.—Neb. Test No. 184; Max. Belt 40.36; Max. D.B. 29.52; Max. lbs. pull 4,650 at 2.25 m.p.h. Weight as tested (with operator) 5,670 lbs. Number of plows recommended: Three to four, 14 in.
Engine: Waukesha, 6ML; 4x$4\frac{3}{4}$, 1,416 r.p.m., 6 cylinders, vertical, cast en bloc; removable sleeves, no.
Pulley: 16x8, 625 r.p.m. and 2,600 f.p.m. at normal engine speed.
Speeds: M.P.H. forward 3, and 1 reverse.

1939-1946

EAGLE "6A"

HUBER MANUFACTURING CO.
Marion, Ohio

Huber "B"   1939-1944
Huber "OB" Orchard   1939-1944

Air Cleaner: Donaldson, oil bath.
Carburetor: Zenith, 1 in.
Clutch: Rockford, dry plate.
Governor: Handy, centrifugal.
Ignition: Wico, magneto.
Lighting: Delco-Remy.
Oil Filter: ------------------------
Radiator: McCord, tubular.
Radiator Cover: Own.
Spark Plugs: Champion C-7.
Starting: Delco-Remy.
Data: H.P.—Neb. Test No. 292; Max. Belt 27.5; Max. D.B. 20.7 on steel and 22.94 on rubber; Max. lbs. pull 3,059 at 2.34 m.p.h. Weight as tested (with operator) 3,745 lbs. with steel wheels, 4,465 lbs. on rubber. Number of plows recommended: Two, 14 in.
Engine: Buda, 1P205; 3 13/16x4½, 1,300 r.p.m., 4 cylinders, vertical, L-head, cast en bloc; removable sleeves, no.
Pulley: 10x7¾, 990 r.p.m. and 2,617 f. p.m. at normal engine speed.
Speeds: M.P.H. forward 2, 3.2, 4.3, 10, and 1.8 reverse.

HUBER "B"
Huber Manufacturing Co., Marion, O.

HUBER "OB" ORCHARD
Huber Manufacturing Co., Marion, O.

Air Cleaner: Donaldson, oil bath.
Carburetor: Zenith, 1 in.
Clutch: Rockford, dry plate.
Governor: Handy, centrifugal.
Ignition: Wico, magneto.
Lighting: Delco-Remy.
Oil Filter: ------------------------
Radiator: McCord, tubular.
Radiator Cover: Own.
Spark Plugs: Champion C-7.
Starting: Delco-Remy.
Data: H.P.—Neb. Test No. (not tested). Number of plows recommended: Two, 14 in.
Engine: Buda 1P205; 3 13/16x4½, 1,300 r.p.m., 4 cylinders, L-head, cast en bloc; removable sleeves, no.
Pulley: 10x7⅜, 990 r.p.m. and 2,617 f. p.m. at normal engine speed.
Speeds: M.P.H. forward 1.46, 2.77, 3.89, 7.3, and 1.29 reverse.

INTERNATIONAL HARVESTER CO.

Chicago, Illinois

International TD-18 Diesel Tractractor   1939-1945

INTERNATIONAL TD-18 DIESEL TRACTRACTOR

International Harvester Co., Chicago, Ill.

Air Cleaner: Donaldson, Oil.
Clutch: Rockford, single plate, over-center, with automatic clutch brake.
Diesel: Bosch injection pump.
Governor: Bosch, centrifugal, variable speed.
Ignition: Compression.
Lighting: Delco-Remy, special.
Oil Filter: Purolator, replaceable element.
Radiator: Own, with circulating pump.
Starting: Delco-Remy.
Data: H.P.—Neb. Test No. 315; Max. Belt 80.54; Max. D.B. 72.38; Max. lbs. pull 18,973 at 1.43 m.p.h. Weight as tested (with operator) 23,360 lbs. Number of plows recommended:...................
Engine: Own; $4\frac{3}{4} \times 6\frac{1}{2}$, 1,200 r.p.m., 6 cylinders, cast en bloc, vertical, valve-in-head; removable sleeves, yes.
Pulley: $13\frac{1}{4} \times 12\frac{1}{2}$, 750 r.p.m. and 2,601 f.p.m. at normal engine speed.
Speeds: M.P.H. forward 1.5, 2.0, 2.5, 3.3, 4.6, 5.7, and 1.5, 3.3 reverse.

MASSEY-HARRIS CO.

Racine, Wisconsin

Massey-Harris Twin Power "101" Std.	1939-1946
Massey-Harris Twin Power "101" Jr. Std.	1939-1946
Massey-Harris Twin Power "101" Row Crop	1939-1946
Massey-Harris Twin Power "101" Jr. Row Crop	1939-1946

MASSEY-HARRIS TWIN POWER "101" STD.

Massey-Harris Co., Racine, Wis.

Air Cleaner: United, oil.
Carburetor: Marvel-Schebler, 1 in.
Clutch: Borg & Beck, dry disc.
Governor: Novi, centrifugal.
Ignition: Auto-Lite, battery.
Oil Filter: Purolator.
Radiator: Modine, tubular.
Spark Plugs: Auto-Lite A-7.
Starting: Battery.
Data: H.P.—Neb. Test No. 306; Max. Belt 35.02 at 1,500 r.p.m. and 40.04 at 1,800 r.p.m.; Max. D.B. 30.80 on rubber and 23.11 on steel; Max. lbs. pull 3,571 at 2.11 m.p.h. on rubber and 3,076 at 2.43 m.p.h. on steel. Weight as tested (with operator) 3,805 on steel and 5,725 on rubber. Number of plows recommended: Two to three, 14 in.
Engine: 3⅛x4⅜, 1,500-1,800 r.p.m., 6 cylinders, cast en bloc; removable sleeves, no.
Pulley: 13½x6¼, 837 r.p.m. and 2,958 f.p.m. at normal engine speed.
Speeds: M.P.H. forward 2.4, 3.3, 4.4, 15.9, and 2.1 reverse.

Air Cleaner: Donaldson, oil.
Carburetor: Marvel-Schebler, 1 in.
Clutch: Borg & Beck, dry.
Governor: Pierce, centrifugal.
Ignition: Auto-Lite, battery.
Lighting: _____
Oil Filter: Purolator.
Radiator: Modine, tubular.
Radiator Cover: _____
Spark Plugs: Auto-Lite A-7.
Starting: Battery.
Data: H.P.—Neb. Test No. (not tested). Number of plows recommended: Two, 14 in.
Engine: Continental; 3x4⅜, 1,500-1,800 r.p.m., 4 cylinders, cast en bloc; removable sleeves, no.
Pulley: 13½x6¼, 694 r.p.m.
Speeds: M.P.H. forward 2.4, 3.4, 4.5, 16.1, and 2.3 reverse.

MASSEY-HARRIS TWIN POWER "101" JR. STD.

Massey-Harris Co., Racine, Wis.

Air Cleaner: United, oil.
Carburetor: Marvel-Schebler, 1 in.
Clutch: Borg & Beck, dry disc.
Governor: Novi, centrifugal.
Ignition: Auto-Lite, battery.
Oil Filter: Purolator.
Radiator: Modine, tubular.
Spark Plugs: Auto-Lite A-7.
Starting: Auto-Lite.
Data: H.P.—Neb. Test No. 307; Max. Belt 35.40 at 1,500 r.p.m. and 40.67 at 1,800 r.p.m.; Max. D.B. 31.50 on rubber and 25.38 on steel. Max. lbs. pull 3,233 at 3.39 m.p.h. on rubber and 3,265 at 2.53 m.p.h. on steel. Weight as tested (with operator) 5,400 on rubber and 3,800 on steel. Number of plows recommended: Two to three, 14 in.
Engine: Chrysler; $3\frac{1}{8} \times 4\frac{3}{8}$, 1,500-1,800 r.p.m., 6 cylinders, L-head, cast en bloc; removable sleeves, no.
Pulley: $13\frac{1}{2} \times 6\frac{1}{4}$, 837 r.p.m. and 2,958 f.p.m. at normal engine speed.
Speeds: M.P.H. forward 2.4, 3.3, 4.4, 15.9, and 2.1 reverse.

MASSEY-HARRIS TWIN POWER "101" ROW CROP

Massey-Harris Co., Racine, Wis.

MASSEY-HARRIS TWIN POWER "101" JR. ROW CROP

Massey-Harris Co., Racine, Wis.

Air Cleaner: Donaldson, oil.
Carburetor: Marvel-Schebler, 1 in.
Clutch: Borg & Beck, dry.
Governor: Pierce, centrifugal.
Ignition: Auto-Lite, battery.
Lighting: _____
Oil Filter: Purolator.
Radiator: Modine, tubular.
Radiator Cover: _____
Spark Plugs: Auto-Lite A-7.
Starting: Battery.
Data: H.P.—Neb. Test No. 318: Max. Belt 26.27; Max. D.B. 20.47; Max. lbs. pull 1,738 at 4.42 m.p.h. Weight as tested (with operator) 4,612 lbs. Number of plows recommended: Two, 14 in.
Engine: Continental; $3 \times 4\frac{3}{8}$, 1,500-1,800 r.p.m., 4 cylinders, cast en bloc; removable sleeves, no.
Pulley: $13\frac{1}{2} \times 6\frac{1}{4}$.
Speeds: M.P.H. forward 2.59, 3.63, 4.85, 17.35, and 2.3 reverse.

MINNEAPOLIS-MOLINE POWER IMPLEMENT CO.

Minneapolis, Minnesota

MM Model "GT"	1939-1942
MM Model "RTU"	1939-1950
MM Model "UTS"	1939-1950
MM Model "UTU"	1939-1950
MM Model "ZTU"	1939-1948

MM MODEL "GT"
Minneapolis-Moline Power Impl. Co.,
Minneapolis, Minn.

Air Cleaner: Donaldson, oil wash.
Carburetor: Schebler, 1 in.
Clutch: Twin Disc, over center.
Governor: Own, flyball, variable speed.
Ignition: Fairbanks-Morse, magneto.
Lighting: Optional; Delco-Remy, 6-volt.
Oil Filter: H-W, renewable waste type.
Radiator: Modine.
Radiator Cover: _____
Spark Plugs: Champion O, 7/8 in.
Starting: Optional; Delco-Remy.
Data: H.P.—Neb. Test No. 317: Max. Belt 55.08; Max. D.B. 47.85; Max. lbs. pull 5,068 at 2.34 m.p.h. Weight as tested (with operator) 9,445 lbs. Number of plows recommended: Four to five, 14 in.
Engine: Own GE; 4 5/8 x6, 1,075 r.p.m., 4 cylinders, vertical, cast in removable pairs; removable sleeves, no.
Pulley: 16x7 1/2, 650 r.p.m. and 2,720 f.p. m. at normal engine speed.
Speeds: M.P.H. forward 2.7, 3.8, 4.8, 9.6, and 2.8 reverse.

MM MODEL "RTU"
Minneapolis-Moline Power Impl. Co.,
Minneapolis, Minn.

Air Cleaner: United, oil wash.
Carburetor: Schebler, 7/8 in.
Clutch: Twin Disc, over center.
Governor: Own, flyball, variable speed.
Ignition: Fairbanks-Morse, magneto.
Lighting: Optional; Delco-Remy, 6-volt.
Oil Filter: H-W, renewable waste type.
Radiator: Modine.
Radiator Cover: _____
Spark Plugs: Champion, J8, 14 mm.
Starting: Optional; Delco-Remy.
Data: H.P.—Neb. Test No. (not tested). Number of plows recommended: Two 12 in.
Engine: Own, EE; 3 5/8 x4, 1,400 r.p.m., 4 cylinders, vertical, side valve, cast in removable pairs; removable sleeves, no.
Pulley: 12 1/4 x6, 933 r.p.m. and 2,990 f.p. m. at normal engine speed.
Speeds: M.P.H. forward 2.3, 3.3, 4.2, 12, and 2.6 reverse.

Minneapolis-Moline "RTE", "RTS", "RTU"

MM MODEL "UTS"
Minneapolis-Moline Power Impl. Co.,
Minneapolis, Minn.

Air Cleaner: United, oil wash.
Carburetor: Schebler, 1 in.
Clutch: Twin Disc, over center.
Governor: Own, fly ball, variable speed.
Ignition: Fairbanks-Morse, magneto.
Lighting: Optional; Delco-Remy, 6-volt.
Oil Filter: H-W, renewable waste type.
Radiator: Perfex.
Radiator Cover: _____
Spark Plugs: Champion O, 7/8 in.
Starting: Optional; Delco-Remy.
Data: H.P.—Neb. Test No. 310: Max. Belt 42.88; Max. D.B. 39; Max. lbs. pull 4,959 at 2.27 m.p.h. Weight as tested (with operator) 7,940 lbs. Number of plows recommended: Three to four, 14 in.
Engine: Own, KEC; 4¼x5, 1,275 r.p.m., 4 cylinders, vertical, valve-in-head, cast en bloc; removable sleeves, no.
Pulley: 15½x7, 727 r.p.m. and 2,960 f.p.m. at normal engine speed.
Speeds: M.P.H. forward 2.7, 3.5, 4.7, 6.2, 20.2, and 1.3 reverse.

Minneapolis-Moline "UTS"

Air Cleaner: United, oil wash.
Carburetor: Schebler, 1 in.
Clutch: Twin Disc, over center.
Governor: Own, flyball, variable speed.
Ignition: Fairbanks-Morse, magneto.
Lighting: Optional, Delco-Remy, 6-volt.
Oil Filter: H-W, renewable waste type.
Radiator: Perfex.
Spark Plugs: Champion O, ⅞ in.
Starting: Optional; Delco-Remy.
Data: H.P.—Neb. Test No. 319: Max. Belt 42.71; Max. D.B. 36.40; Max. lbs. pull 4,585 at 2.66 m.p.h. Weight as tested (with operator) 6,773 lbs. No. of plows recommended: Three to four, 14 in.
Engine: Own, KEC; 4¼x5, 1,275 r.p.m., 4 cylinders, vertical, valve-in-head, cast en bloc; removable sleeves, no.
Pulley: 15½x7, 727 r.p.m. and 2,960 f.p. m. at normal engine speed.
Speeds: M.P.H. forward 2.5, 3.2, 4.3, 5.7, 18.5, and 1.2 reverse.

MM MODEL "UTU"
Minneapolis-Moline Power Impl. Co.

Minneapolis-Moline "UTU"
Minneapolis-Moline Co., Minneapolis, Minn.

MM MODEL "ZTU"
Minneapolis-Moline Power Impl. Co.

Air Cleaner: United, oil wash.
Carburetor: Schebler, 1 in.
Clutch: Twin Disc, over center.
Governor: Own, flyball, variable speed.
Ignition: Fairbanks-Morse, magneto.
Lighting: Optional; Delco-Remy, 6-volt.
Oil Filter: H-W, renewable waste type.
Radiator: Modine.
Spark Plugs: Champion J8, 14 mm.
Starting: Optional, Delco-Remy.
Data: H.P.—Neb. Test No. (not tested).
Engine: Own, RE; 3⅝ x 4½, 1,500 r.p.m., 4 cylinders, vertical, side-valve, cast in removable pairs; removable sleeves, no.
Pulley: 14x7, 786 r.p.m. and 2,880 f.p.m. at normal engine speed.
Speeds: M.P.H. forward 2.3, 2.8, 3.9, 4.9, 15.3, and 1.2 reverse.

OLIVER FARM EQUIPMENT CO.
Tractor Division
Charles City, Iowa

Oliver "90"   1939-1953
Oliver "99"   1939-1953

Air Cleaner: Donaldson, oil-wash.
Carburetor: Schebler, 1¼ in.
Clutch: Borg & Beck, 14", single plate, dry.
Governor: Own, centrifugal, flyball, variable speed.
Ignition: Bosch, high tension.
Lighting: Delco-Remy—Guide L., electric, storage battery.
Oil Filter: Michiana, H-W.
Radiator: Modine, tubular-fin.
Radiator Cover: Own.
Spark Plugs: Champion 2.
Starting: Delco-Remy.
Data: H.P.—Neb. Test No. (not tested). No. of plows recommended: Four, 14".
Engine: Own; 4¾x6¼, 1,125 r.p.m., 4 cylinders, vertical, cast en bloc; removable sleeves, yes.
Pulley: 16¾x8¼, 596 r.p.m. and 2,600 f.p.m. at normal engine speed.
Speeds: M.P.H. forward 2.23, 3.32, 4.32, 5.55, and 3.23 reverse.

OLIVER "90"
Oliver Farm Equipment Co.,
Tractor Div., Charles City, Ia.

OLIVER "99"
Oliver Farm Equipment Co.,
Tractor Div., Charles City, Ia.

Air Cleaner: Donaldson, oil wash.
Carburetor: Schebler, 1¼ in.
Clutch: Borg & Beck, 14", single plate, dry.
Governor: Own, centrifugal, flyball, variable speed.
Ignition: Bosch, high tension.
Lighting: Delco-Remy—Guide L., electric, storage battery.
Oil Filter: Michiana, H-W.
Radiator: Modine, tubular-fin.
Radiator Cover: Own.
Spark Plugs: Champion 2.
Starting: Delco-Remy.
Data: H.P.—Neb. Test No. (not tested). No. of plows recommended: Five, 14".
Engine: Own; 3¾x6¼, 1,125 r.p.m., 4 cylinders, vertical, cast en bloc; removable sleeves, yes.
Pulley: 16¾x8¼, 596 r.p.m. and 2,600 f.p.m. at normal engine speed.
Speeds: M.P.H. forward 2.23, 3.32, 4.32, 5.55, and 3.23 reverse.

1940

In 1940, 39 models of 11 makes not included in 1939 were added. Harry Ferguson Inc. and Ford Motor Co. announced the 9N tractor, which would not become available until 1943.

ALLIS-CHALMERS MANUFACTURING CO.

Milwaukee, Wisconsin

Allis-Chalmers Model HD-7	1940-1948
Allis-Chalmers Model HD-10	1940-1948
Allis-Chalmers Model HD-14	1940-1947

ALLIS-CHALMERS MODEL HD-7
Allis-Chalmers Mfg. Co., Milwaukee, Wis.

Air Cleaner: United, oil.
Clutch: Atwood.
Diesel: General Motors injection pump.
Governor: General Motors, centrifugal.
Lighting: Delco-Remy.
Oil Filter: A-C.
Radiator: Perfex, fin tube.
Radiator Cover: Pines Winterfront.
Starting: Delco-Remy.
Data: H.P.—Neb. Test No. (not tested). Number of plows recommended: Six, 14 inch.
Engine: General Motors "71"; 4¼x5, 1,500 r.p.m., 3 cylinders, two-cycle diesel, vertical, cast en bloc; removable sleeves, yes.
Speeds: M.P.H. forward 1.84, 2.55, 3.45, 5.82, and 2.19 reverse.

Air Cleaner: United, oil.
Clutch: Rockford.
Diesel: General Motors injection pump.
Governor: General Motors, centrifugal.
Lighting: Delco-Remy.
Oil Filter: A-C.
Radiator: Perfex, fin tube.
Radiator Cover: Pines Winterfront.
Starting: Delco-Remy.
Data: H.P.—Neb. Test No. (not tested).
Engine: General Motors "71"; 4¼x5, 1,600 r.p.m., 4 cylinders, two cycle diesel, vertical, cast en bloc; removable sleeves, yes.
Speeds: M.P.H. forward 1.69, 2.06, 2.68, 3.78, 4.62, 6.03, and 1.86, 4.17 reverse.

ALLIS-CHALMERS MODEL HD-10
Allis-Chalmers Mfg. Co., Milwaukee, Wis.

Allis-Chalmers "HD-10"
Allis-Chalmers Mfg. Co., Milwaukee, Wis.

ALLIS-CHALMERS MODEL HD-14
Allis-Chalmers Mfg. Co., Milwaukee, Wis.

Air Cleaner: United, oil.
Clutch: Rockford.
Diesel: General Motors injection pump.
Governor: General Motors, centrifugal.
Lighting: Delco-Remy.
Oil Filter: A-C.
Radiator: Perfex, fin tube.
Radiator Cover: Pines Winterfront.
Starting: Delco-Remy.
Data: H.P.—Neb. Test No. (not tested).
Engine: General Motors "71"; 4 ¼ x5, 1,500 r.p.m., 6 cylinders, two-cycle diesel, vertical, cast en bloc; removable sleeves, yes.
Speeds: M.P.H. forward 1.72, 2.18, 2.76, 3.50, 4.36, 7.00, and 2.00, 3.20 reverse.

DAVID BRADLEY MANUFACTURING WORK

Bradley, Illinois

Graham-Bradley 32 H.P.	1940-1941
Graham-Bradley Model 104	1940-1941

GRAHAM-BRADLEY 32 H.P.

Air Cleaner: Donaldson, oil.
Carburetor: Schebler, 1 in.
Clutch: Long, double disc.
Governor: Handy, flyball.
Ignition: Delco-Remy, battery.
Lighting: Delco-Remy.
Oil Filter: _____
Radiator: McCord, tubular.
Radiator Cover: _____
Spark Plugs: Champion C-7.
Starting: Delco-Remy.
Data: H.P.—Neb. Test No. 296; Max. Belt 30.38; Max. D.B. 25.20; Max. lbs. pull 3,013 at 2.38 m.p.h. Weight as tested (with operator) 4,955 lbs. Number of plows recommended: Two, 14 in.
Engine: Own "103"; 3¼x4⅜; 1,500 r. p.m., 6 cylinders, vertical, L-head, cast en bloc.
Pulley: 15x7¼, 714 r.p.m. and 2,800 f.p.m. at normal engine speed.
Speeds: M.P.H. forward 2.77 to 19.8, and 2.03 reverse.

Air Cleaner: Donaldson, oil.
Carburetor: Schebler, 1 in.
Clutch: Long, double disc.
Governor: Handy, flyball.
Ignition: Delco-Remy, battery.
Lighting: Delco-Remy.
Oil Filter: _____
Radiator: McCord, tubular.
Radiator Cover: _____
Spark Plugs: Champion C-7.
Starting: Delco-Remy.
Data: H.P. Neb. Test No. (not tested). Number of plows recommended: Three, 14 in.
Engine: Own "104"; 3¼x4⅜, 1,500 r.p.m., 6 cylinders, vertical, L-head, cast en bloc.
Pulley: 15x7¼, 714 r.p.m. and 2,800 f.p.m. at normal engine speed.
Speeds: M.P.H. forward 2.3 to 16.4, and 1.68 reverse.

GRAHAM-BRADLEY MODEL 104

J. I. CASE CO.

Racine, Wisconsin

Case Model "D"	1940-1955
Case Model "DC"	1940-1952
Case "DH"	1940
Case Industrial, Model "DI"	1940-1948
Case "DO"	1940-1955
Case "V"	1940-1942
Case "VC"	1940-1942
Case "VI"	1940-1942

Air Cleaner: Own, oil wash.
Carburetor: Zenith, 1¼ in.
Clutch: Twin Disc.
Governor: Own, flyball.
Ignition: Own, magneto.
Lighting: Electric.
Oil Filter: _____
Radiator: Own.
Radiator Cover: Shutters.
Spark Plugs: AC 75.
Starting: Electric.
Data: H.P.—Neb. Test No. (not tested). Number of plows recommended: Two to three, 14 in.
Engine: Own; 3⅞x5½, 1,100 r.p.m., 4 cylinders, valve-in-head; removable sleeves yes.
Pulley: 10¼x6½, 973 r.p.m. and 2,600 f.p.m. at normal engine speed.
Speeds: M.P.H. forward 2⅓, 3⅓, 4⅔, 9⅓, and 2½ reverse.

CASE MODEL "D"
J. I. Case Co., Racine, Wis.

CASE MODEL "DC"
J. I. Case Co., Racine, Wis.

Air Cleaner: Own, oil wash.
Carburetor: Zenith, 1¼ in.
Clutch: Twin Disc.
Governor: Own, flyball.
Ignition: Own, magneto.
Lighting: Electric.
Oil Filter: _____
Radiator: Own.
Radiator Cover: Shutters.
Spark Plugs: AC 75.
Starting: Electric.
Data: H.P.—Neb. Test No. (not tested). Number of plows recommended: Two to three, 14 in.
Engine: Own; 3⅞x5½, 1,100 r.p.m., 4 cylinders, valve-in-head; removable sleeves, yes.
Pulley: 11¾x6¼, 846 r.p.m. and 2,600 f.p.m. at normal engine speed.
Speeds: M.P.H. forward 2½, 3½, 4¾, 9¾, and 2½ reverse.

Air Cleaner: Own, oil wash.
Carburetor: Zenith, 1¼ in.
Clutch: Twin Disc.
Governor: Own, flyball.
Ignition: Own, magneto.
Lighting: Electric.
Oil Filter: _____
Radiator: Own.
Radiator Cover: Shutters.
Spark Plugs: AC 75.
Starting: Electric.
Data: H.P.—Neb. Test No. (not tested). Number of plows recommended: Two to three, 14 in.
Engine: Own; 3⅞x5½, 1,100 r.p.m., 4 cylinders, valve-in-head; removable sleeves, yes.
Pulley: 11¾x6¼, 846 r.p.m. and 2,600 f.p.m. at normal engine speed.
Speeds: M.P.H. forward 2½, 3½, 4¾, 9¾, and 2½ reverse.

CASE "DH"
J. I. Case Co., Racine, Wis.

CASE INDUSTRIAL, MODEL "DI"
J. I. Case Co., Racine, Wis.

Air Cleaner: Own, oil bath.
Carburetor: Zenith, 1¼ in.
Clutch: Twin Disc.
Governor: Own, flyball.
Ignition: Own, magneto.
Lighting: Electric.
Oil Filter: _____
Radiator: Own.
Radiator Cover: _____
Spark Plugs: ⅞ in.
Starting: Electric.
Data: H. P.—Neb. Test No. (not tested).
Engine: Own; 3⅞x5½, 1,100 r.p.m., 4 cylinders, valve-in-head; removable sleeves, yes.
Pulley: 10¼x6¼, 973 r.p.m. and 2,600 f.p.m. at normal engine speed.
Speeds: M.P.H. forward 2.89, 4.14, 5.67, 11.45, and 3.38 reverse.

Air Cleaner: Own, oil wash.
Carburetor: Zenith, 1¼ in.
Clutch: Twin Disc.
Governor: Own, flyball.
Ignition: Own, magneto.
Lighting: Electric.
Oil Filter: _____
Radiator: Own.
Radiator Cover: Shutters.
Spark Plugs: AC 75.
Starting: Electric.
Data: H.P.—Neb. Test No. (not tested). Number of plows recommended: Two to three, 14 in.
Engine: Own; 3⅞x5½, 1,100 r.p.m., 4 cylinders, valve-in-head; removable sleeves, yes.
Pulley: 10¼x6¼, 973 r.p.m. and 2,600 f.p.m. at normal engine speed.
Speeds: M.P.H. forward 1¾, 3⅓, 4⅔, 9⅓, and 2½ reverse.

CASE "DO"
J. I. Case Co., Racine, Wis.

Air Cleaner: United, oil wash.
Carburetor: _____
Clutch: Dry plate.
Governor: _____
Ignition: Splitdorf, magneto.
Lighting: Electric.
Oil Filter: _____
Radiator: _____
Radiator Cover: _____
Spark Plugs: AC 75.
Starting: Electric.
Data: H.P.—Neb. Test No. (not tested). Number of plows recommended: One to two, 14 in.
Engine: 3x4⅜, 1,425 r.p.m., 4 cylinders, L-head; removable sleeves, yes.
Pulley: 10¼x6½, 969 r.p.m. and 2,600 f.p.m. at normal engine speed.
Speeds: M.P.H. forward 2.28, 3.14, 4.03, 8.65, and 1.9 reverse.

CASE "V"
J. I. Case Co., Racine, Wis.

CASE "VC"
J. I. Case Co., Racine, Wis.

Air Cleaner: United, oil wash.
Carburetor: _____
Clutch: Dry plate.
Governor: _____
Ignition: Splitdorf, magneto.
Lighting: Electric.
Oil Filter: _____
Radiator: _____
Radiator Cover: _____
Spark Plugs: AC 75.
Starting: Electric.
Data: H.P.—Neb. Test No. (not tested). Number of plows recommended: One to two, 14 in.
Engine: 3x4⅜, 1,425 r.p.m., 4 cylinders, L-head, removable sleeves, yes.
Pulley: 10¼x6½, 969 r.p.m. and 2,600 f.p.m. at normal engine speed.
Speeds: M.P.H. forward 2.4, 3.4, 4.3, 9.2, and 1.9 reverse.

CASE "VI"
J. I. Case Co., Racine, Wis.

Air Cleaner: United, oil wash.
Carburetor: _____
Clutch: Dry plate.
Governor: _____
Ignition: Splitdorf, magneto.
Lighting: Electric.
Oil Filter: _____
Radiator: _____
Radiator Cover: _____
Spark Plugs: AC 75.
Starting: Electric.
Data: H.P.—Neb. Test No. (not tested).
Engine: 3x4⅜, 1,425 r.p.m., 4 cylinders, L-head, removable sleeves, yes.
Pulley: 10¼x6½, 969 r.p.m. and 2,600 f.p.m. at normal engine speed.
Speeds: M.P.H. forward 2.2, 3.1, 4, 8.6, and 1.9 reverse.

CENTAUR CORP.
Division LeRoi Co.
Greenwich, Ohio

Centaur, Model KV   1940-1944

Air Cleaner: Vortox, oil filter.
Carburetor: Zenith, 1 in.
Clutch: Thelander, automotive.
Governor: Own, enclosed flyball.
Ignition: Wico, high tension.
Lighting: Auto-Lite, generator and battery.
Oil Filter: DeLuxe.
Radiator: Young, tubular.
Radiator Cover: Own.
Spark Plugs: Champion, 1 Com, ⅞ in.
Starting: Auto-Lite.
Data: H.P.—Neb. Test No. (not tested). Number of plows recommended: One 14 in. or two 12 in.
Engine: Le Roi, D133; 3¼x4, 1,400 r.p.m., 4 cylinders, 4 cycle, cast en bloc; removable sleeves, no.
Pulley: 6 13/16x6⅜, 1,400 r.p.m. and 1,660 f.p.m. at normal engine speed.
Speeds: M.P.H. forward 1 to 25, and 1.8 reverse.

CENTAUR, MODEL KV
Centaur Corp., Greenwich, O.

CLEVELAND TRACTOR CO.
Cleveland, Ohio

Cletrac "ED-42"	1940-1941
Cletrac EG-42	1940-1941
Cletrac EG-62	1940
Cletrac EHG-68	1940-1941

CLETRAC "ED-42"
Cleveland Tractor Co., Cleveland, O.

Air Cleaner: Vortox and A-C, oil bath and wire screen.
Clutch: Long, double plate, dry.
Diesel: American Bosch, injection pump.
Governor: Timken, flyball.
Lighting: K. D. Co., 12-volt.
Oil Filter: Purolator.
Radiator: McCord, tube and fin.
Radiator Cover: _____
Starting: Leece-Neville.
Data: H.P.—Neb. Test No. (not tested). Number of plows recommended: Three to four, 14 in.
Engine: Hercules, DOOC; 4x4½, 1,250 r. p.m., 4 cylinders, valve-in-head, cast en bloc; removable sleeves, yes.
Pulley: 10½x8½, 920 r.p.m. and 2,580 f.p.m. at normal engine speed.
Speeds: M.P.H. forward 2.03, 2.67, 3.82, and 1.56 reverse.

CLETRAC EG-42-62
Cleveland Tractor Co., Cleveland, O.

Air Cleaner: Vortox and A-C, oil bath and wire screen.
Carburetor: Tillotson, 1⅛ in.
Clutch: Long, double plate, dry.
Governor: Hercules, flyball.
Ignition: Wico, magneto.
Lighting: K. D. Co., 6-volt.
Oil Filter: Michiana.
Radiator: McCord, tube and fin.
Radiator Cover: _____
Spark Plugs: 1 com., ⅞ in.
Starting: Delco-Remy.
Data: H.P.—Neb. Test No. 261 (tested as "E"); Max. Belt 28.76; Max. D.B. 20.47; Max. lbs. pull 3,867 at 1.84 m.p.h. Weight as tested (with operator), 6,100 lbs. Number of plows recommended: Two to three, 14 in.
Engine: Hercules, OOC; 4x4½, 1,300 r. p.m., 4 cylinders, L-head, cast en bloc; removable sleeves, no.
Pulley: 12x8½, 860 r.p.m. and 2,700 f. p.m. at normal engine speed.
Speeds: M.P.H. forward 2.1, 2.78, 3.97, and 1.62 reverse.

Air Cleaner: Vortox and A-C, oil bath and wire screen.
Carburetor: Tillotson, 1⅛ in.
Clutch: Long, double plate, dry.
Governor: Hercules, flyball.
Ignition: Wico, magneto.
Lighting: K. D. Co., 6-volt.
Oil Filter: Michiana.
Radiator: McCord, tube and fin.
Radiator Cover: _____
Spark Plugs: 1 com., ⅞ in.
Starting: Delco-Remy.
Data: H.P.—Neb. Test No. (not tested). Number of plows recommended: Three to four, 14 in.
Engine: Hercules, OOC; 4x4½, 1,300 r. p.m., 4 cylinders, L-head, cast en bloc; removable sleeves, no.
Pulley: 12x8½, 860 r.p.m. and 2,700 f. p.m. at normal engine speed.
Speeds: M.P.H. forward 2.2, 3.2, 4.6, and 1.67 reverse.

CLETRAC EHG-68
Cleveland Tractor Co., Cleveland, O.

DEERE & CO.
Moline, Illinois

John Deere Model "HN"   1940-1946

JOHN DEERE GENERAL PURPOSE "H"
(Model "HN" Single Front Wheel)
Deere & Co., Moline, Ill.

Air Cleaner: Donaldson, oil washed.
Carburetor: Marvel-Schebler, 1 in.
Clutch: Own, dry disc, hand operated.
Governor: Own, centrifugal, variable speed.
Ignition: Wico, high tension magneto.
Lighting: K. W., generator.
Oil Filter: Purolator.
Radiator: Modine, fin tube.
Radiator Cover: Pines Winterfront, optional.
Spark Plugs: Regular, 18 mm.
Starting: _____
Data: H.P.—Neb. Test No. 312; Max. Belt 14.84; Max. D.B. 12.48; Max. lbs. pull 1,839 at 2.38 m.p.h. Weight as tested (with operator) 3,035 lbs. Number of plows recommended: One, 16 in.
Engine: Own "H"; 3 9/16x5, 1,400 r.p.m., 2 cylinders, horizontal, cast en bloc; removable sleeves, no.
Pulley: 12¼x4½, 700 r.p.m. and 2,245 f.p.m. at normal engine speed.
Speeds: M.P.H. forward 1-2½, 2-3½, 3-5¾, and 1¾ reverse.

FATE-ROOT-HEATH CO.
Plymouth, Ohio

Silver King Model 340	1940-1944
Silver King Model 380	1940
Silver King Model 440	1940-1944
Silver King Model 600	1940-1944
Silver King Model 660	1940-1944
Silver King Model 720	1940

Air Cleaner: Donaldson, oil bath.
Carburetor: Schebler, 1 in.
Clutch: Borg & Beck, single dry plate.
Governor: Pierce, centrifugal.
Ignition: Wico or Bosch, high tension magneto.
Lighting: Delco-Remy.
Oil Filter: Fram.
Radiator: Modine, fin and tube.
Radiator Cover: None; thermostat control.
Spark Plugs: Champion, No. 6, com., 18 mm.
Starting: Delco-Remy.
Data: H.P.—Neb. Test No. (present model not tested). Number of plows recommended: Two to three, 14 in.
Engine: Own, No. 41; 3.438x4.375, 1,500-1,800 r.p.m., 4 cylinders, vertical, L-head, cast en bloc; removable sleeves, no.
Pulley: 8x6½, 1,500-1,800 r.p.m. and 3,150-3,780 f.p.m. at normal engine speed.
Speeds: M.P.H. forward 2.5, 4, 5.6 and 25; 1.9 reverse.

SILVER KING MODEL 340
Fate-Root-Heath Co., Plymouth, O.

SILVER KING MODEL 380 AND 440
Fate-Root-Heath Co., Plymouth, O.

Air Cleaner: Donaldson, oil bath.
Carburetor: Schebler, 1 in.
Clutch: Borg & Beck, single dry plate.
Governor: Handy, centrifugal.
Ignition: Wico, high tension magneto.
Lighting: Delco-Remy.
Oil Filter: Fram.
Radiator: Modine, fin and tube.
Radiator Cover: None.
Spark Plugs: Champion, J-10, 14 mm.
Starting: Auto-Lite.
Data: H.P.—Neb. Test No. (present model not tested). Number of plows recommended: One, 14 in.
Engine: Hercules, IXB3; 3¼x4, 1,500-1,800 r.p.m., 4 cylinders, vertical, L-head, cast en bloc; removable sleeves, no.
Pulley: 6¾x6½, 1,500-1,800 r.p.m. and 2,650-3,180 f.p.m. at normal engine speed.
Speeds: M.P.H. forward 2.5, 4.1, 5.7 and 25; 1.9 reverse.

SILVER KING MODEL 600, 660 AND 720
Fate-Root-Heath Co., Plymouth, O.

Air Cleaner: Donaldson, oil bath.
Carburetor: Schebler, 1 in.
Clutch: Borg & Beck, single dry plate.
Governor: Pierce, centrifugal.
Ignition: Wico, high tension magneto.
Lighting: Delco-Remy.
Oil Filter: Fram.
Radiator: Modine, fin and tube.
Radiator Cover: None; thermostat control.
Spark Plugs: Champion, No. 6, com. 18 mm.
Starting: Delco-Remy.
Data: H.P.—Neb. Test No. (present model not tested). Number of plows recommended: Two, 14 in.
Engine: Own, No. 41; 3.438x4.375, 1,500-1,800 r.p.m., 4 cylinders, vertical, L-head, cast en bloc; removable sleeves, no.
Pulley: 8x6½, 1,500-1,800 r.p.m. and 3,150-3,780 f.p.m. at normal engine speed.
Speeds: M.P.H. forward 2, 3.3, 4.6 and 25; 1.5 reverse.

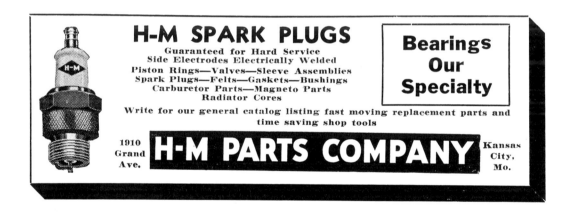
INTERNATIONAL HARVESTER CO.

Chicago, Illinois

Farmall "H"	1940-1947
Farmall "M"	1940-1947
Farmall "MD"	1940-1947
I-4	1940-1948
I-6	1940-1948
ID-6	1940-1948
I-9	1940-1948
ID-9	1940-1948
International Industrial I-30	1940
International ID-40	1940

FARMALL "H"

International Harvester Co., Chicago, Ill.

Air Cleaner: Donaldson, oil.
Carburetor: Own, 1¼ in.
Clutch: Rockford, 11 in., single plate, dry disc.
Governor: Own, variable speed, centrifugal.
Ignition: Own, high tension, automatic impulse magneto.
Lighting: Special.
Oil Filter: Purolator, replaccable element.
Radiator: Own, circulating pump.
Radiator Cover: _____
Spark Plugs: AC 84.
Starting: Special.
Data: H.P.—Neb. Test No. 328 (gasoline) : Max. Belt 36.66; Max. D.B. 33.05; Max. lbs. pull 4,233 at 2.17 m.p.h. Test No. 327 (distillate): Max. Belt 34.82; Max. D.B. 30.65; Max. lbs. pull 4,365 at 2.19 m.p.h. Weight as tested (with operator) 6,770. Number of plows recommended: Three, 14 in.
Engine: Own; 3⅞x5¼, 950-1,450 r.p.m., 4 cylinders, vertical, valve-in-head, cast en bloc; removable sleeves, yes.
Pulley: 11x7½, 899 r.p.m. and 2,588 f.p.m. at normal engine speed.
Speeds: M.P.H. forward on steel 2⅝, 3½, 4¼, 5⅛, and 3⅛ reverse; on 11-38 rubber 2⅝, 3½, 4¼, 5⅛, 16¼ forward, and 3⅛ reverse.

Air Cleaner: Donaldson, oil.
Carburetor: Own, 1 in.
Clutch: Rockford, 10 in., single plate, dry disc.
Governor: Own, variable speed, centrifugal.
Ignition: Own, high tension, automatic impulse magneto.
Lighting: Special.
Oil Filter: Purolator, replaceable element.
Radiator: Own, circulating pump.
Radiator Cover: _____
Spark Plugs: AC 84.
Starting: Special.
Data: H.P.—Neb. Test No. 333 (gasoline): Max. Belt 26.20; Max. D.B. 24.17; Max. lbs. pull 3,603 at 2.06 m.p.h. Test No. 334 (distillate): Max. Belt 23.31; Max. D.B. 21.37; Max. lbs. pull 3,169 at 2.29 m.p.h. Weight as tested (with operator) 5,550 lbs. Number of plows recommended: Two, 14 in.
Engine: Own; 3⅜x4¼, 1,050-1,650 r.p.m., 4 cylinders, vertical, valve-in-head, cast en bloc; removable sleeves, yes.
Pulley: 9¾x7½, 1,019 r.p.m. and 2,601 f.p.m. at normal engine speed.
Speeds: M.P.H. forward on steel 2⅝, 3½, 4¼, 5⅜, and 3 reverse; on 10-38 rubber 2½, 3⅜, 4⅛, 5⅛, 15⅝ forward, and 2⅞ reverse.

FARMALL "M"

International Harvester Co., Chicago, Ill.

McCormick Farmall "M"
International Harvester Co., Chicago, Ill.

Clutch: Rockford, single dry disc, spring-loaded.
Diesel: Bosch injection pump.
Governor: Bosch, flyball, variable speed.
Ignition: Own, magneto.
Lighting: Delco-Remy.
Oil Filter: Purolator.
Radiator: Own, fin and tube.
Radiator Cover: Own.
Spark Plugs: Champion 49 or AC 18-A.
Starting: Delco-Remy.
Data: H.P.—Neb. Test No. (not tested). Number of plows recommended: _____
Engine: Own; 3⅞x5¼, 1,450 r.p.m., 4 cylinders, diesel, cast en bloc, removable sleeves, yes.
Pulley: 11x7½, 879 r.p.m. and 2,588 f. p.m. at normal engine speed.
Speeds: M.P.H. forward_____ and _____ reverse.

Air Cleaner: Donaldson, oil bath.
Carburetor: Own, ¾ in.

FARMALL "MD"
International Harvester Co., Chicago, Ill.

Air Cleaner: Donaldson, oil bath.
Carburetor: Own, 1 in.
Clutch: Rockford, single dry disc, spring-loaded.
Governor: Own, flyball, variable speed.
Ignition: Own, magneto.
Lighting: Delco-Remy.
Oil Filter: Purolator.
Radiator: Own, fin and tube.
Radiator Cover: Own.
Spark Plugs: Champion 15.
Starting: Delco-Remy.
Data: H.P.—Neb. Test No. (not tested); Manufacturer's rating: Max. Belt 27.5; Max. D.B. 25. Number of plows recommended: _____
Engine: Own; 3⅜x4¼, 1,650 r.p.m., 4 cylinders, valve-in-head, cast en bloc; removable sleeves, yes.
Pulley: 9¾x7½, 1,019 r.p.m. and 2,601 f.p.m. at normal engine speed.
Speeds: M.P.H. forward 2.1, 3.5, 5, 7.1, 14.9 and 2.9 reverse.

I-4
International Harvester Co., Chicago, Ill.

Air Cleaner: Donaldson, oil bath.
Carburetor: Own, 1¼ in.
Clutch: Rockford, single dry disc, spring-loaded.
Governor: Own, flyball, variable speed.
Ignition: Own, magneto.
Lighting: Delco-Remy.
Oil Filter: Purolator.
Radiator: Own, fin and tube.
Radiator Cover: Own.
Spark Plugs: Champion 15.
Starting: Delco-Remy.
Data: H.P.—Neb. Test No. (not tested). Manufacturer's rating: Max. Belt 38.5; Max. D.B. 33.5. Number of plows recommended: _____
Engine: Own; 3⅞x5¼, 1,450 r.p.m., 4 cylinders, valve-in-head, cast en bloc; removable sleeves, yes.
Pulley: 11x7½, 899 r.p.m. and 2,588 f.p.m. at normal engine speed.
Speeds: M.P.H. forward 2.1, 3.6, 5.2, 7.3, 14.1, and 2.5 reverse.

I-6
International Harvester Co., Chicago, Ill.

ID-6

International Harvester Co., Chicago, Ill.

Air Cleaner: Donaldson, oil bath.
Carburetor: Own, ¾ in.
Clutch: Rockford, single dry disc, spring-loaded.
Diesel: Bosch injection pump.
Governor: Bosch, flyball, variable speed.
Ignition: Own, magneto.
Lighting: Delco-Remy.
Oil Filter: Purolator.
Radiator: Own, fin and tube.
Radiator Cover: Own.
Spark Plugs: Champion 49 or AC 18-A.
Starting: Delco-Remy.
Data: H.P.—Neb. Test No. (not tested). Manufacturer's rating: Max. Belt 36; Max. D.B. 31. Number of plows recommended: _____
Engine: Own; 3⅞x5¼, 1,450 r.p.m., 4 cylinders, diesel, cast en bloc; removable sleeves, yes.
Pulley: 11x7½, 899 r.p.m. and 2,588 f. p.m. at normal engine speed.
Speeds: M.P.H. forward 2.1, 3.6, 5.2, 7.3, 14.1, and 2.5 reverse.

I-9

International Harvester Co., Chicago, Ill.

Air Cleaner: Donaldson, oil bath.
Carburetor: Own, 1⅜ in.
Clutch: Own, single dry disc, spring-loaded.
Governor: Own, flyball, variable speed.
Ignition: Own, magneto.
Lighting: Delco-Remy.
Oil Filter: Purolator.
Radiator: Own, fin and tube.
Radiator Cover: Own.
Spark Plugs: Champion 1 Com.-A or AC Tractor 9.
Starting: Delco-Remy.
Data: H.P.—Neb. Test No. (not tested). Manufacturer's rating: Max. Belt 50.5; Max. D.B. 43. Number of plows recommended: _____
Engine: Own; 4.4x5.5, 1,500 r.p.m., 4 cylinders, valve-in-head, cast en bloc; removable sleeves, yes.
Pulley: 14x8½, 707 r.p.m. and 2,593 f. p.m. at normal engine speed.
Speeds: M.P.H. forward 2.3, 3.1, 5.2, 7.3, 15.1, and 2.8 reverse.

Clutch: Own, single dry disc, spring-loaded.
Diesel: Bosch injection pump.
Governor: Bosch, flyball, variable speed.
Ignition: Own, magneto.
Lighting: Delco-Remy.
Oil Filter: Purolator.
Radiator: Own, fin and tube.
Radiator Cover: Own.
Spark Plugs: Champion 49 or AC 18-A.
Starting: Delco-Remy.
Data: H.P.—Neb. Test No. (not tested). Manufacturer's rating: Max. Belt 48; Max. D.B. 41. Number of plows recommended: _____
Engine: Own; 4.4x5.5, 1,500 r.p.m., 4 cylinders, diesel, cast en bloc; removable sleeves, yes.
Pulley: 14x8½, 707 r.p.m. and 2,593 f. p.m. at normal engine speed.
Speeds: M.P.H. forward 2¼, 3, 4¼, 5⅛, 14⅞, and 2¾ reverse.

Air Cleaner: Donaldson, oil bath.
Carburetor: Own, ¾ in.

WD-9
International Harvester Co., Chicago, Ill.

INTERNATIONAL INDUSTRIAL I-30
International Harvester Co., Chicago, Ill.

Air Cleaner: Own, oil.
Carburetor: Zenith, 1¼ in.
Clutch: Own, single disc.
Governor: Own, variable speed.
Ignition: Own, high tension magneto.
Lighting: Delco-Remy.
Oil Filter: _____
Radiator: Own, tubular.
Radiator Cover: _____
Spark Plugs: AC 77.
Starting: Delco-Remy, special.
Data: H.P.—Neb. Test No. (not tested). Number of plows recommended: _____
Engine: Own; 4¼x5, 1,200 r.p.m., 4 cylinders, vertical, valve-in-head; removable sleeves, yes.
Pulley: 14⅜x7, 704 r.p.m. and 2,650 f.p. m. at normal engine speed.
Speeds: M.P.H. forward 2½ to 12¼.

INTERNATIONAL ID-40
International Harvester Co., Chicago, Ill.

Air Cleaner: Donaldson, oil.
Carburetor: Own, for starting only.
Clutch: Own, single disc.
Diesel: _____injection pump.
Governor: Own, fly ball.
Ignition: Compression.
Lighting: Robert Bosch.
Oil Filter: _____
Radiator: Own, tubular.
Radiator Cover: _____
Data: H.P.—Neb. Test No. (not tested). Number of plows recommended: _____
Engine: Own; 4¾x6½, 1,200 r.p.m., 4 cylinders, vertical, valve-in-head; removable sleeves, yes.
Pulley: 16¾x9, 640 r.p.m. and 2,815 f. p.m. at normal engine speed.
Speeds: M.P.H. forward 2¼, 4¼, 7⅝, 11¼, and 3½ reverse.

MASSEY-HARRIS CO.
Racine, Wisconsin

Massey-Harris Distillate "101" Jr.   1940-1941

Air Cleaner: Donaldson, dry.
Carburetor: Marvel-Schebler, 1 in.
Clutch: Borg & Beck, dry.
Governor: Pierce, centrifugal.
Ignition: Auto-Lite, battery.
Oil Filter: Purolator.
Radiator: Modine, tubular.
Radiator Cover: Pines Winterfront.
Spark Plugs: Auto-Lite A-7.
Starting: Battery.
Data: H.P.—Neb. Test No. (not tested). Number of plows recommended: Two, 14 in.
Engine: Continental; $3\frac{3}{16}$x$4\frac{3}{8}$, 1,500-1,800 r.p.m., 4 cylinders, cast en bloc; removable sleeves, no.
Pulley: $13\frac{1}{2}$x6, 837 r.p.m. and 2,958 f. p.m. at normal engine speed.
Speeds: M.P.H. forward 2.4, 3.4, 4.5, 16.1, and 2.3 reverse.

MASSEY-HARRIS DISTILLATE "101" JR.
Massey-Harris Co., Racine, Wis.

MINNEAPOLIS-MOLINE POWER IMPLEMENT CO.
Minneapolis, Minnesota

MM Model "RTS"   1940-1950
MM Model "UDLX"   1940-1941

MM MODEL "RTS"
Minneapolis-Moline Power Impl. Co.

Air Cleaner: United, oil wash.
Carburetor: Schebler, $\frac{7}{8}$ in.
Clutch: Twin Disc, over center.
Governor: Own, flyball, variable speed.
Ignition: Fairbanks-Morse, magneto.
Lighting: Optional, Delco-Remy, 6-volt.
Oil Filter: H-W, renewable waste.
Radiator: Modine.
Spark Plugs: Champion J8, 14 mm.
Starting: Optional; Delco-Remy.
Data: H.P.—Neb. Test No. (not tested). No. of plows recommended: Two, 12 in.
Engine: Own, EE; $3\frac{5}{8}$x4, 1,400 r.p.m., 4 cylinders, vertical, side valve, cast in removable pairs; removable sleeves, no.
Pulley: $12\frac{1}{4}$x6, 933 r.p.m. and 2,990 f.p. m. at normal engine speed.
Speeds: M.P.H. forward 2.3, 3.3, 4.2, 12 and 2.6 reverse.

Air Cleaner: Donaldson, oil wash.
Carburetor: Schebler, 1 in.
Clutch: Rockford, spring loaded.
Governor: Own, flyball.
Ignition: Delco-Remy, battery.
Lighting: Delco-Remy, battery.
Oil Filter: H-W, renewable waste type.
Radiator: Perfex.
Radiator Cover: _____
Spark Plugs: Champion O, ⅞ in.
Starting: Delco-Remy.
Data: H.P.—Neb. Test No. (not tested). Number of plows recommended: Three to four, 14 in.
Engine: Own, KED; 4¼x5, 1,275 r.p.m., 4 cylinders, vertical, valve-in-head, cast en bloc; removable sleeves, no.
Pulley: 15½x7, 727 r.p.m. and 2,960 f.p.m. at normal engine speed.
Speeds: M.P.H. forward 2.7, 3.4, 4.7, 10.1, 20.1, 28.1, and 1.3 reverse.

MM MODEL "UDLX"
Minneapolis-Moline Power Impl. Co., Minneapolis, Minn.

SHAW MANUFACTURING CO.
Galesburg, Kansas

Shaw Du-All HY8   1940-1947

SHAW DU-ALL HY8
Shaw Mfg. Co., Galesburg, Kan.

Air Cleaner: United, oil bath.
Carburetor: Zenith.
Clutch: Rockford, automotive.
Governor: Own, air vane.
Ignition: Wico, high tension magneto with impulse starter.
Lighting: _____
Oil Filter: _____
Radiator: _____
Radiator Cover: _____
Spark Plugs: Champion, 18 mm.
Data: H.P.—Neb. Test No. (not tested). Number of plows recommended: One, 12 in.
Engine: Wisconsin, air cooled; 3⅝x4, 2,200 r.p.m., 1 cylinder, vertical, L-head.
Pulley: 4¼x4½, 2,200 r.p.m. and 2,400 f.p.m. at normal engine speed.
Speeds: M.P.H. forward 2 to 7, and 1¾ reverse.

1941

In 1941, 31 models of ten makes not included in 1940 were announced. In December, the attack on Pearl Harbor issued in the start of World War II. The Supply Priorities and Applications Board was set up to try to maintain production machinery at an adequate level.

ALLIS-CHALMERS MANUFACTURING CO.

Milwaukee, Wisconsin

Allis-Chalmers Model "C"   1941-1950

ALLIS-CHALMERS MODEL "C"
Allis-Chalmers Mfg. Co., Milwaukee, Wis.

Air Cleaner: Donaldson, oil bath.
Carburetor: Zenith, ⅞ in.
Clutch: Rockford, single dry plate.
Governor: Own, centrifugal.
Ignition: Fairbanks-Morse high tension magneto.
Lighting: Guide Lamp and Delco-Remy.
Oil Filter: Own.
Radiator: McCord or Perfex, fin and tube.
Radiator Cover: Hardy shutter.
Spark Plugs: AC 45-Gas; AC 47-Kero.
Starting: Delco-Remy or Auto-Lite.
Data: H. P.—Neb. Test No. 363 (distillate); Max. Belt 19.40; Max. D.B. 15.97; Max. lbs. pull 2,368 at 1.87 m. p.h. H.P. Test No. 364 (gasoline); Max. Belt 23.30; Max. D.B. 18.43; Max. lbs. pull 2,352 at 1.93 m.p.h. Number of plows recommended: One, 16 in.
Engine: Own "C"; 3⅜x3½, 1,500 r.p.m., 4 cylinders, vertical, valve-in-head, cast en bloc; removable sleeves, yes.
Pulley: 8x5½, 1,125 r.p.m.
Speeds: M.P.H. forward 2½, 3¾, 7½ and 2¾ reverse, on air tires; 2¼, 3⅓, 6½ forward and 2½ reverse on steel wheels.

Allis-Chalmers "C"
Allis-Chalmers Mfg. Co., Milwaukee, Wis.

J. I. CASE CO.

Racine, Wisconsin

Case "LA"	1941-1955
Case "S"	1941-1955
Case "SC"	1941-1954
Case "SO"	1941-1955
Case "VO"	1941-1942

CASE "LA"
J. I. Case Co., Racine, Wis.

Air Cleaner: Own, oil bath.
Carburetor: Zenith.
Clutch: Disc.
Governor: Own, flyball.
Ignition: Own, magneto.
Lighting: Electric.
Oil Filter: _____
Radiator: Fin and tube.
Radiator Cover: Shutters and screen.
Spark Plugs: 7/8 in.
Starting: Electric.
Data: H.P.—Neb. Test No. (not tested). Number of plows recommended: Four to five, 14 in.
Engine: Own "LA"; 4 5/8 x 6, 1,100 r.p.m., 4 cylinders, valve-in-head; removable sleeves, yes.
Pulley: 13x8 1/4, 779 r.p.m. and 2,660 f.p.m. at normal engine speed.
Speeds: M.P.H. forward 2 3/4, 3 3/4, 4 1/2, 10, and 3 reverse on 13-30 rear tires.

J. I. Case "LA"
J. I. Case Co., Racine, Wis.

Air Cleaner: Oil bath.
Carburetor: Zenith, 1 in.
Clutch: Disc, toggle action.
Governor: Own, flyball.
Ignition: Magneto.
Lighting: Electric.
Oil Filter: _____
Radiator: Fin and tube.
Radiator Cover: Shutter, extra.
Spark Plugs: 14 mm.
Starting: Optional.
Data: H.P.—Neb. Test No. (not tested).
  Number of plows recommended: Two,
  14 in.
Engine: Own "S"; 3½x4, 1,550 r.p.m.,
  4 cylinders, valve-in-head, cast en bloc;
  removable sleeves, yes.
Pulley: 9¼x6¼, 1,078 r.p.m. and 2,600
  f.p.m. at normal engine speed.
Speeds: M.P.H. forward 2½, 3½, 4¾,
  10, and 2¾ reverse on 10-26 rubber
  tires.

CASE "S"
J. I. Case Co., Racine, Wis.

CASE "SC"
J. I. Case Co., Racine, Wis.

Air Cleaner: Oil bath.
Carburetor: Zenith.
Clutch: Disc, toggle action.
Governor: Own, flyball.
Ignition: Magneto.
Lighting: Electric.
Oil Filter: _____
Radiator: Fin and tube.
Radiator Cover: Shutter, extra.
Spark Plugs: 14 mm.
Starting: Optional.
Data: H.P.—Neb. Test No. 367; Max. Belt 22.29; Max. D.B. 19.44; Max. lbs. pull 3166 at 2.29 m.p.h.
Engine: Own "S"; 3½x4, 1,550 r.p.m., 4 cylinders, valve-in-head, cast en bloc, removable sleeves, yes.
Pulley: 9¼x6¼, 1,078 r.p.m. and 2,600 f.p.m. at normal engine speed.
Speeds: M.P.H. forward 2½, 3½, 4¾, 10 and 2¾ reverse on 9-38 rubber tires.

Air Cleaner: Oil bath.
Carburetor: Zenith, 1 in.
Clutch: Disc, toggle action.
Governor: Own, flyball.
Ignition: Magneto.
Lighting: Electric.
Oil Filter: _____
Radiator: Fin and tube.
Radiator Cover: Shutter, extra.
Spark Plugs: 14 mm.
Starting: Optional.
Data: H.P.—Neb. Test No. (not tested). Number of plows recommended: Two, 14 in.
Engine: Own "S"; 3½x4, 1,550 r.p.m., 4 cylinders, valve-in-head, cast en bloc, removable sleeves, yes.
Pulley: 9¼x6¼, 1,078 r.p.m. and 2,600 f.p.m. at normal engine speed.
Speeds: M.P.H. forward 2½, 3½, 4¾, 10, and 2¾ reverse on 10-26 rubber tires.

CASE "SO"
J. I. Case Co., Racine, Wis.

CASE "VO"
J. I. Case Co., Racine, Wis.

Air Cleaner: United, oil wash.
Carburetor: ⅞ in.
Clutch: Dry Plate.
Governor: _____
Ignition: Magneto.
Lighting: Electric.
Oil Filter: _____
Radiator: _____
Radiator Cover: _____
Spark Plugs: 18 mm.
Starting: Electric.
Data: H.P.—Neb. Test No. (not tested). Number of plows recommended:_____
Engine: 3x4⅜, 1,425 r.p.m., 4 cylinders, L-head; removable sleeves, yes.
Pulley: 10¼x6½, 969 r.p.m. and 2,600 f.p.m. at normal engine speed.
Speeds: M.P.H. forward 2.3, 3.1, 4.0, 8.7 (4.7, 10.1 at 1,650 r.p.m.). 1.9 reverse at 1,425 r.p.m.

DEERE & CO.
Moline, Illinois

John Deere Model "LA"

1941-1945

JOHN DEERE MODEL "LA"
Deere & Co., Moline, Ill.

Air Cleaner: United, oil bath.
Carburetor: Marvel-Schebler, ⅞ in.
Clutch: Thelander, dry, single plate.
Governor: Own, centrifugal, variable speed.
Ignition: Edison-Splitdorf, high tension magneto.
Lighting: Guide, battery.
Oil Filter: _____
Radiator: Modine, fin tube.
Spark Plugs: Champion H-10, 14 mm.
Starting: Delco-Remy.
Data: H.P.—Neb. Test No. 373; Max. Belt 14.34; Max. D. B. 13.10; Max. lbs. pull 1,936 at 2.44 m.p.h. Number of plows recommended: One, 16 in.
Engine: Own "LA"; 3½x4, 1,850 r.p.m. 2 cylinders, vertical; cast en bloc.
Pulley: 6¾x6⅜, 1,770 r.p.m. and 3,115 f.p.m. at normal engine speed.
Speeds: M.P.H. forward 2½, 3½, 8 and 2½ reverse.

FERGUSON-SHERMAN MANUFACTURING CO.
Dearborn, Michigan

Ford-Ferguson System 9N

1941-1942

Governor: Novi, variable speed, centrifugal.
Ignition: Own, battery and distributor.
Lighting: Hall electric, extra.
Oil Filter: Ford Fram, renewable waste pack element.
Radiator: Own, fin and tube.
Radiator Cover: None.
Spark Plugs: Champion H9, 14 mm.
Starting: Own, electric.
Data: H.P.—Neb. Test No. 339; Max. Belt 23.56; Max. D.B. 16.31; Max. lbs. pull 2,146 at 2.85 m.p.h. Weight as tested (with operator) 3,375. Number of plows recommended: Two, 14 in.
Engine: Own, 9N; 3.187x3.75; r.p.m., D. B. 1,400; Belt 2,000; 4 cylinders, cast en bloc; removable sleeves.
Pulley: 9x6½, 1,352 r.p.m. and 3,190 f. p.m. at normal engine speed.
Speeds: M.P.H. forward 2.51, 3.23 and 7.48; 2.69 reverse.

Air Cleaner: United, oil bath.
Carburetor: Marvel Schebler, ⅞ in.
Clutch: Long, single dry plate.

FORD-FERGUSON SYSTEM 9N
Ferguson-Sherman Mfg. Corp., Dearborn, Mich.

HUBER MANUFACTURING CO.

Marion, Ohio

Huber "HK" 1941-1944
Huber "HS" 1941-1944

HUBER "HK"
Huber Manufacturing Co., Marion, O.

Air Cleaner: Donaldson, oil bath.
Carburetor: Zenith, 1½ in.
Clutch: Twin Disc, dry plate.
Governor: Waukesha, centrifugal.
Ignition: Bosch, magneto.
Lighting: Delco-Remy.
Oil Filter: DeLuxe.
Radiator: Young, tubular.
Radiator Cover: Own.
Spark Plugs: 3X, ⅞ in.
Starting: Delco-Remy.
Data: H.P.—Neb. Test No. (not tested). Number of plows recommended: **Four to five, 14 in.**
Engine: Waukesha, CHK; 5⅛x6¼, 1,150 r.p.m., 4 cylinders, valve-in-head, **cast en bloc; removable cylinder sleeves, yes.**
Pulley: 17x8½, 616 r.p.m. and 2,840 f. p.m. at normal engine speed.
Speeds: M.P.H. forward 2.32, 3.08, and 1.8 reverse.

Air Cleaner: Donaldson, oil bath.
Carburetor: Zenith, 1½ in.
Clutch: Twin Disc, dry plate.
Governor: Waukesha, centrifugal.
Ignition: Bosch, magneto.
Lighting: Delco-Remy.
Oil Filter: DeLuxe.
Radiator: Young, tubular.
Radiator Cover: Own.
Spark Plugs: 3X, ⅞ in.
Starting: Delco-Remy.
Data: H.P.—Neb. Test No. (not tested). Number of plows recommended: Three to four, 14 in.
Engine: Waukesha, CHS; 4¾x6¼, 1,150 r.p.m., 4 cylinders, overhead valves, cast en bloc; removable cylinder sleeves, yes.
Pulley: 17x8½, 616 r.p.m. and 2,840 f. p.m. at normal engine speed.
Speeds: M.P.H. forward 2.32, 3.08, and 1.8 reverse.

HUBER "HS"
Huber Manufacturing Co., Marion, O.

INTERNATIONAL HARVESTER CO.
Chicago, Illinois

O-4	1941-1947
W-4	1941-1947
International T-9	1941-1956
International Trac Trac Tor T-6	1941-1945
International Trac Trac Tor TD-6	1941-1945
International Trac Trac Tor TD-9	1941-1945
International Trac Trac Tor T-14	1941-1945
International Trac Trac Tor TD-14	1941-1945
McCormick-Deering O-6	1941-1947
McCormick-Deering W-6	1941-1947
McCormick-Deering WD-6	1941-1947
McCormick-Deering W-9	1941-1947
McCormick-Deering WD-9	1941-1947

O-4
International Harvester Co., Chicago, Ill.

Air Cleaner: Donaldson, oil bath.
Carburetor: Own, 1 in.
Clutch: Rockford, single dry disc, over center.
Governor: Own, flyball, variable speed.
Ignition: Own, high tension, automatic impulse magneto.
Lighting: Delco-Remy, special.
Oil Filters: Purolator, replaceable element.
Radiator: Own, fin and tube.
Radiator Cover: Defiance shutter, regular for distillate and special for gas.
Spark Plugs: Champion 15 or AC-87, 18 mm.
Starting: Delco-Remy, special.
Data: H.P.—Neb. Test No. (not tested); H.P. is approximately same as W-4, tests 342 and 353. Number of plows recommended _____
Engine: Own; 3⅜x4¼, 1,650 r.p.m., 4 cylinders, valve-in-head, cast en bloc; removable sleeves, yes.
Pulley: 9¾x7½, 1,019 r.p.m. and 2,601 f.p.m. at normal engine speed. Special.
Speeds: M.P.H. forward 1½, 3⅛, 3⅞, 4⅞, 14⅛, and 1¾ reverse on 11.25-24 tires.

Air Cleaner: Donaldson, oil bath.
Carburetor: Own, 1 in.
Clutch: Rockford, single dry disc, spring loaded.

W-4
International Harvester Co., Chicago, Ill.

Governor: Own, flyball, variable speed.
Ignition: Own, high tension, automatic impulse magneto.
Lighting: Delco-Remy, special.
Oil Filters: Purolator, replaceable element.
Radiator: Own, fin and tube.
Radiator Cover: Defiance shutter, regular for distillate, special for gas.
Spark Plugs: Champion 15 or AC-87, 18 mm.
Starting: Delco-Remy, special.
Data: H.P.—Neb. Test No. 342 (distillate); Max. Belt 23.11; Max. D.B. 21.38; Max. lbs. pull 3,297 at 2.21 m.p.h. Weight as tested (with operator) 5,690 lbs. H.P. Test No. 353 (gasoline); Max. Belt 26.21; Max. D.B. 23.97; Max. lbs. pull 3,671 at 2.16 m.p.h. Weight as tested (with operator) 5,850 lbs.
Engine: Own; 3⅜x4¼, 1,650 r.p.m., 4 cylinders, valve-in-head, cast en bloc; removable sleeves, yes.
Pulley: 9¾x7½, 1,019 r.p.m. and 2,601 f.p.m. at normal engine speed. Special.
Speeds: M.P.H. forward 2¼, 3⅛, 3⅞, 4⅞, 14⅛ and 2⅝ reverse on 11.25-24 tires; 2⅜, 3⅛, 4, 5, and 2¾ reverse on steel wheels.

Clutch: Rockford, single dry disc, over-center, with automatic clutch brake.
Governor: Own, flyball, variable speed.
Ignition: Own, high tension, automatic impulse magneto.
Lighting: Delco-Remy, special.
Oil Filter: Purolator, replaceable element.
Radiator: Own, fin and tube.
Radiator Cover: Defiance, special.
Spark Plugs: Champion 1-Com.-A or AC Tractor 9, 18 mm.
Starting: Delco-Remy, special.
Data: H.P.—Neb. Test No. 372; Max. Belt 46.46; Max. D. B. 40.59; Max. lbs. pull 9,868 at 1.49 m.p.h. Weight as tested (with operator) 10,830 lbs. Number of plows recommended: _____
Engine: Own; 4.4x5.5, 900-1,400 r.p.m., 4 cylinders, valve-in-head, cast en bloc; removable sleeves, yes.
Speeds: M.P.H. forward 1.5, 2.2, 3.2, 3.9, 5.3, and 1.7 reverse.

Air Cleaner: Donaldson, oil bath.
Carburetor: Own, 1⅜ in.

INTERNATIONAL T-9
International Harvester Co., Chicago, Ill.

Ignition: Own, high tension magneto, automatic impulse.

Lighting: Delco-Remy, special.

Oil Filter: Purolator, replaceable element.

Radiator: Own, fin and tube.

Radiator Cover: Defiance shutter, regular for distillate, special for gas.

Spark Plugs: 18 mm. Champion 15 or AC-87.

Starting: Delco-Remy, special.

Data: H.P.—Neb. Test No. 346 (gasoline); Max. Belt 36.96; Max. D.B. 30.85; Max. lbs. pull 7,652 at 1.40 m.p.h. Weight as tested (with operator) 7,680 lbs. Test No. 347 (distillate); Max. Belt 34.54; Max. D.B. 29.53; Max. lbs. pull 7,434 at 1.44 m.p.h. Number of plows recommended:........

Engine: Own; 3⅞x5¼, 950-1,450 r.p.m., 4 cylinders, vertical, valve-in-head, cast en bloc; removable sleeves, yes.

Pulley: 12¼x8, 811 r.p.m. and 2,600 f.p.m. at normal engine speed. Special.

Speeds: M.P.H. forward 1.5, 2.2, 3.1, 3.8, 5.4, and 1.7 reverse.

Air Cleaner: Donaldson, oil.

Carburetor: Own, 1¼ in.

Clutch: Rockford, single plate, over-center, with automatic clutch brake.

Governor: Own, flyball, variable speed.

INTERNATIONAL TRAC TRAC TOR T-6
International Harvester Co., Chicago, Ill.

INTERNATIONAL TRAC TRAC TOR TD-6
International Harvester Co., Chicago, Ill.

Air Cleaner: Donaldson, oil.

Clutch: Rockford, single plate, over-center, with automatic clutch brake.

Diesel: Bosch injection pump.

Governor: Bosch, flyball, variable speed.

Lighting: Delco-Remy, special.

Oil Filter: Purolator, replaceable element.

Radiator: Own, fin and tube.

Radiator Cover: Defiance shutter, special.

Starting: Delco-Remy, special.

Data: H.P.—Neb. Test No. 345; Max. Belt 34.54; Max. D.B. 28.14; Max. lbs. pull 7,160 at 1.40 m.p.h. Weight as tested (with operator) 7,950 lbs. Number of plows recommended:........

Engine: Own; 3⅞x5¼, 800-1,450 r.p.m., 4 cylinders, vertical, valve-in-head, cast en bloc; removable sleeves, yes.

Pulley: 12¼x8, 811 r.p.m. and 2,600 f.p.m., at normal engine speed. Special.

Speeds: M.P.H. forward 1.5, 2.2, 3.1, 3.8, 5.4, and 1.7 reverse.

INTERNATIONAL TRAC TRAC TOR TD-9
International Harvester Co., Chicago, Ill.

Air Cleaner: Donaldson, oil.
Clutch: Rockford, single plate, over-center, with automatic clutch brake.
Diesel: Bosch injection pump.
Governor: Bosch, flyball, variable speed.
Lighting: Delco-Remy, special.
Oil Filter: Purolator, replaceable element.
Radiator: Own, fin and tube.
Radiator Cover: Defiance shutter, special.
Starting: Delco-Remy, special.
Data: H.P.—Neb. Test No. 344; Max. Belt 43.93; Max. D.B. 37.21; Max. lbs. pull 9,014 at 1.43 m.p.h. Weight as tested (with operator) 10,955 lbs. Number of plows recommended:.........
Engine: Own; 4.4x5.5, 800-1,400 r.p.m., 4 cylinders, vertical, valve-in-head; removable sleeves, yes.
Pulley: $11\frac{5}{16}$x9, 878 r.p.m. and 2,600 f. p.m. at normal engine speed, special.
Speeds: M.P.H. forward 1.5, 2.2, 3.2, 3.9, 5.3, and 1.7 reverse.

Air Cleaner: Donaldson, oil.
Carburetor: Zenith, 1½ in.
Clutch: Rockford, single plate, over-center, with automatic clutch brake.
Governor: Own, flyball, variable speed.
Ignition: Own, magneto.
Lighting: Delco-Remy, battery, special.
Oil Filter: Purolator, replaceable element.
Radiator: Own, fin and tube.
Radiator Cover: Defiance shutter, regular for distillate and special for gas.
Spark Plugs: 18 mm. Champion Com.-A or AC-75.
Starting: Delco-Remy, special.
Data: H.P.—Neb. Test No. (not tested); Number of plows recommended:_____
Engine: Own; 4¾x6½, 1,350 r.p.m., 4 cylinders, valve-in-head, cast en bloc; removable sleeves, yes.
Pulley: 12¼x11, 844 r.p.m.
Speeds: M.P.H. forward 1½, 2, 2½, 3⅜, 4¾, 5¾, and 1½, 3⅜ reverse.

INTERNATIONAL TRAC TRAC TOR T-14
International Harvester Co., Chicago, Ill.

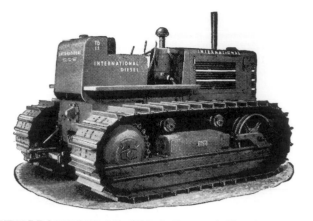

INTERNATIONAL TRAC TRAC TOR TD-14

International Harvester Co., Chicago, Ill.

Air Cleaner: Donaldson, oil.
Clutch: Rockford, single plate, over-center, with automatic clutch brake.
Diesel: Bosch injection pump.
Governor: Bosch, flyball, variable speed.
Lighting: Delco-Remy special.
Oil Filter: Purolator, replaceable element.
Radiator: Own, with circulating pump.
Radiator Cover: Defiance shutter, special.
Starting: Delco-Remy, special.
Data: H.P.—Neb. Test No. 343; Max. Belt 61.56; Max. D.B. 51.82; Max. lbs. pull 13,426 lbs. at 1.44 m.p.h. Weight as tested (with operator) 17,595 lbs. Number of plows recommended:.........
Engine: Own; $4\frac{3}{4}$x$6\frac{1}{2}$, 800-1,350 r.p.m., 4 cylinders, vertical, valve-in-head, cast en bloc; removable sleeves, yes.
Pulley: $12\frac{1}{4}$x11, 844 r.p.m. and 2,706 f.p.m. at normal engine speed. Special.
Speeds: M.P.H. forward 1.5. 2.1, 2.5, 3.4, 4.8, 5.8, and 1.5, 5.4 reverse.

Air Cleaner: Donaldson, oil bath.
Carburetor: Own, $1\frac{1}{4}$ in.
Clutch: Rockford, single dry disc, over center.

McCORMICK-DEERING O-6

International Harvester Co., Chicago, Ill.

Governor: Own, flyball, variable speed.
Ignition: Own, high tension, automatic impulse magneto.
Lighting: Delco-Remy, special.
Oil Filter: Purolator, replaceable element.
Radiator: Own, fin and tube.
Radiator Cover: Defiance shutter, regular for distillate and special for gas.
Spark Plugs: Champion 15 or AC-87, 18 mm.
Starting: Delco-Remy, special.
Data: H.P.—Neb. Test No. (not tested). H.P. approximately same as W-6, tests 354 and 355. Number of plows recommended: _ _ _ _ _ _ _ _ _ _ _ _ _ _ _ _ _
Engine: Own; $3\frac{7}{8}$x$5\frac{1}{4}$, 950-1,450 r.p.m., 4 cylinders, valve-in-head, cast en bloc; removable sleeves, yes.
Pulley: 11x$7\frac{1}{2}$, 899 r.p.m. and 2,588 f.p.m. at normal engine speed, special.
Speeds: M.P.H. forward $1\frac{1}{2}$, 3, 4, $4\frac{7}{8}$, $14\frac{3}{8}$, and $1\frac{3}{4}$ reverse on 12.75-24 tires.

Air Cleaner: Donaldson, oil bath.
Carburetor: Own, 1¼ in.
Clutch: Rockford, single dry disc, spring-loaded.
Governor: Own, flyball, variable speed.
Ignition: Own, high tension, automatic impulse magneto.
Lighting: Delco-Remy, special.
Oil Filter: Purolator, replaceable element.
Radiator: Own, fin and tube.
Radiator Cover: Defiance shutter, regular for distillate and special for gas.
Spark Plugs: Champion 15 or AC-87, 18 mm.
Starting: Delco-Remy, special.
Data: H.P.—Neb. Test No. 354 (distillate); Max. Belt 34.23; Max. D.B. 31.40; Max. lbs. pull 4,755 at 1.96 m. p.h. Weight as tested (with operator) 7,744 lbs. H.P. Test No. 355 (gasoline): Max. Belt 36.97; Max. D.B. 32.48; Max. lbs. pull 4,777 at 1.97 m.p.h. Weight as tested (with operator) 7,610 lbs. Number of plows recommended: ------------------------------------
Engine: Own; 3⅞x5¼, 950-1,450 r.p.m., 4 cylinders, valve-in-head, cast en bloc; removable sleeves, yes.
Pulley: 11x7½, 899 r.p.m. and 2,588 f. p.m. at normal engine speed. Special.
Speeds: M.P.H. forward 2⅜, 3⅛, 4, 4⅞, and 2⅞ reverse on steel; 2¼, 3, 4, 4⅞, 14⅜ forward and 2¾ reverse on 12.75-24 tires.

McCORMICK-DEERING W-6
International Harvester Co., Chicago, Ill.

Diesel: Bosch injection pump.
Governor: Bosch, flyball, variable speed.
Ignition: Own, magneto, for starting only.
Lighting: Delco-Remy, special.
Oil Filter: Purolator, replaceable element.
Radiator: Own, fin and tube.
Radiator Cover: Defiance shutter, special.
Spark Plugs: Champion 49 or AC 18-A, 18 mm., for starting only.
Starting: Delco-Remy, special.
Data: H.P.—Neb. Test No. 356; Max. Belt 34.75; Max. D.B. 31.02; Max. lbs. pull 4,806 at 1.97 m.p.h Weight as tested (with operator) 7,995 lbs. Number of plows recommended: --------------
Engine: Own; 3⅞x5¼, 800-1,450 r.p.m., 4 cylinders, diesel, cast en bloc; removable sleeves, yes.
Pulley: 11x7½, 899 r.p.m. and 2,588 f. p.m. at normal engine speed. Special.
Speeds: M.P.H. forward 2⅜, 3⅛, 4, 4⅞, and 2⅞ reverse on steel; 2¼, 3, 4, 4⅞, 14⅜ and 2¾ reverse on 12.75-24 tires.

Air Cleaner: Donaldson, oil bath.
Carburetor: Own, ¾ in. for starting only.
Clutch: Rockford, single dry disc, spring-loaded.

McCORMICK-DEERING WD-6
International Harvester Co., Chicago, Ill.

Lighting: Delco-Remy, special.

Oil Filter: Purolator, replaceable element.

Radiator: Own, fin and tube.

Radiator Cover: Defiance shutter, regular for distillate and special for gas.

Spark Plugs: Champion 1 Com.-A or AC Tractor 9, ⅞-18.

Starting: Delco-Remy, special.

Data: H.P.—Neb. Test No. 369 (gasoline); Max. Belt 49.40; Max. D. B. 44.15; Max. lbs. pull 6,414 at 1.95 m.p.h. Test No. 371 (distillate): Max. Belt 46.36; Max. D. B. 42.67; Max. lbs. pull 6,577 at 2.02 m.p.h. Number of plows recommended: _____

Engine: Own; 44x5.5, 900-1,500 r.p.m., 4 cylinders, valve-in-head, cast en bloc; removable sleeves, yes.

Pulley: 14x8½, 707 r.p.m. and 2,593 f. p.m. at normal engine speed. Special.

Speeds: M.P.H. forward 2¼, 3, 4¼, 5¼, 15⅛, and 2¾ reverse on 12.75-32 tires; 2¼, 3, 4¼, 5⅛ and 2¾ reverse on steel.

Air Cleaner: Donaldson, oil bath.

Carburetor: Own, 1⅜ in.

Clutch: Own, single dry disc, spring-loaded.

Governor: Own, flyball, variable speed.

Ignition: Own, high tension, automatic impulse magneto.

McCORMICK-DEERING W-9
International Harvester Co., Chicago, Ill.

Air Cleaner: Donaldson, oil bath.

Carburetor: Own, ¾ in., for starting only.

Clutch: Own, single dry disc, spring-loaded.

Diesel: Bosch injection pump.

McCORMICK-DEERING WD-9
International Harvester Co., Chicago, Ill.

Governor: Bosch, flyball, variable speed.

Ignition: Own, magneto, for starting only.

Lighting: Delco-Remy, special.

Oil Filter: Purolator, replaceable element.

Radiator: Own, fin and tube.

Radiator Cover: Defiance shutter, special.

Spark Plugs: Champion 49 or AC 18-A, ⅞-18, for starting only.

Starting: Delco-Remy, special.

Data: H.P.—Neb. Test No. 370; Max. Belt 46.43; Max. D. B. 42.57; Max. lbs. pull 6,367 at 1.98 m.p.h. Weight as tested (with operator) 10,260 lbs. Number of plows recommended: _____

Engine: Own; 4.4x5.5, 800-1,500 r.p.m., 4 cylinders, diesel, cast en bloc; removable sleeves, yes.

Pulley: 14x8½, 707 r.p.m. and 2,593 f. p.m. at normal engine speed, special.

Speeds: M.P.H. forward 2¼, 3, 4¼, 5¼, 14⅛, and 2¾ reverse on 12.75-32 tires; same on steel except high speed omitted.

MASSEY-HARRIS CO.

Racine, Wisconsin

Massey-Harris "81"   1941-1946
Massey-Harris "201" Distillate   1941
Massey-Harris "202"   1941-1942

MASSEY-HARRIS "81"

Massey-Harris Co., Racine, Wis.

Air Cleaner: Donaldson, 4⅜.
Carburetor: Schebler, ⅞ in.
Clutch: Borg & Beck, single plate, foot operated.
Governor: Pierce, centrifugal.
Ignition: Auto-Lite, battery.
Lighting: _____
Oil Filter: Purolator.
Radiator: Modine, tubular.
Radiator Cover: _____
Spark Plugs: Auto-Lite B-7—5 Champion.
Starting: Auto-Lite.
Data: H.P.—Neb. Test No. 376; Max. Belt 27.07; Max. D.B. 20.79; Max. lbs. pull 2,898 at 2.19 m.p.h. Number of Plows Recommended: Two, 14 in
Engine: Continental, F124; 3x4⅜; r.p.m. 1,500 D.B. and 1,800 Belt; 4 cylinders, vertical, cast en bloc; removable sleeves, no.
Pulley: 9½x6, 1,224 r.p.m. and 3,044 f. p.m. at normal engine speed.
Speeds: M.P.H. forward 2.5, 3.6, 4.7, 16 and 2.5 reverse.

Air Cleaner: United, oil.
Carburetor: Schebler, 1¼ in.
Clutch: Borg & Beck, dry disc.
Governor: Pierce, centrifugal.
Ignition: Auto-Lite, battery.
Lighting: _____
Oil Filter: Purolator.
Radiator: Modine, tubular.
Radiator Cover: _____
Spark Plugs: _____
Starting: Auto-Lite.
Data: H.P.—Neb. Test No. (not tested). Number of plows recommended: Four to five 14 in.
Engine: Continental; 4x4⅜; r.p.m. 1,700 D.B., 2,000 Belt; 6 cylinders, vertical, cast en bloc; removable sleeves, yes.
Pulley: 13½x8, 839 r.p.m. and 2,962 f. p.m. at normal engine speed.
Speeds: M.P.H. forward 2.46, 3.51, 4.32, 12.7 and 2¼ reverse.

MASSEY-HARRIS "201" DISTILLATE

Massey-Harris Co., Racine, Wis.

MASSEY-HARRIS "202"

Massey-Harris Co., Racine, Wis.

Air Cleaner: United, oil.
Carburetor: Schebler, 1¼ in.
Clutch: Borg & Beck, dry disc.
Governor: Pierce, centrifugal.
Ignition: Auto-Lite, battery.
Lighting: _____
Oil Filter: Purolator.
Radiator: Modine, tubular.
Radiator Cover: _____
Spark Plugs: _____
Starting: Auto-Lite.
Data: H.P.—Neb. Test No. (not tested). Number of plows recommended: Four to five, 14 in.
Engine: Continental, M290; 3¾x4⅜; r.p.m. 1,700 D.B. 2,000 Belt; 6 cylinders, vertical, cast en bloc; removable sleeves, yes.
Pulley: 13½x8, 839 r.p.m. and 2,962 f. p.m. at normal engine speed.
Speeds: M.P.H. forward 2.46, 3.51, 4.32, 12.7 and 2¼ reverse.

MINNEAPOLIS-MOLINE POWER IMPLEMENT CO.

Minneapolis, Minnesota

MM Twin City "RTN"	1941-1948
MM Twin City "ZTN"	1941-1948

MM TWIN CITY "RTN"
Minneapolis-Moline Power Impl. Co.,
Minneapolis, Minn.

Air Cleaner: United, Oil wash.
Carburetor: Schebler, 1 in. S.A.E. flange.
Clutch: Twin Disc, O. C.
Governor: Own, flyball, V.S.
Ignition: Fairbanks-Morse magneto.
Lighting: Delco (optional).
Oil Filter: Michiana, removable waste type.
Radiator: Modine.
Radiator Cover: _____
Spark Plugs: Champion, J8, Std. C.R.
Starting: Delco (optional).
Data: H.P.—Neb. Test No. (not tested). Number of plows recommended:_____
Engine: Own, EE; 3⅝x4, 1,400 r.p.m., 4 cylinders, cast in pairs; removable cylinders.
Pulley: 12¼x6, 933 r.p.m. and 2,990 f. p.m. at normal engine speed.
Speeds: M.P.H. forward 2.3, 3.3, 4.2, 12, and 2.6 reverse.

MM TWIN CITY "ZTN"
Minneapolis-Moline Power Impl. Co.,

Air Cleaner: United, oil wash.
Carburetor: Schebler, 1 in.
Clutch: Twin Disc, O. C.
Governor: Own, flyball, V.S.
Ignition: Fairbanks-Morse, magneto.
Lighting: Delco (optional).
Oil Filter: Michiana, renewable waste type.
Radiator: Modine.
Radiator Cover: _____
Spark Plugs: Champion, J8 for Std. C.R.
Starting: Delco (optional).
Data: H.P.—Neb. Test No. (not tested). Number of plows recommended:_____
Engine: Own, RE; 3⅝x4½, 1,500 r.p.m., 4 cylinders, cast in pairs; removable cylinders.
Pulley: 14x7, 786 r.p.m. and 2,880 f.p.m. at normal engine speed.
Speeds: M.P.H. forward 2.2, 2.7, 3.7, 4.7, 14.6, and 1.1 reverse.

OLIVER FARM EQUIPMENT CO.
Tractor Division
Charles City, Iowa

Oliver Row Crop "60" HC   1941-1948

OLIVER ROW CROP "60" HC
Oliver Farm Equipment Co.,
Tractor Div., Charles City, Ia.

Air Cleaner: Donaldson, oil wash.
Carburetor: Schebler, 1 in.
Clutch: Borg & Beck, 8", single plate, dry.
Governor: Own, centrifugal, flyball, variable speed.
Ignition: Wico high tension, vertical magneto.
Lighting: Delco-Remy-Guide Lamp, electric, storage battery.
Oil Filter: Michiana.
Radiator: Modine, fin tube.
Radiator Cover: Own.
Spark Plugs: Champion, 5 Comm.
Starting: Delco-Remy.
Data: H.P.—Neb. Test No. 375; Max. Belt 18.76; Max. D.B. 16.92; Max. lbs. pull 2,496 at 2.28 m.p.h. Weight as tested (with operator) 4,040 lbs. No. of plows recommended: One to two, 14 in.
Engine: Own; 3 5/16x3½, 1,500 r.p.m., 4 cylinders, vertical, cast en bloc; removable sleeves, yes.
Pulley: 10x5½, 647-1,143 r.p.m. and 1,700-3,000 f.p.m. at normal engine speed.
Speeds: M.P.H. forward 2.58, 3.45, 4.57, 6.10, and 3.32 reverse.

POND GARDEN TRACTOR CO.
Ravenna, Ohio

Speedex Model B   1941-1946

SPEEDEX MODEL B
Pond Garden Tractor Co., Ravenna, O.

Air Cleaner: United, oil bath.
Carburetor: Briggs & Stratton, 15/16 in.
Clutch: _____
Governor: Briggs & Stratton, gear driven, centrifugal.
Ignition: Briggs & Stratton, flywheel enclosed magneto.
Oil Filter: _____
Radiator: _____
Spark Plugs: Champion 6M.
Engine: Briggs & Stratton ZZ; 3x3¼, 2,200-3,200 r.p.m., 1 cylinder.

Figuring Pulley Sizes and Speeds

The diameter of the tractor pulley times its r.p.m. gives what is known as the "belt constant," so called because it is a virtually constant quantity. Dividing the belt constant by the desired speed gives the diameter of the driven pulley necessary to maintain this speed. This is expressed by the formula

$$\frac{D \times R}{r} = d$$

in which D is the diameter of the tractor pulley; R, its speed in r.p.m.; r, the r.p.m. of the driven pulley, and d, the diameter of the driven pulley.

For instance, it is desired to operate an ensilage machine at a speed of 700 r.p.m. with a tractor having a 14-inch pulley which operates at 900 r.p.m. According to this formula, 900(R)x14(D), which is the belt constant, divided by 700(r), equals d. In this case 900x14 is 12,600, the belt constant, and 12,600 ÷ 700 is 18, the size of the driven pulley.

When any three quantities are known, the foregoing formula can be transformed and the fourth quantity ascertained.

This calculation makes no allowance for slippage of the belt. This will usually amount to from 3 to 5 per cent. This can be allowed for either by slightly decreasing the size of the driven pulley or by slightly increasing the speed of the motor.

1941

1942

In 1942, seven models of three makes were announced, the drop in action taking place because of the need to maintain equipment production at an adequate level under war conditions and still provide means to maintain the growing military needs.

J. I. CASE CO.

Racine, Wisconsin

Case "SI"   1942-1948
Case "LAI"   1942-1948

CASE "SI"
J. I. Case Co., Racine, Wis.

Air Cleaner: Oil bath.
Carburetor: Zenith.
Clutch: Single plate.
Governor: Own, flyball.
Ignition: Magneto.
Lighting: Electric.
Oil Filter: Purolator (extra).
Radiator: Fin and tube.
Radiator Cover: Shutter, extra.
Spark Plugs: 14 mm.
Starting: Extra.
Data: H.P.—Neb. Test No. (not tested). Number of plows recommended_____
Engine: Own "S"; 3½ x 4, 1,550 r.p.m., 4 cylinders, valve-in-head, cast en bloc; removable sleeves, yes.
Pulley: _____
Speeds: M.P.H. forward 2½, 3½, 4¾, 9¾ and 2¾ reverse on 10-26 tires.

Air Cleaner: Own, oil bath.
Carburetor: Zenith.
Clutch: Disc.
Governor: Own, flyball.
Ignition: Own, magneto.
Lighting: Electric.
Oil Filter: Purolator (extra).
Radiator: Fin and tube.
Radiator Cover: Shutter and Screen.
Spark Plugs: ⅞ in.
Starting: Electric (extra).
Data: H.P.—Neb. Test No. (not tested).
Engine: Own "LA"; 4⅝x6, 1,100 r.p.m., 4 cylinders, valve-in-head, cast en bloc, removable sleeves, yes.
Pulley: 13x8¼, 779 r.p.m. and 2,660 f. p.m. at normal engine speed.
Speeds: M.P.H. forward 2.81, 3.85, 4.78, 10.6, and 3.08 reverse on 15-28 low pressure tires.

CASE "LAI"
J. I. Case Co., Racine, Wis.

DEERE & CO.

Moline, Illinois

John Deere Model "LI"   1942-1944

JOHN DEERE MODEL "LI"
Deere & Co., Moline, Ill.

Air Cleaner: United, oil bath.
Carburetor: Marvel-Schebler, ⅞ in.
Clutch: Thelander, dry, single plate.
Governor: Own, centrifugal, variable speed.
Ignition: Wico, high tension magneto.
Lighting: Guide, battery.
Oil Filter: _____
Radiator: Modine, fin tube.
Radiator Cover: _____
Spark Plugs: Champion H-10, 14 mm.
Starting: Delco-Remy.
Data: H.P.—Neb. Test No. (not tested).
Engine: Own "LI"; 3½x4, 1,550 r.p.m., 2 cylinders, vertical, cast en bloc.
Pulley: 6¾x6⅜, 1,480 r.p.m. and 2,615 f.p.m. at normal engine speed.
Speeds: M.P.H. forward 3, 4¼, 8½. Transporting speeds 13 to 16 m.p.h.; 2½ reverse.

MASSEY-HARRIS CO.
Racine, Wisconsin

Massey-Harris "82" Std.   1942-1946
Massey-Harris Distillate "102" Jr.   1942-1946
Massey-Harris "102" Sr. Std.   1942-1946
Massey-Harris "203" Distillate   1942-1946

Air Cleaner: Donaldson, 4⅜.
Carburetor: Schebler, ⅞ in.
Clutch: Borg & Beck, single plate, foot operated.
Governor: Pierce, centrifugal.
Ignition: Auto-Lite, battery.
Lighting: K. D. Electric.
Oil Filter: Purolator.
Radiator: Modine, tubular.
Radiator Cover: Pines.
Spark Plugs: Auto-Lite, B-7, 5 Champion.
Starting: Auto-Lite.
Data: H.P.—Neb. Test No. (not tested). Number of plows recommended: Two, 14 in.
Engine: Continental F-140; $3\frac{3}{16}$x4⅜; 1,500 D.B., 1,800 belt r.p.m., 4 cylinders, vertical, cast en bloc; removable sleeves, no.
Pulley: 9½x6¼, 1,224 r.p.m. and 3,044 f.p.m. at normal engine speed.
Speeds: M.P.H. forward 2.5, 3.6, 4.7, 16.0, and 2.5 reverse.

MASSEY-HARRIS "82" STD. (Dist.)
Massey-Harris Co., Racine, Wis.

MASSEY-HARRIS DISTILLATE "102" JR.
Massey-Harris Co., Racine, Wis.

Air Cleaner: Donaldson, dry.
Carburetor: Marvel-Schebler, 1 in.
Clutch: Borg & Beck, dry.
Governor: Pierce, centrifugal.
Ignition: Electro-magneto.
Oil Filter: Purolator.
Radiator: Modine, tubular.
Radiator Cover: Pines Winterfront.
Spark Plugs: Auto-Lite A-7.
Starting: _____
Data: H.P.—Neb. Test No. (not tested). Number of plows recommended: Two, 16 in.
Engine: Continental; $3\frac{7}{16}$x4⅜, 1,500-1,800 r.p.m., 4 cylinders, cast en bloc; removable sleeves, no.
Pulley: 13½x6, 837 r.p.m. and 2,958 f.p.m. at normal engine speed.
Speeds: M.P.H. forward 2.5, 3.4, 4.3, 16.4, and 2.2 reverse.

Air Cleaner: United, oil.
Carburetor: Marvel-Schebler, 1 in.
Clutch: Borg & Beck, dry disc.
Governor: Novi, centrifugal.
Ignition: Electro-magneto.
Lighting: K. D. Electric.
Oil Filter: Purolator.
Radiator: Modine, tubular.
Radiator Cover: Pines.
Spark Plugs: Auto-Lite, A-7.
Starting: _____
Data: H.P.—Neb. Test No. (not tested).
Number of plows recommended: Three,
14 in.
Engine: Continental A-244; $3\frac{7}{16}$x4⅜,
1,600 D.B., 1,900 belt r.p.m.; 6 cylin-
ders, vertical, cast en bloc; removable
sleeves, no.
Pulley: 13½x6¼, 885 r.p.m. and 3,124
f.p.m. at 1,900 engine speed.
Speeds: M.P.H. forward 2.56, 3.58, 4.45,
17.0, and 2.29 reverse.

MASSEY-HARRIS "102" SR. STD.
(Distillate)
Massey-Harris Co., Racine, Wis.

MASSEY-HARRIS "203" DISTILLATE

Massey-Harris Co., Racine, Wis.

Air Cleaner: United, oil.
Carburetor: Schebler, 1¼ in.
Clutch: Borg & Beck, dry disc.
Governor: Pierce, centrifugal.
Ignition: Electro-magneto.
Lighting: _____
Oil Filter: Purolator.
Radiator: Modine, tubular.
Radiator Cover: _____
Spark Plugs: _____
Starting: _____
Data: H.P.—Neb. Test No. (not tested).
Number of plows recommended: Four
to five 14 in.
Engine: Continental; 4x4⅜; r.p.m. 1,700
D.B., 2,000 Belt; 6 cylinders, vertical,
cast en bloc; removable sleeves, no.
Pulley: 13½x8, 839 r.pm. and 2,962 f.
p.m. at normal engine speed.
Speeds: M.P.H. forward 2.46, 3.51, 4.32,
12.7 and 2¼ reverse.

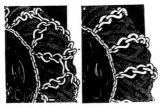

1943

In 1943, nine models of seven makes were announced, including the John Deere "GM" and Harry Ferguson 9N. Part of the confusion connected with the wartime red tape is illustrated in the story of the Ford-Ferguson 2N first listed in 1944. Potential equipment shortages required that certain components be placed on the "available" list to provide a magneto assembly and steel wheels for alternative use if needed. The problem was solved by providing a new model (2N) which would be substituted for the 9N, the 2N being the same tractor as the 9N with only the steel wheels, magneto, and attaching units included. The alternative "Model Number" remains on the records although never actually used in production.

B. F. AVERY & SONS CO.
Louisville, Kentucky

B. F. Avery "A"   1943-1950

Air Cleaner: Vortox "R," oil bath.
Carburetor: Tillotson, ⅞ in.
Clutch: Long, single plate, dry.
Governor: Hercules-Handy, flyball.
Ignition: Wico.
Lighting: Auto-Lite.
Oil Filter: Michiana.
Radiator: McCord, tube and fin.
Radiator Cover: None.
Spark Plugs: Champion No. 1, Com.
Starting: Auto-Lite.
Data: H.P.—Neb. Test No. (not tested). Number of plows recommended: One 16 in. or two 12 in.
Engine: Hercules "IXK"; 3⅛x4, 1450 r.p.m., 4 cylinders, L-head, cast en bloc, removable sleeves, no.
Pulley: 8½x6½, 1035 r.p.m. at normal engine speed.
Speeds: M.P.H. forward 2.25, 3.50, 6.00 and 2.50 reverse.

B. F. AVERY "A"
B. F. Avery & Sons Co., Louisville, Ky.

J. I. CASE CO.
Racine, Wisconsin

Case "VA"	1943-1956
Case "VAC"	1943-1956
Case "VAI"	1943-1948

CASE "VA"
J. I. Case Co., Racine, Wis.

Air Cleaner: Oil wash.
Carburetor: Marvel-Schebler.
Clutch: Spring loaded.
Governor: Flyball.
Ignition: Own, magneto or distributor.
Lighting: Electric.
Oil Filter: _____
Radiator: _____
Radiator Cover: _____
Spark Plugs: 18 mm.
Starting: Electric, extra.
Data: H.P.—Neb. Test No. (not tested). Number of plows recommended: One to two, 14 in.
Engine: 3¼ x 3¾, 1425 r.p.m.; 4 cylinders, valve-in-head, removable sleeves.
Pulley: 10¼ x 6¼, 1105 r.p.f. and 2600 f.p. m. at normal engine speed.
Speeds: M.P.H. forward 2¼, 3¼, 4¼, 8¾, and 3.32 reverse.

CASE "VAI"
J. I. Case Co., Racine, Wis.

Air Cleaner: Oil wash.
Carburetor: Marvel-Schebler.
Clutch: Spring loaded.
Governor: Flyball.
Ignition: Own, magneto or distributor.
Lighting: Electric.
Oil Filter: _____
Radiator: _____
Radiator Cover: _____
Spark Plugs: 18 mm.
Starting: Electric, extra.
Data: H.P.—Neb. Test No. (not tested). Number of plows recommended: One to two 14 in.
Engine: 3¼ x 3¾, 1425 r.p.m.; 4 cylinders, valve-in-head, removable sleeves.
Pulley: 10¼ x 6, 969 r.p.m. and 2600 f.p. m. at loaded engine speed.
Speeds: M.P.H. forward 2¼, 2¾, 3¾, 8, and 3 reverse.

CASE "VAC"
J. I. Case Co., Racine, Wis.

Air Cleaner: Oil wash.
Carburetor: Marvel-Schebler.
Clutch: Spring loaded.
Governor: Own, flyball,
Ignition: Own, magneto or distributor.
Lighting: Electric.
Oil Filter: Michiana, extra.
Radiator: _____
Radiator Cover: _____
Spark Plugs: 18 mm.
Starting: Electric, extra.
Data: H.P.—Neb. Test No. (not tested). Number of plows recommended:_____
Engine: 3¼ x 3¾, 1425 r.p.m., 4 cylinders, valve-in-head, removable sleeves.
Pulley: 10¼ x 6, 969 r.p.m. and 2600 f.p. m. at loaded engine speed, extra.
Speeds: M.P.H. forward 2.8, 4.9, 6.4, 15.2, and 4 reverse.

HELP FOR

Owners report: "Plows an acre an hour on a gallon of fuel"—with Ferguson 2-bottom plow. 93% of all Ferguson plows used are this type—mostly 14-inch.

Even though current production of the Ford Tractor with Ferguson System is rationed, there will still be new help available for the hard-pressed, short-handed farmer.

With rubber tires for new tractors no longer to be had, today's production is on steel tires. But because the Ferguson System was originally engineered for steel tires, its comparative outstanding efficiency remains unchanged.

The Ford Tractor with Ferguson System has proved its ability to do more farm work in less time and at less cost—on steel tires—than any other farm equipment in its class.

THE FORD TRACTOR WITH FERGUSON

FARMERS

"We plow 14½ acres a day, on 13 gallons of gas — averaging less than a gallon an acre, even with a 3-bottom plow — one third of our former operating cost."

Fred C. Bowles,
Groton, S. Dak.

Here is one light-weight all-purpose tractor that steel tires have not forced off the market — a fact made possible by the rugged construction of the tractor and by the exclusive advantages of the Ferguson System.

HARRY FERGUSON, INC.
Dearborn, Michigan

Ford Tractor

FERGUSON SYSTEM

© Ford Motor Co.

SYSTEM PROVED ON STEEL TIRES

DEERE & CO.
Moline, Illinois

John Deere General Purpose Model "GM"   1943-1946

Air Cleaner: Donaldson, oil washed.
Carburetor: Marvel-Schebler, 1¼ in., venturi.
Clutch: Own, dry disk, hand operated.
Governor: Own, centrifugal, variable speed.
Ignition: Wico, high tension, enclosed impulse.
Lighting: Delco-Remy, battery.
Oil Filter: Purolator.
Radiator: Modine, fin tube.
Radiator Cover: Pines Winterfront, dash controlled.
Spark Plugs: 18 mm.
Starting: Delco-Remy.
Data: H.P.—Neb. Test No. (not tested). Number of plows recommended: Three, 14 in.
Engine: Own "GM"; 6⅛x7, 975 r.p.m., 2 cylinders, horizontal, cast en bloc.
Pulley: 12¾x8½, 975 r.p.m. and 3,270 f.p.m. at normal engine speed.
Speeds: M.P.H. forward 1-2½, 2-3½, 3-4½, 4-6⅓, 5-8½, 6-12, and 3¼ reverse.

JOHN DEERE GENERAL PURPOSE MODEL "GM"
Deere & Co., Moline, Ill.

HARRY FERGUSON, INC.
Dearborn, Michigan

Ford-Ferguson System 9N   1943

Air Cleaner: United, oil bath.
Carburetor: Marvel Schebler, ⅞ in.
Clutch: Long, single dry plate.

FORD-FERGUSON SYSTEM 9N
Harry Ferguson, Inc., Dearborn, Mich.

Governor: Novi, variable speed, centrifugal.
Ignition: Own, battery and distributor.
Lighting: Hall electric, extra.
Oil Filter: Ford Fram, renewable waste pack element.
Radiator: Own, fin and tube.
Radiator Cover: None.
Spark Plugs: Champion H9, 14 mm.
Starting: Own, electric.
Data: H.P.—Neb. Test No. 339; Max. Belt 23.56; Max. D.B. 16.31; Max. lbs. pull 2,146 at 2.85 m.p.h. Weight as tested (with operator) 3,375. Number of plows recommended: Two, 14 in.
Engine: Own, 9N; 3.187x3.75; r.p.m., D. B. 1,400; Belt 2,000; 4 cylinders, cast en bloc; removable sleeves.
Pulley: 9x6½, 1,352 r.p.m. and 3,190 f. p.m. at normal engine speed.
Speeds: M.P.H. forward 2.51, 3.23 and 7.48; 2.69 reverse at 1400 r.p.m.

MASSEY-HARRIS CO.
Racine, Wisconsin

Massey-Harris "203G"

Air Cleaner: United, oil.
Carburetor: Schebler, 1¼ in.
Clutch: Borg & Beck, dry disc.
Governor: Pierce, centrifugal.
Ignition: Electro-magneto.
Lighting: _____
Oil Filter: Purolator.
Radiator: Modine, tubular.
Radiator Cover: _____
Spark Plugs: _____
Starting: _____
Data: H.P.—Neb. Test No. (not tested).
Number of plows recommended: Four
to five, 14 in.
Engine: Continental, M330; 4x4⅜; r.p.m.
1,700 D.B. 2,000 Belt; 6 cylinders, ver-
tical, cast en bloc; removable sleeves,
no.
Pulley: 13½x8, 839 r.p.m. and 2,962 f.
p.m. at normal engine speed.
Speeds: M.P.H. forward 2.46, 3.51, 4.32,
12.7 and 2¼ reverse.

MASSEY-HARRIS "203G"

Massey-Harris Co., Racine, Wis.

MINNEAPOLIS-MOLINE POWER IMPLEMENT CO.
Minneapolis, Minnesota

MM Model "GTA"

Air Cleaner: Donaldson, oil wash.
Carburetor: Schebler, 1¼ in.
Clutch: Twin Disc, over center.
Governor: Own, flyball, variable speed.
Ignition: Fairbanks-Morse, magneto.
Lighting: Optional; Delco-Remy, 6-volt.
Oil Filter: H-W, renewable waste type.
Radiator: Modine.
Radiator Cover: _____
Spark Plugs: Champion O, ⅞ in. Std. CR.
Starting: Optional; Delco-Remy.
Data: H.P.—Neb. Test No. (not tested).
Number of plows recommended: _____
Engine: Own LE; 4⅝x6, 1,075 r.p.m., 4
cylinders, vertical, cast in removable
pairs; removable sleeves, no.
Pulley: 16x7½, 650 r.p.m. and 2,720 f.p.
m. at normal engine speed.
Speeds: M.P.H. forward 2.8, 3.9, 4.9, 9.9,
and 2.9 reverse.

MM MODEL "GTA"
Minneapolis-Moline Power Impl. Co.,
Minneapolis, Minn.

OLIVER FARM EQUIPMENT CO.
Tractor Division
Charles City, Iowa

Oliver Standard "60" HC   1943-1948

Air Cleaner: Donaldson, oil wash.
Carburetor: Schebler, 1 in.
Clutch: Borg & Beck, 8 in. single plate, dry.
Governor: Own, centrifugal, flyball, variable speed.
Ignition: Wico high tension vertical magneto.
Lighting: Delco-Remy-Guide Lamp, electric, battery.
Oil Filter: Michiana.
Radiator: Modine, fin tube.
Radiator Cover: Own.
Spark Plugs: Champion, 5 Com.
Starting: Delco-Remy.
Data: H.P.—Neb. Test No. (not tested). Number of plows recommended: One or two, 14 in.
Engine: Own; $3\frac{5}{16}$x$3\frac{1}{2}$, 1,500 r.p.m., 4 cylinders, vertical, cast en bloc; removable sleeves, yes.
Pulley: 10x$5\frac{1}{2}$, 647-1,143 r.p.m. and 1,700-3,000 f.p.m. at normal engine speed.
Speeds: M.P.H. forward $2\frac{1}{2}$, $3\frac{1}{2}$, $4\frac{1}{2}$, 6, and $3\frac{1}{4}$ reverse.

OLIVER STANDARD "60" HC
Oliver Farm Equipment Co.,
Tractor Div., Charles City, Ia.

HORSEPOWER OR HORSES

CASE

ANY BREED—
"It's how you feed 'em that counts!"

Popular Zenith 62 Series, tractor model

A TRACTOR can get "off its feed" just as easily as the old "hay-burner" . . . and the result is just the same—lost pulling power.

Tractor engineers know that Zenith Carburetors provide a good, wholesome diet for engines that face the tough service of a tractor. High temperatures, heavy fuels, high engine speeds, low vehicle speeds, rough going, dust—what a life!

Zenith is engineered to take these things in its stride and deliver top economy.

Every tractor dealer should be set up to sell and service Zenith Carburetors. There's profit in it, and it builds up good will for other business. Write—

ZENITH CARBURETOR DIVISION
Bendix Aviation Corporation
696 Hart Avenue • Detroit, Michigan

Readily Installed by any intelligent mechanic

ZENITH CARBURETORS

Air Cleaner: Donaldson, oil bath.
Battery: Auto-Lite (special).
Brakes: Two; operated by foot pedals, individually or locked together.
Carburetor: Own, 1¼ in.
Clutch: Rockford, single plate, dry disc, spring-loaded.
Generator: Delco-Remy (special).
Governor: Own, centrifugal, variable speed.
Ignition: Own, high tension magneto with automatic impulse coupling.
Lamps: Guide Lamp (special).
Lighting: Delco-Remy (special).
Oil Filter: Purolator, replaceable element.
Radiator: Own or McCord, fin and flat tube.
Radiator Cover: Hardy shutter.
Spark Plugs: Champion 15-A or AC-87, 18 m.m.
Starting: Delco-Remy (special).
Data: H.P.—Neb. Test No. (not tested). Horsepower is approximtely the same as Farmall M, test Nos. 328 and 327. Number of Plows Recommended: three, 14 in.
Engine: Own; 3⅞x5¼, 1450 r.p.m., 4 cylinders, vertical, valve-in-head, cast en bloc; piston displacement 247.7 cu. in.
Pulley: 11x7½, 899 r.p.m. and 2588 f.p.m. at normal engine speed (special).
Speeds: M.P.H. forward 2½, 3⅜, 4⅛, 5, 16 and 3⅛ reverse on 10.00-36 tires.

McCORMICK-DEERING FARMALL MV
International Harvester Co., Chicago, Ill.

McCORMICK-DEERING OS-4

Air Cleaner: Donaldson, oil bath.
Battery: Auto-Lite (special).
Brakes: Two, operated by foot pedals, individually.
Carburetor: Own, 1-in.
Clutch: Rockford, single plate, dry disc, over center.
Generator: Delco-Remy (special).
Governor: Own, certrifugal, variable speed.
Ignition: Own, high tension magneto with automatic impulse coupling.
Lamps: Guide Lamp (special).
Oil Filter: Purolator, replaceable element.
Radiator: Own, fin and flat tube.
Radiator Cover: Hardy shutter.
Spark Plugs: Champion 15-A or AC-87, 18 m.m.
Starting: Delco-Remy (special).
Data: H.P.—Neb. Test No. (not tested). Horsepower is approximately the same as W-4, tests 342 and 353. Number of plows recommended: two, 14-in.
Engine: Own; 3⅜x4¼, 1650 r.p.m., 4 cylinders, vertical, valve-in-head, cast en bloc; piston displacement 152.1 cu. in.; removable sleeves, yes.
Pulley: 9¾x7½, 1019 r.p.m. and 2601 f.p.m. at normal engine speed.
Speeds: M.P.H. forward 1½, 3, 3⅞, 4⅞, 14, and 1⅝ reverse on 11-26 tires.

Air Cleaner: Donaldson, oil bath.
Battery: Auto-Lite (special).
Brakes: Two; operated by foot pedals, individually.
Carburetor: Own, 1¼-in.
Clutch: Rockford, single plate, dry disc, over center.
Generator: Delco-Remy (special).
Governor: Own, centrifugal, variable speed.
Ignition: Own, high tension magneto with automatic impulse coupling.
Lamps: Guide Lamp (special).
Oil Filter: Purolator, replaceable element.
Radiator: Own, fin and flat tube.
Radiator Cover: Hardy shutter.
Spark Plugs: Champion 15-A or AC 87, 18 m.m.
Starting: Delco-Remy (special).
Data: H.P.—Neb. Test No. (not tested). Horsepower is approximately the same as W-6, tests 354 and 355. Number of plows recommended: three, 14-in.
Engine: Own, 3⅞x5¼, 1450 r.p.m., 4 cylinders, vertical, valve-in-head, cast en bloc; piston displacement 247.7 cu. in. Removable sleeves, yes.
Pulley: 11x7½, 899 r.p.m. and 2588 f.p.m. at normal engine speed.

Speeds: M.P.H. forward 1½, 3, 3⅞, 4¾, 14, and 1¾ reverse on 12-26 tires.

McCORMICK-DEERING OS-6
International Harvester Co., Chicago, Ill.

THE OLIVER CORP.
Cletrac Division

Cleveland, Ohio

Cletrac "FDE"   1946-1948

Air Cleaner: Vortox, oil bath and wire screen.
Battery: Willard, RHD-25-6.
Brakes: Two; operated by hand.
Clutch: Long, 17 plate, single, dry.
Diesel: American Bosch, injection pump.
Generator: Delco-Remy.
Governor: Hercules, flyball.
Lamps: Corcoran Brown.
Lighting: 12-volt Delco-Remy.
Oil Filter: Purolator.
Radiator: Modine, tube and fin.
Radiator Cover: ....
Starting: Delco-Remy, 24 volts.
Data: H.P.—Neb. Test No. (not tested). Manufacturers rating: Max. Belt 146; Max. D.B. 120.5; Max. pounds pull 28,600 at 1.61 m.p.h. Weight 29,760 lbs. Number of plows recommended: Twelve to fourteen, 14 in.
Engine: Hercules, DFXE; 5⅝x6, 1,300 r.p.m., 6 cylinders, valve-in-head, cast in pairs; piston displacement 895 cu. in.; removable sleeves, yes.
Pulley: 24½x15, 535 r.p.m. and 3,350 f.p.m. at normal engine speed.
Speeds: M.P.H. forward 1.61, 2.75, 3.66, 5 and 1.58, 2.82 reverse.

CLETRAC "FDE"
The Oliver Corp., Cletrac Div., Cleveland, O.

1947

The 1947 list includes 36 models of nine makes. A newcomer, home from the war, is synthetic rubber which has been improved as experience is gained. New in the equipment line, is the Economy tractor manufactured by Engineering Products Co. of Milwaukee, Wisconsin, and powered by a Briggs & Stratton engine. Also beginning to come into limited use as a fuel was LP gas.

1947 is also noted as the year in which Henry Ford, in the United States, and Harry Ferguson, in England, abrogated their verbal agreement which had produced 258,000 tractors over a period of five years. As a result of the argument, Ferguson sued Ford for $342 million, but settled in 1953 for $9 1/4 million. The Ferguson tractor was built in England at the time. The first TE-20 (made in England) was produced in 1948 as was the first Ford 8N.

AERCO CORP.

Hollydale, California

Earthmaster "C"	1947
Earthmaster "CH"	1947
Earthmaster "S"	1947

EARTHMASTER "C" and "CH"
Aerco Corp., Hollydale, Calif.

Air Cleaner: Vortox.
Battery: Auto-Lite.
Brakes: Two, operated by foot, individually or simultaneously.
Carburetor: Zenith, ⅝-in.
Clutch: Auburn, 6½-in.
Generator: Auto-Lite.
Governor: Continental, built-in.
Radiator: McCord.
Spark Plugs: Auo-Lite B7 or Champion 7 Com.
Data: H.P.—Neb. test No.; not tested.
Number of Plows Recommended: One, 14-in.
Engine: Continental N-62; 2⅔x3½, 1800 r.p.m., 4 cylinders, L Head.
Piston Displacement: 62 cu. in.
Pulley: 7x5, 1540 r.p.m., and 2820 f.p.m. at 2200 engine speed.
Speeds: M.P.H. Forward 2.54, 3.64, 5.81, and 3.03 reverse.

Earthmaster

Guarantee of Quality

Real quality and product performance have established the Earthmaster name in a remarkably short time. Those behind the Earthmaster line take pride in this rapid acceptance and proof of their conviction that the most effective salesman is a *superior product*.

Model C—General Purpose Tractor

Fills all needs for 10 to 60 acre farms or for auxiliary service on large acreage, featuring: high clearance . . . easy wheel adjustment for row crops . . . short wheel base for minimum turning radius . . . 2-way hydraulic system for full line of mounted implements.

Air Cleaner: Oil bath.

Governor: Briggs & Stratton.

Ignition: Briggs & Stratton.

Magneto: Briggs & Stratton.

Engine: Briggs & Stratton "A"; 2¼x2¼, 3200 r.p.m., 1 cylinder.

Piston Displacement: 8.94 cu. in.

Pulley: 3200 r.p.m. and 2600 f.p.m. at normal engine speed.

Speeds: M.P.H. Forward: ¾, 2¾, and ¾, 2¾ reverse.

EARTHMASTER "S"

Aerco Corp., Hollydale, Calif.

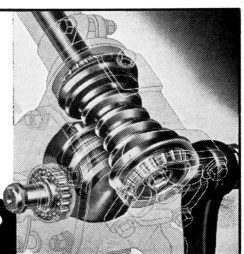

ALLIS-CHALMERS MANUFACTURING CO.
Milwaukee, Wisconsin

Allis-Chalmers HD-5   1947-1955

Air Cleaner: United, oil bath.
Battery: Exide—Auto-Lite.
Brakes: Two, operated by foot pedals.
Clutch: Auburn, single plate (over center).
Diesel: General Motors injection pump (unit injectors).
Generator: Delco-Remy.
Governor: General Motors, centrifugal.
Lamps: Guide Lamp.
Oil Filter: AC.
Radiator: Perfex, fin and tube.
Radiator Cover: Own (special equipment)
Starting: Delco-Remy.
Data: H.P.—Neb. Test No. (not tested).
Engine: General Motors "2-71"; 4¼x5, 1,800 r.p.m., 2 cylinders, 2 cycle, cast en bloc (vertical); piston displacement 142 cu. in.; removable sleeves, yes (dry).
Pulley: 12x8¾, 963 r.p.m. and 3,025 f.p.m. at normal engine speed.
Speeds: M.P.H forward 1.46, 2.44, 3.30, 3.96, 5.47, and 2 reverse.

ALLIS-CHALMERS HD-5
Allis-Chalmers Mfg. Co., Milwaukee, Wis.

Allis-Chalmers "HD-5"

B. F. AVERY & SONS CO.
Louisville, Kentucky

B. F. Avery "V"   1947-1951

Air Cleaner: Vortox.
Battery: Delco-Remy.
Brakes: Operated by foot.
Carburetor: Tillotson, ⅝-in.
Clutch: Rockford, single plate, dry disc.
Generator: Delco-Remy.
Governor: Handy, flyball.
Ignition: Delco-Remy.
Lamps: ....
Oil Filter: Fram.
Radiator: McCord, fin and rudder.
Radiator Cover: None.
Spark Plugs: Champion H-10.
Starting: Delco-Remy.
Data: H.P.—Neb. Test No. (not tested).
  Number of plows recommended: One 14 in.
Engine: Hercules "ZBX"; 2⅝x3, 1,800
  r.p.m., 4 cylinders, L-head, cast en bloc,
  piston displacement 64.9 cu. in.; remov-
  able sleeves, no.
Pulley: 6x5½, 540 r.p.m. and 3,100 f.p.m. at
  normal engine speed.
Speeds: M.P.H. forward 2.74, 3.60, 7.33, and
  3.22 reverse.

B. F. AVERY "V"
B. F. Avery & Sons Co., Louisville, Ky.

B. F. Avery "V"
B. F. Avery & Sons Co., Louisville, Ky.

DEERE & CO.
Moline, Illinois

John Deere General Purpose Model "G"   1947-1953

JOHN DEERE GENERAL PURPOSE MODEL "G"

Deere & Co., Moline, Ill.

Air Cleaner: Donaldson, oil washed.
Battery: Delco-Remy—Auto-Lite.
Brakes: Two, operated by foot.
Carburetor: Marvel-Schebler, 1¼ in., venturi.
Clutch: Own, dry disk, hand operated.
Generator: Delco-Remy.
Governor: Own, centrifugal, variable speed.
Ignition: Wico, high tension, enclosed impulse.
Lamps: Guide Lamp.
Lighting: Delco-Remy, battery.
Oil Filter: Purolator.
Radiator: Modine, fin tube.
Radiator Cover: Hardy, dash controlled.
Spark Plugs: 18 mm.
Starting: Delco-Remy.
Data: H.P.—Neb. Test No. (not tested). Number of plows recommended: Three, 14 in.
Engine: Own "G," 6⅛x7, 975 r.p.m., 2 cylinders, horizontal, cast en bloc; piston displacement 412.5 cu. in.
Pulley: 12¾x8½, 975 r.p.m. and 3,270 f.p.m. at normal engine speed.
Speeds: M.P.H. forward 1-2½, 2-3½, 3-4½, 4-6⅓, 5-8½, 6-12, and 3¼ reverse.

John Deere "G"   **Deere & Co., Moline, Ill.**

ENGINEERING PRODUCTS CO.
Milwaukee, Wisconsin

Economy

1947

Air Cleaner: Oil bath.

Clutch: Borg-Warner, single plate disc, ball bearing throughout.

Governor: Speed.

Starting: Rope.

Engine: Briggs & Stratton ZZP or Wisconsin AEH, 1 cylinder.

Speeds: Three forward and one reverse.

ECONOMY
Engineering Products Co., Milwaukee 3, Wis.

THE FATE-ROOT-HEATH CO.
Plymouth, Ohio

Silver King Model 347   1947
Silver King Model 447   1947

SILVER KING MODEL 347
The Fate-Root-Heath Co., Plymouth, O.

Air Cleaner: Donaldson, oil washed.

Battery: Exide.

Brakes: Two, operated by foot.

Carburetor: Marvel-Schebler, 1 in.

Clutch: Borg & Beck, single dry disc.

Generator: Delco-Remy.

Governor: Pierce, centrifugal.

Ignition: Delco-Remy, battery, coil and distributor.

Lamps: Guide Lamp.

Lighting: Delco-Remy.

Oil Filter: Fram.

Radiator: Modine, fin and tube.

Spark Plugs: Champion, 18 mm, 8 Com.

Starting: Delco-Remy.

Data: H.P.—Neb. Test No. (not tested at Nebraska). Number of Plows Recommended: Two, 14-in.

Engine: Continental F-162; $3\frac{7}{16}$ x $4\frac{3}{8}$, 1,800 r.p.m., 4 cylinders, L-head, cast en bloc; piston displacement 162 cu. in.; removable sleeves, no.

Pulley: 6.6x8.5, 1,800 r.p.m. and 3,100 f.p.m. at normal engine speed.

Speeds: M.P.H. forward 2.76, 4.10, 5.93, 19.10 and 1.97 reverse.

Air Cleaner: Donaldson, oil washed.
Battery: Exide.
Brakes: Two, operated by foot.
Carburetor: Marvel-Schebler, 1 in.
Clutch: Borg & Beck, single dry disc.
Generator: Delco-Remy.
Governor: Pierce, centrifugal.
Ignition: Delco-Remy, battery, coil and distributor.
Lamps: Guide Lamp.
Lighting: Delco-Remy.
Oil Filter: Fram.
Radiator: Modine, fin and tube.
Spark Plugs: Champion, 18 mm, 8 Com.
Starting: Delco-Remy.
Data: H.P.—Neb. Test No. (not tested at Nebraska). Number of Plows Recommended: Two, 14 in.
Engine: Continental, F162; $3\frac{7}{16}$ x $4\frac{3}{8}$, 1,800 r.p.m., 4 cylinders, L-head, cast en bloc; piston displacement 162 cu. in.; removable sleeves, no.
Pulley: 6.6x8.5, 1,800 r.p.m. and 3,100 f.p.m. at normal engine speed.
Speeds: M.P.H. forward 3.25, 5.18, 7.20, 23.20 and 2.39 reverse.

SILVER KING MODEL 447
The Fate-Root-Heath Co., Plymouth, O.

INTERNATIONAL HARVESTER CO.

Chicago, Illinois

International T-6 Crawler	1947-1958
International TD-6 Diesel Crawler	1947-1958
McCormick-Deering Farmall A	1947
McCormick-Deering Farmall AV	1947
McCormick-Deering Farmall B	1947
McCormick-Deering Farmall BN	1947
McCormick-Deering Farmall HV	1947
McCormick-Deering Farmall MDV Diesel	1947
McCormick-Deering ODS-6 Diesel	1947
McCormick-Deering WDR-9 Diesel	1947
McCormick-Deering WR-9	1947

Air Cleaner: Donaldson, oil bath.
Battery: Auto-Lite (special).
Brakes: Two; operated by individual foot pedals.
Carburetor: Own, 1¼ in.
Clutch: Rockford, single plate, over-center, with automatic clutch brake.
Generator: Delco-Remy (special).
Governor: Own, centrifugal, variable speed.
Ignition: Own, high tension magneto with automatic impulse coupling.
Lamps: Guide Lamp (special).
Lighting: Delco-Remy (special).
Oil Filter: Purolator, replaceable element.
Radiator: Own, fin and flat tube.
Radiator Cover: Hardy shutter.
Spark Plugs: Champion 15-A or AC-87, 18 mm.
Starting: Delco-Remy (special).
Data: H.P.—Neb. Test No. 346 (gasoline); Max. Belt 36.96; Max. D.B. 30.85; Max. lbs. pull 7,652 at 1.40 m.p.h. Weight as tested (with operator) 7,680 lbs. Test No. 347 (distillate); Max. Belt 34.54; Max. D.B. 29.53; Max. lbs. pull 7,434 at 1.44 m.p.h. Number of plows recommended:........
Engine: Own; 3⅞x5¼, 1,450 r.p.m., 4 cylinders, vertical, valve-in-head, cast en bloc; piston displacement 247.7 cu. in.; removable sleeves, yes.
Pulley: 12½x8½, 811 r.p.m. and 2,654 f. p.m. at normal engine speed (special).
Speeds: M.P.H. forward 1.5, 2.2, 3.1, 3.8, 5.4, and 1.7 reverse.

INTERNATIONAL T-6 CRAWLER
International Harvester Co., Chicago, Ill.

INTERNATIONAL TD-6 DIESEL CRAWLER
International Harvester Co., Chicago, Ill.

Air Cleaner: Donaldson, oil.
Battery: Auto-Lite (special).
Brakes: Two; operated by individual foot pedals.
Carburetor: Own, ¾ in. (for starting only).
Clutch: Rockford, single plate, over-center, with automatic clutch brake.
Diesel: Own injection pump.
Generator: Delco-Remy (special).
Governor: Own, centrifugal, variable speed.
Ignition: Own magneto (for starting only.)
Lamps: Guide Lamp (special).
Lighting: Delco-Remy (special).
Oil Filter: Purolator, replaceable element.
Radiator: Own, fin and flat tube.
Radiator Cover: Hardy shutter (special).
Spark Plugs: Champion 49 or AC 18-A, 18 m.m. (for starting only).
Starting: Delco-Remy (special).
Data: H.P.—Neb. Test No. 345; Max. Belt 34.54; Max. D.B. 28.14; Max. lbs. pull 7,160 at 1.40 m.p.h. Weight as tested (with operator) 7,950 lbs. Number of plows recommended............
Engine: Own; 3⅞x5¼, 1,450 r.p.m., 4 cylinders, vertical, valve-in-head, cast en bloc; piston displacement 247.7 cu. in.; removable sleeves, yes.
Pulley: 12½x8½, 811 r.p.m. and 2,654 f.p.m., at normal engine speed (special).
Speeds: M.P.H. forward 1.5, 2.2, 3.1, 3.8. 5.4, and 1.7 reverse.

Air Cleaner: Donaldson, oil bath.
Battery: Auto-Lite (Special).
Brakes: Two; operated by foot pedals, individually or locked together.
Carburetor: Zenith or Marvel-Schebler, ⅞ in.
Clutch: Rockford or Atwood, single plate, dry disc, spring loaded.
Generator: Delco-Remy (special).
Governor: Own, centrifugal, variable speed.
Ignition: Own, high tension magneto with automatic impulse coupling.
Lamps: Guide Lamp (special).
Lighting: Delco-Remy (special).
Oil Filter: Purolator, replaceable element.
Radiator: Own, fin and flat tube.
Radiator Cover: Hardy shutter (special).
Spark Plugs: Champion 15-A or AC-87, 18 mm.
Starting: Delco-Remy (special).
Data: H.P.—Neb. Test No. 329 (gasoline): Max. Belt 18.34; Max. D.B. 16.32; Max lbs. pull 2,387 at 1.93 m. p.h. Test No. 330 (distillate): Max. Belt 16.51; Max. D.B. 15.17; Max. lbs. pull 2,360 at 1.97 m.p.h. Weight as tested (with operator) 3,570 lbs. Number of plows recommended: One, 16 in.
Engine: Own; 3x4, 1,400 r.p.m., 4 cylinders, vertical, valve-in-head, cast en bloc; piston displacement 113.1 cu. in.; removable sleeves, yes.
Pulley: 8½x6, 1,157 r.p.m. and 2,574 f. p.m. at normal engine speed (special).
Speeds: M.P.H. forward 2¼, 3½, 4⅝, 9⅝, and 2¾ reverse on 8-24 tires.

McCORMICK-DEERING FARMALL A
International Harvester Co., Chicago, Ill.

Air Cleaner: Donaldson, oil bath.
Battery: Auto-Lite (special).
Brakes: Two; operated by foot pedals, individually or locked together.
Carburetor: Zenith or Marvel-Schebler, ⅞ in.
Clutch: Rockford or Atwood, single plate, dry disc, spring-loaded.
Generator: Delco-Remy (special).
Governor: Own, centrifugal, variable speed.
Ignition: Own, high tension magneto with automatic impulse coupling.
Lamps: Guide Lamp (special).
Lighting: Delco-Remy (special).
Oil Filter: Purolator, replaceable element.
Radiator: Own, fin and flat tube.
Radiator Cover: Hardy shutter (special).
Spark Plugs: Champion 15-A or AC-87, 18 mm.
Starting: Delco-Remy (special).
Data: H.P.—Neb. Test No. (not tested). Horsepower is approximately same as Farmall A, tests 329 and 330. Number of plows recommended: One, 16 in.
Engine: Own; 3x4, 1,400 r.p.m., 4 cylinders, vertical, valve-in-head, cast en bloc; piston displacement 113.1 cu. in.; removable sleeves, yes.
Pulley: 8½x6, 1,157 r.p.m. and 2,574 4. p.m. at normal engine speed (special).
Speeds: M.P.H. forward 2⅞, 4⅝, 6⅛, 12¾ and 3⅝ reverse, on 8-36 tires.

McCORMICK-DEERING FARMALL AV
International Harvester Co., Chicago, Ill.

Air Cleaner: Donaldson, oil bath.
Battery: Auto-Lite (Special).
Brakes: Two; operated by foot pedals, individually or locked together.
Carburetor: Zenith or Marvel-Schebler, ⅞ in.
Clutch: Rockford or Atwood, single plate, dry disc, spring-loaded.
Generator: Delco-Remy (special).
Governor: Own, centrifugal, variable speed.
Ignition: Own, high tension magneto with automatic impulse coupling.
Lamps: Guide Lamp (special).
Lighting: Delco-Remy (special).
Oil Filter: Purolator, replaceable element.
Radiator: Own, fin and flat tube.
Radiator Cover: Hardy shutter (special).
Spark Plugs: Champion 15-A or AC-87, 18 mm.
Starting: Delco-Remy (special).
Data: H.P.—Neb. Test No. 331 (gasoline): Max. Belt 18.39; Max. D.B. 16.21; Max. lbs. pull 2,377 at 1.90 m.p.h. Test No. 332 (distillate): Max. Belt 16.00; Max. D.B. 14.73; Max. lbs. pull 2,463 at 1.83 m.p.h. Weight as tested (with operator) 3,740 lbs. Number of plows recommended: One, 16 in.
Engine: Own; 3x4, 1,400 r.p.m., 4 cylinders, vertical, valve-in-head, cast en bloc; piston displacement 113.1 cu. in.; removable sleeves, yes.
Pulley: 8½x6, 1,157 r.p.m. and 2,574 f.p.m. at normal engine speed, special
Speeds: M.P.H. forward 2¼, 3½, 4⅝, 9⅝, and 2¾ reverse, on 8-24 tires.

McCORMICK-DEERING FARMALL B
(McCormick-Deering BN similar except for narrower rear treads).
International Harvester Co., Chicago, Ill.

McCORMICK-DEERING FARMALL HV
International Harvester Co., Chicago, Ill.

Air Cleaner: Donaldson, oil bath.
Battery: Auto-Lite (special).
Brakes: Two; operated by foot pedals, individually or locked together.
Carburetor: Own, 1-in.
Clutch: Rockford, single plate, dry disc, spring loaded.
Generator: Delco-Remy (special).
Governor: Own, centrifugal, variable speed.
Ignition: Own, high tension magneto with automatic impulse coupling.
Lamps: Guide Lamp (special).
Oil Filter: Purolator, replaceable element.
Radiator: Own or Young, fin and flat tube.
Radiator Cover: Hardy shutter.
Spark Plugs: Champion 15-A or AC-87, 18 m.m.
Starting: Delco-Remy (special).
Data: H.P. — Neb. Test No. (not tested). Horsepower is approximately same as Farmall H, tests 333 and 334. Number of plows recommended: Two, 14 in.
Engine: Own; 3⅜x4¼, 1,650 r.p.m., 4 cylinders, vertical, valve-in-head; piston displacement 152.1 cu. in. Removable sleeves, yes.
Pulley: 9¾x7½, 1919 r.p.m. and 2601 f.p.m. at normal engine speed.
Speeds: M.P.H. Forward 2½, 3⅜, 4, 5, 15¼ and 2⅞ reverse.

McCORMICK-DEERING FARMALL MDV DIESEL

International Harvester Co., Chicago, Ill.

Air Cleaner: Donaldson, oil bath.
Battery: Auto-Lite (special) (2).
Brakes: Two; operated by foot pedals, individually or locked together.
Carburetor: Own, for starting only, ¾-in.
Clutch: Rockford, single plate, dry disc, spring-loaded.
Diesel: Own injection pump.
Generator: Delco-Remy (special).
Governor: Own, centrifugal, variable speed.
Ignition: Own magneto, for starting only.
Lamps: Guide Lamp (special).
Oil Filter: Purolator, replaceable element.
Radiator: Own or McCord, fin and flat tube.
Radiator Cover: Hardy shutter (special).
Spark Plugs: Champion 49 or AC 18-A, 18 m.m. (for starting only).
Starting: Delco-Remy (special).
Data: H.P. — Neb. Test No. (not tested). Horsepower is approximately the same as Farmall MD, test 368. Number of plows recommended: three, 14-in.
Engine: Own; 3⅞x5¼, 1450 r.p.m. 4 cylinders, vertical, valve-in-head, cast en bloc; piston displacement 247.7 cu. in.; removable sleeves, yes.
Pulley: 11x7½, 899 r.p.m and 2588 f.p.m. at normal engine speed.
Speeds: M.P.H. forward 2½, 3⅜, 4⅛, 5, 16 and 3⅛ reverse.

McCORMICK-DEERING ODS-6 DIESEL
International Harvester Co., Chicago, Ill.

Air Cleaner: Donaldson, oil bath.
Battery: Auto-Lite (special) (2).
Brakes: Two; operated by foot pedals, individually.
Carburetor: Own, ¾-in. (for starting only).
Clutch: Rockford, single plate, dry disc, over center.
Diesel: Own injection pump.
Generator: Delco-Remy (special).
Governor: Own, centrifugal, variable speed.
Ignition: Own magneto (for starting only).
Lamps: Guide Lamp (special).
Oil Filter: Purolator, replaceable element.
Radiator: Own, fin and flat tube.
Radiator Cover: Hardy shutter (special).
Spark Plugs: Champion 49 or AC 18-A, 18 m.m. (for starting only).
Starting: Delco-Remy (special).
Data: H.P.—Neb. Test No. (not tested). Horsepower is approximately the same as WD-6, test 356. Number of plows recommended: three, 14-in.
Engine: Own; 3⅞x5¼, 1450 r.p.m., 4 cylinders, valve-in-head, cast en bloc; piston displacement 247.7 cu. in. Removable sleeves, yes.
Pulley: 11x7½, 899 r.p.m. and 2588 f.p.m. at normal engine speed.
Speeds: M.P.H. forward 1½, 3, 3⅞, 4¾, 14, and 1¾ reverse on 12-26 tires.

Air Cleaner: Donaldson, oil bath.
Battery: Auto-Lite (special) (2).
Brakes: Two; operated by foot pedals, individually or locked together.
Carburetor: Own, ¾-in. (for starting only).
Clutch: Rockford, single plate, dry disc, over center.
Diesel: Own, injection pump.
Generator: Delco-Remy (special).
Governor: Own, centrifugal, variable speed.
Ignition: Own, magneto (for starting only).
Lamps: Guide Lamp (special).
Oil Filter: Purolator, replaceable element.
Radiator: Own, fin and flat tube.
Radiator Cover: Hardy shutter (special).
Spark Plugs: Champion 49 or AC 18-A, 18 m.m. (for starting only).
Starting: Delco-Remy (special).
Data: H.P.—Neb. Test No. (not tested). Horsepower is approximately the same as WD-9, test 370. Number of plows recommended: four, 14-in.
Engine: Own; 4.4x5.5, 1500 r.p.m., 4 cylinders, vertical, valve-in-head, cast en bloc; piston displacement 334.5 cu. in.
Pulley: 14x8½, 707 r.p.m. and 2593 f.p.m. at normal engine speed.
Speeds: M.P.H. forward 2⅝, 3½, 4⅞, 6, and 3⅛ reverse on 54-in. steel wheels. 2½, 3⅝, 4¾, 5⅞, 16⅞ forward and 3⅛ reverse on 15-34 tires.

McCORMICK-DEERING WDR-9 DIESEL
International Harvester Co., Chicago, Ill.

Air Cleaner: Donaldson, oil bath.
Battery: Auto-Lite (special).
Brakes: Two; operated by foot pedals, individually or locked together.
Carburetor: Own, 1⅜-in.
Clutch: Rockford, single plate, dry disc, over center.
Generator: Delco-Remy (special).
Governor: Own, centrifugal, variable speed.
Ignition: Own, high tension magneto with automatic impulse coupling.
Lamps: Guide Lamp (special).
Oil Filter: Purolator, replaceable element.
Radiator: Own, fin and flat tube.
Radiator Cover: Hardy shutter.
Spark Plugs: Champion 1 Com. A or AC-77 (kerosene and distillate); Champion O Com. or AC-75 (gasoline); ⅞-18.
Starting: Delco-Remy (special).
Data: H.P.—Neb. Test No. (not tested). Horsepower is approximately the same as W-9, tests 369 and 371. Number of plows recommended: four, 14-in.
Engine: Own; 4.4x5.5, 1500 r.p.m., 4 cylinders, vertical, valve-in-head, cast en bloc; piston displacement 334.5 cu. in.; removable sleeves, yes.
Pulley: 14x8½, 707 r.p.m. and 2593 f.p.m. at normal engine speed.
Speeds: M.P.H. forward 2⅝, 3½, 4⅞, 6, and 3⅛ reverse on 54 in. steel wheels. 2½, 3⅜, 4¾, 5⅞, 16⅞ forward, and 3⅛ reverse on 15-34 tires.

McCORMICK-DEERING WR-9
International Harvester Co., Chicago, Ill.

MASSEY-HARRIS CO.

Racine, Wisconsin

Massey-Harris "20"	1947-1948
Massey-Harris "20-K"	1947-1948
Massey-Harris "30"	1947-1949
Massey-Harris "30 Standard"	1947-1953
Massey-Harris "30-K"	1947-1949
Massey-Harris "44"	1947-1949
Massey-Harris "44-6"	1947-1948
Massey-Harris "44-K"	1947-1948
Massey-Harris "44-RC"	1947-1954
Massey-Harris "55"	1947-1949
Massey-Harris "55-K"	1947-1949

MASSEY-HARRIS "20"
Massey-Harris Co., Racine, Wis.

Air Cleaner: Donaldson, oil bath.
Battery: Exide.
Brakes: Two; operated by foot pedals.
Carburetor: Marvel Schebler.
Clutch: Borg & Beck, single plate, dry.
Generator: Auto-Lite.
Governor: Novi, centrifugal.
Ignition: Auto-Lite distributor.
Lamps: K. D.
Oil Filter: Purolator.
Radiator: Modine, fin and tube.
Radiator Cover: None.
Spark Plugs: Auto-Lite, B7.
Starting: Auto-Lite.
Data: H.P.—Neb. Test No. (Not tested).
Engine: Continental "F124"; 3x4⅜, 1,500 r.p.m., 4 cylinders, L-head, cast en bloc; piston displacement 124 cu. in.; removable sleeves, no.
Pulley: 9½x6, 1,228 r.p.m.
Speeds: M.P.H forward, Std. 2.45, 3.51, 4.62, 13.02, and 2.45 reverse. Row Crop, 2.57, 3.69, 4.85, 13.68 M.P.H. forward, and 2.57 reverse.

Air Cleaner: Donaldson, oil bath.
Battery: Exide.
Brakes: Two; operated by foot pedals.
Carburetor: Marvel Schebler.
Clutch: Borg & Beck, single plate, dry.
Generator: Auto-Lite.
Governor: Novi, centrifugal.
Ignition: Auto-Lite distributor.
Lamps: K. D.
Oil Filter: Purolator.
Radiator: Modine, fin and tube.
Radiator Cover: None.
Spark Plugs: Champion 8 Comm. D.
Starting: Auto-Lite.
Data: H.P.—Neb. Test No. (Not tested).
Engine: Continental "F140"; 3³⁄₁₆x4⅜, 1,500 r.p.m., 4 cylinders, L-head, cast en bloc; piston displacement 140 cu. in.; removable sleeves, no.
Pulley: 9½x6, 1,228 r.p.m.
Speeds: M.P.H. forward, Std. 2.45, 3.5, 4.62, 13.02, and 2.45 reverse. Row Crop, 2.57, 3.69, 4.85, 13.68 M.P.H. forward, and 2.57 reverse.

MASSEY-HARRIS "20-K"
Massey-Harris Co., Racine, Wis.

MASSEY-HARRIS "30"
Massey-Harris Co., Racine, Wis.

Air Cleaner: Donaldson, oil bath.
Battery: Exide.
Brakes: Two; operated by foot pedals.
Carburetor: Marvel Schebler.
Clutch: Borg & Beck, single plate, dry.
Generator: Auto-Lite.
Governor: Novi, centrifugal.
Ignition: Auto-Lite distributor.
Lamps: K. D.
Oil Filter: Purolator.
Radiator: Modine, fin and tube.
Radiator Cover: None.
Spark Plugs: Auto-Lite, B7.
Starting: Auto-Lite.
Data: H.P.—Neb. Test No. (Not tested).
Engine: Continental "F162"; $3\frac{7}{16}$x$4\frac{3}{8}$, 1,500 r.p.m., 4 cylinders, L-head, cast en bloc; piston displacement 162 cu. in.; removable sleeves, no.
Pulley: $13\frac{1}{2}$x6, 838 r.p.m.
Speeds: M.P.H. forward, Std. 2.19, 3.06, 3.82, 5.35, 10.71, and 2.48 reverse. Row Crop 2.58, 3.61, 4.51, 6.31, 12.63 M.P.H. forward, and 2.93 reverse.

Air Cleaner: Donaldson, oil bath.
Battery: Exide.
Brakes: Two; operated by foot pedals.
Carburetor: Marvel Schebler.
Clutch: Borg & Beck, single plate, dry.
Generator: Auto-Lite.
Governor: Novi, centrifugal.
Ignition: Auto-Lite distributor.
Lamps: K. D.
Oil Filter: Purolator.
Radiator: Modine, fin and tube.
Radiator Cover: None.
Spark Plugs: Champion 8 Comm. D.
Starting: Auto-Lite.
Data: H.P.—Neb. Test No. (Not tested).
Engine: Continental "F162"; $3\frac{7}{16}$x$4\frac{3}{8}$, 1,500 r.p.m., 4 cylinders, L-head, cast en bloc; piston displacement 162 cu. in.; removable sleeves, no.
Pulley: $13\frac{1}{2}$x6, 838 r.p.m.
Speeds: M.P.H. forward, Std. 2.19, 3.06, 3.82, 5.35, 10.71, and 2.48 reverse. Row Crop, 2.58, 3.61, 4.51, 6.31, 12.63 M.P.H. forward, and 2.93 reverse.

MASSEY-HARRIS "30-K" AND "STD"
Massey-Harris Co., Racine, Wis.

MASSEY-HARRIS "44" AND "44-K"
Massey-Harris Co., Racine, Wis.

Air Cleaner: Donaldson, oil bath.
Battery: Exide.
Brakes: Two; operated by foot pedals.
Carburetor: Zenith, 1¼ in.
Clutch: Borg & Beck, single plate, dry.
Generator: Auto-Lite.
Governor: Own, centrifugal.
Ignition: Auto-Lite, distributor.
Lamps: K. D.
Oil Filter: Purolator.
Radiator: Modine, fin and tube.
Radiator Cover: None.
Spark Plugs: Champion 8 Comm. C.
Starting: Auto-Lite.
Data: H.P.—Neb. Test No. (Not tested).
Engine: Own "H260"; 3⅞x5½, 1,350 r.p.m., 4 cylinders, overhead; piston displacement 260 cu. in.; removable sleeves, yes.
Pulley: 13½x6, 863 r.p.m.
Speeds: M.P.H. forward, Std. 2.21, 3.33, 4.43, 5.75, 12.28, and 2.89 reverse. Row Crop 2.48, 3.75, 4.97, 6.46, 13.82 M.P.H. forward, and 3.26 reverse.

Massey-Harris "44"
The Massey-Harris Co., Racine, Wis.

Air Cleaner: Donaldson, oil bath.
Battery: Exide.
Brakes: Two; operated by foot pedals.
Carburetor: Marvel Schebler, 1¼ in.
Clutch: Borg & Beck, single plate, dry.
Generator: Auto-Lite.
Governor: Novi.
Ignition: Auto-Lite, distributor.
Lamps: K. D.
Oil Filter: Purolator.
Radiator: Modine, fin and tube.
Radiator Cover: None.
Spark Plugs: Champion 8 Comm. C.
Starting: Auto-Lite.
Data: H.P.—Neb. Test No. (Not tested).
Engine: Continental "F226"; $3\frac{5}{16}$x4⅜, 1,500 r.p.m., 6 cylinders, L-head, cast en bloc; piston displacement 226 cu. in.; removable sleeves, no.
Pulley: 13½x6, 838 r.p.m.
Speeds: M.P.H. forward 2.76, 2.85, 4.81, 6.74, 13.48, and 3.12 reverse.

MASSEY-HARRIS "44-6"
Massey-Harris Co., Racine, Wis.

MASSEY-HARRIS "44-RC"
Massey-Harris Co., Racine, Wis.

Air Cleaner: Donaldson "A."
Battery: Exide.
Brakes: Two; operated by foot individually or interlocked.
Carburetor: Zenith.
Clutch: Borg & Beck "11A6."
Generator: Auto-Lite.
Ignition: Auto-Lite.
Lamps: Not standard equipment.
Oil Filter: Purolator.
Radiator: Modine, tubular.
Radiator Cover: Not standard equipment.
Spark Plugs: Champion 8 comm.
Starting: Auto-Lite.
Data: H.P.—Neb. Test No. (not tested). Number of plows recommended: three, 14-in.
Engine: Own H-260; 3⅞x5½, 1,350 r.p.m., 4 cylinders, valve-in-head, cast en bloc; piston displacement 260 cu. in.; removable sleeves, yes.
Pulley: 13½x6¼, 863 f.p.m. at normal engine speed.
Speeds: M.P.H. forward 2.48, 3.86, 4.97, 6.46, 13.82, and 3.45 reverse.

MASSEY-HARRIS "55" AND "55-K"
Massey-Harris Co., Racine, Wis.

Air Cleaner: Donaldson, oil bath.
Battery: Exide.
Brakes: Two; operated by foot pedals.
Carburetor: Zenith, 1¼ in.
Clutch: Borg & Beck, single plate, dry.
Generator: Auto-Lite.
Governor: Own, centrifugal.
Ignition: Auto-Lite, distributor.
Lamps: K. D.
Oil Filter: Purolator.
Radiator: Modine, fin and tube.
Radiator Cover: None.
Spark Plugs: Champion 8 Comm. C.
Starting: Auto-Lite.
Data: H.P.—Neb. Test No. (Not tested).
Engine: Own "J382"; 4½x6, 1,350 r.p.m., 4 cylinders, overhead, cast en bloc; piston displacement 382 cu. in.; removable sleeves, yes.
Pulley: 16x8, 730 f.p.m. at normal engine speed.
Speeds: M.P.H. forward 2.96, 4.22, 5.21, 12.07 and 2.54 reverse.

THE OLIVER CORP.
Tractor Division
Charles City, Iowa

Oliver Industrial "60"	1947-1948
Oliver Industrial "70"	1947-1948
Oliver Industrial "80"	1947
Oliver Industrial "99"	1947
Oliver Industrial "900"	1947-1948

OLIVER INDUSTRIAL "60"
The Oliver Corp., Tractor Div., Charles City, Ia.

Air Cleaner: Donaldson, oil wash.
Battery: Delco-Remy.
Brakes: ....
Carburetor: Schebler, 1-in.
Clutch: Borg & Beck, 8-in., single plate, dry.
Governor: Own, centrifugal, flyball, variable speed.
Ignition: Delco-Remy, battery and distributor.
Lamps: Guide.
Oil Filter: Michiana.
Radiator: Modine, fin and tube.
Radiator Cover: Own.
Spark Plugs: Champion, 6 Comm.
Starting: Delco-Remy.
Data: H.P.—Neb. Test No. (not tested).
Engine: Own, 3⁵⁄₁₆x3½, 1,500 r.p.m., 4 cylinders, vertical, cast en bloc; removable sleeves, yes.
Pulley: 10x6¼, 674-1,143 r.p.m. and 1,700-3,000 f.p.m. at normal engine speeds.
Speeds: M.P.H. forward 2.60, 3.48, 4.61, 6.16, 11.67, and 3.35, 5.90 reverse on 9-24 tires.

Air Cleaner: Donaldson, oil wash.
Brakes: ....
Carburetor: Zenith.
Clutch: Borg & Beck, 9-in., single plate, dry.
Governor: Own, centrifugal, flyball, variable speed.
Ignition: Bosch, high tension magneto.
Lamps: Guide.
Oil Filter: Michiana.
Radiator: Modine or Young, tubular-fin.
Radiator Cover: Own.
Spark Plugs: Champion, 6 Comm.
Starting: Delco-Remy.
Data: H.P.—Neb. Test No. (not tested). H.P. approximately same as Standard "70" HC test 283.
Engine: Own; 3⅛x4⅜, 1,500 r.p.m., 6 cylinders, vertical, cast en bloc; removable sleeves, yes.
Pulley: 12¾x7¼, 774 r.p.m. and 2,600 f.p.m. at normal engine speed.
Speeds: M.P.H. forward 2.52, 3.42, 4.47, 6.07, 7.48, 13.22, and 2.52 reverse.

OLIVER INDUSTRIAL "70"
The Oliver Corp., Tractor Div., Charles City, Ia.

Air Cleaner: Donaldson, oil wash.
Brakes: ....
Carburetor: Schebler, 1¼-in.
Clutch: Rockford, 12-in., single plate, dry.
Governor: Own, centrifugal, flyball, variable speed.
Ignition: Bosch, high tension magneto.
Lamps: Guide.
Oil Filter: Michiana.
Radiator: Modine or Young, tubular-fin.
Radiator Cover: Own.
Spark Plugs: Champion, 0 Comm.
Starting: Delco-Remy.
Data: H.P.—Neb. Test No. (not tested). H.P. approximately same as Standard "80" HC test 365.
Engine: Own; 4¼x5¼, 1,200 r.p.m., 4 cylinders, vertical, cast en bloc; removable sleeves, yes.
Pulley: 14⁷⁄₁₆x7¼, 731 r.p.m. and 2,750 f.p.m. at normal engine speed.
Speeds: M.P.H. forward 2.47, 4.26, 5.74, 10.62, and 3.03 reverse.

OLIVER INDUSTRIAL "80"
The Oliver Corp., Tractor Div., Charles City, Ia.

OLIVER INDUSTRIAL "99"
The Oliver Corp., Tractor Div., Charles City, Ia.

Air Cleaner: Donaldson, oil wash.
Brakes: ....
Carburetor: Schebler, 1¼-in.
Clutch: Borg & Beck, 14-in., single plate, dry.
Governor: Own, centrifugal, flyball, variable speed.
Ignition: Bosch, high tension magneto.
Lamps: Guide.
Oil Filter: Michiana, Duo-Flo.
Radiator: Modine, tubular-fin
Radiator Cover: Own.
Spark Plugs: Champion 0 Comm.
Starting: Delco-Remy.
Data: H.P.—Neb. Test No. (not tested).
Engine: Own; 4¾x6¼, 1,200 r.p.m., 4 cylinders, vertical, cast en bloc; removable sleeves, yes.
Pulley: 16¾x8¼, 635 r.p.m. and 3,300 f.p.m. at normal engine speed.
Speeds: M.P.H. forward 2.62, 5.08, 8.38, 16.63, and 3.81 reverse.

Air Cleaner: Donaldson, oil wash.
Brakes: ....
Carburetor: Schebler, 1¼-in.
Clutch: Rockford, 14-in., single plate, dry.
Governor: Own, centrifugal, flyball, variable speed.
Ignition: Bosch, high tension magneto.
Lamps: Guide.
Oil Filter: Michiana, Duo-Flo.
Radiator: Modine, tubular-fin.
Radiator Cover: Own.
Spark Plugs: Champion 0 Comm.
Starting: Delco-Remy.
Data: H.P.—Neb. Test No. (not tested).
Engine: Own; 4¾x6¼, 1,200 r.p.m., 4 cylinders, vertical, cast en bloc; removable sleeves, yes.
Pulley: None.
Speeds: M.P.H. forward 2.38, 4.63, 7.64, 15.15, and 3.48 reverse.

OLIVER INDUSTRIAL "900"
The Oliver Corp., Tractor Div., Charles City, Ia.

1948

The 1948 list includes 19 tractor manufacturers producing 47 tractor models. Allis-Chalmers Manufacturing Company produced their "Grasshopper" (G) and HD19H at the top and bottom of the line. International Harvester Company introduced 24 models from the "Cub" to the WDR-9.

The Ferguson Tractor Division merged with Massey-Harris and imported the Ferguson tractor from England. The Ford Motor Company formed Dearborn Motors Corporation to market their Ford 8N and established line of farm equipment.

ALLIS-CHALMERS MANUFACTURING CO.

Milwaukee, Wisconsin

Allis-Chalmers Model "G"	1948-1958
Allis-Chalmers HD19H	1948

ALLIS-CHALMERS MODEL "G"
Allis-Chalmers Mfg. Co., Milwaukee, Wis.

Air Cleaner: Donaldson, oil bath.
Battery: Auto-Lite.
Brakes: Two, operated by foot pedals.
Carburetor: Marvel-Schebler, ⅝ in.
Clutch: Rockford, single dry plate.
Generator: Delco-Remy.
Governor: Continental, centrifugal.
Ignition: Delco-Remy, distributor and coil.
Lamps: Guide Lamp.
Oil Filter: Own.
Radiator: Perfex or McCord, fin and tube.
Radiator Cover: ....
Spark Plugs: Auto-Lite AN-7.
Starting: Delco-Remy.
Data: H.P.—Neb. Test No. (not tested). Number of plows recommended: One, 12-in.
Engine: Continental N-62; 2⅜x3½, 1800 r.p.m., 4 cylinders, L-head, cast en bloc. Piston displacement 62 cu. in.
Pulley: 6x4, 1950 r.p.m. and 3070 f.p.m. at normal engine speed.
Speeds: M.P.H. Forward 1.58, 2.19, 3.46, 6.71 and 2.54 reverse.

Allis-Chalmers "G"

ALLIS-CHALMERS HD19H
Allis-Chalmers Mfg. Co., Milwaukee, Wis.

Air Cleaner: United, two, oil bath.
Battery: Exide or Auto-Lite.
Brakes: Two, operated by foot pedals.
Clutch. Twin Disc.
Diesel: General Motors injection pump, unit injectors.
Generator: Delco-Remy.
Governor: General Motors, centrifugal.
Lamps: Guide Lamp.
Oil Filter: Own.
Radiator: Perfex, fin and tube.
Starting: Delco-Remy.
Data: H.P.—Neb. Test No. (not tested at Nebraska).
Engine: General Motors "71"; 4¼x5, 1750 r.p.m., 6 cylinders, two cycle diesel, vertical, cast en bloc, removable dry sleeves. Piston displacement 426 cu. in.
Pulley: 20x15, 800 r.p.m. at no load high idle to 430 r.p.m. at maximum B.H.P. Rotation clockwise viewed from tractor left hand side.
Speeds: M.P.H. Forward; Low range 0 to 3; high range 0 to 7 and 0 to 5.5 reverse.

COCKSHUTT PLOW CO. LTD.

Brantford, Ontario, Canada

Cockshutt "30"   1948-1958

Air Cleaner: Donaldson, oil washed wire screen filter.
Battery: Exide.

COCKSHUTT "30"
(Also designated as Co-op E-3 or Farmcrest 30)
Cockshutt Plow Co., Ltd., Brantford, Ont., Can.

Brakes: Two brake pedals that can be locked together.
Carburetor: Marvel-Schebler, ⅞ in.
Clutch: Borg & Beck, single plate, operated by foot pedal.
Generator: Auto-Lite.
Governor: Novi, mechanical flyball
Ignition: Auto-Lite, distributor.
Lamps: Guide.
Oil Filter: Kralinator K-55.
Radiator: Perfex and National, tubular.
Radiator Cover: ....
Spark Plugs: Champion, J-5.
Starting: Auto-Lite.
Data: H.P.—Neb. Test No. 382; Max. Belt 31.88; Max. D.B. 27.25; Max. lbs. pull 3,745 at 2.36 m.p.h. Weight as tested (with operator) 5,528. Number of plows recommended: Two to three, 14-in.
Engine: Buda 4B-153; $3\frac{7}{16}$x$4\frac{1}{8}$, 1,650 r.p.m., 4 cylinders, vertical, cast en bloc; piston displacement 153 cu. in.; removable sleeves, yes.
Pulley: $8\frac{1}{4}$x$7\frac{1}{2}$, 1,350 r.p.m. and 2,915 f.p.m. at normal engine speed.
Speeds: M.P.H. forward 2.75, 4, 5.5, 12 and 3.5 reverse. With 8-speed attachment additional speeds, 1.65, 2.4, 3.3, 6.5 and 2.21 reverse.

Cockshutt "30"
Cockshutt Plow Co., Ltd., Brantford, Canada

DEARBORN MOTORS CORP.
Detroit, Michigan

Ford Model 8-N   1948

Air Cleaner: Oakes-United, oil bath with dust receptacle.

Battery: Ford.

Brakes: Two, operated by foot individually or together.

Carburetor: Marvel-Schebler, 7/8 in.

Clutch: Long, dry plate, semi-centrifugal.

Generator: Ford.

Governor: Novi, variable speed, mechanically operated.

Ignition: Ford distributor.

Lamps: Available as accessory.

Oil Filter: Fram, replaceable element.

Radiator: Ford and Long, tube and fin.

Radiator Cover: Ford.

Spark Plugs: Champion H-10.

Starting: Ford.

Data: H.P.—Neb. Test No. 393; Max. Belt 25.77; Max. D.B. 21.72; Max. lbs. pull 2751 at 2.71 m.p.h.. Weight as Tested (With Operator) 4,140. Number of Plows recommended: Two, 14 in.

Engine: Ford 8N; $3\frac{3}{16}$x3¾, 2,000 r.p.m. 4 cylinders, vertical, L-head. Piston displacement 119.7 cu. in. Removable Sleeves: Yes.

Pulley: 9x6½, 1,018 r.p.m., and 2,399 f.p.m. at normal engine speed.

Speeds: M.P.H. Forward at 1,500 r.p.m., 2.77, 3.56, 4.90, 10.23 and 4.55 reverse. At 2,000 r.p.m., 3.69, 4.75, 6.53, 13.64 m.p.h. forward and 6.07 reverse.

FORD MODEL 8-N
Dearborn Motors Corp., Detroit 3, Mich.

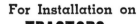

HARRY FERGUSON, INC.
Detroit, Michigan

Ferguson TO20

1948-1952

Air Cleaner: Donaldson or Vortox, circulating oil bath and multiple screen.
Battery: Own.
Brakes: Two; mechanical, operated by foot pedal.
Carburetor: Marvel-Schebler, ⅞ in.
Clutch: Rockford, single dry disc.
Generator: Auto-Lite or Delco-Remy.
Governor: Continental Motors, centrifugal.
Ignition: Auto-Lite or Delco-Remy distributor.
Lamps: Hall.
Oil Filter: Michiana No. 5A-15217-S.
Radiator: Own, fin and tube.
Radiator Cover: None.
Spark Plugs: 18 m.m. Champion 8 com. or equivalent.
Starting: Auto-Lite or Delco-Remy.
Data: H.P.—Neb. Test No. (not tested). Number of plows recommended: Two, 14-in.
Engine: Own, Z-120; $3\frac{3}{16}$x3¾, 1,940 r.p.m., 4 cylinders, vertical, overhead, cast en bloc, removable sleeves; piston displacement 119.7 cu. in.
Pulley: 9x6½, 1,316 r.p.m. and 3,100 f.p.m. at normal engine speed.

Speeds: M.P.H. forward with 1,500 engine r.p.m. 2.48, 3.42, 4.71, 9.84 and 2.87 reverse. With 2,000 engine r.p.m. 3.32, 4.57, 6.29, 13.13 and 3.83 reverse.

FERGUSON TO20
Harry Ferguson, Inc., Detroit 11, Mich.

FRAZER FARM EQUIPMENT CORP.
York, Pennsylvania

Jaques-Frazer Model T

1948

JAQUES-FRAZER MODEL T
Frazer Farm Equip. Corp., York, Pa.

Air Cleaner: Donaldson, oil bath.
Brakes: Two; operated by foot pedal.
Carburetor: Tillotson, 1-in.
Clutch: Twin Disc, V 4½.
Ignition: High tension magneto.
Magneto: Edison-Splitdorf or Fairbanks-Morse, gear driven-impulse starter.
Spark Plugs: One, Champion, 18 mm.
Starting: Cable and pulley (self rewind).
Data: H.P.—Neb. Test No. (not tested). Number of plows recommended: One, 14-in.
Engine: Simar-Swiss; 3x3¼, 1,250-2,500 r.p.m., 1 cylinder; piston displacement 22.97 cu. in.
Speeds: M.P.H. forward .532, .849, 1.385, 1.835, 2.933, 4.781 and .391, 1.352 reverse at 2,000 engine r.p.m.

FRIDAY TRACTOR CO.
Hartford, Michigan

Friday Orchard Model O48

1948-1952

FRIDAY ORCHARD MODEL 048
Friday Tractor Co., Hartford, Mich.

Air Cleaner: United, oil bath.
Battery: Auto-Lite.
Brakes: Four; two hand hydraulic steering, one foot service, one hand emergency.
Carburetor: Ball & Ball, 1½-in.
Clutch: Borg & Beck, single plate dry.
Generator: Auto-Lite.
Governor: Pierce, centrifugal, flyball variable speed.
Ignition: Auto-Lite battery and distributor.
Lamps: Guide.
Oil Filter: Purolator.
Radiator: Seven tube.
Spark Plugs: Auto-Lite A-5, 14 mm.
Starting: Auto-Lite.
Data: H.P.—Neb. Test No. (not tested). Number of plows recommended: Three, 14-in.
Engine: Chrysler IND-5; 3¼x4⅜, 6 cylinders, L-Head, cast en bloc; piston displacement 217.7 cu. in.
Speeds: M.P.H. forward 1.9, 2.8, 3.4, 5.1, 6.4, 9.2, 10.3, 15.2, 22.6, 32.4 and 1.9, 2.8 reverse.

GIBSON MANUFACTURING CORP.
Longmont, Colorado

Gibson Model D

1948-1949

Air Cleaner: United, oil bath.
Brakes: Two, operated individually.
Carburetor: Stromberg 426020, ⅞ in.
Clutch: Own, V-belts.
Governor: Built in motor, flyball.
Ignition: Wico, impulse coupling magneto.
Magneto: Wico, impulse coupling.
Spark Plugs: 18 mm.
Number of Plows Recommended: One, 12-in.
Engine: Wisconsin AEH; 3x3¼, 2,000 r.p.m., 1 cylinder, air cooled. Piston displacement 23 cu. in.
Speeds: M.P.H Forward, 2, 4, 7 and 2.5 reverse.

GIBSON MODEL D
Gibson Mfg. Corp., Longmont, Colo.

GRAND HAVEN STAMPED PRODUCTS CO.
Grand Haven, Michigan

GH Model BC   1948
GH Model CC   1948

GH MODEL BC and CC
Grand Haven Stamped Products Co.,
Grand Haven, Mich.

Brakes: Two; operated by foot.
Carburetor: Briggs & Stratton.
Clutch: Twin Disc, XA3265, model 1045 over center friction type disc.
Ignition: Briggs & Stratton, built in flywheel magneto.
Spark Plugs: 18 mm, C-7.
Data: H.P.—Calculated; Max. Belt 6.5; Max. D.B. 4.8; Max. lbs. pull 1,090 at 1.5 m.p.h. Weight 1,215 lbs. Number of plows recommended: One, 10-in.
Engine: Briggs & Stratton ZZ; 2,000-3,200 r.p.m.; 1 cylinder, 4-cycle; piston displacement 22.97 cu. in.
Speeds: M.P.H. forward 0.6 to 7.2 and 1.0 to 3.0 reverse.

INEXCO TRACTOR CORP.
New York, New York

Tiger 3, Motor Cultivator   1948
Tiger 12 Model IXA-12   1948

Clutch: Sliding motor base.
Dimensions: Length over all, 7 ft.; height, 40 in.; width, 26 in.; width tread to tread, 20 in.; wheelbase, 6 ft.; turning radius, 7ft. 10 in.; net weight, 375 lbs; gross weight crated, 440 lbs.
Drive: Primary, V-belt; secondary, roller chain.
Engine: 3.5 H.P. Lauson, Wisconsin or Clinton, air cooled.
Speeds: Two forward and one reverse.
Starting: Rope.
Wheels: Rear tires 5.00-16; front, 4.00-8.

TIGER 3, MOTOR CULTIVATOR
Inexco Tractor Corp., New York, N. Y.

TIGER 12 MODEL IXA-12
Inexco Tractor Corp., New York, N. Y.

Air Cleaner: United, oil bath.
Brakes: Two; operated by foot pedals.
Carburetor: Wisconsin, 7/8-in.
Clutch: Wisconsin, twin disc.
Generator: Delco-Remy.
Governor: Wisconsin, flyball.
Ignition: Wisconsin, high tension magneto.
Lamps: Guide (Special).
Oil Filter: Purolator.
Radiator: ....
Radiator Cover: ....
Spark Plugs: Champion.
Starting: Hand crank.
Data—H.P.—Neb. Test No. (not tested);
Manufacturer's rating: Max. Belt 13.3;
Max. D.B. 14½; Max lbs. pull 1,685 at 2
m.p.h. Weight 1,720. Number of plows
recommended: One, 14-in.
Engine: Wisconsin TF; 3x3¼, 1,600-2,600
r.p.m., 2 cylinders, air cooled, cast en
bloc; piston displacement 53.9 cu. in.
Pulley: 8x5½, 1,100 r.p.m. and 2,700 f.p.m.
at normal engine speed.
Speeds: M.P.H. forward 2½, 4, 10 and 2½
reverse.

INTERNATIONAL HARVESTER CO.

Chicago, Illinois

International Super-A	1948-1949
International TD-24 Diesel Crawler Tractor	1948-1952
McCormick-Deering Farmall Super-A	1948-1949
McCormick-Deering Farmall Super-AV	1948-1954
McCormick-Deering Farmall C	1948-1951
McCormick-Deering Farmall H	1948-1952
McCormick-Deering Farmall HV	1948-1952
McCormick-Deering Farmall M	1948-1952
McCormick-Deering Farmall MD Diesel	1948-1952
McCormick-Deering Farmall MDV Diesel	1948-1952
McCormick-Deering Farmall MV	1948-1952
McCormick-Deering Farmall Cub	1948-1958
McCormick-Deering O-4	1948-1953
McCormick-Deering OS-4	1948-1953
McCormick-Deering O-6	1948-1953
McCormick-Deering OS-6	1948-1953
McCormick-Deering ODS-6 Diesel	1948-1953
McCormick-Deering W-4	1948-1953
McCormick-Deering W-6	1948-1952
McCormick-Deering WD-6 Diesel	1948-1952
McCormick-Deering W-9	1948-1953
McCormick-Deering WD-9 Diesel	1948-1952
McCormick-Deering WR-9	1948-1954
McCormick-Deering WDR-9 Diesel	1948-1954

Air Cleaner: Donaldson, oil bath.
Battery: Auto-Lite (special).
Brakes: Two; operated by foot pedals, individually or locked together.
Carburetor: Zenith or Marvel-Schebler, ⅞ in.
Clutch: Rockford or Atwood single plate, dry disc, spring-loaded.
Generator: Delco-Remy (special).
Governor: Own, centrifugal, variable speed.
Ignition: Own, high tension magneto with automatic impulse coupling.
Lamps: Guide Lamp (special).
Lighting: Delco-Remy (special).
Oil Filter: Purolator, replaceable element.
Radiator: Own, fin and flat tube.
Radiator Cover: Hardy shutter (special).
Spark Plugs: Champion 15-A or AC-87, 18 m.m.
Starting: Delco-Remy (special).
Data: H.P.—Manufacturers rating: Max. belt 19.06; Max. D. B. 17.35; Max. pounds pull 2272 at 2.1 m.p.h. with operating weight of 3672 lbs.
Engine: Own, 3x4, 1400 r.p.m., 4 cylinders, vertical, valve-in-head, cast en bloc; piston displacement 113.1 cu. in. Removable sleeves.
Pulley: 8½x6, 1157 r.p.m. and 2574 f.p.m. at normal engine speed (special).
Speeds: M.P.H. forward 2.1, 3.4, 4.5, 9.3 and 2.7 reverse on 8-24 tires.

INTERNATIONAL SUPER-A
International Harvester Co., Chicago, Ill.

INTERNATIONAL TD-24 DIESEL CRAWLER TRACTOR
International Harvester Co., Chicago, Ill.

Air Cleaner: Donaldson, oil bath.
Battery: Auto-Lite.
Brakes: Two, operated hydraulically and manual (foot).
Carburetor: Own, 1¼-in.
Clutch: Rockford, double plate, spring loaded, dry disk.
Diesel: Own injection pump.
Generator: Delco-Remy.
Governor: Own, centrifugal, variable speed.
Ignition: Delco-Remy distributor
Lamps: Guide Lamp.
Oil Filter: Purolator.
Radiator: Own, fin and flat tube.
Radiator Cover: Hardy shutter (special).
Spark Plugs: Champion 44 or AC 18.
Starting: Delco-Remy.
Data: H.P.—Neb. Test No. (not tested). Manufacturer's rating: Max. belt 167; Max. D.B. 140; Max. lbs. pull 33,600 at 1.6 m.p.h. Weight 37,350 lbs.
Engine: Own, D-24; 5¾x7, 1,375 r.p.m., 6 cylinders, cast en bloc; piston displacement 1,090.6 cu. in.
Speeds: M.P.H. forward 1,6, 2.0, 2.4, 3.1, 4.0, 5.2, 6.2, 7.8, and 1.6, 2.0, 2.4, 3.0, 4.0, 5.0, 6.0, and 7.7 reverse.

International "TD-24" Crawler Tractor
International Harvester Co., Chicago, Ill.

Air Cleaner: Donaldson, oil bath.
Battery: Auto-Lite (Special).
Brakes: Two; operated by foot pedals, individually or locked together.
Carburetor: Zenith or Marvel-Schebler, 7/8 in.
Clutch: Rockford or Atwood, single plate, dry disc, spring loaded.
Generator: Delco-Remy (special).
Governor: Own, centrifugal, variable speed.
Ignition: Own, high tension magneto with automatic impulse coupling.
Lamps: Guide Lamp (special).
Lighting: Delco-Remy (special).
Oil Filter: Purolator, replaceable element.
Radiator: Own, fin and flat tube.
Radiator Cover: Hardy shutter (special).
Spark Plugs: Champion 15-A or AC-85S com., Auto-Lite BT8 or Edison Z147; 18 mm.
Starting: Delco-Remy (special).
Data: H.P.—Neb. Test No. 329 (gasoline): Max. Belt 18.34; Max. D.B. 16.32; Max lbs. pull 2,387 at 1.93 m.p.h. Test No. 330 (distillate): Max. Belt 16.51; Max. D.B. 15.17; Max. lbs. pull 2,360 at 1.97 m.p.h. Weight as tested (with operator) 3,570 lbs. Number of plows recommended: One, 16 in.
Engine: Own; 3x4, 1,400 r.p.m., 4 cylinders, vertical, valve-in-head, cast en bloc; piston displacement 113.1 cu. in.; removable sleeves, yes.

Pulley: 8½x6, 1,157 r.p.m. and 2,574 f. p.m. at normal engine speed (special).
Speeds: M.P.H. forward 2⅜, 3⅝, 4⅞, 10, and 2⅞ reverse on 9-24 tires.

McCORMICK-DEERING FARMALL SUPER-A
International Harvester Co., Chicago, Ill.

McCormick Farmall "Super-A"

Air Cleaner: Donaldson, oil bath.
Battery: Auto-Lite (special).
Brakes: Two; operated by foot pedals, individually or locked together.
Carburetor: Zenith or Marvel-Schebler, ⅞ in.

McCORMICK-DEERING FARMALL SUPER-AV
International Harvester Co., Chicago, Ill.

Clutch: Rockford or Atwood, single plate, dry disc, spring-loaded.
Generator: Delco-Remy (special).
Governor: Own, centrifugal, variable speed.
Ignition: Own, high tension magneto with automatic impulse coupling.
Lamps: Guide Lamp (special).
Lighting: Delco-Remy (special).
Oil Filter: Purolator, replaceable element.
Radiator: Own, fin and flat tube.
Radiator Cover: Hardy shutter (special).
Spark Plugs: Champion 15-A, AC-85S com., Auto-Lite BT8 or Edison Z147; 18 mm.
Starting: Delco-Remy (special).
Data: H.P.—Neb. Test No. (not tested). Horsepower is approximately same as Farmall A, tests 329 and 330. Number of plows recommended: One, 16 in.
Engine: Own; 3x4, 1,400 r.p.m., 4 cylinders, vertical, valve-in-head, cast en bloc; piston displacement 113.1 cu. in.; removable sleeves, yes.
Pulley: 8½x6, 1,157 r.p.m. and 2,574 f. p.m. at normal engine speed (special).
Speeds: M.P.H. forward 3, 4⅞, 6⅜, 13¼, and 3¾ reverse, on 9-36 tires.

Air Cleaner: Donaldson, oil bath.
Battery: Auto-Lite (Special).
Brakes: Two; operated by foot pedals individually or locked together.
Carburetor: Zenith or Marvel-Schebler, 7/8-in.
Clutch: Rockford or Atwood, single plate, dry disc, spring loaded.
Generator: Delco-Remy (Special).
Governor: Own, centrifugal, variable speed.
Ignition: Own, high tension magneto with automatic impulse coupling.
Lamps: Guide Lamp (special).
Oil Filter: Purolator, replaceable element.
Radiator: Young, fin and flat tube.
Radiator Cover: Hardy shutter (special).
Spark Plugs: Champion 15-A, AC-85S com., Auto-Lite BT8 or Edison Z147.
Starting: Delco-Remy (special).
Data: H.P.—Neb. Test No. (not tested). Number of plows recommended: One, 16-in. or Two, 12-in.
Engine: Own; 3x4, 1,650 r.p.m., 4 cylinders, vertical, valve-in-head, cast en bloc. Removable sleeves: yes. Piston displacement 113.1 cu. in.
Pulley: 8½x6, 1,363 r.p.m. and 3,033 f.p.m. at normal engine speed (special).
Speeds: M.P.H. forward 2⅜, 3¾, 5, 10¼, and 3 reverse, on 9-36 tires.

McCORMICK-DEERING FARMALL C
International Harvester Co., Chicago, Ill.

McCormick Farmall "C"
International Harvester Co., Chicago, Ill.

Air Cleaner: Donaldson, oil bath.
Battery: Auto-Lite (Special).
Brakes: Two; operated by foot pedals, individually or locked together.

McCORMICK-DEERING FARMALL H
International Harvester Co., Chicago, Ill.

Carburetor: Own, 1 in.
Clutch: Rockford, single plate, dry disc, spring-loaded.
Generator: Delco-Remy (special).
Governor: Own, centrifugal, variable speed.
Ignition: Own, high tension magneto with automatic impulse coupling.
Lamps: Guide Lamp (special).
Lighting: Delco-Remy (special).
Oil Filter: Purolator, replaceable element.
Radiator: Own or Young, fin and flat tube.
Radiator Cover: Hardy shutter (special).
Spark Plugs: Champion 15-A or AC-85S com., Auto-Lite BT8 or Edison Z147; 18 mm.
Starting: Delco-Remy (special).
Data: H.P.—Neb. Test No. 333 (gasoline): Max. Belt 26.20; Max. D.B. 24.17; Max. lbs. pull 3,603 at 2.06 m.p.h. Test No. 334 (distillate): Max. Belt 23.31; Max. D.B. 21.37; Max. lbs. pull 3,169 at 2.29 m.p.h. Weight as tested (with operator) 5,550 lbs. Number of plows recommended: Two, 14 in.
Engine: Own; 3⅜x4¼, 1,650 r.p.m, 4 cylinders, vertical, valve-in-head, cast en bloc; piston displacement 152.1 cu. in.; removable sleeves, yes.
Pulley: 9¾x7½, 1,019 r.p.m. and 2,601 f.p.m. at normal engine speed (special).
Speeds: M.P.H. forward 2½, 3⅜, 4⅛, 5⅛, 15⅝, and 2⅞ reverse, on 10-38 tires.

Air Cleaner: Donaldson, oil bath.
Battery: Auto-Lite (special).
Brakes: Two; operated by foot pedals, individually or locked together.
Carburetor: Own, 1-in.
Clutch: Rockford, single plate, dry disc, spring loaded.
Generator: Delco-Remy (special).
Governor: Own, centrifugal, variable speed.
Ignition: Own, high tension magneto with automatic impulse coupling.
Lamps: Guide Lamp (special).
Oil Filter: Purolator, replaceable element.
Radiator: Own or Young, fin and flat tube.
Radiator Cover: Hardy shutter (special).
Spark Plugs: Champion 15-A, AC-85S com., Auto-Lite BT8 or Edison Z147; 18 mm.
Starting: Delco-Remy (special).
Data: H.P.—Neb. Test No. (not tested). Horsepower is approximately same as Farmall H, tests 333 and 334. Number of plows recommended: Two, 14 in.
Engine: Own; 3⅜x4¼, 1,650 r.p.m., 4 cylinders, vertical, valve-in-head; piston displacement 152.1 cu. in. Removable sleeves, yes.

Pulley: 9¾x7½, 1019 r.p.m. and 2601 f.p.m. at normal engine speed.
Speeds: M.P.H. Forward 2½, 3⅜, 4, 5, 15¼ and 2⅞ reverse, on 9:00-36 tires.

McCORMICK-DEERING FARMALL HV

McCORMICK-DEERING FARMALL M

International Harvester Co., Chicago, Ill.

Air Cleaner: Donaldson, oil bath.
Battery: Auto-Lite (special) (2).
Brakes: Two; operated by foot pedals, individually or locked together.
Carburetor: Own, ¾ in. (for starting only).
Clutch: Rockford, single plate, dry disc, spring-loaded.
Diesel: Own injection pump.
Generator: Delco-Remy (special).
Governor: Own, centrifugal, variable speed.
Ignition: Own, magneto (for starting only).
Lamps: Guide Lamp (special).
Lighting: Delco-Remy (special).
Oil Filter: Purolator, replaceable element.
Radiator: Own or McCord, fin and flat tube.
Radiator Cover: Hardy shutter (special).
Spark Plugs: Champion 49 or AC 18-A, 18 mm. (for starting only).
Starting: Delco-Remy (special).
Data: H.P.—Neb. Test No. 368; Max. Belt 35.02; Max. D.B. 31.05; Max. lbs. pull 4,541 at 2.22 m.p.h. Weight as tested (with operator) 7,570 lbs. Number of plows recommended: three, 14 in.
Engine: Own, 3⅞x5¼, 1,450 r.p.m., 4 cylinders, vertical, valve-in-head, cast en bloc; piston displacement 247.7 cu. in.; removable sleeves, yes.
Pulley: 11x7½, 899 r.p.m. and 2,588 f. p.m. at normal engine speed (special).
Speeds: M.P.H. forward 2⅝, 3½, 4¼, 5⅛, 16¼, and 3⅛ reverse, on 11-38 tires.

Air Cleaner: Donaldson, oil bath.
Battery: Auto-Lite (special).
Brakes: Two; operated by foot pedals, individually or locked together.
Carburetor: Own, 1¼ in.
Clutch: Rockford, single plate, dry disc, spring-loaded.
Generator: Delco-Remy (special).
Governor: Own, centrifugal, variable speed.
Ignition: Own, high tension magneto with automatic impulse coupling.
Lamps: Guide Lamp (special).
Lighting: Delco-Remy (special).
Oil Filter: Purolator, replaceable element.
Radiator: Own or McCord, fin and flat tube.
Radiator Cover: Hardy shutter (special).
Spark Plugs: Champion 15-A, AC-85S com., Auto-Lite BT8 or Edison Z147; 18 mm.
Starting: Delco-Remy (special).
Data: H.P.—Neb. Test No. 328 (gasoline) : Max. Belt 36.66; Max. D.B. 33.05; Max. lbs. pull 4,233 at 2.17 m.p.h. Test No. 327 (distillate): Max. Belt 34.82; Max. D.B. 30.62; Max. lbs. pull 4,365 at 2.19 m.p.h. Weight as tested (with operator) 6,770. Number of plows recommended: Three, 14 in.
Engine: Own; 3⅞x5¼, 1,450 r.p.m., 4 cylinders, vertical, valve-in-head, cast en bloc; piston displacement 247.7 cu. in.; removable sleeves, yes.
Pulley: 11x7½, 899 r.p.m. and 2,588 f.p. m. at normal engine speed (special).
Speeds: M.P.H. forward 2⅝, 3½, 4¼, 5⅛, 16¼, and 3⅛ reverse, on 11-38 tires.

McCORMICK-DEERING FARMALL MD DIESEL

International Harvester Co., Chicago, Ill.

Air Cleaner: Donaldson, oil bath.
Battery: Auto-Lite (special) (2).
Brakes: Two; operated by foot pedals, individually or locked together.
Carburetor: Own, for starting only, ¾-in.
Clutch: Rockford, single plate, dry disc, spring-loaded.
Diesel: Own injection pump.
Generator: Delco-Remy (special).
Governor: Own, centrifugal, variable speed.
Ignition: Own magneto, for starting only.
Lamps: Guide Lamp (special).
Oil Filter: Purolator, replaceable element.
Radiator: Own or McCord, fin and flat tube.
Radiator Cover: Hardy shutter (special).
Spark Plugs: Champion 49 or AC 18-A, 18 m.m. (for starting only).
Starting: Delco-Remy (special).
Data: H.P.— Neb. Test No. (not tested). Horsepower is approximately the same as Farmall MD, test 368. Number of plows recommended: three, 14-in.
Engine: Own; 3⅞x5¼, 1450 r.p.m. 4 cylinders, vertical, valve-in-head, cast en bloc; piston displacement 247.7 cu. in.; removable sleeves, yes.
Pulley: 11x7½, 899 r.p.m and 2588 f.p.m. at normal engine speed (special).
Speeds: M.P.H. forward 2½, 3⅜, 4⅛, 5, 16 and 3⅛ reverse, on 10.00-36 tires.

McCORMICK-DEERING FARMALL MDV DIESEL

International Harvester Co., Chicago, Ill.

McCORMICK-DEERING FARMALL MV
International Harvester Co., Chicago, Ill.

Air Cleaner: Donaldson, oil bath.
Battery: Auto-Lite (special).
Brakes: Two; operated by foot pedals, individually or locked together.
Carburetor: Own, 1¼ in.
Clutch: Rockford, single plate, dry disc, spring-loaded.
Generator: Delco-Remy (special).
Governor: Own, centrifugal, variable speed.
Ignition: Own, high tension magneto with automatic impulse coupling.
Lamps: Guide Lamp (special).
Lighting: Delco-Remy (special).
Oil Filter: Purolator, replaceable element.
Radiator: Own or McCord, fin and flat tube.
Radiator Cover: Hardy shutter (special).
Spark Plugs: Champion 15-A, AC-85S com., Auto-Lite BT8 or Edison Z147; 18 mm.
Starting: Delco-Remy (special).
Data: H.P.—Neb. Test No. (not tested). Horsepower is approximtely the same as Farmali M, test Nos. 328 and 327. Number of Plows Recommended: three, 14 in.
Engine: Own; 3⅞x5¼, 1450 r.p.m., 4 cylinders, vertical, valve-in-head, cast en bloc; piston displacement 247.7 cu. in.; removable sleeves, yes.
Pulley: 11x7½, 899 r.p.m. and 2588 f.p.m. at normal engine speed (special).
Speeds: M.P.H. forward 2½, 3⅜, 4⅛, 5, 16 and 3⅛ reverse, on 10.00-36 tires.

McCORMICK-DEERING FARMALL CUB
International Harvester Co., Chicago, Ill.

Air Cleaner: Donaldson, oil bath.
Battery: Auto-Lite (Special).
Brakes: Two; operated by foot pedal individually or locked together.
Carburetor: Own, ¾-in.
Clutch: Rockford or Atwood, single plate, dry disc, spring loaded.
Generator: Delco-Remy (Special).
Governor: Own, centrifugal, variable speed.
Ignition: Own, high tension magneto with automatic impulse coupling.
Lamps: Guide Lamp (Special).
Oil Filter: Purolator, replaceable element.
Radiator: Modine core, fin and flat tube.
Radiator Cover: None.
Spark Plugs: Champion 15-A, AC-85S com., Auto-Lite BT8 or Edison Z147, 18 mm.
Starting: Delco-Remy (Special).
Data: H.P.—Neb. Test No. 386 (gasoline); Max. Belt. 9.23; Max. D.B. 8.47; Max. lbs. pull 1,596 at 1.96 m.p.h. Weight as tested (with operator) 2,701. Number of plows recommended: One, 12-in.
Engine: Own; 2⅝x2¾, 1,600 r.p.m., 4 cylinders, vertical, L-head, cast en bloc; removable sleeves: no; piston displacement 59.5 cu. in.
Pulley: 9x4½, 1,322 r.p.m. and 3,114 f.p.m. at normal engine speed (special).
Speeds: M.P.H. forward 2, 3, 6⅛ and 2¼ reverse, on 7-24 tires.

McCormick Farmall "Cub"

Air Cleaner: Donaldson, oil bath.

Battery: Auto-Lite (special).

Brakes: Two; operated by foot pedals, individually.

Carburetor: Own, 1 in.

Clutch: Rockford, single plate, dry disc, over center.

Generator: Delco-Remy (special).

Governor: Own, centrifugal, variable speed.

Ignition: Own, high tension magneto with automatic impulse coupling.

Lamps: Guide Lamp (special).

Lighting: Delco-Remy (special).

Oil Filters: Purolator, replaceable element.

Radiator: Own, fin and flat tube.

Radiator Cover: Hardy shutter (special).

Spark Plugs: Champion 15-A, AC-85S com., Auto-Lite BT8 or Edison Z147; 18 mm.

Starting: Delco-Remy (special).

Data: H.P.—Neb. Test No. (not tested); H.P. is approximately same as W-4, tests 353 and 342. Number of plows recommended: two, 14-in.

Engine: Own; 3⅜x4¼, 1,650 r.p.m., 4 cylinders, vertical, valve-in-head, cast en bloc; piston displacement 152.1 cu. in.; removable sleeves, yes.

Pulley: 9¾x7½, 1,019 r.p.m. and 2,601 f.p.m. at normal engine speed (special).

Speeds: M.P.H. forward 1½, 3⅛, 4, 5, 14⅝, and 1¾ reverse, on 12-26 tires.

McCORMICK-DEERING O-4
Orchard and Grove
International Harvester Co., Chicago, Ill.

McCORMICK-DEERING OS-4
Orchard and Grove
International Harvester Co., Chicago, Ill.

Air Cleaner: Donaldson, oil bath.

Battery: Auto-Lite (special).

Brakes: Two, operated by foot pedals, individually.

Carburetor: Own, 1-in.

Clutch: Rockford, single plate, dry disc, over center.

Generator: Delco-Remy (special).

Governor: Own, certrifugal, variable speed.

Ignition: Own, high tension magneto with automatic impulse coupling.

Lamps: Guide Lamp (special).

Oil Filter: Purolator, replaceable element.

Radiator: Own, fin and flat tube.

Radiator Cover: Hardy shutter (special).

Spark Plugs: Champion 15-A, AC-85S com., Auto-Lite BT8 or Edison Z147; 18 mm.

Starting: Delco-Remy (special).

Data: H.P.—Neb. Test No. (not tested). Horsepower is approximately the same as W-4 tests 353 and 342. Number of plows recommended: two, 14-in.

Engine: Own; 3⅜x4¼, 1650 r.p.m., 4 cylinders, vertical, valve-in-head, cast en bloc; piston displacement 152.1 cu. in.; removable sleeves, yes.

Pulley: 9¾x7½, 1019 r.p.m. and 2601 f.p.m. at normal engine speed (special).

Speeds: M.P.H. forward 1½, 3⅛, 4, 5, 14⅝, and 1¾ reverse, on 12-26 tires.

Air Cleaner: Donaldson, oil bath.
Battery: Auto-Lite (special).
Brakes: Two; operated by foot pedals, individually.
Carburetor: Own, 1¼-in.
Clutch: Rockford, single plate, dry disc, over center.
Generator: Delco-Remy (special).
Governor: Own, certrifugal, variable speed.
Ignition: Own, high tension magneto with automatic impulse coupling.
Lamps: Guide Lamp (special).
Lighting: Delco-Remy (special).
Oil Filter: Purolator, replaceable element.
Radiator: Own, fin and flat tube.
Radiator Cover: Hardy shutter (special).
Spark Plugs: Champion 15-A, AC-85S com., Auto-Lite BT8 or Edison Z147; 18 mm.
Starting: Delco-Remy (special).
Data: H.P.—Neb. Test No. (not tested). H.P. approximately same as W-6, tests 355 and 354. Number of plows recommended: three, 14-in.
Engine: Own; 3⅞x5¼, 1,450 r.p.m., 4 cylinders, vertical, valve-in-head, cast en bloc; piston displacement 247.7 cu. in.; removable sleeves, yes.
Pulley: 11x7½, 899 r.p.m. and 2,588 f. p.m. at normal engine speed (special).
Speeds: M.P.H. forward 1½, 3⅛, 4⅛, 4⅞, 14⅝, and 1⅞ reverse, on 13-26 tires.

McCORMICK-DEERING O-6
Orchard and Grove
International Harvester Co., Chicago, Ill.

McCORMICK-DEERING OS-6
Orchard and Grove
International Harvester Co., Chicago, Ill.

Air Cleaner: Donaldson, oil bath.
Battery: Auto-Lite (special).
Brakes: Two; operated by foot pedals, individually.
Carburetor: Own, 1¼-in.
Clutch: Rockford, single plate, dry disc, over center.
Generator: Delco-Remy (special).
Governor: Own, centrifugal, variable speed.
Ignition: Own, high tension magneto with automatic impulse coupling.
Lamps: Guide Lamp (special).
Oil Filter: Purolator, replaceable element.
Radiator: Own, fin and flat tube.
Radiator Cover: Hardy shutter (special).
Spark Plugs: Champion 15-A, AC-85S com., Auto-Lite BT8 or Edison Z147; 18 mm.
Starting: Delco-Remy (special).
Data: H.P.—Neb. Test No. (not tested). Horsepower is approximately the same as W-6, tests 355 and 354. Number of plows recommended: three, 14-in.
Engine: Own, 3⅞x5¼, 1450 r.p.m., 4 cylinders, vertical, valve-in-head, cast en bloc; piston displacement 247.7 cu. in. Removable sleeves, yes.
Pulley: 11x7½, 899 r.p.m. and 2588 f.p.m. at normal engine speed (special).
Speeds: M.P.H. forward 1½, 3⅛, 4⅛, 4⅞, 14⅝, and 1⅞ reverse, on 13-26 tires.

Air Cleaner: Donaldson, oil bath.
Battery: Auto-Lite (special) (2).
Brakes: Two; operated by foot pedals, individually.
Carburetor: Own, ¾-in. (for starting only).
Clutch: Rockford, single plate, dry disc, over center.
Diesel: Own injection pump.
Generator: Delco-Remy (special).
Governor: Own, centrifugal, variable speed.
Ignition: Own magneto (for starting only).
Lamps: Guide Lamp (special).
Oil Filter: Purolator, replaceable element.
Radiator: Own, fin and flat tube.
Radiator Cover: Hardy shutter (special).
Spark Plugs: Champion 49 or AC 18-A, 18 m.m. (for starting only).
Starting: Delco-Remy (special).
Data: H.P.—Neb. Test No. (not tested). Horsepower is approximately the same as WD-6, test 356. Number of plows recommended: three, 14-in.
Engine: Own; 3⅞x5¼, 1450 r.p.m., 4 cylinders, valve-in-head, cast en bloc; piston displacement 247.7 cu. in. Removable sleeves, yes.
Pulley: 11x7½, 899 r.p.m. and 2588 f.p.m. at normal engine speed (special).
Speeds: M.P.H. forward 1½, 3⅛, 4⅛, 4⅞, 14⅝, and 1⅞ reverse, on 13-26 tires.

McCORMICK-DEERING ODS-6 DIESEL
Orchard and Grove
International Harvester Co., Chicago, Ill.

Air Cleaner: Donaldson, oil bath.
Battery: Auto-Lite (special).
Brakes: Two; operated by foot pedals, individually or locked together.
Carburetor: Own, 1 in.
Clutch: Rockford, single plate, dry disc, spring-loaded.
Generator: Delco-Remy (special).
Governor: Own, centrifugal, variable speed.
Ignition: Own, high tension magneto with automatic impulse coupling.
Lamps: Guide Lamp (special).
Lighting: Delco-Remy (special).
Oil Filters: Purolator, replaceable element.
Radiator: Own, fin and flat tube.
Radiator Cover: Hardy shutter (special).
Spark Plugs: Champion 15-A, AC-85S com., Auto-Lite BT8 or Edison Z147; 18 mm.
Starting: Delco-Remy (special).
Data: H.P.—Neb. Test No. 353 (gasoline); Max. Belt 26.21; Max. D.B. 23.97; Max. lbs. pull 3,671 at 2.16 m.p.h. Weight as tested (with operator) 5,850 lbs. Test No. 342 (distillate); Max. Belt 23.11; Max. D.B. 21.38; Max. lbs. pull 3,297 at 2.21 m.p.h. Weight as tested (with operator) 5,690 lbs. Number of plows recommended: two, 14-in.
Engine: Own; 3⅜x4¼, 1,650 r.p.m., 4 cylinders, vertical, valve-in-head, cast en bloc; piston displacement 152.1 cu. in.; removable sleeves, yes.
Pulley: 9¾x7½, 1,019 r.p.m. and 2,601 f.p.m. at normal engine speed (special).
Speeds: M.P.H. forward 2⅜, 3⅛, 4, 5, 14⅝, and 2¾ reverse, on 12-26 tires.

McCORMICK-DEERING W-4
International Harvester Co., Chicago, Ill.

Air Cleaner: Donaldson, oil bath.
Battery: Auto-Lite (special).
Brakes: Two; operated by foot pedals, individually or locked together.
Carburetor: Own, 1¼ in.
Clutch: Rockford, single plate, dry disc, spring-loaded.
Generator: Delco-Remy (special).
Governor: Own, centrifugal, variable speed.
Ignition: Own, high tension magneto with automatic impulse coupling.
Lamps: Guide Lamp (special).
Lighting: Delco-Remy (special).
Oil Filter: Purolator, replaceable element.
Radiator: Own, fin and flat tube.
Radiator Cover: Hardy shutter (special).
Spark Plugs: Champion 15-A, AC-85S com., Auto-Lite BT8 or Edison Z147; 18 mm.
Starting: Delco-Remy (special).
Data: H.P.—Neb. Test No. 355 (gasoline); Max. Belt 36.97; Max. D.B. 32.48; Max. lbs. pull 4,777 at 1.97 m.p.h. Weight as tested (with operator) 7,610 lbs. Test No. 354 (distillate); Max. Belt 34.23; Max. D.B. 30.74; Max. lbs. pull 4,755 at 1.96 m.p.h. Weight as tested (with operator) 7,744 lbs. Number of plows recommended: three, 14-in.

Engine: Own; 3⅞x5¼, 1,450 r.p.m.,4 cylinders, vertical, valve-in-head, cast en bloc; piston displacement 247.7 cu. in; removable sleeves, yes.
Pulley: 11x7½, 899 r.p.m. and 2,588 f. p.m. at normal engine speed (special).
Speeds: M.P.H. forward 2⅜, 3⅜, 4⅜, 5⅜, 15⅞, and 2⅞ reverse, on 13-30 tires.

McCORMICK-DEERING W-6
International Harvester Co., Chicago, Ill.

Air Cleaner: Donaldson, oil bath.
Battery: Auto-Lite (special) (2).
Brakes: Two; operated by foot pedals, individually or locked together.

McCORMICK-DEERING WD-6 DIESEL
International Harvester Co., Chicago, Ill.

Carburetor: Own, ¾ in. (for starting only).
Clutch: Rockford, single plate, dry disc, spring-loaded.
Diesel: Own injection pump.
Generator: Delco-Remy (special).
Governor: Own, centrifugal, variable speed.
Ignition: Own, magneto (for starting only).
Lamps: Guide Lamp (special).
Lighting: Delco-Remy (special).
Oil Filter: Purolator, replaceable element.
Radiator: Own, fin and flat tube.
Radiator Cover: Hardy shutter (special).
Spark Plugs: Champion 49 or AC 18-A, 18 mm. (for starting only).
Starting: Delco-Remy (special).
Data: H.P.—Neb. Test No. 356; Max. Belt 34.75; Max. D.B. 30.58; Max. lbs. pull 4,806 at 1.97 m.p.h Weight as tested (with operator) 7,995 lbs. Number of plows recommended: three, 14-in.
Engine: Own; 3⅞x5¼, 1,450 r.p.m., 4 cylinders, vertical, valve-in-head, cast en bloc; piston displacement 247.7 cu. in.; removable sleeves, yes.
Pulley: 11x7½, 899 r.p.m. and 2,588 f. p.m. at normal engine speed (special).
Speeds: M.P.H. forward 2⅜, 3⅜, 4⅜, 5⅜, 15⅞, and 2⅞ reverse, on 13-30 tires.

Air Cleaner: Donaldson, oil bath.
Battery: Auto-Lite (special).
Brakes: Two; operated by foot pedals, individually or locked together.
Carburetor: Own, 1⅜ in.
Clutch: Rockford, single plate, dry disc, spring-loaded.
Generator: Delco-Remy (special).
Governor: Own, centrifugal, variable speed.
Ignition: Own, high tension magneto with automatic impulse coupling.
Lamps: Guide Lamp (special).
Lighting: Delco-Remy (special).
Oil Filter: Purolator, replaceable element.
Radiator: Own, fin and flat tube.
Radiator Cover: Hardy shutter (special).
Spark Plugs: Champion O Com. or AC-73 Com. (gasoline); Champion 1 Com. or AC-75 Com. (distillate or kerosene); ⅞-18.
Starting: Delco-Remy (special).
Data: H.P.—Neb. Test No. 369 (gasoline); Max. Belt 49.40; Max. D. B. 44.15; Max. lbs. pull 6,414 at 1.95 m.p.h. Weight as tested (with operator), 10,090 lbs. Test No. 371 (distillate); Max. Belt 46.36; Max. D.B. 42.67; Max. lbs. pull 6,577 at 2.02 m.p.h. Weight as tested (with operator) 10,190 lbs. Number of plows recommended: four, 14-in.
Engine: Own; 4.4x5.5, 1,500 r.p.m., 4 cylinders, vertical, valve-in-head, cast en bloc; piston displacement 334.5 cu. in.; removable sleeves, yes.
Air Cleaner: Donaldson, oil bath.
Battery: Auto-Lite (special) (2).
Brakes: Two; operated by foot pedals, individually or locked together.

McCORMICK-DEERING WD-9 DIESEL
International Harvester Co., Chicago, Ill.

Pulley: 14x8½, 707 r.p.m. and 2,593 f. p.m. at normal engine speed (special).
Speeds: M.P.H. forward 2⅜, 3¼, 4⅝, 5⅝, 16¼, and 3 reverse on 14-34 tires.

McCORMICK-DEERING W-9
International Harvester Co., Chicago, Ill.

Carburetor: Own, ¾ in. (for starting only).
Clutch: Rockford, single plate, dry disc, spring-loaded.
Diesel: Own injection pump.
Generator: Delco-Remy (special).
Governor: Own, centrifugal, variable speed.
Ignition: Own, magneto (for starting only).
Lamps: Guide Lamp (special).
Lighting: Delco-Remy (special).
Oil Filter: Purolator, replaceable element.
Radiator: Own, fin and flat tube.
Radiator Cover: Hardy shutter (special).
Spark Plugs: Champion 49 or AC 18-A, 18 mm. (for starting only).
Starting: Delco-Remy (special).
Data: H.P.—Neb. Test No. 370; Max. Belt 46.43; Max. D. B. 42.57; Max. lbs. pull 6,367 at 1.98 m.p.h. Weight as tested (with operator) 10,260 lbs. Number of plows recommended: four, 14-in.
Engine: Own; 4.4x5.5, 1,500 r.p.m., 4 cylinders, vertical, valve-in-head, cast en bloc; piston displacement 334.5 cu. in.; removable sleeves, yes.
Pulley: 14x8½, 707 r.p.m. and 2,593 f. p.m. at normal engine speed (special).
Speeds: M.P.H. forward 2⅜, 3¼, 4⅝, 5⅝, 16¼, and 3 reverse, on 14-34 tires.

Air Cleaner: Donaldson, oil bath.
Battery: Auto-Lite (special).
Brakes: Two; operated by foot pedals, individually or locked together.
Carburetor: Own, 1⅜-in.
Clutch: Rockford, single plate, dry disc, over center.
Generator: Delco-Remy (special).
Governor: Own, centrifugal, variable speed.
Ignition: Own, high tension magneto with automatic impulse coupling.
Lamps: Guide Lamp (special).
Oil Filter: Purolator, replaceable element.
Radiator: Own, fin and flat tube.
Radiator Cover: Hardy shutter (special).
Spark Plugs: Champion O Com. or AC-73 Com. (gasoline); Champion 1 Com. or AC-75 Com. (distillate or kerosene); ⅞-18.
Starting: Delco-Remy (special).
Data: H.P.—Neb. Test No. (not tested). Horsepower is approximately the same as W-9, tests 369 and 371. Number of plows recommended: four, 14-in.
Engine: Own; 4.4x5.5, 1500 r.p.m., 4 cylinders, vertical, valve-in-head, cast en bloc; piston displacement 334.5 cu. in.; removable sleeves, yes.
Pulley: 14x8½, 707 r.p.m. and 2593 f.p.m. at normal engine speed (special).

Speeds: M.P.H. forward 2⅝, 3½, 4⅞, 6, and 3⅛ reverse on 54 in. steel wheels; 2½, 3⅜, 4¾, 5¾, 16¾ forward, and 3 reverse on 15-34 tires.

McCORMICK-DEERING WR-9
Rice Field Special
International Harvester Co., Chicago, Ill.

McCORMICK-DEERING WDR-9 DIESEL
Rice Field Special
International Harvester Co., Chicago, Ill.

Air Cleaner: Donaldson, oil bath.
Battery: Auto-Lite (special) (2).
Brakes: Two; operated by foot pedals, individually or locked together.
Carburetor: Own, ¾-in. (for starting only).
Clutch: Rockford, single plate, dry disc, over center.
Diesel: Own, injection pump.
Generator: Delco-Remy (special).
Governor: Own, centrifugal, variable speed.
Ignition: Own, magneto (for starting only).
Lamps: Guide Lamp (special).
Oil Filter: Purolator, replaceable element.
Radiator: Own, fin and flat tube.
Radiator Cover: Hardy shutter (special).
Spark Plugs: Champion 49 or AC 18-A, 18 m.m. (for starting only).
Starting: Delco-Remy (special).
Data: H.P.—Neb. Test No. (not tested). Horsepower is approximately the same as WD-9, test 370. Number of plows recommended: four, 14-in.
Engine: Own; 4.4x5.5, 1500 r.p.m., 4 cylinders, vertical, valve-in-head, cast en bloc; piston displacement 334.5 cu. in.; removable sleeves, yes.
Pulley: 14x8½, 707 r.p.m. and 2593 f.p.m. at normal engine speed (special).
Speeds: M.P.H. forward 2⅝, 3½, 4⅞, 6, and 3⅛ reverse on 54-in. steel wheels. 2½, 3⅝, 4¾, 5¾, 16¾ forward, and 3 reverse, on 15-34 tires.

LEADER TRACTOR CO.
Cleveland, Ohio

Leader Model 48D

1948

Air Cleaner: Air Maize, oil bath.
Battery: Willard, 15 plate.
Brakes: Two, operated by foot, individually or interlocked.
Carburetor: Zenith No. 161-7, 7/8-in.
Clutch: Rockford, 9M. single disc.
Generator: Auto-Lite.
Governor: Hercules (Handy).
Ignition: Auto-Lite, 6-volt.
Lamps: Dietz Seal Beam.
Oil Filter: Fram.
Radiator: Hercules, tubular.
Radiator Cover: Own.
Spark Plugs: Champion (4).
Starting: Auto-Lite.
Data: H.P.—Neb. Test No. (not tested). Number of plows recommended: Two, 12-in.
Engine: Hercules, IXB; 3¼x4, 1,800 r.p.m., 4 cylinders, L-head; piston displacement 133 cu. in.
Pulley: 7x7, 1,510 r.p.m. and 2,770 f.p.m. at normal engine speed.
Speeds: M.P.H. forward 3 to 4, 5 to 7, 8 to 12½, and 2 to 4 reverse.

LEADER MODEL 48D
Leader Tractor Co., Cleveland, O.

MASSEY-HARRIS CO.
Racine, Wisconsin

Massey-Harris "Pony"

1948-1957

MASSEY-HARRIS "PONY"
Massey-Harris Co., Racine, Wis.

Air Cleaner: Donaldson, oil bath.
Battery: Exide.
Brakes: Two, operated by foot.
Carburetor: Marvel Schebler, 5/8-in.
Clutch: Rockford, single disc, heavy duty.
Generator: Auto-Lite, GBM4804A.
Governor: Continental, weight actuated.
Ignition: Auto-Lite.
Lamps: Canadian Motor Lamp Co.
Oil Filter: Purolator.
Radiator: National Auto.
Radiator Cover: None.
Spark Plugs: 18M, 1-in. hex.
Starting: Auto-Lite.
Data: H.P.—Neb. Test No. (not tested). Number of plows recommended:.......
Engine: Continental, N62; 2⅜x3½, 1,800 r.p.m., 4 cylinders, L-head; piston displacement 62 cu. in.
Pulley: 6x4¼, 1,990 r.p.m. and 3,130 f.p.m. at normal engine speed.
Speeds: M.P.H. forward 2.74, 3.59, 7.00, and 3.22 reverse.

MINNEAPOLIS-MOLINE POWER IMPLEMENT CO.
Minneapolis, Minnesota

MM Model "GTB"   1948-1950

Air Cleaner: Donaldson, oil wash.
Battery: ....
Brakes: Two; operated by foot.
Carburetor: Marvel Schebler, 1¼ in.
Clutch: Twin Disc, over center.
Generator: Delco-Remy.
Governor: Own, flyball, variable speed.
Lamps: Guide.
Lighting: Optional; Delco-Remy, 6-volt.
Magneto: Fairbanks-Morse, RF flange.
Oil Filter: Michiana, replaceable cartridge.
Radiator: Modine, tubular core, cast top
and bottom tanks.
Radiator Cover: ....
Spark Plugs: Champion, ⅞ in. O Com.
Starting: Delco-Remy.
Data: H.P.—Neb. Test No. (not tested).
Number of plows recommended:.........
Engine: Own 403A-4; 4⅝x6, 1,100 r.p.m.,
4 cylinders, vertical, cast in pairs; piston
displacement 403.2 cu. in.; no sleeves.
Pulley: 15½x7, 627 r.p.m. and 2,670 f.p.m.
at normal engine speed.
Speeds: M.P.H. forward 2.5, 3.5, 4.1, 6.0,
13.8, and 2.0 reverse.

MM MODEL "GTB"

Minneapolis-Moline "GTB"
Minneapolis-Moline Co., Minneapolis, Minn.

THE OLIVER CORP.
Charles City, Iowa

Oliver Industrial "88" HC   1948
Oliver Standard "88" HC   1948-1954
Oliver Row Crop "88" HC   1948-1954

OLIVER INDUSTRIAL "88" HC
The Oliver Corp., Charles City, Ia.

Air Cleaner: Donaldson, oil wash.
Battery: Delco-Remy.
Brakes: Two, operated by foot.
Carburetor: Schebler, 1-in.
Clutch: Borg & Beck, single plate, dry.
Generator: Delco-Remy.
Governor: Own, centrifugal, flyball, variable speed.
Ignition: Delco-Remy, battery and distributor.
Lamps: Guide.
Oil Filter: Michiana.
Radiator: Modine, fin-tube.
Radiator Cover: Own.
Spark Plugs: Champion, 6 Com.
Starting: Delco-Remy.
Data: H.P.—Neb. Test No. (not tested).
Engine: Own; $3\frac{1}{2}$x4, 1,600 r.p.m., 6 cylinders, vertical, cast en bloc; piston displacement 231 cu. in.
Pulley: $11\frac{7}{8}$x$7\frac{1}{4}$, 992 r.p.m. and 3,080 f.p.m. at normal engine speed.
Speeds: M.P.H. forward $2\frac{1}{8}$, $2\frac{3}{4}$, $3\frac{5}{8}$, $4\frac{3}{4}$, $9\frac{3}{4}$, $16\frac{7}{8}$, and $2\frac{1}{8}$, $3\frac{3}{4}$ reverse.

Air Cleaner: Donaldson, oil wash.
Battery: Delco-Remy.
Brakes: Two, operated by foot.
Carburetor: Schebler, 1-in.
Clutch: Borg & Beck, single plate, dry.
Generator: Delco-Remy.
Governor: Own, centrifugal, flyball, variable speed.
Ignition: Delco-Remy, battery and distributor.
Lamps: Guide.
Oil Filter: Michiana.
Radiator: Modine, fin-tube.
Radiator Cover: Own.
Spark Plugs: Champion, 6 Com.
Starting: Delco-Remy.
Data: H.P.—Neb. Test No. (not tested). Number of plows recommended: three, 14-in.
Engine: Own; $3\frac{1}{2}$x4, 1,600 r.p.m., 6 cylinders, vertical, cast en bloc; piston displacement 231 cu. in.
Pulley: $11\frac{7}{8}$x$7\frac{1}{4}$, 992 r.p.m. and 3,080 f.p.m. at normal engine speed.
Speeds: M.P.H. forward $2\frac{1}{2}$, $3\frac{1}{4}$, 4 1/3, $5\frac{1}{2}$, $6\frac{7}{8}$, $11\frac{7}{8}$, and $2\frac{1}{2}$, 4 1/3 reverse.

OLIVER STANDARD "88" HC
The Oliver Corp., Charles City, Ia.

Air Cleaner: Donaldson, oil wash.
Battery: Delco-Remy.
Brakes: Two, operated by foot.

OLIVER ROW CROP "88" HC
The Oliver Corp., Charles City, Ia.

Carburetor: Schebler, 1-in.
Clutch: Borg & Beck, single plate, dry.
Generator: Delco-Remy.
Governor: Own, centrifugal, flyball, variable speed.
Ignition: Delco-Remy, battery and distributor.
Lamps: Guide.
Oil Filter: Michiana.
Radiator: Modine, fin-tube.
Radiator Cover: Own.
Spark Plugs: Champion, 6 Com.
Starting: Delco-Remy.
Data: H.P.—Neb. Test No. 388; Max belt 41.99; Max. D.B. 36.97; Max lbs. pull 5,173 at 2.51 m.p.h. Weight as tested (with operator) 8,484 lbs. Number of plows recommended: three, 14-in.
Engine: Own; 3½x4, 1,600 r.p.m., 6 cylinders, vertical, cast en bloc; piston displacement 231 cu. in.
Pulley: 11⅞x7¼, 992 r.p.m. and 3,080 f.p.m. at normal engine speed.
Speeds: M.P.H. forward 2⅝, 3¼, 4½, 5¾, 7⅛, 12 1/3, and 2⅝, 4⅝ reverse.

OSCO MOTORS CORP.

Philadelphia, Pennsylvania

Osco   1948

Air Cleaner: Heavy duty, oil bath.
Brakes: Individual rear wheel; self energizing forward and reverse.
Clutch: Fully automatic; no foot pedal.
Dimensions: Length 79 in.; height 48 in.; width 24, 34, 38 or 48 inches; weight approximately 945 lbs.; wheel base 47 inches.
Drive: Enclosed worm gear.
Power Take-off: Two shafts, front and rear.
Engine: 6.5 H.P. heavy duty, air cooled.
Speeds: Three forward, 0 to 10 M.P.H. and one speed reverse.
Steering: Rack and pinion.
Tires: Front 4.00x12; rear 7.00x24.
Turning Radius: 93 inches.

OSCO
Osco Motors Corp., Philadelphia 34, Pa.

SOLLBERGER ENGINEERING CO., INC.

Marshall, Texas

C24   1948

C24

Sollberger Engineering Co., Inc., Marshall, Tex.

Air Cleaner: Donaldson.
Battery: Exide (any standard).
Brakes: External, operated mechanically.
Carburetor: Up draft (any standard).
Clutch: Rockwell 10 in., dry disc.
Generator: Auto-Lite.
Governor: Continental.
Ignition: Auto-Lite.
Lamps: C. M. Hall seal-beam.
Oil Filter: Renewable cartridge type.
Radiator: Modine.
Spark Plugs: A-C.
Starting: Auto-Lite.
Data: H.P.—Neb. Test No. (not tested). Manufacturer's rating: Max. Belt 29; Max. D.B. 26. Number of plows recommended: Two to three 14-in.
Engine: Continental F162; $3\frac{7}{16}$x$4\frac{3}{8}$, 1,500 r.p.m., 4 cylinders, L-head, cast in line. Piston displacement 162 cu. in. Removable sleeves, no.
Pulley: 10x$16\frac{1}{2}$, 532 r.p.m. and 3,212 f.p.m. at normal engine speed.
Speeds: Four forward and one reverse.

U.S. TRACTOR SALES DIVISION, INC.

Peoria, Illinois

Ustrac Model 10   1948

Air Cleaner: Own, oil bath.
Battery: Auto-Lite.
Brakes: Two, band contracted about steering drum.
Carburetor: Zenith.
Clutch: Rockford, multiple disc, wet type.
Generator: Auto-Lite.
Governor: Novo, variable speed.
Ignition: Auto-Lite distributor.
Oil Filter: Fram.
Radiator: Blackstone, core and fin integral.
Radiator Cover:
Spark Plugs:
Starting: Auto-Lite.
Data: H.P.—Neb. Test. No. (not tested). Manufacturer's estimated H.P.—Max. belt 27, Max. D.B. 20. Number of plows recommended: Three, 14-in.
Engine: Continental F-124; 3x4⅜, 1,900 r.p.m., 4 cylinders, L-head. Piston displacement 123.7 cu. in.
Speeds: M.P.H. Forward 1.09, 2.22, 4.12, 6.95 and 1.25, 2.55, 4.75, 8.10 reverse.

USTRAC MODEL 10

U. S. Tractor Sales Div., Inc., Peoria 3, Ill.

1949

For 1949, the list includes 21 tractor manufacturers producing 57 tractor models. About 1949, some tractors were equipped to burn propane which became a popular fuel for a few years.

ALLIS-CHALMERS MANUFACTURING CO.

Milwaukee, Wisconsin

Allis-Chalmers "HD5B"	1949-1951
Allis-Chalmers "HD7W"	1949-1951
Allis-Chalmers "HD10W"	1949-1951
Allis-Chalmers "WD"	1949-1953

Allis-Chalmers "WD"
Allis-Chalmers Mfg. Co., Milwaukee, Wis.

General	Allis-Chalmers "HD5B"	"HD7W"
Number and Size Plows	4-16	6, 8-16
Shipping Weight—Lbs.	11250	14000
Nebraska Test Number	396	360
Observed Drawbar Horsepower ...	38.24	57.29
Observed Belt Horsepower	47.85	68.68
Maximum Pull—Lbs.	10059	12171
Speed @ Maximum Pull	1.41	1.77
Weight @ Maximum Pull—Lbs. ...	11815	14175
Tread—Inches	60	63
Height Overall—Inches	60⅜	66 9/16
Length Overall—Inches	124⅞	127¼
Starting—Crank, Electric	Elec.	Elec.
D.B. Adjustable Laterally?	Yes	Yes
D.B. Adjustable Vertically?	No	No
Cultivating Clearance—Inches	11¼	9 13/16
Hydraulic Power Unit	Opt.	Opt.

Transmission of Power

Clutch—Single Plate?	Yes	Yes
Clutch—Dry, Wet	Dry	Dry
Clutch—Spring Loaded?	Yes	Yes
Final Drive—Spur, Chain	Spur	Spur
High Gear Ratio	27.42	25.83
Low Gear Ratio	102.5	81.69
Speeds—Number Forward	5	4
Speeds—Number Reverse	1	1
Sliding Gear Speed Change?	Yes	Yes

Belt Pulley—P.T.O.—Engine

Belt Pulley Diameter—Inches	12	10-12
Belt Pulley Face Width—Inches	8¾	8¾
Belt Pulley Speed—rpm	963	889
Belt Pulley Speed—fpm	3025	2793
Power Take-off—Standard, Optional.	Opt.	Opt.
Is Power for P.T.O. Continuous? ...	No	No
Engine—Make	G.M.	G.M.
Engine—Model	2-71	3-71
Displacement—Cubic Inches	142	213
Rated rpm	1800	1500
Piston Speed fpm @ Rated rpm	1500	1250

Steering Brakes—Tracks

Type	Band	Band
Location—Steering Clutch		
Compartment?	Yes	Yes
Hydraulic or Mechanical	Mech.	Mech.
Brake Units per Tractor	2	2
Steering Make	Own	Own
Type—Multiple Disc Clutch?	Yes	Yes
Track Face Width—Inches	13	16
Ground Contacting Area of Tracks—		
Square Inches	1670	2144

Allis-Chalmers "HD5B"

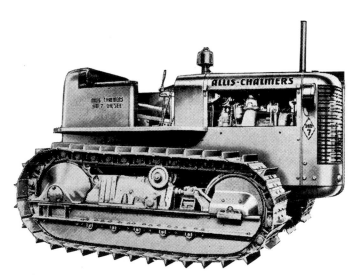

Allis-Chalmers "HD7W"

ALLIS-CHALMERS MFG. CO.
Milwaukee, Wisconsin

General

	Allis-Chalmers "HD10W"
Number and Size Plows..............	10-16
Type—Adj. Axle, Tricycle..........	Crawl.
Shipping Wt. on Rubber—Lbs........	22000
Nebraska Test Number .....(Diesel)	361
Observed Drawbar Horsepower ...	82.19
Observed Belt Horsepower	98.47
Maximum Pull—Lbs.	19002
Speed @ Maximum Pull	1.60
Weight @ Maximum Pull—Lbs.	21630
Track Tread—Inches	74
Height Overall—Inches	$75\frac{1}{8}$
Length Overall—Inches	$150\frac{7}{16}$
Starting—Crank, Electric	Elec.
D.B. Adjustable Laterally?	Yes
D.B. Adjustable Vertically?	No
Cultivating Clearance—Inches	$11\frac{5}{8}$
Hydraulic Power Unit	Opt.

Transmission of Power

Clutch—Single Dry Plate?	Yes
Clutch—Spring Loaded, Overcenter..	OC
Final Drive—Bevel, Chain, Spur......	Spur
High Gear Ratio	24.54
Low Gear Ratio	94.54
Speeds—Number Forward	6
Speeds—Number Reverse	2
Sliding Gear Speed Change?	Yes

Belt Pulley—P.T.O.—Engine

Belt Pulley Diameter—Inches	$13\frac{3}{8}$
Belt Pulley Face Width—Inches	10
Belt Pulley Speed—High—rpm	929
Belt Pulley Speed—Low—rpm	412
Belt Pulley Speed—High—fpm	3253
Belt Pulley Speed—Low—fpm	1443
Power Take-off—Standard, Optional.	Opt.
Is Power for P.T.O. Continuous? ...	No
Engine—Make	GM
Engine—Model	4-71
Displacement—Cubic Inches	284
Rated rpm	1600
Piston Speed fpm @ Rated rpm......	1333

Brakes

Make	Own
Type	Band
Location—Bull Pinion Shafts, Steering Clutch Shafts	SCS
Actuation—Hydraulic, Mechanical	Mech.
Brake Units per Tractor	2

Steering—Tires

	"HD10W"
Steering—Make	Own
Type—Multiple Disc Clutch, Worm & Gear	MDC
Track Face Width—Inches	18
Ground Contacting Area of Tracks—Square Inches	3058

Allis-Chalmers "HD10W"

ALLIS-CHALMERS MFG. CO.
Milwaukee, Wisconsin

Allis-Chalmers "WD"

ALLIS-CHALMERS MFG. CO.

Milwaukee, Wisconsin

*WD has two clutches. Engine clutch is single plate, spring loaded, dry type. Transmission clutch is multiple disc, overcenter, wet type.

General

Number and Size Plows	2-14
Type—Adjustable Axle, Tricycle	Tri.
Shipping Weight on Rubber—Lbs.	3975
Nebraska Test Number	399
Observed Drawbar Horsepower	24.31
Observed Belt Horsepower	26.14
Maximum Pull—Lbs.	3425
Speed @ Maximum Pull	2.30
Weight @ Maximum Pull—Lbs.	5042
Rear Tread, Minimum—Inches	56
Rear Tread, Maximum—Inches	90
Front Tread, Minimum—Inches	8⅞
Front Tread, Maximum—Inches	8⅞
Height Overall—Inches	81½
Length Overall—Inches	127.1
Wheelbase—Inches	88
Starting—Crank, Electric	Elec.
D.B. Adjustable Laterally?	Yes
D.B. Adjustable Vertically?	Yes
Cultivating Clearance—Inches	28¼
Hydraulic Power Unit	Opt.

Transmission of Power

Clutch—Dry Single Plate?	*
Clutch—Spring Loaded?	*
Final Drive—Bevel, Spur	Spur
High Gear Ratio	19.5
Low Gear Ratio	72.5
Speeds—Number Forward	4
Speeds—Number Reverse	1
Sliding Gear Speed Change?	Yes

Belt Pulley—P.T.O.—Engine

Belt Pulley Diameter—Inches	9
Belt Pulley Face Width—Inches	6½
Belt Pulley Speed—rpm	1260
Belt Pulley Speed—fpm	2960
Power Take-off—Standard, Optional.	Opt.
Is Power for P.T.O. Continuous?	Yes
Engine—Make	Own
Engine—Model	W
Displacement—Cubic Inches	201
Rated rpm	1400
Piston Speed fpm @ Rated rpm	933

Brakes

Type	Shoe
Location—Rear Axle, Diff. Shafts	D.S.
Hydraulic or Mechanical	Mech.

Steering—Tires

Steering Make	Own
Type—Cam & Lever, Worm & Segment	W&S
Tire Size—Standard Rear—Inches	11x28
Tire Size—Standard Front—Inches	5.5x16

BROCKWAY TRACTOR CO.
Bedford, Ohio

Brockway "49G"
Brockway "49D"

1949-1952
1949-1952

General

	Brockway "49G" "49D"
Number and Size Plows	2-14
Type—Axle, Adjustable Axle	A.A.
Shipping Wt. on Rubber—Lbs...(49G)	3100
(49D)	3600
Nebraska Test Number	None
Rear Tread, Minimum—Inches	48
Rear Tread, Maximum—Inches	76
Front Tread, Minimum—Inches	48
Front Tread, Maximum—Inches	76
Height Overall—Inches	66
Length Overall—Inches (49G)	110
(49D)	114
Wheelbase—Inches (49G)	71
(49D)	75
Starting—Crank, Electric	Elec.
D.B. Adjustable Laterally?	Yes
D.B. Adjustable Vertically?	Yes
Cultivating Clearance—Inches	20
Hydraulic Power Unit	Std.
Steel Tire Wheels Optional?	Yes

Transmission of Power

Clutch—Dry Single Plate?	Yes
Clutch—Spring Loaded?	Yes
Final Drive—Spur, Chain	Chain
High Gear Ratio	16.5
Low Gear Ratio	106.0
Speeds—Number Forward	4
Speeds—Number Reverse	1
Sliding Gear Speed Change?	No
Planetary Gear Speed Change?	Yes

Belt Pulley—P.T.O.—Engine

Belt Pulley Diameter—Inches	8½
Belt Pulley Face Width—Inches	6¼
Belt Pulley Speed—rpm	1072
Belt Pulley Speed—fpm	2385
Power Take-Off—Std., Optional	Opt.
Is Power to P.T.O. Continuous?	No
Engine—Make	Cont'l
Engine—Model (49G)	F162
(49D)	GD157
Displacement—Cu. In. (49G)	162
(49D)	157
Rated rpm	1650
Piston Speed fpm @ Rated rpm	1204

Brockway "49G" and "49D"

THE BROCKWAY TRACTOR CO.
Bedford, Ohio

Brakes

Make	Bendix
Type—Contracting Band, Internal Expanding	I.E.
Location—Bull Pinion Shaft, Intermediate Axle	IA
Hydraulic or Mechanical	Mech.
Brake Units per Tractor	2

Steering—Tires

Steering Make	Saginaw
Type—Cam & Lever, Worm & Sector	W&S
Tire Size—Standard Rear—Inches	11x28
Tire Size—Standard Front—Inches	5.5x16

346

1949

THE J. I. CASE CO.
Racine, Wisconsin

Case "VAH"   1949-1956
Case "VAO"   1949-1956

General	J. I. Case "VAH"
Number and Size Plows	1, 2-14
Type—Adjustable Axle, Tricycle	A.A.
Shipping Weight on Rubber—Lbs.	RNA
Nebraska Test Number ...(Gasoline)	None
Nebraska Test Number (Trac. Fuel)	None
Rear Tread, Minimum—Inches	60
Rear Tread, Maximum—Inches	88
Front Tread, Minimum—Inches	61
Front Tread, Maximum—Inches	85
Height Overall—Inches	63½
Length Overall—Inches	125
Wheelbase—Inches	84
Electric Starting—Std. or Opt.	Std.
D.B. Adjustable Laterally?	Yes
D.B. Adjustable Vertically?	No
Cultivating Clearance—Inches	30
Hydraulic Power Unit	Std.

Transmission of Power

Clutch—Single Plate?	Yes
Clutch—Dry, Wet	Dry
Clutch—Spring Loaded?	Yes
Final Drive—Spur, Chain	Spur
Speeds—Number Forward	4
Speeds—Number Reverse	1
Sliding Gear Speed Change?	Yes

Belt Pulley—P.T.O.—Engine

Belt Pulley Diameter—Inches	10¼
Belt Pulley Face Width—Inches	6
Belt Pulley Speed—rpm	969
Belt Pulley Speed—fpm	2600
Power Take-off—Standard, Optional.	Opt.
Is Power to P.T.O. Continuous?	No
Engine—Make	Own
Engine—Model	VA
Displacement—Cubic Inches	124
Rated rpm	1425
Piston Speed fpm @ Rated rpm	891

Brakes

Type	Disc
Location—Differential Side Gears?	Yes
Hydraulic or Mechanical	Mech.

Steering—Tires

Steering Make	Own
Type—Worm & Wheel?	Yes
Tire Size—Standard Rear—Inches	9x36
Tire Size—Standard Front—Inches	6x16

Case "VAH"

J. I. CASE CO.
Racine, Wisconsin

RNA—Release of information not authorized.

General

	J. I. Case "VAO"
Number and Size Plows	1, 2-14
Type—Axle, Tricycle	Axle
Shipping Weight—Lbs.	RNA
Nebraska Test Number	None
Rear Tread, Minimum—Inches	48
Rear Tread, Maximum—Inches	72
Front Tread, Minimum—Inches	43
Front Tread, Maximum—Inches	43
Height Overall—Inches	53¼
Length Overall—Inches	113½
Wheelbase—Inches	75¼
Electric Starting—Std., Optional	Std.
D.B. Adjustable Laterally?	Yes
D.B. Adjustable Vertically?	No
Cultivating Clearance—Inches	16⅞
Hydraulic Power Unit	Opt.
Steel Tire Wheels Optional?	No

Transmission of Power

Clutch—Double or Single Plate?	Sgl.
Clutch—Dry, Wet	Dry
Clutch—Spring Loaded?	Yes
Clutch—Overcenter?	No
Final Drive—Spur, Chain	Spur
Speeds—Number Forward	4
Speeds—Number Reverse	1
Sliding Gear Speed Change?	Yes

Belt Pulley—P.T.O.—Engine

Belt Pulley Diameter—Inches	10¼
Belt Pulley Face Width—Inches	6
Belt Pulley Speed—rpm	969
Belt Pulley Speed—fpm	2600
Power Take-off—Standard, Optional	Opt.
Is Power to P.T.O. Continuous?	No
Engine—Make	Own
Engine—Model	VA
Displacement—Cubic Inches	124
Rated rpm	1425
Piston Speed fpm @ Rated rpm	891

Brakes

Type	Disc
Location—Diff. Side Gears?	Yes
Hydraulic or Mechanical	Mech.
Brake Units per Tractor	2

Steering—Tires

Steering Make	Own
Type—Worm & Wheel?	Yes
Tire Size—Standard Rear—Inches	9x24
Tire Size—Standard Front—Inches	5x15

Case "VAO"

J. I. CASE CO.
Racine, Wisconsin

CORBITT CO.

Henderson, North Carolina

Corbitt "D50"   1949-1952
Corbitt "G50"   1949-1952
Corbitt "K50"   1949-1952

	Corbitt "G50" "K50" "D50"
General	
Number and Size Plows	2-14
Type—Axle, Tricycle	Tri.
Shipping Weight on Rubber—Lbs.	3400
Nebraska Test Number	None
Rear Tread, Minimum—Inches	56
Rear Tread, Maximum—Inches	84
Front Tread, Minimum—Inches	8
Front Tread, Maximum—Inches	8
Height Overall—Inches	69½
Length Overall—Inches	128
Wheelbase—Inches	86
Electric Starting—Std. or Opt.	Std.
D.B. Adjustable Laterally?	Yes
D. B. Adjustable Vertically?	No
Cultivating Clearance—Inches	26
Hydraulic Power Unit	Opt.
Steel Tire Wheels Optional?	Yes

Transmission of Power

Clutch—Single Plate?	Yes
Clutch—Dry, Wet	Dry
Clutch—Spring Loaded?	Yes
Separate Clutch for P.T.O.?	No
Final Drive—Bevel, Spur	Bevel
High Gear Ratio	24.2
Low Gear Ratio	96.8
Speeds—Number Forward	4
Speeds—Number Reverse	1
Sliding Gear Speed Change?	Yes

Belt Pulley—Engine

Belt Pulley Diameter—Inches	8
Belt Pulley Face Width—Inches	6½
Belt Pulley Speed—High—rpm	1210
Belt Pulley Speed—High—fpm	2500
Cooling—Pump, Thermo-Syphon	Pump
Engine—Make	Hercules
Engine—Model	DIX4D Diesel
Displacement—Cubic Inches	166
Rated rpm	1500

Brakes

Make	Timken
Type—Clamping Internal External Shoes or Internal Expanding Shoe	CIES
Location—Diff. Shaft or Rear Wheel	DS
Actuation—Hydraulic, Mechanical	Mech.
Brake Units per Tractor	2
Gear Reduction—Drum to Rear Wheel	5.10

Corbitt "D50"

CORBITT COMPANY
Henderson, N. C.

Steering—Tires

Steering Make	Ross
Type—Cam & Lever?	Yes
Tire Size—Standard Rear—Inches	10x38
Tire Size—Standard Front—Inches	5.5x16

General

	Corbitt "G50" "K50"
Number and Size Plows	2-14
Type—Axle, Adj. Axle, Tricycle	Tri.
Shipping Wt. on Rubber—Lbs.	3400
Nebraska Test Number (Gas.) (G50)	422
Observed Drawbar Horsepower	30.74
Observed Belt Horsepower	34.63
Maximum Pull—Lbs.	3556
Speed @ Maximum Pull	2.65
Weight @ Maximum Pull—Lbs.	5699
Rear Tread, Minimum—Inches	56
Rear Tread, Maximum—Inches	84
Front Tread, Minimum—Inches	8
Front Tread, Maximum—Inches	8
Height Overall—Inches	69½
Length Overall—Inches	128
Wheelbase—Inches	86
Electric Starting—Std. or Opt.	Std.
D.B. Adjustable Laterally?	Yes
D.B. Adjustable Vertically?	Yes
Cultivating Clearance—Inches	26
Hydraulic Power Unit—Std., Optional.	Opt.
Steel Tire Wheels Optional?	Yes

Transmission of Power

Clutch—Dry Single Plate?	Yes
Clutch—Spring Loaded, Overcenter	SL
Final Drive—Bevel, Chain, Spur	Bevel
High Gear Ratio	24.2
Low Gear Ratio	96.8
Speeds—Number Forward	4
Speeds—Number Reverse	1
Sliding Gear Speed Change?	Yes

Belt Pulley—P.T.O.—Engine

Belt Pulley Diameter—Inches	8
Belt Pulley Face Width—Inches	6½
Belt Pulley Speed—rpm	1210
Belt Pulley Speed—fpm	2500
Power Take-Off—Std., Optional	Std.
Is Power to P.T.O. Continuous?	No
Engine—Make	[1]
Engine—Model	[1]
Displacement—Cubic Inches	[1]
Rated rpm	1800
Piston Speed, fpm, @ Rated rpm	1200

Brakes

Make	Timken
Type—Clamping Shoes?	Yes
Location—Differential Shafts?	Yes
Actuation—Hydraulic, Mechanical	Mech.
Brake Units per Tractor	2

Steering—Tires

Steering—Make	Ross
Type—Cam & Lever, Worm & Gear	C&L
Tire Size—Std. Rear—Inches	10x38
Tire Size—Std. Front—Inches	5.5x16

[1] G50, LeRoi model D176 (Displacement 176 cu. in.)
  K50, LeRoi model D201 (Displacement 201 cu. in.)

Corbett "G50"

CORBETT COMPANY
Henderson, North Carolina

CUSTOM MANUFACTURING CORP.
Shelbyville, Indiana

Custom "B"   1949
Custom "C"   1949

General

	Custom "B"
Number and Size Plows	2, 3-14
Type—Axle, Tricycle	Tri.
Shipping Weight on Rubber—Lbs.	3450
Nebraska Test Number	None
Rear Tread, Minimum—Inches	56
Rear Tread, Maximum—Inches	84
Front Tread, Minimum—Inches	8
Front Tread, Maximum—Inches	11½
Height Overall—Inches	71
Length Overall—Inches	130
Wheelbase—Inches	87⅞
Electric Starting—Std. or Opt.	Std.
D.B. Adjustable Laterally?	Yes
D. B. Adjustable Vertically?	Yes
Cultivating Clearance—Inches	25
Hydraulic Power Unit	Opt.
Steel Tire Wheels Optional?	No

Transmission of Power

Clutch—Single Plate?	Yes
Clutch—Dry, Wet	Dry
Clutch—Spring Loaded?	Yes
Separate Clutch for P.T.O.?	No
Final Drive—Bevel, Spur	Bevel
High Gear Ratio	13.58
Low Gear Ratio	101.93
Speeds—Number Forward	4
Speeds—Number Reverse	1
Sliding Gear Speed Change?	Yes

Belt Pulley—Engine

Belt Pulley Diameter—Inches	11
Belt Pulley Face Width—Inches	7½
Belt Pulley Speed—High—rpm	1011
Belt Pulley Speed—Low—rpm	675
Belt Pulley Speed—High—fpm	2910
Belt Pulley Speed—Low—fpm	1944
Cooling—Pump, Thermo-Syphon	Pump
Engine—Make	Chrys.
Engine—Model	Ind.5
Displacement—Cubic Inches	217.7
Rated rpm	1800

Brakes

Make	Wagner
Type—Clamping Internal External Shoes or Internal Expanding Shoe	IES
Location—Diff. Shaft or Rear Wheel	RW
Actuation—Hydraulic, Mechanical	Hyd.
Brake Units per Tractor	3
Gear Reduction—Drum to Rear Wheel	None

Custom "B"

CUSTOM MANUFACTURING CORP.
Shelbyville, Indiana

Steering—Tires

Steering Make	Ross
Type—Cam & Lever?	Yes
Tire Size—Standard Rear—Inches	10x38
Tire Size—Standard Front—Inches	6x16

General

	Custom "C"
Number and Size Plows	2, 3-14
Type—Axle, Adj. Axle, Tricycle	Axle
Shipping Weight on Rubber—Lbs.	3450
Nebraska Test Number ...(All Fuel)	None
Nebraska Test Number....(Gasoline)	None
Rear Tread, Minimum—Inches	64
Rear Tread, Maximum—Inches	74⅜
Front Tread, Minimum—Inches	54
Front Tread, Maximum—Inches	57½
Height Overall—Inches	68
Length Overall—Inches	128
Wheelbase—Inches	87⅞
Electric Starting—Std. or Opt.	Std.
D.B. Adjustable Laterally?	Yes
D.B. Adjustable Vertically?	Yes
Hydraulic Power Unit	Opt.
Steel Tire Wheels Optional?	No

Transmission of Power

Clutch—Single, Dry Plate or Double, Dry Disc	SDP
Clutch—Spring Loaded, Overcenter..	SL
Separate Clutch for P.T.O.?	No
Final Drive—Bevel, Spur	Bevel
High Gear Ratio	13.58
Low Gear Ratio	101.93
Speeds—Number Forward	4
Speeds—Number Reverse	1
Sliding Gear Speed Change?	Yes

Belt Pulley—Engine

Belt Pulley Diameter—Inches	11
Belt Pulley Face Width—Inches	7½
Belt Pulley Speed—High—rpm	1011
Belt Pulley Speed—Low—rpm	675
Belt Pulley Speed—High—fpm	2910
Belt Pulley Speed—Low—fpm	1944
Cooling—Pump, Thermo-Syphon	Pump
Engine—Make	Chrys.
Engine—Model	Ind.5
Displacement—Cubic Inches	217.7
Rated rpm	1800

Brakes

Make	Wagner
Type—Internal Expanding?	Yes
Location—Rear Wheel, Separate Shaft Driven by Bull Gear	RW
Actuation—Hydraulic, Mechanical	Hyd.
Brake Units per Tractor	3
Gear Reduction—Drum to Rear Wheel	None

Steering—Tires

Steering—Make	Ross
Type—Cam & Lever, Worm & Sector	C&L
Tire Size—Std. Rear—Inches	11x28
Tire Size—Std. Front—In.	6x16

Custom "C"
CUSTOM MANUFACTURING CORP.
Shelbyville, Indiana

DEERE & CO.
Moline, Illinois

Deere "M"	1949-1953
Deere "MT"	1949-1953
Deere "R" Diesel	1949-1955

General

	John Deere "M"	"MT"
Number and Size Plows	1-16 or 2-14	
Type—Adjustable Axle, Tricycle	A.A.	Tri.
Shipping Weight on Rubber—Lbs.	2750	3200
Nebraska Test Number	387	None
Observed Drawbar Horsepower	18.15	
Observed Belt Horsepower	20.45	
Maximum Pull—Lbs.	2329	
Speed @ Maximum Pull	1.61	
Weight @ Maximum Pull—Lbs.	3952	
Rear Tread, Minimum—Inches	38	48
Rear Tread, Maximum—Inches	52	96
Front Tread, Minimum—Inches	38	$6\frac{11}{16}$
Front Tread, Maximum—Inches	52	$11\frac{13}{16}$
Height Overall—Inches	66	$73\frac{3}{4}$
Length Overall—Inches	110	$125\frac{3}{8}$
Wheelbase—Inches	70	$82\frac{1}{4}$
Electric Starting—Std. or Opt.	Std.	Std.
D.B. Adjustable Laterally?	No	No
D.B. Adjustable Vertically?	Yes	Yes
Cultivating Clearance—Inches	21	21
Hydraulic Power Unit	Std.	Std.
Steel Tire Wheels Optional?	Yes	Yes

Transmission of Power

Clutch—Single Plate?	Yes	Yes
Clutch—Dry, Wet	Dry	Dry
Clutch—Spring Loaded?	Yes	Yes
Separate Clutch for P.T.O.?	No	No
Final Drive—Spur, Chain	Spur	Spur
High Gear Ratio	18.2	21.1
Low Gear Ratio	98.4	114.01
Speeds—Number Forward	4	4
Speeds—Number Reverse	1	1
Sliding Gear Speed Change?	Yes	Yes

Belt Pulley—Engine

Belt Pulley Diameter—Inches	$7\frac{1}{4}$	$7\frac{1}{4}$
Belt Pulley Face Width—Inches	$6\frac{3}{8}$	$6\frac{3}{8}$
Belt Pulley Speed—High—rpm	1575	1575
Belt Pulley Speed—Low—rpm	525	525
Belt Pulley Speed—High—fpm	2990	2990
Belt Pulley Speed—Low—fpm	1000	1000
Cooling—Pump, Thermo-Syphon	T.S.	T.S.
Engine—Make	Own	Own
Displacement—Cubic Inches	100.5	100.5
Rated rpm	1650	1650

Brakes

Make—Auto Specialty, Lambert	A.S.	Lamb.
Type—Single or Double Disc	S.D.	D.D.
Location—Final Drive Shaft?	Yes	Yes
Actuation—Hydraulic, Mechanical	Mech.	Mech.
Brake Units per Tractor	2	2
Gear Reduction—Drum to Rear Wheel	4.05	5.02

Steering—Tires

	"M"	"MT"
Steering Make	Ross	Ross
Type—Cam & Lever?	Yes	Yes
Tire Size—Standard Rear—Inches	9x24	9x34
Tire Size—Standard Front—Inches	5x15	5x15

Deere "M"

Deere "MT"

DEERE & COMPANY
Moline, Illinois

General

	Deere "R"
Number and Size Plows	4, 5-14
Type—Axle, Adjustable Axle, Tricycle	Axle
Shipping Weight on Rubber—Lbs.	7400
Nebraska Test Number	406
Observed Drawbar Horsepower	43.15
Observed Belt Horsepower	48.58
Maximum Pull—Lbs.	6644
Speed @ Maximum Pull	1.88
Weight @ Maximum Pull—Lbs.	10398
Rear Tread, Minimum—Inches	62½
Rear Tread, Maximum—Inches	62½
Front Tread, Minimum—Inches	54
Front Tread, Maximum—Inches	54
Height Overall—Inches	78⅛
Length Overall—Inches	147
Wheelbase—Inches	85½
Starting—Crank, Elec. or Aux. Engine	A.E.
D.B. Adjustable Laterally?	Yes
D.B. Adjustable Vertically?	Yes
Cultivating Clearance—Inches	13⅝
Hydraulic Power Unit	Opt.

Transmission of Power

Clutch—Single Plate or Multiple Disc	MD
Clutch—Spring Loaded or Overcenter	OC
Separate Clutch for P.T.O. & B.P.?	Yes
Final Drive—Spur, Chain	Spur
High Gear Ratio	14.71
Low Gear Ratio	77.83
Speeds—Number Forward	5
Speeds—Number Reverse	1
Sliding Gear Speed Change?	Yes

Belt Pulley—Engine

Belt Pulley Diameter—Inches	$12\frac{7}{32}$
Belt Pulley Face Width—Inches	9
Belt Pulley Speed—rpm	1000
Belt Pulley Speed—fpm	3199
Cooling—Pump, Thermo-Syphon	T.S.
Engine—Make	Own
Engine—Model	R
Displacement—Cubic Inches	416
Rated rpm	1000

Brakes

Type—Internal Expanding?	Yes
Location—Separate Shaft Driven by Bull Gear, Jack Shaft	SS
Actuation—Hydraulic, Mechanical	Mech.
Brake Units per Tractor	2
Gear Reduction—Drum to Rear Wheel	6.27

Steering—Tires

Type—Worm & Gear, Brakes on Jack Shaft	W&G
Tire Size—Standard Rear—Inches	14x34
Tire Size—Standard Front—Inches	7.5x18

Deere "R" Diesel

DEERE & COMPANY
Moline, Illinois

DETROIT TRACTOR CORP.
Detroit, Michigan

Detroit "44-16-B"   1949-1950

General

	Detroit "44-16"
Number and Size Plows	1-16
Type—Axle, Adjustable Axle, Tricycle [1]	——
Shipping Weight on Rubber—Lbs.	1660
Nebraska Test Number	None
Rear Tread, Minimum—Inches	46
Rear Tread, Maximum—Inches	58
Front Tread, Minimum—Inches	46
Front Tread, Maximum—Inches	58
Height Overall—Inches	51
Length Overall—Inches	78
Wheelbase—Inches	34
Starting—Crank, Elec. or Aux. Engine	El.-Opt.
D.B. Adjustable Laterally?	Yes
D.B. Adjustable Vertically?	No
Cultivating Clearance—Inches	20
Hydraulic Power Unit	Opt.

Transmission of Power

Clutch—Single Plate or Multiple Disc	SP
Clutch—Spring Loaded or Overcenter	SL
Separate Clutch for P.T.O. & B.P.? ..	Yes
Final Drive—Spur, Chain	Chain
High Gear Ratio	33.5
Low Gear Ratio	53.7
Speeds—Number Forward	2
Speeds—Number Reverse	1
Sliding Gear Speed Change?	Yes

Belt Pulley—Engine

Belt Pulley Diameter—Inches	8
Belt Pulley Face Width—Inches	5
Belt Pulley Speed—rpm	1070
Belt Pulley Speed—fpm	2240
Cooling—Pump, Thermo-Syphon	T.S.
Engine—Make	Cont'l
Engine—Model	N62
Displacement—Cubic Inches	62
Rated rpm	1800

Brakes

Type—Internal Expanding?	Yes
Location—Separate Shaft Driven by Bull Gear, Jack Shaft	JS
Actuation—Hydraulic, Mechanical ...	Hyd.
Brake Units per Tractor	2
Gear Reduction—Drum to Rear Wheel	2.5

Detroit "44-16-B"

DETROIT TRACTOR CORPORATION
Detroit, Michigan

Steering—Tires

Type—Worm & Gear, Brakes on Jack Shaft	BoJS
Tire Size—Standard Rear—Inches ..	6x16
Tire Size—Standard Front—Inches..	6x16

[1] 4-Wheel Drive Tractor.

EARTHMASTER FARM EQUIPMENT
Burbank, California

Earthmaster "CN"	1949
Earthmaster "D"	1949
Earthmaster "DH"	1949

General

	Earthmaster "CN"
Number and Size Plows	1-14
Type—Adjustable Axle, Tricycle	A.A.
Shipping Weight—Lbs.	1505
Nebraska Test Number	None
Rear Tread, Minimum—Inches	38
Rear Tread, Maximum—Inches	58
Front Tread, Minimum—Inches	38
Front Tread, Maximum—Inches	58
Height Overall—Inches	61
Length Overall—Inches	98
Wheelbase—Inches	66
Electric Starting—Std. or Opt.	Std.
D.B. Adjustable Laterally?	Yes
D.B. Adjustable Vertically?	Yes
Cultivating Clearance—Inches	20
Hydraulic Power Unit	Std.

Transmission of Power

Clutch—Dry, Single Plate?	Yes
Clutch—Spring Loaded?	Yes
Separate Clutch for P.T.O.?	No
Final Drive—Spur, Chain	Spur
High Gear Ratio	37.1
Low Gear Ratio	85.6
Speeds—Number Forward	3
Speeds—Number Reverse	1
Sliding Gear Speed Change?	Yes

Belt Pulley—Engine

Belt Pulley Diameter—Inches	7
Belt Pulley Face Width—Inches	5
Belt Pulley Speed—rpm	1540
Belt Pulley Speed—fpm	2830
Cooling—Pump, Thermo-Syphon	T.S.
Engine—Make	Cont'l.
Engine—Model	N62
Displacement—Cubic Inches	62
Rated RPM	1800

Brakes

Make—Auto Specialties?	Yes
Type	Disc
Location—Bull Pinion Shaft?	Yes
Actuation—Hydraulic, Mechanical	Mech.
Brake Units per Tractor	2
Gear Reduction—Drum to Rear Wheel	5.9

Steering—Tires

	"CN"
Steering Make	Ross
Type—Cam & Lever?	Yes
Tire Size—Std. Rear—Inches	8x24
Tire Size—Std. Front—Inches	4x15

Earthmaster "CN"

EARTHMASTER FARM EQUIPMENT
Burbank, California

General

	Earthmaster "D" "DH"
Number and Size Plows	1-14
Type—Adjustable Axle, Tricycle	A.A.
Shipping Weight on Rubber ......(D)	1600
(DH)	1610
Nebraska Test Number	None
Rear Tread, Minimum—Inches	56
Rear Tread, Maximum—Inches	84
Front Tread, Minimum—Inches	56
Front Tread, Maximum—Inches	84
Height Overall—Inches ....(D)	61
(DH)	64
Length Overall—Inches ....(D)	98
(DH)	100
Wheelbase—Inches	66
Electric Starting—Std. or Opt.	Std.
D.B. Adjustable Laterally?	Yes
D.B. Adjustable Vertically?	Yes
Cultivating Clearance—Inches ..(D)	20
(DH)	24½
Hydraulic Power Unit	Std.

Transmission of Power

Clutch—Dry, Single Plate?	Yes
Clutch—Spring Loaded?	Yes
Separate Clutch for P.T.O.?	No
Final Drive—Spur, Chain	Spur
High Gear Ratio	37.1
Low Gear Ratio	85.6
Speeds—Number Forward	3
Speeds—Number Reverse	1
Sliding Gear Speed Change?	Yes

Belt Pulley—Engine

Belt Pulley Diameter—Inches	7
Belt Pulley Face Width—Inches	5
Belt Pulley Speed—High—rpm	1540
Belt Pulley Speed—High—fpm	2830
Cooling—Pump, Thermo-Syphon	T.S.
Engine—Make	Cont'l.
Engine—Model	N62
Displacement—Cubic Inches	62
Rated rpm	1800

Brakes

Make—Auto Specialty, Timken	A.S.
Type—Disc or Clamping Shoes	Disc
Location—Final Drive Shafts or Differential Side Gears	FD
Actuation—Hydraulic, Mechanical ...	Mech.
Brake Units per Tractor	2
Gear Reduction—Drum to Rear Wheel	5.9

Steering—Tires

Steering Make	Ross
Type—Cam & Lever, Worm & Sector	C&L
Tire Size—Std. Rear—Inches ...(D)	9x24
(DH)	7x30
Tire Size—Standard Front—Inches..	4x15

Earthmaster "D"

EARTHMASTER FARM EQUIPMENT
Burbank, California

FARMASTER CORP.
Clifton, New Jersey

Farmaster "FD-33"   1949-1951
Farmaster "FG-33"   1949-1951

General

	Far-master "FD-33"
Number and Size Plows	2, 3-14
Type—Adjustable Axle, Tricycle	Tri.
Shipping Weight on Rubber	3300
Nebraska Test Number	None
Rear Tread, Minimum—Inches	56
Rear Tread, Maximum—Inches	84
Front Tread, Minimum—Inches	9
Front Tread, Maximum—Inches	9
Height Overall—Inches	60
Length Overall—Inches	132
Wheelbase—Inches	87
Electric Starting—Std. or Opt.	Std.
D.B. Adjustable Laterally?	Yes
D.B. Adjustable Vertically?	Yes
Cultivating Clearance—Inches	12
Hydraulic Power Unit	Opt.

Transmission of Power

Clutch—Dry, Single Plate?	Yes
Clutch—Spring Loaded?	Yes
Separate Clutch for P.T.O.?	No
Final Drive—Spur, Chain	Spur
High Gear Ratio	24.2
Low Gear Ratio	96.0
Speeds—Number Forward	4
Speeds—Number Reverse	1
Sliding Gear Speed Change?	Yes

Belt Pulley—Engine

Belt Pulley Diameter—Inches	8¼
Belt Pulley Face Width—Inches	6½
Belt Pulley Speed—High—rpm	1349
Belt Pulley Speed—Low—rpm	818
Belt Pulley Speed—High—fpm	2915
Belt Pulley Speed—Low—fpm	1767
Cooling—Pump, Thermo-Syphon	Pump
Engine—Make	Buda
Engine—Model	4BD-153
Displacement—Cubic Inches	153
Rated rpm	1650

Brakes

Make—Auto Specialty, Timken	Timken
Type—Disc or Clamping Shoes	C.S.
Location—Final Drive Shafts or Differential Side Gears	DSG
Actuation—Hydraulic, Mechanical	Mech.
Brake Units per Tractor	2
Gear Reduction—Drum to Rear Wheel	5.1

Farmaster "FD-33"

FARMASTER CORPORATION
Clifton, New Jersey

Steering—Tires

Steering Make	Sag'nw
Type—Cam & Lever, Worm & Sector	W&S
Tire Size—Std. Rear—Inches	11x38
Tire Size—Standard Front—Inches	5.5x16

General

	Far-master "FG-33"
Number and Size Plows	2, 3-14
Type—Adjustable Axle, Tricycle	Tri.
Shipping Weight on Rubber—Lbs.	3200
Nebraska Test Number	None
Rear Tread, Minimum—Inches	56
Rear Tread, Maximum—Inches	84
Front Tread, Minimum—Inches	9
Front Tread, Maximum—Inches	9
Height Overall—Inches	60
Length Overall—Inches	132
Wheelbase—Inches	87
Electric Starting—Std. or Opt.	Std.
D.B. Adjustable Laterally?	Yes
D.B. Adjustable Vertically?	Yes
Cultivating Clearance—Inches	12
Hydraulic Power Unit	Opt.

Transmission of Power

Clutch—Dry, Single Plate?	Yes
Clutch—Spring Loaded?	Yes
Separate Clutch for P.T.O.?	No
Final Drive—Bevel, Spur	Spur
High Gear Ratio	24.2
Low Gear Ratio	96.0
Speeds—Number Forward	4
Speeds—Number Reverse	1
Speed Change—Sliding Gear, Constant Mesh	SG

Belt Pulley—Engine

Belt Pulley Diameter—Inches	8¼
Belt Pulley Face Width—Inches	6½
Belt Pulley Speed—High—rpm	1349
Belt Pulley Speed—Low—rpm	818
Belt Pulley Speed—High—fpm	2915
Belt Pulley Speed—Low—fpm	1767
Cooling—Pump, Thermo-Syphon	Pump
Engine—Make	Buda
Engine—Model	4B-153
Displacement—Cubic Inches	153
Rated rpm—Belt	1650
Drawbar	1650

Brakes

Make	Timken
Type—Clamping Shoes, Internal Expanding Shoes	CS
Location—Differential Side Gears, Rear Wheels	DSG
Actuation—Hydraulic, Mechanical	Mech.
Brake Units per Tractor	2
Gear Reduction—Drum to Rear Wheel	5.1

Steering—Tires

Steering Make	Sag'nw
Type—Worm & Sector, Bevel Pinion & Twin Sector	W&S
Tire Size—Standard Rear—Inches	11x38
Tire Size—Standard Front—Inches	5.5x16

Farmaster "FG-33"

FARMASTER CORPORATION
Clifton, New Jersey

FATE-ROOT-HEATH CO.
Plymouth, Ohio

Silver King "349"   1949-1950
Silver King "449"   1949-1950

General	Silver King "349"	"449"
Number and Size Plows	2, 3-14	2-14
Type—Axle, Tricycle	Tri.	Axle
Shipping Weight on Rubber—Lbs. ...	3550	3200
Nebraska Test Number	None	None
Rear Tread, Minimum—Inches	56	44
Rear Tread, Maximum—Inches	84	72
Front Tread—Inches	None	48
Height Overall—Inches	78	66
Length Overall—Inches	131	114
Wheelbase—Inches	83¼	66 5/16
Electric Starting—Std. or Opt.	Std.	Std.
D.B. Adjustable Laterally?	Yes	Yes
D.B. Adjustable Vertically?	No	No
Cultivating Clearance—Inches	27⅝	15¼
Hydraulic Power Unit	Opt.	Opt.

Transmission of Power

Clutch—Dry, Single Plate?	Yes	Yes
Clutch—Spring Loaded?	Yes	Yes
Separate Clutch for P.T.O.?	No	No
Final Drive—Spur, Chain	Spur	Spur
High Gear Ratio	15.13	10.51
Low Gear Ratio	108.2	75.15
Speeds—Number Forward	4	4
Speeds—Number Reverse	1	1
Sliding Gear Speed Change?	Yes	Yes

Belt Pulley—Engine

Belt Pulley Diameter—Inches ......:	6½	6½
Belt Pulley Face Width—Inches	8	8
Belt Pulley Speed—rpm	1800	1800
Belt Pulley Speed—fpm	3100	3100
Cooling—Pump, Thermo-Syphon	Pump	Pump
Engine—Make	Cont'l.	Cont'l.
Engine—Model	F162	F162
Displacement—Cubic Inches	162	162
Rated rpm	1800	1800

Brakes

Make	Own	Own
Type—Contracting Band?	Yes	Yes
Location—Bull Pinion Shaft?	Yes	Yes
Actuation—Hydraulic, Mechanical ...	Mech.	Mech.
Brake Units per Tractor	2	2
Gear Reduction—Drum to Rear Wheel	3.31	2.30

Steering—Tires

Steering Make	Ross	Ross
Type—Cam & Lever?	Yes	Yes
Tire Size—Standard Rear—Inches ..	10x38	10x28
Tire Size—Standard Front—Inches..	7.5x16	6.5x16

Silver King "349"

Silver King "449"

FATE-ROOT-HEATH COMPANY
Plymouth, Ohio

FORD MOTOR CO.
Dearborn, Michigan

Ford "8N"

General

	Ford "8N"
Number and Size Plows	2-14
Type—Axle, Adjustable Axle	A.A.
Shipping Weight on Rubber—Lbs.	2410
Nebraska Test Number	393
Observed Drawbar Horsepower	21.72
Observed Belt Horsepower	25.77
Maximum Pull—Lbs.	2751
Speed @ Maximum Pull	2.71
Weight @ Maximum Pull—Lbs.	4140
Rear Tread, Minimum—Inches	48
Rear Tread, Maximum—Inches	76
Front Tread, Minimum—Inches	48
Front Tread, Maximum—Inches	76
Height Overall—Inches	54½
Length Overall—Inches	115
Wheelbase—Inches	70
Electric Starting—Std. or Opt.	Std.
D.B. Adjustable Laterally?	Yes
D.B. Adjustable Vertically?	Yes
Cultivating Clearance—Inches	21
Hydraulic Power Unit	Std.

Transmission of Power

Clutch—Dry, Single Plate?	Yes
Clutch—Semi-Centrifugal?	Yes
Clutch—Spring Loaded?	Yes
Separate Clutch for P.T.O.?	No
Final Drive—Bevel, Spur	Bevel
High Gear Ratio	19.86
Low Gear Ratio	73.33
Speeds—Number Forward	4
Speeds—Number Reverse	1
Speed Change—Constant Mesh, Syncro-Mesh	CM

Belt Pulley—Engine

Belt Pulley Diameter—Inches	9
Belt Pulley Face Width—Inches	6½
Belt Pulley Speed—High—rpm	1358
Belt Pulley Speed—Low—rpm	1018
Belt Pulley Speed—High—fpm	3199
Belt Pulley Speed—Low—fpm	2398
Cooling—Pump, Thermo-Syphon	Pump
Engine—Make	Own
Engine—Model	8N
Displacement—Cubic Inches	119.7
Rated rpm—Belt	2000
Drawbar	1750

Brakes

	"8N"
Make—Bendix, New Process	Bendix
Type—Internal Expanding Shoes, Contracting Band	IES
Location—Rear Wheels, Final Drive Shafts	RW
Actuation—Hydraulic, Mechanical	Mech.
Brake Units per Tractor	2
Gear Reduction—Drum to Rear Wheel	None

Steering—Tires

Steering—Make	Sag'nw
Type—Worm & Ball Nut, Cam & Lever	W&BN
Tire Size—Standard Rear—Inches	10x28
Tire Size—Standard Front—Inches	4x19

Ford "8N"

FORD MOTOR COMPANY
Dearborn, Michigan

362   1949

GIBSON MANUFACTURING CORP.
Longmont, Colorado

Gibson "H"   1949-1952
Gibson "I"   1949-1952

Gibson "H"

Gibson "I"

GIBSON MANUFACTUING CORPORATION
Longmont, Colorado

	Gibson "H"	"I"
General		
Number and Size Plows	2-14	2, 3-14
Shipping Weight on Rubber—Lbs.	3560	4020
Nebraska Test Number	407	408
Observed Drawbar Horsepower	22.77	36.73
Observed Belt Horsepower	24.54	41.03
Maximum Pull—Lbs.	3583	4676
Speed @ Maximum Pull	1.69	2.56
Weight @ Maximum Pull—Lbs.	5816	7495
Rear Tread, Minimum—Inches	47	49
Rear Tread, Maximum—Inches	85	90
Front Tread—Inches	7¾	9
Height Overall—Inches	67	67
Length Overall—Inches	127¼	127¼
Wheelbase—Inches	86	94
Electric Starting—Std. or Opt.	Std.	Std.
D.B. Adjustable Only Laterally?	Yes	Yes
Cultivating Clearance—Inches	25	25
Hydraulic Power Unit	Std.	Std.
Transmission of Power		
Clutch—Dry, Single Plate?	Yes	Yes
Clutch—Spring Loaded?	Yes	Yes
Separate Clutch for P.T.O.?	No	No
Final Drive—Spur, Chain	Spur	Spur
High Gear Ratio	24.63	24.63
Low Gear Ratio	158.0	158.0
Speeds—Number Forward	4	4
Belt Pulley—Engine		
Belt Pulley Diameter—Inches	$9\frac{3}{16}$	$9\frac{3}{16}$
Belt Pulley Face Width—Inches	7½	7½
Belt Pulley Speed—rpm	1487	1487
Belt Pulley Speed—fpm	3539	3539
Engine—Make	Herc.	Herc.
Engine—Model	IXB3	QXD5
Displacement—Cubic Inches	133	230
Rated rpm	1800	1800
Brakes		
Type—Contracting Band?	Yes	Yes
Location—Bull Pinion Shaft?	Yes	Yes
Hydraulic or Mechanical	Mech.	Mech.
Brake Units per Tractor	2	2
Gear Reduction—Drum to Rear Wheel	3.7	3.7
Steering—Tires		
Type—Worm & Gear?	Yes	Yes
Tire Size—Standard Rear—Inches	10x38	12x38
Tire Size—Standard Front—Inches	5x15	5.5x16

LOVE TRACTOR, INC.
Eau Claire, Michigan

Love "T50"   1949-1950

General

	Love "T50"
Number and Size Plows	3-14
Type—Axle, Adjustable Axle	A.A.
Shipping Weight on Rubber—Lbs.	3780
Nebraska Test Number	None
Rear Tread, Minimum—Inches	57
Rear Tread, Maximum—Inches	77
Front Tread, Minimum—Inches	54
Front Tread, Maximum—Inches	78
Height Overall—Inches	66½
Length Overall—Inches	115
Wheelbase—Inches	75¾
Electric Starting—Std. or Opt.	Std.
D.B. Adjustable Laterally?	Yes
D.B. Adjustable Vertically?	Yes
Cultivating Clearance—Inches	21½
Hydraulic Power Unit	Opt.

Transmission of Power

Clutch—Dry, Single Plate?	Yes
Clutch—Spring Loaded?	Yes
Separate Clutch for P.T.O. & B.P.?	Yes
Final Drive—Chain, Bevel	Bevel
High Gear Ratio	9.35
Low Gear Ratio	66.75
Speeds—Number Forward	8
Speeds—Number Reverse	2
Sliding Gear Speed Change?	Yes

Belt Pulley—Engine

Belt Pulley Diameter—Inches	9
Belt Pulley Face Width—Inches	6½
Belt Pulley Speed—rpm	1360
Belt Pulley Speed—fpm	3200
Cooling—Pump, Thermo-Syphon	Pump
Engine—Make	Chrys.
Engine—Model	Ind.5
Displacement—Cubic Inches	217
Rated RPM	1800

Brakes

Make	Wagner
Type—Contracting Band, Internal Expanding	IE
Location—Bull Pinion Shaft, Rear Wheels	RW
Actuation—Hydraulic, Mechanical	Hyd.
Brake Units per Tractor	2
Gear Reduction—Drum to Rear Wheel	None

Steering—Tires

	"T50"
Type—Worm & Gear, Cam & Lever	C&L
Tire Size—Standard Rear—Inches	13x24
Tire Size—Standard Front—Inches	6x16

Love "T50"
LOVE TRACTOR, INC.
Eau Claire, Mich.

MASSEY-HARRIS CO.
Racine, Wisconsin

Massey-Harris "44D"   1949

General	Massey-Harris "44D"
Number and Size Plows	4-14
Type—Axle, Tricycle	Axle
Shipping Wt. on Rubber—Lbs.	4565
Nebraska Test Number	None
Rear Tread, Minimum—Inches	54⅛
Rear Tread, Maximum—Inches	54⅛
Front Tread, Minimum—Inches	47½
Front Tread, Maximum—Inches	47½
Length Overall—Inches	127½
Wheelbase—Inches	79⅛
Electric Starting—Std. or Opt.	Std.
D.B. Adjustable Laterally?	Yes
D.B. Adjustable Vertically?	Yes
Cultivating Clearance—Inches	12
Hydraulic Power Unit	None

Transmission of Power	
Clutch—Dry, Single Plate?	Yes
Clutch—Spring Loaded?	Yes
Final Drive—Spur, Chain	Spur
High Gear Ratio	16.68
Low Gear Ratio	93.1
Speeds—Number Forward	5

Belt Pulley—Engine	
Belt Pulley Diameter—Inches	13½
Belt Pulley Face Width—Inches	6
Belt Pulley Speed—rpm	863
Belt Pulley Speed—fpm	3050
Engine—Make	Cont'l.
Engine—Model	HD-260
Displacement—Cubic Inches	260
Rated rpm	1350

Brakes	
Type—Internal Expanding?	Yes
Location—Differential Pinion?	Yes
Actuation—Hydraulic, Mechanical	Mech.
Gear Reduction—Drum to Rear Wheel	4.12

Steering—Tires	
Type—Worm & Sector?	Yes
Tire Size—Std. Rear—Inches	13x30
Tire Size—Std. Front—Inches	6x16

Massey-Harris "44D"
MASSEY-HARRIS COMPANY
Racine, Wisconsin

MAYRATH, INC.
Dodge City, Kansas

General   Mayrath

Number and Size Plows—Inches	1-10
Number of Ground Contacting Wheels	4
Type—Riding, Walking	R
Axle or Tricycle Type	Axle
Shipping Weight, Standard—Lbs.	525
Nebraska Test Number	None
Wheel Tread, Minimum—Inches	37
Wheel Tread, Maximum—Inches	37
Wheelbase—Inches	50
Starting—Rope, Electric	Rope
Equipped with Drawbar?	Yes
D.B. Adjustable Laterally?	Yes
D.B. Adjustable Vertically?	Yes
Cultivating Clearance—Inches	10

Transmission of Power

Method Obtaining Ratio Reductions, Crankshaft to Driving Wheels	
1st Reduction	Belt
2nd, 3rd, 4th Reduction— Transmission Gearset?	Yes
5th Reduction	Gear
Number of Forward Speeds	3
Additional Ratios Obtained by Belt Shifting	3
Speed Ratio, Crankshaft to Wheels ....(Highest)	9.3
(Lowest)	59.5
Number of Reverse Speeds	1
Tractor Speed Range—mph	6-30
Sliding Gear Speed Change?	Yes
Final Drive	Gear

Aux. Power Belt Pulley—P.T.O.

Belt Pulley—Std., Opt., None	None
Power Take-off—Std., Opt., None ..	None

Engine

Make—Briggs & Stratton, Clinton ..	B&S
Model	23
Bore—Inches	3
Stroke—Inches	3¼
Displacement—Cubic Inches	23
Maximum Continuous Horsepower ...	7
RPM @ Max. Continuous Horsepower	3200

Mayrath Mobile Tractor

MAYRATH, INC.
Dodge City, Kansas

Steering—Tires—Brakes

Steering Type—Drum, Guide Handles	Drum
Tire Size, Standard—Inches ..(Rear)	5x16
(Front)	5x16
Brakes Make	Own
Brakes Type—Contracting Band? ...	Yes
Brake Drum Location—Rear Wheels?	Yes
Brake Units Per Tractor	2
Brake Actuation—Hyd., Mechanical ..	Mech.

MINNEAPOLIS-MOLINE CO.
Minneapolis, Minnesota

Minneapolis-Moline "RTE"	1949-1950
Minneapolis-Moline "ZAE"	1949-1950
Minneapolis-Moline "ZAN"	1949-1950
Minneapolis-Moline "ZAU"	1949-1950
Minneapolis-Moline "ZAS"	1949-1950

General

	Minneapolis-Moline "GTB" "RTE"
Number and Size Plows	2-14
Type—Axle, Adjustable Axle	A.A.
Shipping Weight on Rubber —Lbs.	3250
Nebraska Test Number	None
Rear Tread, Minimum—Inches	52
Rear Tread, Maximum—Inches	88
Front Tread, Minimum—Inches	56
Front Tread, Maximum—Inches	84
Height Overall—Inches	68½
Length Overall—Inches	125
Wheelbase—Inches	84½
Electric Starting—Std. or Opt.	Std.
D.B. Adjustable Laterally?	Yes
D.B. Adjustable Vertically?	No
Cultivating Clearance—Inches	22
Hydraulic Power Unit	Opt.

Transmission of Power

Clutch—Dry, Single Plate?	Yes
Clutch—Overcenter?	Yes
Separate Clutch for P.T.O.?	No
Final Drive—Spur, Chain	Spur
High Gear Ratio	16.78
Low Gear Ratio	86.55
Speeds—Number Forward	4
Speeds—Number Reverse	1
Sliding Gear Speed Change?	Yes

Belt Pulley—Engine

Belt Pulley Diameter—Inches	12¼
Belt Pulley Face Width—Inches	6
Belt Pulley Speed—rpm	933
Belt Pulley Speed—fpm	2990
Cooling—Pump, Thermo-Syphon	Pump
Engine—Make	Own
Engine—Model	EE
Displacement—Cubic Inches	165
Rated rpm	1400

Minneapolis-Moline "RTE"

MINNEAPOLIS-MOLINE COMPANY
Minneapolis, Minnesota

Brakes

Make	Lamb't
Type—Internal Expanding, Disc	Disc
Location—Wheel Axle Shafts?	Yes
Actuation—Hydraulic, Mechanical	Mech.
Brake Units per Tractor	2
Gear Reduction—Drum to Rear Wheel	None

Steering—Tires

Steering Make	Own
Type—Cam & Lever, Worm & Sector	W&S
Tire Size—Standard Rear—Inches	9x36
Tire Size—Standard Front—Inches	5x15

General

<table>
<tr><td></td><td colspan="2">Minneapolis-Moline</td></tr>
<tr><td></td><td>"ZAE"</td><td>"ZAN"
"ZAU"</td></tr>
<tr><td>Number and Size Plows ....</td><td>2, 3-14</td><td>2, 3-14</td></tr>
<tr><td>Type—Adjustable Axle, Tricycle ....</td><td>A.A.</td><td>Tri.</td></tr>
<tr><td>Shipping Weight on Rubber—Lbs. ...</td><td>4100</td><td>3750</td></tr>
<tr><td>Nebraska Test Number ....</td><td>None</td><td>None</td></tr>
<tr><td>Rear Tread, Minimum—Inches ......</td><td>54</td><td>54</td></tr>
<tr><td>Rear Tread, Maximum—Inches .....</td><td>88</td><td>88</td></tr>
<tr><td>Front Tread, Minimum—Inches ....</td><td>56</td><td>7¾</td></tr>
<tr><td>Front Tread, Maximum—Inches ....</td><td>88</td><td>12⅞</td></tr>
<tr><td>Height Overall—Inches ....</td><td>78</td><td>78</td></tr>
<tr><td>Length Overall—Inches ......(ZAN)</td><td>136</td><td>128</td></tr>
<tr><td>(ZAU)</td><td></td><td>129</td></tr>
<tr><td>Wheelbase—Inches ....</td><td>90</td><td>83</td></tr>
<tr><td>Electric Starting—Std. or Opt. .....</td><td>Std.</td><td>Std.</td></tr>
<tr><td>D.B. Adjustable Laterally? ....</td><td>Yes</td><td>Yes</td></tr>
<tr><td>D.B. Adjustable Vertically? ....</td><td>No</td><td>No</td></tr>
<tr><td>Cultivating Clearance—Inches ....</td><td>25</td><td>25</td></tr>
<tr><td>Hydraulic Power Unit ....</td><td>Opt.</td><td>Opt.</td></tr>
</table>

Transmission of Power

<table>
<tr><td>Clutch—Dry, Single Plate? ....</td><td>Yes</td><td>Yes</td></tr>
<tr><td>Clutch—Overcenter? ....</td><td>Yes</td><td>Yes</td></tr>
<tr><td>Separate Clutch for P.T.O.? ....</td><td>No</td><td>No</td></tr>
<tr><td>Final Drive—Spur, Chain ....</td><td>Spur</td><td>Spur</td></tr>
<tr><td>High Gear Ratio ....</td><td>18.77</td><td>18.77</td></tr>
<tr><td>Low Gear Ratio ....</td><td>100.89</td><td>100.89</td></tr>
<tr><td>Speeds—Number Forward ....</td><td>4</td><td>4</td></tr>
<tr><td>Speeds—Number Reverse ....</td><td>1</td><td>1</td></tr>
<tr><td>Sliding Gear Speed Change? ....</td><td>Yes</td><td>Yes</td></tr>
</table>

Belt Pulley—Engine

<table>
<tr><td>Belt Pulley Diameter—Inches ......</td><td>15⅛</td><td>15⅛</td></tr>
<tr><td>Belt Pulley Face Width—Inches ....</td><td>7</td><td>7</td></tr>
<tr><td>Belt Pulley Speed—rpm ....</td><td>786</td><td>786</td></tr>
<tr><td>Belt Pulley Speed—fpm ....</td><td>3100</td><td>3100</td></tr>
<tr><td>Cooling—Pump, Thermo-Syphon .....</td><td>Pump</td><td>Pump</td></tr>
<tr><td>Engine—Make ....</td><td>Own</td><td>Own</td></tr>
<tr><td>Engine—Model ....</td><td>206B-4</td><td>206B-4</td></tr>
<tr><td>Displacement—Cubic Inches ....</td><td>206</td><td>206</td></tr>
<tr><td>Rated rpm ....</td><td>1500</td><td>1500</td></tr>
</table>

Brakes

<table>
<tr><td>Make ....</td><td>Own</td><td>Own</td></tr>
<tr><td>Type—Internal Expanding? ....</td><td>Yes</td><td>Yes</td></tr>
<tr><td>Location—Bull Pinion Shaft? ....</td><td>Yes</td><td>Yes</td></tr>
<tr><td>Actuation—Hydraulic, Mechanical ...</td><td>Mech.</td><td>Mech.</td></tr>
<tr><td>Brake Units per Tractor ....</td><td>2</td><td>2</td></tr>
<tr><td>Gear Reduction—Drum to Rear Wheel</td><td>5.666</td><td>5.666</td></tr>
</table>

Steering—Tires

<table>
<tr><td>Make ....</td><td>Own</td><td>Own</td></tr>
<tr><td>Type—Worm & Sector? ....</td><td>Yes</td><td>Yes</td></tr>
<tr><td>Tire Size—Standard Rear—Inches ..</td><td>11x38</td><td>11x38</td></tr>
<tr><td>Tire Size—Std. Front—Inches (ZAN)</td><td>5.5x16</td><td>7.5x10</td></tr>
<tr><td>(ZAU)</td><td></td><td>5.5x16</td></tr>
</table>

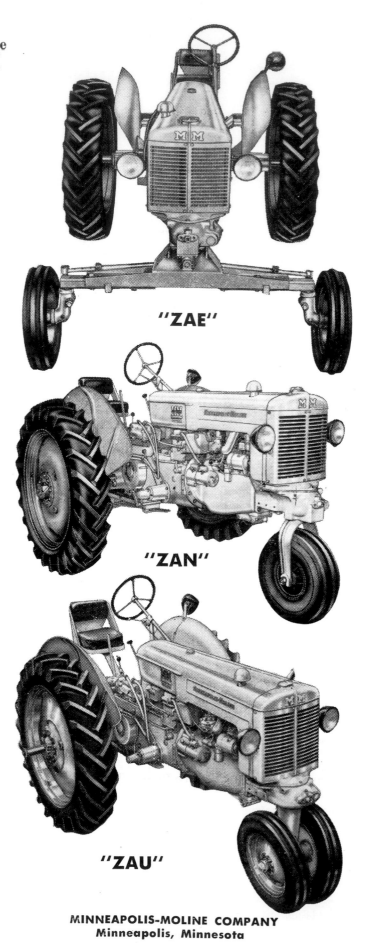

"ZAE"

"ZAN"

"ZAU"

MINNEAPOLIS-MOLINE COMPANY
Minneapolis, Minnesota

General

	Minneapolis-Moline "ZAS"
Number and Size Plows	2, 3-14
Type—Axle, Tricycle	Axle
Shipping Wt. on Rubber—Lbs.	3760
Nebraska Test Number	None
Rear Tread, Minimum—Inches	54
Rear Tread, Maximum—Inches	54
Front Tread, Minimum—Inches	48
Front Tread, Maximum—Inches	48
Height Overall—Inches	69
Length Overall—Inches	124
Wheelbase—Inches	72¾
Electric Starting—Std. or Opt.	Std.
D.B. Adjustable Laterally?	Yes
D.B. Adjustable Vertically?	No
Cultivating Clearance—Inches	24
Hydraulic Power Unit	Opt.

Transmission of Power

Clutch—Dry, Single Plate?	Yes
Clutch—Spring Loaded, Overcenter?	OC
Separate Clutch for P.T.O.?	No
Final Drive—Spur, Chain	Spur
High Gear Ratio	18.77
Low Gear Ratio	100.89
Speeds—Number Forward	4
Speeds—Number Reverse	1
Sliding Gear Speed Change?	Yes

Belt Pulley—Engine

Belt Pulley Diameter—Inches	15⅛
Belt Pulley Face Width—Inches	7
Belt Pulley Speed—rpm	786
Belt Pulley Speed—fpm	3100
Cooling—Pump, Thermo-Syphon	Pump
Engine—Make	Own
Engine—Model	206B-4
Displacement—Cubic Inches	206
Rated rpm	1500

Brakes

Type—Internal Expanding, Contracting Band	IE
Location—Bull Pinion Shaft?	Yes
Actuation—Hydraulic, Mechanical	Mech.
Brake Units per Tractor	2
Gear Reduction—Drum to Rear Wheel	5.666

Steering—Tires

Steering Make	Ross
Type—Cam & Lever, Worm & Sector	C&L
Tire Size—Standard Rear—Inches	11x38
Tire Size—Standard Front—Inches	5.5x16

"ZAS"
MINNEAPOLIS-MOLINE COMPANY
Minneapolis, Minnesota

THE OLIVER CORP.
Charles City, Iowa

Oliver Row Crop "66HC"	1949-1954
Oliver Row Crop "66KD"	1949-1951
Oliver Standard "66HC"	1949-1954
Oliver Standard "66KD"	1949-1951
Oliver Row Crop "77HC"	1949-1954
Oliver Row Crop "77KD"	1949-1951
Oliver Standard "77HC"	1949-1954
Oliver Standard "77KD"	1949-1951
Oliver Row Crop "88HC"	1949-1954
Oliver Row Crop "88KD"	1949-1951
Oliver Standard "88HC"	1949-1954
Oliver Standard "88KD"	1949-1951

Oliver "66" Row Crop
THE OLIVER CORPORATION
Charles City, Iowa

	Oliver Row Crop "66HC" "66KD"
General	
Number and Size Plows	2-14
Type—Axle, Tricycle	Tri.
Shipping Wt. on Rubber—Lbs. (66HC)	2500
(66KD)	2515
Nebraska Test Number	None
Rear Tread, Minimum—Inches	58
Rear Tread, Maximum—Inches	88
Front Tread, Minimum—Inches	6 9/16
Front Tread, Maximum—Inches	11¾
Height Overall—Inches	72
Length Overall—Inches	131¾
Wheelbase—Inches	86¾
Electric Starting—Std. or Opt.	Std.
D.B. Adjustable Laterally?	Yes
D.B. Adjustable Vertically?	Yes
Cultivating Clearance—Inches	24½
Hydraulic Power Unit	Opt.
Transmission of Power	
Clutch—Dry, Single Plate?	Yes
Clutch—Spring Loaded, Overcenter?.	SL
Separate Clutch for P.T.O.?	Yes
Final Drive—Spur, Chain	Spur
High Gear Ratio	19.52
Low Gear Ratio	90.37
Speeds—Number Forward	6
Speeds—Number Reverse	2
Sliding Gear Speed Change?	Yes
Belt Pulley—Engine	
Belt Pulley Diameter—Inches	11⅞
Belt Pulley Face Width—Inches	7¼
Belt Pulley Speed—rpm	987
Belt Pulley Speed—fpm	3065
Cooling—Pump, Thermo-Syphon	Pump
Engine—Make	Own
Engine—Model (66HC)	66HC
(66KD)	66KD
Displacement—Cubic Inches ..(66HC)	129.3
(66KD)	144
Rated rpm	1600

Brakes	
Type—Internal Expanding, Contracting Band	CB
Location—Bull Pinion Shaft?	Yes
Actuation—Hydraulic, Mechanical ...	Mech.
Brake Units per Tractor	2
Gear Reduction—Drum to Rear Wheel	4.679
Steering—Tires	
Steering Make	Own
Type—Cam & Lever, Worm & Sector	W&S
Tire Size—Standard Rear—Inches ..	9x38
Tire Size—Standard Front—Inches..	5x15

	Oliver	
	Standard "66HC" "66KD"	Row Crop "77HC" "77KD"

General

Number and Size Plows	2-14	2, 3-14
Type—Axle, Tricycle	Axle	Tri.
Shipping Wt. on Rubber—Lbs. . .(HC)	2380	3240
(KD)	2395	3260
Nebraska Test Number .....(77HC)	None	404
Observed Drawbar Horsepower ...		28.63
Observed Belt Horsepower		33.98
Maximum Pull—Lbs.		4079
Speed @ Maximum Pull		2.56
Weight @ Maximum Pull—Lbs.		7560
Rear Tread, Minimum—Inches	49¾	60
Rear Tread Maximum—Inches	59¾	92½
Front Tread, Minimum—Inches	46	7 11/16
Front Tread, Maximum—Inches	51	12¾
Height Overall—Inches	66	74
Length Overall—Inches	124½	139¼
Wheelbase—Inches	73½	90⅞
Electric Starting—Std. or Opt.	Std.	Std.
D.B. Adjustable Laterally?	Yes	Yes
D.B. Adjustable Vertically?	Yes	Yes
Cultivating Clearance—Inches	11½	25¼
Hydraulic Power Unit	Opt.	Opt.

Transmission of Power

Clutch—Dry, Single Plate?	Yes	Yes
Clutch—Spring Loaded?	Yes	Yes
Separate Clutch for P.T.O.?	Yes	Yes
Final Drive—Spur, Chain	Spur	Spur
High Gear Ratio	15.54	21.03
Low Gear Ratio	71.95	98.24
Speeds—Number Forward	6	6
Speeds—Number Reverse	2	2

Belt Pulley—Engine

Belt Pulley Diameter—Inches	11⅞	11⅞
Belt Pulley Face Width—Inches	7¼	7¼
Belt Pulley Speed—rpm	987	992
Belt Pulley Speed—fpm	3065	3080
Engine—Make	Own	Own
Displacement—Cubic Inches ...(HC)	129.3	193.9
(KD)	144	216
Rated rpm	1600	1600

Brakes

Type—Contracting Band?	Yes	Yes
Location—Bull Gear Pinion?	Yes	Yes
Actuation—Hydraulic, Mechanical ...	Mech.	Mech.
Gear Reduction—Drum to Rear Wheel	4.679	4.84

Steering—Tires

Type—Worm & Sector?	Yes	Yes
Tire Size—Standard Rear—Inches ..	10x24	11x38
Tire Size—Standard Front—Inches..	5x15	5.5x16

Oliver "66" Standard

Oliver "77" Row Crop
THE OLIVER CORPORATION Charles City, Iowa

General	Oliver Standard "77HC" "77KD"	Oliver Row Crop "88HC" "88KD"
Number and Size Plows	2, 3-14	3, 4-14
Nebraska Test Number (HC)	405	388
Observed Drawbar Horsepower	28.48	36.97
Observed Belt Horsepower	33.56	41.99
Maximum Pull—Lbs.	3802	5173
Speed @ Maximum Pull	2.61	2.51
Weight @ Maximum Pull—Lbs.	7418	8484
Rear Tread, Minimum—Inches	52½	60
Rear Tread, Maximum—Inches	52½	92½
Front Tread, Minimum—Inches	47⅛	8 1/16
Front Tread, Maximum—Inches	52¼	12 1/16
Length Overall—Inches	129½	141⅞
Wheelbase—Inches	78¼	93¾
Cultivating Clearance—Inches	13¼	26
Hydraulic Power Unit	Opt.	Opt.
Transmission of Power		
Clutch—Dry, Single Plate?	Yes	Yes
Clutch—Spring Loaded?	Yes	Yes
Separate Clutch for P.T.O.?	Yes	Yes
Final Drive—Spur, Chain	Spur	Spur
High Gear Ratio	17.31	21.41
Low Gear Ratio	80.83	100.78
Speeds—Number Forward	6	6
Speeds—Number Reverse	2	2
Belt Pulley—Engine		
Belt Pulley Diameter—Inches	11⅞	11⅞
Belt Pulley Face Width—Inches	7¼	7¼
Belt Pulley Speed—rpm	992	992
Belt Pulley Speed—fpm	3080	3080
Engine—Make	Own	Own
Displacement—Cubic Inches (HC)	193.9	230.9
(KD)	216	265
Rated rpm	1600	1600
Brakes		
Type—Contracting Band?	Yes	Yes
Location—Bull Gear Pinion?	Yes	Yes
Gear Reduction—Drum to Rear Wheel	4.84	4.692
Steering—Tires		
Type—Worm & Sector?	Yes	Yes
Tire Size—Standard Rear—Inches	12x26	12x38
Tire Size—Standard Front—Inches	5.5x16	6x16

Oliver "77" Standard

Oliver "88" Row Crop

THE OLIVER CORPORATION
Charles City, Iowa

General

	Oliver Standard "88HC" "88KD"
Number and Size Plows	3, 4-14
Type—Axle, Tricycle	Axle
Shipping Weight on Rubber—Lbs.	
(HC)	4600
(KD)	4625
Nebraska Test Number .....(88HC)	391
Observed Drawbar Horsepower	37.27
Observed Belt Horsepower	43.15
Maximum Pull—Lbs.	5270
Speed @ Maximum Pull	2.26
Weight @ Maximum Pull—Lbs.	7804
Rear Tread, Minimum—Inches	54
Rear Tread, Maximum—Inches	62
Front Tread, Minimum—Inches	48¾
Front Tread, Maximum—Inches	54¾
Height Overall—Inches	68½
Length Overall—Inches	141⅞
Wheelbase—Inches	79¼
Electric Starting—Std. or Opt.	Std.
D.B. Adjustable Laterally?	Yes
D.B. Adjustable Vertically?	Yes
Cultivating Clearance—Inches	13¾
Hydraulic Power Unit	Opt.

Transmission of Power

Clutch—Dry, Single Plate?	Yes
Clutch—Spring Loaded?	Yes
Separate Clutch for P.T.O.?	Yes
Final Drive—Spur, Chain	Spur
High Gear Ratio	18.12
Low Gear Ratio	85.28
Speeds—Number Forward	6
Speeds—Number Reverse	2
Sliding Gear Speed Change?	Yes

Belt Pulley—Engine

Belt Pulley Diameter—Inches	11⅞
Belt Pulley Face Width—Inches	7¼
Belt Pulley Speed—rpm	992
Belt Pulley Speed—fpm	3080
Cooling—Pump, Thermo-Syphon	Pump
Engine—Make	Own
Engine—Model (HC)	88HC
(KD)	88KD
Displacement—Cubic Inches (HC)	230.9
(KD)	265
Rated rpm	1600

Brakes

Make	Own
Type—Contracting Band?	Yes
Location—Bull Gear Pinion?	Yes
Actuation—Hydraulic, Mechanical	Mech.
Brake Units per Tractor	2
Gear Reduction—Drum to Rear Wheel	4.692

Steering—Tires

Steering Make	Own
Type—Worm & Sector?	Yes
Tire Size—Standard Rear—Inches	13x26
Tire Size—Standard Front—Inches	6x16

Oliver "88" Standard

THE OLIVER CORP.
Cletrac Division

Cleveland, Ohio

Oliver Cletrac "AD"	1949
Oliver Cletrac "AG-6"	1949
Oliver Cletrac "BD"	1949-1954
Oliver Cletrac "DG"	1949-1956
Oliver Cletrac "FDE"	1949-1952
Oliver Cletrac "HG"	1949-1951

General

	Oliver Cletrac "AD"	"AG-6"
Number and Size Plows	3-14	3-14
Shipping Weight—Lbs.	7662	7086
Nebraska Test Number	None	None
Tread, Minimum—Inches	42	42
Tread, Maximum—Inches	50	50
Height Overall—Inches	[1]54	[1]54
Length Overall—Inches	101½	103½
Wheelbase—Inches	62	62
Electric Starting—Std. or Opt.	Std.	Crank
D.B. Adjustable Laterally?	Yes	Yes
D.B. Adjustable Vertically?	No	No
Cultivating Clearance—Inches	12	12
Hydraulic Power Unit	Opt.	Opt.

Transmission of Power

Clutch—Dry, Double Plate?	Yes	Yes
Clutch—Semi-Centrifugal?	Yes	Yes
Clutch—Spring Loaded?	Yes	Yes
Separate Clutch for P.T.O. & B.P.? ..	Yes	Yes
Final Drive—Spur, Chain	Spur	Spur
High Gear Ratio	27.03	27.03
Low Gear Ratio	56.52	56.52
Speeds—Number Forward	3	3
Speeds—Number Reverse	1	1
Sliding Gear Speed Change?	Yes	Yes

Belt Pulley—Engine

Belt Pulley Diameter—Inches	10½	10½
Belt Pulley Face Width—Inches	8½	8½
Belt Pulley Speed—rpm	1130	1130
Belt Pulley Speed—fpm	3105	3105
Cooling—Pump, Thermo-Syphon	Pump	Pump
Engine—Make	Herc.	Cont'l.
Engine—Model	DOOC	F226
Displacement—Cubic Inches	226	226
Rated rpm	1530	1530

Steering Brakes—Tracks

Make	Own	Own
Type—Contracting Wet Band?	Yes	Yes
Location—Differential?	Yes	Yes
Actuation—Hydraulic, Mechanical ...	Mech.	Mech.
Brake Units per Tractor	2	2
Gear Reduction—Drum to Track	6.17	6.17
Track Face Width—Inches	12	12
Ground Contacting Area of Tracks—Square Inches	1488	1488

[1] Excluding air intake and exhaust pipes.

Oliver Cletrac "AD"

Oliver Cletrac "AG-6"

THE OLIVER CORPORATION
Cletrac Division
Cleveland, Ohio

1950

For 1950, the list includes four tractor manufacturers producing 11 new tractor models. Sherman Products Company of Detroit introduced a Step-Up transmission which could be installed in all models of Ford or Ford-Ferguson tractors. The Step-Up transmission allowed faster speeds in all gears. This was quickly followed with a Step-Up/Step-Down transmission which gave a greater range of tractor speeds. The auxiliary transmission could be installed on any model of Ford or Ferguson and quickly became a popular accessory.

Massey-Harris Company merged with Ferguson to form Massey-Harris-Ferguson. The merger resulted in an expansion of the Massey-Harris line.

Ford TRACTOR

A POWER UNIT WITH
PLENTY OF OUTSTANDING FEATURES

In every way the Ford Tractor reflects the wealth of Ford Engineering and manufacturing experience *gained* in building over a million tractors. Here are some of the more important things you get in the Ford Tractor—

- Ford-built engine is high compression, L-head type. Removable cylinder liners are dry type. Water jackets extend full length of cylinders.

- Transmission has four forward speeds for greater convenience and economy. Quiet, easy shifting—thanks to helical gears.

- Ford Tractor Hydraulic Touch Control lets the operator utilize hydraulics to raise, lower and otherwise control attached implements.

- Duo-servo type brakes give fast stops. Pedals for both wheels are on right side and may be operated together or separately.

- Other convenience features include Automotive Type Steering Gear, full running boards, swing-back seat and safety starter.

For more complete information see your nearby Ford Tractor dealer or write direct to—
DEARBORN MOTORS CORPORATION • DETROIT 3, MICHIGAN

COPYRIGHT 1948, DEARBORN MOTORS CORPORATION

Dearborn FARM EQUIPMENT

For the Ford Tractor there is a complete line of Dearborn Farm Equipment designed and built to exceptionally high standards. This line includes soil preparation, planting, cultivating and harvesting implements, plus special implements for conservation work and a large number of other farm jobs.

DEARBORN MOTORS CORP.
Birmingham, Michigan

Ford "8N"   1950-1953

General	Ford "8N"
Number and Size Plows	2-14
Type—Axle, Adjustable Axle	A.A.
Shipping Weight on Rubber—Lbs.	2410
Nebraska Test Number	393
Observed Drawbar Horsepower	21.72
Observed Belt Horsepower	25.77
Maximum Pull—Lbs.	2751
Speed @ Maximum Pull	2.71
Weight @ Maximum Pull—Lbs.	4140
Rear Tread, Minimum—Inches	48
Rear Tread, Maximum—Inches	76
Front Tread, Minimum—Inches	48
Front Tread, Maximum—Inches	76
Height Overall—Inches	54½
Length Overall—Inches	115
Wheelbase—Inches	70
Electric Starting—Std. or Opt.	Std.
D.B. Adjustable Laterally?	Yes
D.B. Adjustable Vertically?	Yes
Cultivating Clearance—Inches	21
Hydraulic Power Unit	Std.

Transmission of Power

Clutch—Dry, Single Plate?	Yes
Clutch—Semi-Centrifugal?	Yes
Clutch—Spring Loaded?	Yes
Separate Clutch for P.T.O.?	No
Final Drive—Bevel, Spur	Bevel
High Gear Ratio	19.86
Low Gear Ratio	73.33
Speeds—Number Forward	4
Speeds—Number Reverse	1
Speed Change—Constant Mesh, Syncro-Mesh	CM

Belt Pulley—Engine

Belt Pulley Diameter—Inches	9
Belt Pulley Face Width—Inches	6½
Belt Pulley Speed—High—rpm	1358
Belt Pulley Speed—Low—rpm	1018
Belt Pulley Speed—High—fpm	3199
Belt Pulley Speed—Low—fpm	2398
Cooling—Pump, Thermo-Syphon	Pump
Engine—Make	Own
Engine—Model	8N
Displacement—Cubic Inches	119.7
Rated rpm—Belt	2000
Drawbar	1750

Brakes

Make—Bendix, New Process	Bendix
Type—Internal Expanding Shoes, Contracting Band	IES
Location—Rear Wheels, Final Drive Shafts	RW
Actuation—Hydraulic, Mechanical	Mech.
Brake Units per Tractor	2
Gear Reduction—Drum to Rear Wheel	None

Steering—Tires

	"8N"
Steering—Make	Sag'nw
Type—Worm & Ball Nut, Cam & Lever	W&BN
Tire Size—Standard Rear—Inches	10x28
Tire Size—Standard Front—Inches	4x19

Ford "8N"

FORD MOTOR COMPANY
Dearborn, Michigan

DEERE & CO.
Moline, Illinois

Deere "AH"   1950-1952
Deere "GN"   1950-1953
Deere "GW"   1950-1953

	Deere "AH"
General	
Number and Size Plows	3-14
Type—Adjustable Axle, Tricycle	Tri.
Shipping Wt. on Rubber—Lbs.	6400
Nebraska Test No. (All Fuel)	None
Rear Tread, Minimum—Inches	60
Rear Tread, Maximum—In.	90
Front Tread, Minimum—Inches	60
Front Tread, Maximum—In.	84
Height Overall—Inches	97½
Length Overall—Inches	152½
Wheelbase—Inches	98¼
Electric Starting—Std. or Opt.	Std.
D.B. Adjustable Laterally?	No
D.B. Adjustable Vertically?	Yes
Cultivating Clearance—Inches	32
Hydraulic Power Unit—Std., Optional.	Std.
Transmission of Power	
Clutch—Multiple Disc?	Yes
Clutch—Overcenter?	Yes
Final Drive—Bevel, Chain, Spur	
High Gear Ratio	14.5
Low Gear Ratio	111.2
Speeds—Number Forward	6
Speeds—Number Reverse	1
Sliding Gear Speed Change?	Yes
Belt Pulley—P.T.O.—Engine	
Belt Pulley Diameter—Inches	12¹³⁄₁₆
Belt Pulley Face Width—Inches	7⅜
Belt Pulley Speed—rpm	975
Belt Pulley Speed—fpm	3270
Power Take-Off—Std., Optional	Std.
Is Power to P.T.O. Continuous?	No
Engine—Make	Own
Engine—Model	A
Displacement—Cubic Inches	321
Rated rpm	975
Piston Speed, fpm, @ Rated rpm	1097
Brakes	
Make	Own
Type—Internal Expanding?	Yes
Location—Separate Shaft?	Yes
Actuation—Hydraulic, Mechanical	Mech.
Brake Units per Tractor	2
Steering—Tires	
Steering—Make	Own
Type—Worm & Sector?	Yes
Tire Size—Std. Rear—Inches (A-AH)	11x38
Tire Size—Std. Front—In. (A-AW)	7.5x20

Deere "AH"
Model "GH" Similar

General

	John Deere "GN" "GW"
Number and Size Plows	3-14
Type—Axle, Adj. Axle, Tri. (GW)	Adj.
(GN)	Tri.
Shipping Weight on Rubber—Lbs.	
(GN)	5714
(GW)	5994
Nebraska Test Number	383
Observed Drawbar Horsepower	34.49
Observed Belt Horsepower	38.10
Corrected Drawbar Horsepower	36.0
Corrected Belt Horsepower	39.8
Maximum Pull—Lbs.	4394
Speed @ Maximum Pull	2.07
Weight @ Maximum Pull—Lbs.	7442
Rear Tread, Minimum—Inches	60
Rear Tread, Maximum—Inches	84
Front Tread, Minimum—Inches (GW)	56
Front Tread, Maximum—Inches (GW)	80
Height Overall—Inches (GN)	89½
(GW)	88⅛
Length Overall—Inches (GN)	140¹³⁄₁₆
(GW)	145¹¹⁄₁₆
Wheelbase—Inches (GN)	91¼
(GW)	97⅜
Cultivating Clearance—Inches	26½
Hydraulic Power Unit	Opt.

Belt Pulley—P.T.O.—Engine

Pulley Diameter, Standard—Inches	12⅞
Pulley Face Width—Inches	8½
Pulley Speed, Loaded—rpm	975
Pulley Speed, Loaded—fpm	3270
Power Take-off—Standard, Optional.	Std.
Is Power to P.T.O. Continuous?	No
Engine Make	Own
Displacement—Cubic Inches	413
Compression Ratio, Standard	4.2
Rated rpm	975
Piston Speed fpm @ Rated rpm	1138

Brakes—Steering—Tires

Brakes, Type—Contracting Band, Internal Expanding	IE
Brakes, Location—Separate Shaft Driven by Bull Gear?	Yes
Brake Units per Tractor	2
Steering Type—Worm & Gear, Worm & Sector	W&S
Tire Size—Standard Rear—Inches	12x38
Tire Size—Std. Front—In. (GW)	6x16
(GN)	7.5x16

Transmission of Power

Clutch—Multiple Disc Dry Type?	Yes
Clutch—Overcenter?	Yes
Final Drive—Spur, Chain	Spur
High Gear Ratio	13.27
Low Gear Ratio	66.9
Speeds—Number Forward	6
Speeds—Number Reverse	1

John Deere "G"

DEERE & COMPANY
Moline, Illinois

MASSEY-HARRIS CO.
Racine, Wisconsin

Massey-Harris "22"	1950-1953
Massey-Harris "30"	1950-1953
Massey-Harris "44" Standard	1950-1954
Massey-Harris "44D" Row Crop	1950-1954
Massey-Harris "44D" Standard	1950-1954
Massey-Harris "55"	1950-1956

Massey-Harris "22"

Massey-Harris "30"

	Massey-Harris	
General	**"22"**	**"30"**
Number and Size Plows	2-14	2-14
Type—Axle or Tricycle	Both	Both
Shipping Wt. on Rubber—Lbs. (Axle)	2710	3960
(Tri.)	2560	3770
Nebraska Test Number ..(Row Crop)	403	409
Observed Drawbar Horsepower	22.87	26.24
Observed Belt Horsepower	31.05	34.18
Maximum Pull—Lbs.	2109	3273
Speed @ Maximum Pull	1.91	2.18
Weight @ Maximum Pull—Lbs.	4489	5265
Rear Tread, Minimum—Inches (Axle)	47	52⅛
(Tri.)	48	52
Rear Tread, Maximum—Inches (Axle)	48	52⅛
(Tri.)	88	88
Front Tread, Minimum—Inches (Axle)	45¾	47⅝
(Tri.)	6⅜	7⅜
Front Tread, Maximum—Inches (Axle)	45¾	47⅝
(Tri.)	12⅜	14⅛
Height Overall—Inches (Axle)	73	71⅜
(Tri.)	76	74¼
Length Overall—Inches (Axle)	111½	125⅝
(Tri.)	119½	128
Wheelbase—Inches (Axle)	74¾	79 3/16
(Tri.)	74¾	83
Electric Starting—Std. or Opt.	Std.	Std.
D.B. Adjustable Laterally?	Yes	Yes
D.B. Adjustable Vertically?	Yes	Yes
Cultivating Clearance—Inches (Axle)	11½	9½
(Tri.)	12⅝	13⅝
Hydraulic Power Unit	Std.	Opt.

Transmission of Power

Clutch—Dry, Single Plate?	Yes	Yes
Clutch—Spring Loaded?	Yes	Yes
Separate Clutch for P.T.O.?	No	No
Final Drive—Bevel, Spur	Bevel	Spur
High Gear Ratio	15.02	19.0
Low Gear Ratio	79.80	93.2
Speeds—Number Forward	4	5
Sliding Gear Speed Change?	Yes	Yes

Belt Pulley—Engine

Belt Pulley Diameter—Inches	9½	13½
Belt Pulley Face Width—Inches	6	6
Belt Pulley Speed—rpm	1224	838
Belt Pulley Speed—fpm	3044	2960
Engine—Make	Cont'l.	Cont'l.
Engine—Model	F-140	F-162
Displacement—Cubic Inches	140	162
Rated rpm—Belt	1800	1800
Drawbar	1500	1500

Brakes

Type—Expanding?	Yes	Yes
Location—Axle Sleeve, Differential Pinion Shafts	AS	DP
Actuation—Hydraulic, Mechanical	Mech.	Mech.
Gear Reduction—Drum to Rear Wheel	None	5.077

Steering—Tires

Steering Make	Sag'nw.	Sag'nw.
Type—Worm & Sector?	Yes	Yes
Tire Size—Std. Rear—Inches (Axle)	10x28	11x28
(Tri.)	9x32	10x38
Tire Size—Std. Front—Inches (Axle)	5x15	5x15
(Tri.)	4x15	5x15

General	Massey-Harris "44"	"44D"
Number and Size Plows	4-14	4-14
Type—Axle, Tricycle	Both	Both
Shipping Weight Maximum—Lbs......	4860	5075
Nebraska Test No.... (Gas. & Diesel)	389	426
Observed Drawbar Horsepower....	39.90	37.91
Observed Belt Horsepower........	45.64	41.82
Corrected Drawbar Horsepower...	41.36	39.48
Corrected Belt Horsepower.......	47.04	43.04
Maximum Pull—Lbs.	4612	4351
Speed @ Maximum Pull...........	2.09	1.92
Weight @ Maximum Pull—Lbs.....	6925	7313
Rear Tread, Minimum—Inches (Axle)	54⅛	54⅛
(Tri.)	51¼	51¼
Rear Tread, Maximum—Inches (Axle)	54⅛	54⅛
(Tri.)	88⅜	88⅜
Front Tread, Minimum—Inches (Axle)	47½	47½
(Tri.)	8¹³⁄₁₆	8¹³⁄₁₆
Front Tread, Maximum—Inches (Axle)	47½	47½
(Tri.)	15⁵⁄₁₆	15⁵⁄₁₆
Length Overall—Inches ......(Axle)	129	129
(Tri.)	137	137
Wheelbase—Inches ....(Axle)	79½	79½
(Tri.)	87¾	87¾
Cultivating Clearance—Inches (Axle)	25⅝	25⅝
(Tri.)	26¾	26¾
Hydraulic Power Unit....(Tri. Only)	Std.	Std.

Belt Pulley—P.T.O.—Engine

	"44"	"44D"
Pulley Diameter, Standard—Inches...	13½	13½
Pulley Face Width—Inches..........	6	6
Pulley Speed, Loaded—rpm..........	863	863
Pulley Speed, Loaded—fpm..........	3050	3050
Power Take-Off—Standard, Optional.	Opt.	Opt.
Is Power to P.T.O. Continuous?.....	No	No
Engine—Make	Own	Own
Ignition—Spark, Diesel	Spk.	Die.
Engine—Model	H-260	HD-260
Displacement—Cubic Inches	260	260
Compression Ratio, Standard........	5.65	14.5
Optional	4.65	
Rated rpm	1350	1350
Piston Speed fpm @ Rated rpm......	1238	1238

Brakes—Steering—Tires

	"44"	"44D"
Brakes, Type—Internal Expanding?..	Yes	Yes
Brakes, Location—Diff. Pinions?....	Yes	Yes
Steering Type—Worm & Sector?....	Yes	Yes
Tire Size—Std. Rear—Inches (Axle)	14x30	14x30
(Tri.)	13x38	11x38
Tire Size—Std. Front—Inches (Axle)	6x16	6x16
(Tri.)	5.5x16	5.5x16

Transmission of Power

	"44"	"44D"
Clutch—Dry, Single Plate?	Yes	Yes
Clutch—Spring Loaded?	Yes	Yes
Final Drive—Spur, Chain	Spur	Spur
High Gear Ratio	16.68	16.68
Low Gear Ratio	92.93	92.93
Speeds—Number Forward	5	5
Speeds—Number Reverse	1	1

Massey-Harris "44" (Std.)

Massey-Harris "44D" (R.C.)

MASSEY-HARRIS COMPANY
Racine, Wisconsin

MINNEAPOLIS-MOLINE CO.
Minneapolis, Minnesota

Minneapolis-Moline-Avery "V"   1950-1952

General

	Minneapolis-Moline-Avery "V"
Number and Size Plows	1-14
Type—Axle, Tricycle, Adj. Axle	Axle
Shipping Wt. on Rubber—Lbs.	1612
Nebraska Test Number	None
Rear Tread, Minimum—Inches	40
Rear Tread, Maximum—Inches	40
Front Tread, Minimum—Inches	40
Front Tread, Maximum—Inches	40
Height Overall—Inches	61¼
Length Overall—Inches	105
Wheelbase—Inches	74
Cultivating Clearance—Inches	23
Hydraulic Power Unit	Opt.

Belt Pulley—P.T.O.—Engine

Pulley Diameter, Standard—Inches	6
Pulley Face Width—Inches	5½
Pulley Speed, Loaded—rpm	1990
Pulley Speed, Loaded—fpm	3100
Power Take-Off—Std., Optional	Opt.
Is Power to P.T.O. Continuous?	No
Engine—Make	Herc.
Engine—Model	ZXB3
Displacement—Cubic Inches	64.9
Rated rpm	1800
Piston Speed fpm @ Rated rpm	900

Brakes—Steering—Tires

Brakes, Type—Contracting Band?	Yes
Brakes, Location—Bull Pinion Shafts?	Yes
Steering Make	Ross
Steering, Type—Cam & Lever, Worm & Gear	C&L
Tire Size—Standard Rear—Inches	8x24
Tire Size—Std. Front—Inches	4x15

Transmission of Power

Clutch—Dry, Single Plate?	Yes
Clutch—Spring Loaded?	Yes
Final Drive—Spur, Chain	Spur
High Gear Ratio	26.2
Low Gear Ratio	70.2
Speeds—Number Forward	3
Speeds—Number Reverse	1

Minneapolis-Moline-Avery "V"
MINNEAPOLIS-MOLINE COMPANY
Minneapolis, Minnesota

1951

For 1951, 16 tractor manufacturers produced 39 new tractor models. Willys-Overland Motors convert-ed their popular Jeep to field work by building a three-point hitch and offering plows, post hole diggers and similar tools.

ALLIS-CHALMERS

Milwaukee, Wisconsin

Allis-Chalmers "CA"   1951

General	Allis-Chalmers "CA"
Number and Size Plows	2-14
Type—Axle, Adj. Axle, Tricycle	AA&T
Shipping Weight on Rubber—Lbs.	2835
Nebraska Test Number (Gasoline)	453
Observed Drawbar Horsepower	22.97
Observed Belt Horsepower	25.96
Corrected Drawbar Horsepower	23.55
Corrected Belt Horsepower	26.62
Maximum Pull—Lbs.	3557
Speed @ Maximum Pull	1.7
Weight @ Maximum Pull—Lbs.	5045
Rear Tread, Adj. Range—Inches	52-80
Front Tread, Minimum—Inches (A.A.)	47
(Tri.)	6¼
Front Tread, Maximum—Inches (A.A.)	78
(Tri.)	13
Height Overall—Inches	76⅜
Length Overall—Inches	124⅝
Wheelbase—Inches	81⅞
Cultivating Clearance—Inches	22½
Hydraulic Power Unit	Std.

Belt Pulley—P.T.O.—Engine

Pulley Diameter, Standard—Inches	8
Pulley Face Width—Inches	5½
Pulley Speed, Loaded—rpm	1220
Pulley Speed, Loaded—fpm	2556
Power Take-off—Standard, Optional	Std.
Is Power for P.T.O. Continuous?	Yes
Engine—Make	Own
Engine—Model	CE
Displacement—Cubic Inches	125
Compression Ratio, Standard	6.25
Rated rpm	1650
Piston Speed fpm @ Rated rpm	962

Brakes—Steering—Tires

Brakes Type	Band
Drums Location—Bull Pinion Shaft?	Yes
Steering Type—Cam and Lever?	Yes
Tire Size—Standard Rear—Inches	10x24
Tire Size—Standard Front—Inches	5x15

Transmission of Power

Clutch—Dry Disc Spring Loaded?	Yes
Final Drive—Spur, Chain	Spur
High Gear Ratio	24.75
Low Gear Ratio	76.0
Speeds—Number Forward	4
Speeds—Number Reverse	1

Allis-Chalmers "CA"

AMERICAN TRACTOR CORP.
Churubusco, Indiana

Terratrac "GT-25"
Terratrac "GT-30"

1951-1954
1951-1955

Terratrac "GT-25"

Terratrac "GT-30"

AMERICAN TRACTOR CORP.

Churubusco, Indiana

General	Terratrac "GT-25"	"GT-30"
Number and Size Plows	2-14	3-14
Shipping Weight—Lbs.	3290	3400
Nebraska Test Number	None	471
Observed Drawbar Horsepower		25.16
Observed Belt Horsepower		30.41
Corrected Drawbar Horsepower		26.30
Corrected Belt Horsepower		31.40
Maximum Pull—Lbs.		4518
Speed @ Maximum Pull—mph		1.64
Weight @ Maximum Pull—Lbs.		4471
Tread, Minimum—Inches	36	42
Tread, Maximum—Inches	72	72
Height Overall—Inches	*51	*51
Length, Overall—Inches	96	96
Cultivating Clearance—Inches	20½	18
Hydraulic Power Unit	Opt.	Opt.
Rated Drawbar Horsepower	20.0	
Rated Belt Horsepower	25	

Belt Pulley—P.T.O.—Engine

Pulley Diameter, Standard—Inches	8½	8½
Pulley Face Width—Inches	6½	6½
Pulley Speed, Loaded—rpm	1130	1130
Pulley Speed, Loaded—fpm	2514	2514
Power Take-Off—Standard, Optional	Opt.	Opt.
Is Power to P.T.O. Continuous?	No	No
Engine—Make	Cont'l	Cont'l
Engine—Model	F-124	F-140
Displacement—Cubic Inches	123.7	139.6
Compression Ratio, Standard	6.3	6.5
Rated rpm	1850	1850
Piston Speed fpm @ Rated rpm	1349	1349

Steering Brakes—Tracks

Steering Brakes Type—Contracting Wet Band?	Yes	Yes
Steering Brakes Location—Diff.?	Yes	Yes
Track Face Width—Inches	7½	10
Ground Contacting Area of Tracks—Square Inches	764	1080

Transmission of Power

Clutch—Dry Disc Spring Loaded?	Yes	Yes
Final Drive—Spur, Chain	Spur	Spur
High Gear Ratio	26.21	26.21
Low Gear Ratio	68.27	68.27
Speeds—Number Forward	3	3
Speeds—Number Reverse	1	1

Advertised Speeds, mph, With Standard Transmission—Models GT-25, GT-30: 1.78, 2.81, 4.61; reverse, 2.05.

*To top of cowling.

B. F. AVERY & SONS CO.
Louisville, Kentucky

B. F. Avery "R"   1951

General	B. F. Avery "R"
Number and Size Plows	2-14
Type—Adj. Axle, Tricycle	Both
Shipping Wt. on Rubber—Lbs...(Axle)	2900
(Tri.)	2735
Nebraska Test Number .....(Diesel)	None
Rear Tread, Minimum—Inches	52
Rear Tread, Maximum—Inches	76
Front Tread, Minimum—Inches (Adj.)	52
Front Tread, Maximum—Inches (Adj.)	72
Height Overall—Inches	76
Length Overall—Inches (Adj.)	118⅛
(Tri.)	116¾
Wheelbase—Inches (Adj.)	82½
(Tri.)	79¾
Starting—Crank, Electric	Elec.
D.B. Adjustable Laterally?	Yes
D.B. Adjustable Vertically?	Yes
Cultivating Clearance—Inches (Adj.)	22
(Tri.)	26
Hydraulic Power Unit	Std.

Transmission of Power

Clutch—Single Dry Plate?	Yes
Clutch—Spring Loaded, Overcenter	SL
Final Drive—Bevel, Chain, Spur	Spur
Speeds—Number Forward	4
Speeds—Number Reverse	1
Sliding Gear Speed Change?	Yes

Belt Pulley—P.T.O.—Engine

Power Take-off—Standard, Optional.	Opt.
Is Power for P.T.O. Continuous?	No
Engine—Make	Herc.
Engine—Model	IXB3
Displacement—Cubic Inches	133
Rated rpm	1800
Piston Speed fpm @ Rated rpm	1200

Brakes

Make	Clark
Type	Band
Location—Bull Pinion Shafts, Steering Clutch Shafts	BPS
Actuation—Hydraulic, Mechanical	Mech.
Brake Units per Tractor	2

Steering—Tires

	"R"
Steering—Make	Own
Type—Multiple Disc Clutch, Worm & Gear	W&G
Tire Size—Std. Rear—Inches	10x28
Tire Size—Std. Front—Inches (Adj.)	5x15
(Tri. Single)	6x16
(Tri. Dual)	5x15

B. F. Avery "R"

B. F. AVERY & SONS CO.
Louisville, Kentucky

COCKSHUTT PLOW CO.
Brantford, Ontario, Canada

General | Cockshutt "40"

Number and Size Plows	3, 4-14
Type—Axle, Adj. Axle, Tricycle	All
Shipping Wt. on Rubber—Lbs... (Axle)	4600
Nebraska Test Number (Gas.) (G50)	442
Observed Drawbar Horsepower	37.85
Observed Belt Horsepower	43.30
Maximum Pull—Lbs.	5538
Speed @ Maximum Pull	1.38
Weight @ Maximum Pull—Lbs.	8371
Rear Tread, Minimum—Inches. (Axle)	61¾
(Tri.)	56
Rear Tread, Maximum—Inches. (Axle)	78¾
(Tri.)	84
Front Tread, Minimum—Inches. (Axle)	53⅜
(Tri.)	7¾
Front Tread, Maximum—Inches. (Axle)	57
(Tri.)	11⅜
Height Overall—Inches	79½
Length Overall—Inches (Axle)	132
(Tri.)	135
Wheelbase—Inches (Axle)	$86\frac{9}{16}$
(Tri.)	$89\frac{9}{16}$
Electric Starting—Std. or Opt.	Std.
D.B. Adjustable Laterally?	Yes
D.B. Adjustable Vertically?	Yes
Cultivating Clearance—Inches. (Axle)	17
(Adj.)	24
(Tri.)	28½
Hydraulic Power Unit—Std., Optional.	Opt.
Steel Tire Wheels Optional?	Yes

Transmission of Power

Clutch—Dry Single Plate?	Yes
Clutch—Spring Loaded, Overcenter	SL
Final Drive—Bevel, Chain, Spur	Spur
High Gear Ratio	23.6
Low Gear Ratio	174.5
Speeds—Number Forward	6
Speeds—Number Reverse	2
Sliding Gear Speed Change?	Yes

Belt Pulley—P.T.O.—Engine

Belt Pulley Diameter—Inches	12
Belt Pulley Face Width—Inches	8½
Belt Pulley Speed—rpm	1000
Belt Pulley Speed—fpm	3511
Power Take-Off—Std., Optional	Opt.
Is Power to P.T.O. Continuous?	Yes
Engine—Make	Buda
Engine—Model	6B230
Displacement—Cubic Inches	229.7
Rated rpm	1650
Piston Speed, fpm, @ Rated rpm	1134

Brakes | "40"

Make	Timken
Type—Clamping Shoes?	Yes
Location—Differential Shafts?	Yes
Actuation—Hydraulic, Mechanical	Mech.
Brake Units per Tractor	2

Steering—Tires

Steering—Make	Own
Type—Cam & Lever, Worm & Gear	W&G
Tire Size—Std. Rear—Inches	12x38
Tire Size—Std. Front—Inches	6x16

Cockshutt "40"

COCKSHUTT PLOW CO.
Brantford, Canada

DEERE & CO.
Moline, Illinois

John Deere "MC"

1951-1953

General

	John Deere "MC"
Number and Size Plows.............	3-14
Type—Track, Axle	Track
Shipping Weight on Rubber—Lbs. ...	3875
Nebraska Test Number	448
Observed Drawbar Horsepower ...	17.49
Observed Belt Horsepower	21.24
Corrected Drawbar Horsepower...	18.26
Corrected Belt Horsepower......	22.22
Maximum Pull—Lbs.	4226
Speed @ Maximum Pull	0.84
Weight @ Maximum Pull—Lbs.	4293
Tread, Standard—Inches	36 & 46
Tread, Optional—Inches	38 & 44
Height Overall—Inches	50½
Length Overall—Inches	102
Standard Starting—Elec., Aux. Engine	Elec.
Cultivating Clearance—Inches	14
Hydraulic Power Unit..............	Opt.

Belt Pulley—P.T.O.—Engine

Pulley Diameter, Standard—Inches...	7¼
Pulley Face Width—Inches.........	6⅜
Pulley Speed, Loaded—rpm........	1575
Pulley Speed, Loaded—fpm........	2990
Power Take-off—Standard, Optional.	Std.
Is Power to PTO Continuous?	No
Engine—Make	Own
Displacement—Cubic Inches	100.5
Compression Ratio, Standard.......	6.0
Rated rpm	1650
Piston Speed fpm @ Rated rpm......	1100

Brakes

Type—Expanding, Contracting	Con.
Location—Final Drive Pinion, Sep. Shafts Driven by Bull Gears......	FDS

Steering—Tires—Tracks

Steering Clutches Type—Mult. Disc?.	Yes
Track Face Width, Standard—Inches.	10-12 or 14
Tire Size—Standard Rear—Inches ...	Track
Tire Size—Standard Front—Inches ..	Track

John Deere "MC"

DEERE & COMPANY
Moline, Illinois

Transmission of Power

Clutch—Single Plate, Multiple Disc...	SP
Clutch—Dry, Wet	Dry
Clutch—Spring Loaded, Overcenter..	SL
Final Drive—Spur, Chain	Spur
High Gear Ratio...................	21.8
Low Gear Ratio...................	117.9
Speeds—Number Forward	4
Speeds—Number Reverse	1

FATE-ROOT-HEATH CO.
Plymouth, Ohio

Silver King "3 Wheel Row Crop"   1951-1953
Silver King "4 Wheel Standard"   1951-1953

General	Silver King "Row Crop"	"Std."
Number and Size Plows	2, 3-14	2-14
Type—Axle, Tricycle	Tri.	Axle
Shipping Weight on Rubber—Lbs.	3550	3200
Nebraska Test Number....(Gasoline)	424	None
Observed Drawbar Horsepower	28.03	
Observed Belt Horsepower	33.14	
Corrected Drawbar Horsepower	29.80	
Corrected Belt Horsepower	34.53	
Maximum Pull—Lbs.	3004	
Speed @ Maximum Pull—mph	2.32	
Weight @ Maximum Pull—Lbs.	5357	
Rear Tread, Adj. Range—Inches	56-84	44-72
Front Tread—Inches	None	48
Height Overall—Inches	78	66
Length Overall—Inches	131	114
Wheelbase—Inches	83¼	66¼
Cultivating Clearance—Inches	27⅝	15¼
Hydraulic Power Unit	Opt.	Opt.

Belt Pulley—P.T.O.—Engine

Pulley Diameter, Standard—Inches	6½	6½
Pulley Face Width—Inches	8	8
Pulley Speed, Loaded—rpm	1800	1800
Pulley Speed, Loaded—fpm	3100	3100
Power Take-Off—Standard, Optional.	Opt.	Opt.
Is Power to P.T.O. Continuous?	No	No
Engine—Make	Cont'l.	Cont'l.
Engine—Model	F162	F162
Displacement—Cubic Inches	162	162
Compression Ratio, Standard	6.1	6.1
Rated rpm	1800	1800
Piston Speed fpm @ Rated rpm	1312	1312

Brakes—Steering—Tires

Brakes, Type—Contracting Band?	Yes	Yes
Brakes, Location—Bull Pinion Shaft?	Yes	Yes
Steering Make	Ross	Ross
Steering, Type—Cam & Lever?	Yes	Yes
Tire Size—Standard Rear—Inches	10x38	11x28
Tire Size—Standard Front—Inches	7.5x16	6.5x16

Transmission of Power

Clutch—Dry Disc Spring Loaded?	Yes	Yes
Final Drive—Spur, Chain	Spur	Spur
High Gear Ratio	15.13	10.51
Low Gear Ratio	108.2	75.15
Speeds—Number Forward	4	4
Speeds—Number Reverse	1	1

Advertised Speeds, mph, With Standard Transmission and Standard Tires—Row Crop: 2.67, 4.10, 5.93, 19.10; reverse 1.97. Standard: 3.02, 4.83, 6.06, 21.60; reverse 2.23.

**Silver King
"3 Wheel Row Crop"**

**Silver King
"4 Wheel Standard"**

FATE-ROOT-HEATH COMPANY
Plymouth, Ohio

FEDERAL MACHINE & WELDER CO.
Warren, Ohio

Ustrac "10A"   1951

General

	Ustrac "10A"
Number and Size Plows	3-12
Type—Axle, Crawler	Crawl.
Shipping Weight on Rubber—Lbs.	3425
Nebraska Test Number....(Gasoline)	414
Observed Drawbar Horsepower	15.26
Observed Belt Horsepower	21.33
Maximum Pull—Lbs.	3256
Speed @ Maximum Pull	0.82
Weight @ Maximum Pull—Lbs.	3695
Track Tread, Standard—Inches	29½
Height Overall—Inches	56
Length Overall—Inches	92
Wheelbase—Inches	51½
Electric Starting—Std. or Opt.	Std.
D.B. Adjustable Laterally?	Yes
D.B. Adjustable Vertically?	No
Cultivating Clearance—Inches	6.1
Hydraulic Power Unit	Opt.

Transmission of Power

Clutch—Dry Plate, Wet Disc	Wet
Clutch—Single Plate, Multiple Disc.	MD
Clutch—Spring Loaded, Overcenter	OC
Final Drive—Chain, Gears	Gears
High Gear Ratio	22.0
Low Gear Ratio	141.0
Speeds—Number Forward	4
Speeds—Number Reverse	1
Sliding Gear Speed Change?	Yes

Belt Pulley—P.T.O.—Engine

Belt Pulley Diameter—Inches	8
Belt Pulley Face Width—Inches	6
Belt Pulley Speed—rpm	1700
Belt Pulley Speed—fpm	3560
Power Take-off—Standard, Optional	Opt.
Is Power to P.T.O. Continuous?	No
Engine Make—Continental, Willys	Cont'l
Engine—Model	F124
Displacement—Cubic Inches	124
Rated rpm	1900
Piston Speed fpm @ Rated rpm	1375

Brakes

Make—Own, Lambert	Own
Type—Contracting Band, Disc	CB
Location—Rear Wheels, Transmission	Trans.
Actuation—Hydraulic, Mechanical	Mech.
Brake Units per Tractor	2

Ustrac "10A"

FEDERAL MACHINE & WELDER CO.
Warren, Ohio

Steering—Tires—Tracks

Steering—Make	Own
Type—Cam & Lever, Brakes & Clutches	B&C
Tire Size—Standard Rear—Inches	Track
Tire Size—Standard Front—Inches	Track
Track Face Width—Inches	7½
Ground Contacting Area of Tracks—Square Inches	772

INTERCONTINENTAL MANUFACTURING CO., INC.

Garland, Texas

Intercontinental "DE"	1951-1956
Intercontinental "DF"	1951-1956
Intercontinental "Cultrac"	1951-1952

General	Intercontinental "DE" "DF"
Number and Size Plows	3-14
Type—Axle, Adj. Axle, Tricycle	Tri.
Shipping Weight on Rubber—Lbs.	3250
Nebraska Test	420
Observed Drawbar Horsepower	26.11
Observed Belt Horsepower	28.86
Maximum Pull—Lbs.	3406
Speed @ Maximum Pull	2.78
Weight @ Maximum Pull—Lbs.	6091
Rear Tread, Minimum—Inches	56
Rear Tread, Maximum—Inches	84
Front Tread, Minimum—Inches	9
Front Tread, Maximum—Inches	16
Height Overall—Inches	85½
Length Overall—Inches	122
Wheelbase—Inches	79
Electric Starting—Std. or Opt.	Std.
D.B. Adjustable Laterally?	Yes
D.B. Adjustable Vertically?	Yes
Cultivating Clearance—Inches	25
Hydraulic Power Unit	Opt.

Transmission of Power

Clutch—Single, Dry Plate?	Yes
Clutch—Spring Loaded?	Yes
Final Drive—Chain, Spur	Spur
High Gear Ratio	24.2
Low Gear Ratio	96.0
Speeds—Number Forward	4
Speeds—Number Reverse	1
Sliding Gear Speed Change?	Yes

Belt Pulley—P.T.O.—Engine

Belt Pulley Diameter—Inches	10
Belt Pulley Face Width—Inches	6½
Belt Pulley Speed—rpm	1472
Belt Pulley Speed—fpm	3850
Power Take-Off—Standard, Optional	Std.
Is Power for P.T.O. Continuous?	Opt.
Engine—Make	Buda
Engine—Model (DE)	4BD153
(DF)	4BD182
Displacement—Cubic Inches (DE)	153
(DF)	182
*Rated rpm	1800
*Piston Speed fpm @ Rated rpm	1237

Intercontinental "DE"

INTERCONTINENTAL MFG. CO., INC.
Garland, Texas

Brakes

Make—Duo-Grip?	Yes
Type—Clamping Shoes?	Yes
Location—Differential Shafts?	Yes
Actuation—Hydraulic, Mechanical	Mech.
Brake Units per Tractor	2

Steering—Tires

Steering Make—Saginaw?	Yes
Type—Worm & Sector?	Yes
Tire Size—Std. Rear—Inches	10x38
Tire Size—Std. Front—Inches	5.5x16

*Tractor Manufacturer's Rated rpm.

General

	Intercontinental "Cultrac"
Number and Size Plows	2-14
Type—Crawler?	Yes
Shipping Weight—Lbs.	1750
Nebraska Test Number	None
Tread, Minimum—Inches	32
Tread, Maximum—Inches	48
Height Overall—Inches	69½
Length Overall—Inches	90
Wheelbase—Inches	44½
Starting—Electric, Hand	Hand
D.B. Adjustable Laterally?	Yes
D.B. Adjustable Vertically?	Yes
Cultivating Clearance—Inches	20½
Hydraulic Power Unit	Opt.

Transmission of Power

Clutch—Single, Dry Plate?	Yes
Clutch—Spring Loaded, Overcenter	SL
Final Drive—Chain, Spur	Spur
High Gear Ratio	13.4
Low Gear Ratio	21.4
Speeds—Number Forward	2
Speeds—Number Reverse	1
Sliding Gear Speed Change?	Yes

Belt Pulley—P.T.O.—Engine

Belt Pulley Diameter—Inches	None
Belt Pulley Face Width—Inches	None
Belt Pulley Speed—High—rpm	None
Belt Pulley Speed—Low—rpm	None
Belt Pulley Speed—High—fpm	None
Belt Pulley Speed—Low—fpm	None
Power Take-Off—Standard, Optional	None
Is Power for P.T.O. Continuous?	
Engine Make—Waukesha, Own	Wauk.
Engine—Model	1CK
Displacement—Cubic Inches	61
Rated rpm	2000
Piston Speed fpm @ Rated rpm	1042

Brakes

Make	Own
Type—Contracting Band?	Yes
Location—Final Drive Track Frame Pivot Shaft?	Yes
Actuation—Hydraulic, Mechanical	Mech.
Brake Units per Tractor	2

Steering—Tires

Steering—Make	Own
Type—Brake & Transmission, Clutch & Brake	B&T
Track Face Width—Inches	6 or 8
Ground Contacting Area of Tracks—Square Inches	[2]267

[2] With 8 inch tracks, 356.

Intercontinental "Cultrac"

INTERCONTINENTAL MFG. CO., INC.
Garland, Texas

INTERNATIONAL HARVESTER CO.
Chicago, Illinois

International Crawler "TD-14A"   1951-1956
International Crawler "TD-18A"   1951-1956

General	International "TD-9" "TD-14A"
Engine Type—Diesel, Non-Diesel.....	Diesel
Number and Size Plows.............	8-14
Shipping Weight—Lbs...............	16825
Nebraska Test Number.............	445
Observed Drawbar Horsepower....	62.68
Observed Belt Horsepower........	71.79
Corrected Drawbar Horsepower...	65.90
Corrected Belt Horsepower.......	75.30
Maximum Pull—Lbs..............	14652
Speed @ Maximum Pull...........	1.49
Weight @ Maximum Pull—Lbs.....	18445
Tread, Standard—Inches	56
Tread, Optional—Inches	74
Height Overall—Inches	$90\frac{5}{16}$
Length Overall—Inches	$134\frac{1}{8}$
Ground Clearance—Inches	$11\frac{13}{16}$
Electric Starting—Std. or Opt.......	Std.
Hydraulic Power Unit.............	Opt.

Belt Pulley—P.T.O.—Engine

Pulley Diameter, Standard—Inches...	$11\frac{3}{4}$
Pulley Face Width—Inches..........	11
Pulley Speed, Loaded—rpm.........	875
Pulley Speed, Loaded—fpm.........	2690
Power Take-Off—Standard, Optional.	Opt.
Is Power to P.T.O. Continuous?	No
Engine—Make	Own
Engine—Model	D14A
Displacement—Cubic Inches	460.7
Compression Ratio, Standard........	15.5
Rated rpm	1400
Piston Speed, fpm, @ Rated rpm.....	1541

Steering—Brakes—Tracks

Steering Type—Track Clutches?.....	Yes
Steering Clutches Type—Multiple Disc Spring Loaded?	Yes
Brakes, Type—Contracting Band?...	Yes
Brakes, Location—On Steering Clutches?	Yes
Standard Track Face Width—Inches.	16
Ground Contacting Area of Standard Tracks—Square Inches	2516
(Optional)	2828

International Crawler "TD-14A"

INTERNATIONAL HARVESTER CO.
Chicago, Illinois

Transmission of Power

Clutch—Dry, Single Plate?	Yes
Clutch—Overcenter?	Yes
Final Drive—Spur, Chain	Spur
High Gear Ratio	22.15
Low Gear Ratio	79.67
Speeds—Number Forward	6
Speeds—Number Reverse	2

General

	Minneapolis-Moline	
	"G"	"R" Type E
Number and Size Plows	4, 5-14	2-14
Type—Axle, Adjustable Axle	Axle	A.A.
Shipping Wt., Max., on Rubber—Lbs.	6750	3300
Nebraska Test Number (Gasoline)	437	None
Observed Drawbar Horsepower	49.53	
Observed Belt Horsepower	58.03	
Corrected Drawbar Horsepower	51.87	
Corrected Belt Horsepower	59.50	
Maximum Pull—Lbs.	6410	
Speed @ Maximum Pull—mph	2.12	
Weight @ Maximum Pull—Lbs.	10955	
Rear Tread, Adj. Range—Inches	62	52-88
Front Tread, Adj. Range—Inches	54¼	56-84
Height Overall—Inches	71	68½
Length Overall, Maximum—Inches	133$\frac{5}{16}$	124
Wheelbase—Inches	82½	84½
Cultivating Clearance—Inches	14	18½
Hydraulic Power Unit	Opt.	Opt.

Belt Pulley—P.T.O.—Engine

Pulley Diameter, Standard—Inches	16	12¼
Pulley Face Width—Inches	7	6
Pulley Speed, Loaded—rpm	627	1000
Pulley Speed, Loaded—fpm	2630	3210
Power Take-Off—Standard, Optional	Opt.	Opt.
Is Power to P.T.O. Continuous?	Yes	No
Engine—Make	Own	Own
Engine—Model (Gasoline)	403A	EE
(LP-Gas)	340	
Displacement—Cubic In. (Gasoline)	403	165
(LP-Gas)	340	
Compression Ratio, Standard (403A)	5.4	6.2
Optional (403A)	4.3	5.0
(LP-Gas 340)	RNA	
Rated rpm	1100	1500
Piston Speed fpm @ Rated rpm	1100	1000

Brakes—Steering—Tires

Brakes, Type—Disc?	Yes	Yes
Brakes, Location—Wheel Axle Shafts, Bull Pinion Shafts	BPS	WAS
Steering Make	Ross	Own
Steering, Type—Cam & Lever, Worm & Sector	C&L	W&S
Tire Size—Standard Rear—Inches	14x34	10x34
Tire Size—Standard Front—Inches	7.5x18	5x15

Transmission of Power

Clutch—Dry Disc Overcenter?	Yes	Yes
Final Drive—Spur, Bevel Gear	Spur	BG
High Gear Ratio	13.33	16.78
Low Gear Ratio	73.83	86.55
Speeds—Number Forward	5	4
Speeds—Number Reverse	1	1

Advertised Speeds, mph, With Standard Tires and Standard Transmission—Model G: 2.5, 3.5, 4.1, 6.0, 13.8; reverse, 2.0. Model R Type E: 2.6, 3.6, 4.7, 13.2; reverse, 2.9.

RNA—Manufacturer declines to release this information.

Minneapolis-Moline "G"

Minneapolis-Moline "R" Type E

MINNEAPOLIS-MOLINE COMPANY

Minneapolis, Minnesota

General	Minneapolis-Moline "R" Type S	"R" Type U
Number and Size Plows	2-14	2-14
Type—Axle, Tricycle	Axle	Tri.
Shipping Weight on Rubber—Lbs.	3110	3110
Nebraska Test Number....(Gasoline)	None	468
Observed Drawbar Horsepower		23.90
Observed Belt Horsepower		27.09
Corrected Drawbar Horsepower		24.00
Corrected Belt Horsepower		27.89
Maximum Pull—Lbs.		2801
Speed @ Maximum Pull		2.16
Weight @ Maximum Pull—Lbs.		5036
Rear Tread, Minimum—Inches	52	52
Rear Tread, Maximum—Inches	88	88
Front Tread, Adj. Range—Inches	47½	8-13¼
Height Overall—Inches	68½	68½
Length Overall, Maximum—Inches	108½	116
Wheelbase—Inches	69	76
Cultivating Clearance—Inches	11	22⅜
Hydraulic Power Unit	Opt.	Opt.

Belt Pulley—P.T.O.—Engine

Pulley Diameter, Standard—Inches	12¼	12¼
Pulley Face Width—Inches	6	6
Pulley Speed, Loaded—rpm	1000	1000
Pulley Speed, Loaded—fpm	3210	3210
Power Take-Off—Standard, Optional.	Opt.	Opt.
Is Power to P.T.O. Continuous?	No	No
Engine—Make	Own	Own
Engine—Model	EE	EE
Displacement Cubic Inches	165	165
Compression Ratio, Standard	6.2	6.2
Optional	5.0	5.0
Rated rpm	1500	1500
Piston Speed fpm @ Rated rpm	1000	1000

Brakes—Steering—Tires

Brakes, Type—Disc?	Yes	Yes
Brakes, Location—Wheel Axle Shafts?	Yes	Yes
Steering Make	Ross	Own
Steering, Type—Cam & Lever, Worm & Sector	C&L	W&S
Tire Size—Std. Rear—Inches	10x34	10x34
Tire Size—Std. Front—Inches	5x15	5x15

Transmission of Power

Clutch—Dry Disc Overcenter?	Yes	Yes
Final Drive—Spur, Bevel Gear	BG	BG
High Gear Ratio	16.78	16.78
Low Gear Ratio	86.55	86.55
Speeds—Number Forward	4	4
Speeds—Number Reverse	1	1

Minneapolis-Moline "R" Type S

Minneapolis-Moline "R" Type U

MINNEAPOLIS-MOLINE COMPANY
Minneapolis, Minnesota

General	Minneapolis-Moline "U" Type S	"U" Type U
Number and Size Plows	3, 4-14	3, 4-14
Type—Axle, Tricycle, Adj. Axle	Axle	Tri.
Shipping Wt., Max., on Rubber—Lbs.	5500	5300
Nebraska Test Number....(Gasoline)	310	319
Observed Drawbar Horsepower	39.00	36.40
Observed Belt Horsepower	42.88	42.71
Corrected Drawbar Horsepower	41.15	38.03
Corrected Belt Horsepower	44.85	45.27
Maximum Pull—Lbs.	4959	4585
Speed @ Maximum Pull	2.27	2.66
Weight @ Maximum Pull—Lbs.	7940	6773
Rear Tread, Minimum—Inches	57	54½
Rear Tread, Maximum—In.	62½	84½
Front Tread, Adj. Range—In.	50½	8⅜-13½
Height Overall—Inches	72	70
Length Overall—Inches	130¾	137
Wheelbase—Inches	80	88
Cultivating Clearance—Inches	15	25
Hydraulic Power Unit	Opt.	Opt.

Minneapolis-Moline "U" Type S

Belt Pulley—P.T.O.—Engine

Pulley Diameter, Standard—Inches	16	16
Pulley Face Width—Inches	7	7
Pulley Speed, Loaded—rpm	727	727
Pulley Speed, Loaded—fpm	3050	3050
Power Take-Off—Standard, Optional.	Opt.	Opt.
Is Power to P.T.O. Continuous?	Yes	Yes
Engine—Make	Own	Own
Engine—Model	283A	283A
Displacement—Cubic Inches	283	283
Compression Ratio, Standard..(Gas.)	5.4	5.4
(LP-Gas)	6.8	6.8
Rated rpm	1275	1275
Piston Speed fpm @ Rated rpm	1062	1062

Brakes—Steering—Tires

Brakes, Type—External Expanding?	Yes	Yes
Brakes, Location—Bull Pinion Shafts?	Yes	Yes
Steering Make	Ross	Own
Type—Cam & Lever, Worm & Sector	C&L	W&S
Tire Size—Standard Rear—Inches	12x38	12x38
Tire Size—Std. Front—In.	6x16	6x16

Minneapolis-Moline "U" Type U

Transmission of Power

Clutch—Dry Disc Overcenter?	Yes	Yes
Final Drive—Spur, Chain	Spur	Spur
High Gear Ratio	14.52	14.52
Low Gear Ratio	80.42	80.42
Speeds—Number Forward	5	5
Speeds—Number Reverse	1	1

MINNEAPOLIS-MOLINE COMPANY
Minneapolis, Minnesota

General	Minneapolis-Moline "Z" Type E	"Z" Types N & U
Number and Size Plows	2, 3-14	2, 3-14
Type—Adjustable Axle, Tricycle	A.A.	Tri.
Shipping Weight on Rubber—Lbs.	4100	3750
Nebraska Test Number...(Gasoline)	None	438
Observed Drawbar Horsepower		32.07
Observed Belt Horsepower		36.20
Maximum Pull—Lbs.		3556
Speed @ Maximum Pull—mph		3.04
Weight @ Maximum Pull—Lbs.		5925
Rear Tread, Minimum—Inches	54	54
Rear Tread, Maximum—Inches	88	88
Front Tread, Minimum—Inches	56	7¾
Front Tread, Maximum—Inches	88	12⅞
Height Overall—Inches	78	78
Length Overall, Maximum—Inches	139¼	134⅞
Wheelbase—Inches	90⅛	82
Electric Starting—Std. or Opt.	Std.	Std.
D.B. Adjustable Laterally?	Yes	Yes
D.B. Adjustable Vertically?	No	No
Cultivating Clearance—Inches	25	25
Hydraulic Power Unit	Opt.	Opt.

Transmission of Power

Clutch—Dry, Single Plate?	Yes	Yes
Clutch—Overcenter?	Yes	Yes
Final Drive—Spur, Chain	Spur	Spur
High Gear Ratio	18.77	18.77
Low Gear Ratio	100.89	100.89
Speeds—Number Forward	5	5
Speeds—Number Reverse	1	1
Sliding Gear Speed Change?	Yes	Yes

Belt Pulley—P.T.O.—Engine

Belt Pulley Diameter—Inches	15⅛	15⅛
Belt Pulley Face Width—Inches	7	7
Belt Pulley Speed—rpm	786	786
Belt Pulley Speed—fpm	3100	3100
Power Take-Off—Standard, Optional	Opt.	Opt.
Is Power to P.T.O. Continuous?	No	No
Engine—Make	Own	Own
Engine—Model	206B-4	206B-4
Displacement—Cubic Inches	206	206
Rated rpm	1500	1500
Piston Speed fpm @ Rated rpm	1250	1250

Brakes

Make	Own	Own
Type—Internal Expanding?	Yes	Yes
Location—Bull Pinion Shaft?	Yes	Yes
Actuation—Hydraulic, Mechanical	Mech.	Mech.
Brake Units per Tractor	2	2

Steering—Tires

Make	Own	Own
Type—Worm & Sector?	Yes	Yes
Tire Size—Standard Rear—Inches	11x38	11x38
Tire Size—Std. Front—In...(Type N)	5.5x16	7.5x10
(Type U)		5.5x16

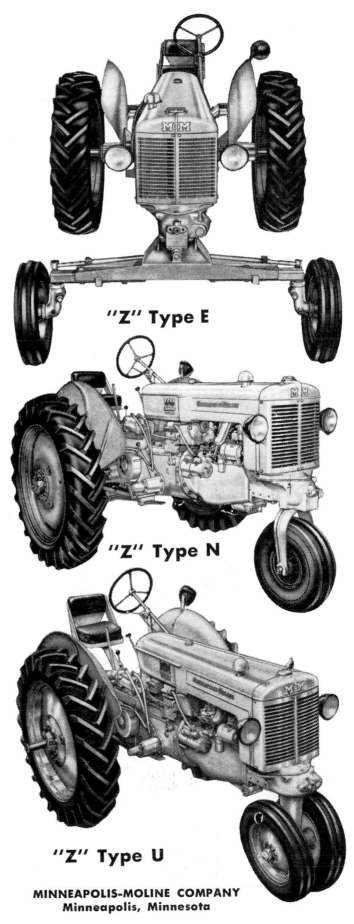

"Z" Type E

"Z" Type N

"Z" Type U

MINNEAPOLIS-MOLINE COMPANY
Minneapolis, Minnesota

General

Number and Size Plows.............. 2, 3-14
Type—Axle, Tricycle .... Axle
Shipping Weight on Rubber—Lbs...... 3750
Nebraska Test Number.............. None
Rear Tread, Adj. Range—Inches.... 54-59
Front Tread, Min. & Max.—Inches... 48
Height Overall—Inches 69
Length Overall, Maximum—Inches.... $120\frac{11}{16}$
Wheelbase—Inches .... $72\frac{7}{16}$
Cultivating Clearance—Inches ..... $12\frac{1}{4}$
Hydraulic Power Unit.............. Opt.

Belt Pulley—P.T.O.—Engine

Pulley Diameter, Standard—Inches... $15\frac{1}{8}$
Pulley Face Width—Inches......... 7
Pulley Speed, Loaded—rpm......... 786
Pulley Speed, Loaded—fpm......... 3100
Power Take-Off—Standard, Optional. Opt.
Is Power to P.T.O. Continuous?..... Yes
Engine—Make .... Own
Engine—Model 206B
Displacement—Cubic Inches 206
Compression Ratio, Standard........ 6.2
                  Optional 4.7
Rated rpm 1500
Piston Speed fpm @ Rated rpm..... 1250

Brakes—Steering—Tires

Brakes, Type—Internal Expanding?.. Yes
Brakes, Location—Bull Pinion Shafts,
   Front Wheel Axle Shafts........ BPS
Steering Make .... Ross
Steering, Type—Cam & Lever,
   Worm & Sector................. C&L
Tire Size—Standard Rear—Inches... 11x38
Tire Size—Standard Front—Inches.. 5.5x16

Transmission of Power

Clutch—Dry, Single Plate, Spring
   Idler & Flat Belt.............. DSP
Clutch—Overcenter? .... OC
Final Drive—Spur, Chain........... Spur
High Gear Ratio.................. 18.77
Low Gear Ratio.................. 100.89
Sliding Gear Speed Change?......... Yes
Variable Dia. V-Belt Pulley In Drive? No
Gearset Speeds—Number Forward... 5
Gearset Speeds—Number Reverse... 1

"Z" Type S

MINNEAPOLIS-MOLINE COMPANY
Minneapolis, Minnesota

R. H. SHEPPARD CO., INC.
Hanover, Pennsylvania

Sheppard Diesel "SDG2"	1951
Sheppard Diesel "SDG3"	1951
Sheppard Diesel "SDO2"	1951
Sheppard Diesel "SDO3"	1951

Sheppard Diesel "SDG3"
("SDG2" is similar)

Sheppard Diesel "SDO3"
("SDO2" is similar)

General

	Sheppard Diesel "SDG2" "SDO2"	"SDG3" "SDO3"
Number and Size Plows	2-14	3-14
Type—Axle, Tricycle	Axle	Axle
Shipping Weight, Maximum—Lbs	5150	5350
Nebraska Test Number	None	None
Rear Tread—Inches	56	56
Front Tread—Inches	59	59
Height Overall—Inches ...(SDG)	67½	67½
(SDO)	70	70
Length Overall—Inches	130	136
Wheelbase—Inches	85	92⅜
Hydraulic Power Unit	Opt.	Opt.

Belt Pulley—P.T.O.—Engine

Pulley Diameter, Standard—Inches	*8¼	*8¼
Pulley Face Width—Inches	7½	7½
Pulley Speed, Loaded—rpm	1325	1325
Pulley Speed, Loaded—fpm	2915	2915
Power Take-Off—Standard, Optional	Opt.	Opt.
Is Power to P.T.O. Continuous?	Yes	Yes
Engine—Make	Own	Own
Engine—Model	13E	6E or 6B
Displacement—Cubic Inches ....(6E)	141.9	212.8
(6B)		188.5
Compression Ratio, Standard	22.0	22.0
Rated rpm	1650	1650
Piston Speed fpm @ Rated rpm	1375	1375

Brakes—Steering—Tires

Brakes, Type—Double Disc?	Yes	Yes
Brakes, Location—Bull Pinion Shafts?	Yes	Yes
Steering, Make	Ross	Ross
Steering, Type—Cam & Lever?	Yes	Yes
Tire Size—Standard Rear—Inches	13x26	13x26
Tire Size—Standard Front—Inches	6x16	6x16

R. H. SHEPPARD CO., INC.
Hanover, Pennsylvania

Transmission of Power

Clutch—Dry Disc Overcenter?	Yes	Yes
Final Drive—Spur, Chain	Spur	Spur
High Gear Ratio	24.2	24.2
Low Gear Ratio	96.0	96.0
Speeds—Number Forward	8	8
Speeds—Number Reverse	2	2

Advertised Speeds, mph, With Standard Tires and Standard Transmission—1.55, 2.24, 2.63, 3.12, 3.8, 5.24, 6.15, 11.3; reverse 2.1 and 3.6.

*Diameters of 9 inches and 9¾ inches also available.

WILLYS-OVERLAND MOTORS, INC.
Toledo, Ohio

Willys Jeep "CJ-3A"   1951

General

	Willys Jeep "CJ-3A"
Number and Size Plows	2-12
Type—Axle, Adj. Axle, Tricycle	Axle
Shipping Weight on Rubber—Lbs.	2203
Nebraska Test Number	432
Observed Drawbar Horsepower	24.32
Observed Belt Horsepower	28.43
Maximum Pull—Lbs.	2148
Speed @ Maximum Pull—Lbs.	4.25
Weight @ Maximum Pull—Lbs.	3537
Rear Tread, Minimum—Inches	48¼
Rear Tread, Maximum—Inches	48¼
Front Tread, Minimum—Inches	48¼
Front Tread, Maximum—Inches	48¼
Height Overall—Inches	66¾
Length Overall—Inches	130
Wheelbase—Inches	80
Electric Starting—Standard or Optional	Std.
D.B. Adjustable Laterally?	Yes
D.B. Adjustable Vertically?	Yes
Cultivating Clearance—Inches	$8\frac{3}{32}$
Hydraulic Power Unit	Opt.

Transmission of Power

Clutch—Single Dry Plate?	Yes
Clutch—Spring Loaded?	Yes
Final Drive—Bevel?	Yes
High Gear Ratio	5.37
Low Gear Ratio	36.5
Speeds—Number Forward	6
Speeds—Number Reverse	2
Sliding Gear Speed Change?	Yes

Belt Pulley—P.T.O.—Engine

Belt Pulley Diameter—Inches	8
Belt Pulley Face Width—Inches	8
Belt Pulley Speed—High—rpm	1550
Belt Pulley Speed—High—fpm	3246
Power Take-off—Standard, Optional	Opt.
Is Power for P.T.O. Continuous?	No
Engine—Make	Own
Engine—Model	CJ3A
Displacement—Cubic Inches	134
Rated rpm	4000
Piston Speed fpm @ Rated rpm	2916

Willys Jeep "CJ-3A"

WILLYS-OVERLAND MOTORS, INC.
Toledo, Ohio

Brakes

Make	Bendix
Type—Internal Expanding?	Yes
Location—Wheel Shafts?	Yes
Actuation—Hydraulic, Mechanical	Hyd.
Brake Units per Tractor	[1]4

Steering—Tires

Steering—Make	Ross
Type—Cam & Lever, Worm & Sector	C&L
Tire Size—Std. Rear—Inches	6x16
Tire Size—Std. Front—Inches	6x16

[1] Plus mechanically operated hand brake located on propeller shaft.

Here is the hard-working vehicle that pays big dividends on any farm! You get more farm work done with the 'Jeep'. It spreads its cost over a greater variety of jobs than any other machine.

The Universal 'Jeep' pulls at tractor speeds for field work — operates both pull-type and hydraulic-lift implements — tows a 5,000 lb. payload on or off the road. In 2-wheel drive, it's a pick-up for fast trips to town or highway hauling. With power take-off it operates shaft or belt driven equipment.

4-WHEEL-DRIVE UNIVERSAL `Jeep`

REG. U. S. PAT. OFF

WILLYS-OVERLAND MOTORS · TOLEDO 1, OHIO

1952

In 1952, nine tractor manufacturers introduced 22 new models. Harry Ferguson, Inc. introduced the TO-30 and Minneapolis-Moline Company brought out the Uni-Tractor "L."

ALLIS-CHALMERS MANUFACTURING CO.

Milwaukee, Wisconsin

Allis-Chalmers "HD9"   1952-1955
Allis-Chalmers "HD15"   1952-1955
Allis-Chalmers "HD20"   1952-1955

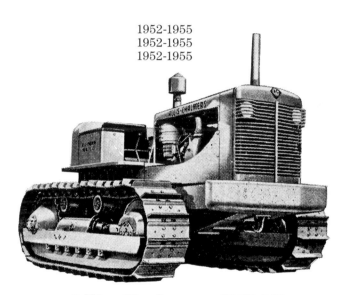

General — Allis-Chalmers "HD9"

	Allis-Chalmers "HD9"
Number and Size Plows	10-16
Shipping Weight—Lbs.	18800
Nebraska Test Number	463
Observed Drawbar Horsepower	67.39
Observed Belt Horsepower	79.10
Corrected Drawbar Horsepower	72.49
Corrected Belt Horsepower	84.57
Maximum Pull—Lbs.	19035
Speed @ Maximum Pull	1.3
Weight @ Maximum Pull—Lbs.	19945
Tread—Inches	74
Height Overall—Inches	*73⅛
Length Overall—Inches	150
Starting—Electric, Sep. Engine	Elec.
Cultivating Clearance—Inches	13 5/16
Hydraulic Power Unit	Opt.

Belt Pulley—P.T.O.—Engine

Pulley Diameter, Standard—Inches	13⅜
Pulley Face Width—Inches	10
Pulley Speed, Loaded—rpm	929
Pulley Speed, Loaded—fpm	3253
Power Take-off—Standard, Optional	Opt.
Is Power for P.T.O. Continuous?	No
Engine—Make	G.M.
Engine—Model	4-71
Displacement—Cubic Inches	284
Compression Ratio, Standard	16.0
Rated rpm	1600
Piston Speed fpm @ Rated rpm	1333

*Without stacks.   RNA—Manufacturer declines to release the information.

Allis-Chalmers "HD9"

Brakes—Steering—Tracks

Brakes Type	Band
Brakes Location—Steering Clutch Compartment?	Yes
Hydraulic or Mechanical Application	Mech.
Steering Clutches Type—Spring Loaded Multiple Disc?	Yes
Track Face Standard Width—Inches	16
Track Face Width, Optional—Inches	18,20,22
Ground Contacting Area of Standard Tracks—Square Inches	2744

Transmission of Power

Clutch—Dry Disc Overcenter?	Yes
Final Drive—Spur, Chain	Spur
High Gear Ratio	RNA
Low Gear Ratio	RNA
Speeds—Number Forward	6
Speeds—Number Reverse	3

General

	Allis-Chalmers "HD15"	"HD20"
Number and Size Plows.............		
Shipping Weight—Lbs...............	27850	41000
Nebraska Test Number.............	464	465
Observed Drawbar Horsepower....	104.37	116.69
Observed Belt Horsepower........	117.68	††N.T.
Corrected Drawbar Horsepower...	109.01	124.25
Corrected Belt Horsepower.......	123.88	††N.T.
Maximum Pull—Lbs..............	29400	41321
Speed @ Maximum Pull...........	1.34	0.96
Weight @ Maximum Pull—Lbs......	30895	42625
Tread—Inches	74&84	84
Height Overall—Inches	*84	*94¼
Length Overall—Inches	172¾	190¾
Starting—Electric, Sep. Engine......	Elec.	Elec.
Cultivating Clearance—Inches	14⅜	16⅛
Hydraulic Power Unit.............	Opt.	Opt.

Allis-Chalmers "HD15"

Belt Pulley—P.T.O.—Engine

Pulley Diameter, Standard—Inches...	18	20
Pulley Face Width—Inches.........	15	15
Pulley Speed, Loaded—rpm........	693	400
Pulley Speed, Loaded—fpm........	3265	2100
Power Take-off—Standard, Optional.	Opt.	None
Is Power for P.T.O. Continuous?....	No	None
Engine—Make	G.M.	G.M.
Engine—Model	6-71	6-110
Displacement—Cubic Inches	426	660
Compression Ratio, Standard.......	16.0	18.0
Rated rpm	1600	1700
Piston Speed fpm @ Rated rpm.....	1333	1588

Brakes—Steering—Tracks

Brakes Type	Band	Band
Brakes Location—Steering Clutch Compartment?	Yes	Yes
Hydraulic or Mechanical Application..	Mech.	Mech.
Steering Clutches Type—Multiple Disc Spring Loaded?..............	†Yes	†Yes
Track Face Standard Width—Inches.	20	24
Track Face Width, Optional—Inches.	18,22,24	22,26,28
Ground Contacting Area of Standard Track—Square Inches	3853	5118

Allis-Chalmers "HD20"

ALLIS-CHALMERS MFG. CO.

Milwaukee, Wisconsin

Transmission of Power

Clutch—Dry Disc Overcenter?......	Yes	Yes
Final Drive—Spur, Chain..........	Spur	Spur
High Gear Ratio..................	RNA	RNA
Low Gear Ratio..................	RNA	RNA
Speeds—Number Forward	6	**2
Speeds—Number Reverse	3	**1
Sliding or Constant Mesh Gear Change	CM	**S

Advertised Speeds, mph, With Std. Transmission—Model HD15: 1.4, 2.1, 3.0, 3.9, 4.5, 5.8; reverse, 1.5, 3.5, 4.5. Model HD20: low, 0-3.0; high, 0-7.0; reverse, 0-5.5.

*Without stacks. **Has torque converter in series with clutch and 2 speed gearset. †Power actuated by hydraulic servo mechanism. ††Not tested due to insufficient dynamometer capacity. See also "Remarks" in complete report of Test 465. RNA—Manufacturer declines to release the information.

AMERICAN TRACTOR CORP.
Churubusco, Indiana

Terratrac "GT-30"   1952-1955

General

	Terratrac "GT-30"
Number and Size Plows	3-14
Shipping Weight—Lbs.	3400
Nebraska Test Number	None
Tread, Minimum—Inches	42
Tread, Maximum—Inches	72
Height Overall—Inches	*51
Length, Overall—Inches	96
Cultivating Clearance—Inches	18
Hydraulic Power Unit	Opt.
Rated Drawbar Horsepower	24.0
Rated Belt Horsepower	30.0

Belt Pulley—P.T.O.—Engine

Pulley Diameter, Standard—Inches	8½
Pulley Face Width—Inches	6½
Pulley Speed, Loaded—rpm	1130
Pulley Speed, Loaded—fpm	3017
Power Take-Off—Standard, Optional	Opt.
Is Power to P.T.O. Continuous?	No
Engine—Make	Cont'l
Engine—Model	F-140
Ignition—Spark, Diesel	Spk.
Displacement—Cubic Inches	139.6
Compression Ratio, Standard	6.3
Rated rpm	1850
Piston Speed fpm @ Rated rpm	1349

Terratrac "GT-30"

Steering Brakes—Tracks

Steering Brakes Make	Clark
Type—Contracting Wet Bands?	Yes
Location—Differential?	Yes
Track Face Width—Inches	10
Ground Contacting Area of Tracks—Square Inches	1060

Transmission of Power

Clutch—Dry, Single Plate?	**Yes**
Clutch—Spring Loaded?	**Yes**
Final Drive—Spur, Chain	Spur
High Gear Ratio	26.21
Low Gear Ratio	68.11
Speeds—Number Forward	3
Speeds—Number Reverse	1

*To top of cowling.

HARRY FERGUSON, INC.
Detroit, Michigan

Ferguson "TO-30"   1952-1954

General

	Ferguson "TO-30"
Number and Size Plows	3-12
Type—Adjustable Axle, Tricycle	A.A.
Shipping Weight, Max., on Rubber	2480
Nebraska Test Number	466
Observed Drawbar Horsepower	24.37
Observed Belt Horsepower	29.32
Corrected Drawbar Horsepower	25.24
Corrected Belt Horsepower	30.27
Maximum Pull—Lbs.	2994
Speed @ Maximum Pull—mph	2.55
Weight @ Maximum Pull—Lbs.	4476
Rear Tread, Adj. Range—Inches	48-76
Front Tread, Adj. Range—Inches	48-80
Height Overall—Inches	51¾
Length Overall—Inches	115
Wheelbase—Inches	70
Cultivating Clearance—Inches	19¾
Hydraulic Power Unit	Std.

Belt Pulley—P.T.O.—Engine

Pulley Diameter, Standard—Inches	9
Pulley Face Width—Inches	6½
Pulley Speed, Loaded rpm	1316
Pulley Speed, Loaded—fpm	3100
Power Take-off—Standard, Optional	Std.
Is Power to P.T.O. Continuous?	No
Engine—Make	Cont'l.
Engine—Model	Z129
Displacement—Cubic Inches	129
Compression Ratio, Standard	6.5
Optional	8.0
Rated rpm	2000
Piston fpm @ Rated rpm	1292

Brakes—Steering—Tires

Brakes, Type—Disc, Internal Expanding Shoes	IES
Brakes, Location—Diff. Shafts, Wheel Axle Shafts	WAS
Steering Make	Own
Steering Type—Cam & Lever, Bevel Pinion & Twin Sector	BP&TS
Tire Size—Std. Rear—Inches....(D)	10x28
Tire Size—Standard Front—Inches	4x19

Ferguson "TO-30"

HARRY FERGUSON, INC.
Detroit, Michigan

Transmission of Power

Clutch—Dry Disc Spring Loaded?	Yes
Final Drive—Spur, Bevel	Bevel
High Gear Ratio	19.86
Low Gear Ratio	78.57
Speeds—Number Forward	4
Speeds—Number Reverse	1
Speed Change—Sliding Gear, Constant Mesh	CM

STANDARD
THROUGH THE YEARS

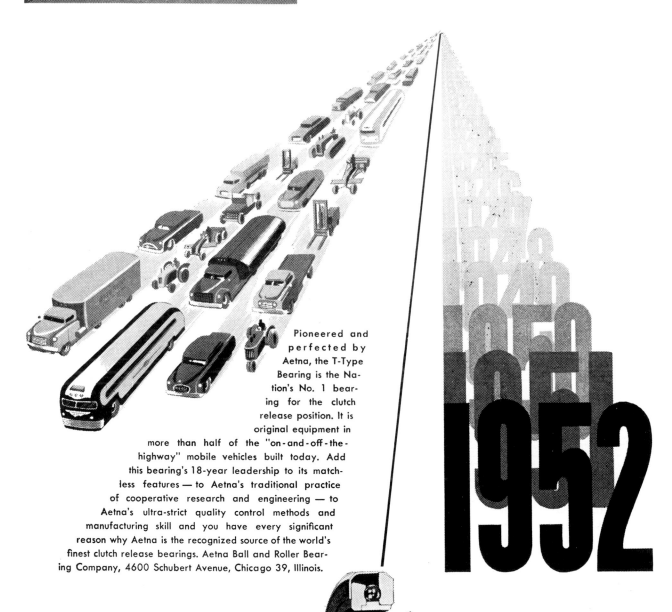

Pioneered and perfected by Aetna, the T-Type Bearing is the Nation's No. 1 bearing for the clutch release position. It is original equipment in more than half of the "on-and-off-the-highway" mobile vehicles built today. Add this bearing's 18-year leadership to its matchless features — to Aetna's traditional practice of cooperative research and engineering — to Aetna's ultra-strict quality control methods and manufacturing skill and you have every significant reason why Aetna is the recognized source of the world's finest clutch release bearings. Aetna Ball and Roller Bearing Company, 4600 Schubert Avenue, Chicago 39, Illinois.

1952

T-TYPE CLUTCH RELEASE BEARINGS

HARRIS MANUFACTURING CO.
Stockton, California

Harris ''PH53''   1952-1953

General

	Harris "PH53"
Number and Size Plows	3-14
Type—Axle, Adjustable Axle	Axle
Shipping Weight on Rubber—Lbs.	4860
Nebraska Test Number....(Gasoline)	479
Observed Drawbar Horsepower	50.11
Observed Belt Horsepower	†——
Corrected Drawbar Horsepower	52.07
Corrected Belt Horsepower	†——
Maximum Pull—Lbs.	6160
Speed @ Maximum Pull	2.01
Weight @ Maximum Pull—Lbs.	9585
Rear Tread, Adj. Range—Inches	48-76
Front Tread, Adj. Range—Inches	48-76
Height Overall—Inches	65
Length Overall—Inches	††99½
Wheelbase—Inches	54
Cultivating Clearance—Inches	18
Hydraulic Power Unit	Opt.

Belt Pulley—P.T.O.—Engine

Pulley Diameter, Standard—Inches	None
Pulley Face Width—Inches	None
Pulley Speed, Loaded—rpm	None
Pulley Speed, Loaded—fpm	None
Power Take-Off—Standard, Optional	Opt.
Is Power to P.T.O. Continuous?	No
Engine—Make	Chry.
Engine—Model	Ind.8A
Displacement—Cubic Inches	250.6
Compression Ratio, Standard	6.6
Optional	7.0
Rated rpm—Drawbar	2000
Piston Speed, fpm @ Rated rpm— Drawbar	1500

Brakes—Steering—Tires

Brakes, Type—Internal Expanding Shoes, Contracting Band	CB
Brakes, Location..Wheel Axle Shafts, On Bull Pinion Shaft	BPS
Brake Units per Tractor	2
Steering Type—Worm & Ball Nut, Steering Clutches & Brakes	SC&B
Tire Size—Standard Rear—Inches	13x24
Tire Size—Standard Front—Inches	13x24

Harris "PH53"
HARRIS MFG. CO.
Stockton, California

Transmission of Power

Clutch—Single Plate, Double Plate	DP
Clutch—Semi-Centrifugal?	No
Clutch—Spring Loaded?	Yes
Final Drive—Bevel, Spur Gear, Chain— (Rear Wheels)	S.Gear
(Front Wheels)	Chain
High Gear Ratio	18.3
Low Gear Ratio	117.2
Speeds—Number Forward	4
Speeds—Number Reverse	5
Speed Change—Constant Mesh, Sliding Gear	SG

†Belt pulley not available. ††Less drawbar.

INTERNATIONAL HARVESTER CO.
Chicago, Illinois

McCormick Farmall "Super C"   1952-1954

General

	McCormick Farmall Super "C"
Number and Size Plows	2-14
Type—Adj. Axle, Axle, Tricycle	T&AA
Shipping Wt., Max., on Rubber—Lbs.	3000
Nebraska Test Number...(Gasoline)	458
Observed Drawbar Horsepower	20.72
Observed Belt Horsepower	23.67
Corrected Drawbar Horsepower	21.67
Corrected Belt Horsepower	24.45
Maximum Pull—Lbs.	3151
Speed @ Maximum Pull	2.08
Weight @ Maximum Pull—Lbs.	5038
Rear Tread, Adj. Range—Inches	48-80
Front Tread, Min.—In...(A.A.)	50
(Tri.)	6¾
Front Tread, Max.—Inches.... (Tri.)	12⅝
(Adj. Axle)	83¼
Height Overall—Inches (Axle)	85½
Length Overall—Inches (Axle)	132⅛
(Tri.)	123
Wheelbase—Inches (Axle)	91½
(Tri.)	82¼
Electric Starting—Std. or Opt.	Std.
Cultivating Clearance—Inches (Axle)	23⅛
(Tri.)	23⅜
Hydraulic Power Unit	Std.

Belt Pulley—P.T.O.—Engine

Pulley Diameter, Standard—Inches	8½
Pulley Face Width—Inches	6
Pulley Speed, Loaded—rpm	1363
Pulley Speed, Loaded—fpm	3033
Power Take-Off—Standard, Optional	Opt.
Is Power to P.T.O. Continuous?	No
Engine—Make	Own
Engine—Model	C-123
Displacement—Cubic Inches	122.7
Compression Ratio, Standard	6.0
Optional	5.0
Rated rpm	1650
Piston Speed fpm @ Rated rpm	1100

Brakes—Steering—Tires

Brakes, Type—Contracting Band, Disc	Disc
Brakes, Location—Bull Pinion Shafts?	Yes
Steering, Type—Worm & Gear?	Yes
Tire Size—Std. Rear—Inches	10x36
Tire Size—Std. Front—Inches	5x15

McCormick Farmall "Super C"

Transmission of Power

Clutch—Dry Disc Spring Loaded?	Yes
Final Drive—Spur, Chain	Spur
Speeds—Number Forward	4
Speeds—Number Reverse	1

MASSEY-HARRIS CO.
Racine, Wisconsin

Massey-Harris "55D"   1952-1956

General

	Massey-Harris "55D"
Number and Size Plows	5-14
Type—Axle, Adjustable Axle	Axle
Shipping Weight on Rubber—Lbs.	6930
Nebraska Test No.	452
Observed Drawbar Horsepower	52.49
Observed Belt Horsepower	59.04
Corrected Drawbar Horsepower	54.49
Corrected Belt Horsepower	60.27
Maximum Pull—Lbs.	5365
Speed @ Maximum Pull	2.62
Weight @ Maximum Pull—Lbs.	10155
Rear Tread, Minimum—Inches	$57\frac{5}{16}$
Rear Tread, Maximum—Inches	$57\frac{5}{16}$
Front Tread, Minimum—Inches	$52\frac{1}{4}$
Front Tread, Maximum—Inches	$52\frac{1}{4}$
Height Overall—Inches	$83\frac{1}{4}$
Length Overall—Inches	$145\frac{1}{2}$
Wheelbase—Inches	$88\frac{1}{2}$
Cultivating Clearance—Inches	$12\frac{1}{2}$
Hydraulic Power Unit	Opt.

Belt Pulley—P.T.O.—Engine

Pulley Diameter, Standard—Inches	16
Pulley Face Width—Inches	8
Pulley Speed, Loaded—rpm	730
Pulley Speed, Loaded—fpm	3059
Power Take-off—Standard, Optional	Opt.
Is Power to P.T.O. Continuous?	No
Engine—Make	Own
Engine—Model	JD-382
Displacement—Cubic Inches	382
Compression Ratio	15.0
Rated rpm	1350
Piston Speed fpm @ Rated rpm	1350

Brakes—Steering—Tires

Brakes, Type—Internal Expanding	IE
Brakes, Location—Separate Shaft Driven by Bull Gears?	Yes
Steering Make	Ross
Steering Type—Cam & Lever?	Yes
Tire Size—Standard Rear—Inches	14x34
Tire Size—Standard Front—Inches	7.5x18

Massey-Harris "55D"

MASSEY-HARRIS COMPANY

Racine, Wisconsin

Transmission of Power

Clutch—Dry, Single Plate?	Yes
Clutch—Spring Loaded?	†Yes
Final Drive—Spur, Chain	Spur
High Gear Ratio	19.17
Low Gear Ratio	78.0
Speeds—Number Forward	4
Speeds—Number Reverse	1

†Western Special and hand clutch models have a Rockford overcenter type.

MERCER ROBINSON CO., INC.

New York, New York

Mercer "30BD"　　　　　　　　　1952-1955
Mercer "30CK"　　　　　　　　　1952-1955

General

	Mercer "30BD"	"30CK"
Number and Size Plows	2, 3-14	2, 3-14
Type—Adjustable Axle, Tricycle	Tri.	Tri.
Shipping Weight on Rubber—Lbs.	3450	3250
Nebraska Test Number	*419	*421
Observed Drawbar Horsepower	21.93	25.26
Observed Belt Horsepower	23.59	28.36
Corrected Drawbar Horsepower	23.22	26.44
Corrected Belt Horsepower	25.23	29.93
Maximum Pull—Lbs.	3055	3202
Speed @ Maximum Pull	2.50	2.41
Weight @ Maximum Pull—Lbs.	5663	5195
Rear Tread, Adj. Range—Inches	56-84	56-84
Front Tread, Adj. Range—Inches	8-11	8-11
Height Overall—Inches	60	60
Length Overall—Inches	132	132
Wheelbase—Inches	87	87
Cultivating Clearance—Inches	23	23
Hydraulic Power Unit	Opt.	Opt.

Belt Pulley—P.T.O.—Engine

	"30BD"	"30CK"
Pulley Diameter, Standard—Inches	8¼	8¼
Pulley Face Width—Inches	6½	6½
Pulley Speed, Loaded—rpm	1335	1335
Pulley Speed, Loaded—fpm	2880	2880
Power Take-Off—Standard, Optional	Std.	Std.
Continuous Power P.T.O.—Std., Opt.	Opt.	Opt.
Engine—Make	Buda	Buda
Engine—Model	4BD153	4B153
Displacement—Cubic Inches	153	153
Compression Ratio, Standard	15.0	6.18
Rated rpm—Belt	1650	1650
Piston Speed, fpm, @ Rated rpm	1134	1134

Brakes—Steering—Tires

	"30BD"	"30CK"
Brakes, Type—Clamping Shoes?	Yes	Yes
Brakes, Location—Diff. Side Gears?	Yes	Yes
Steering Make	—Saginaw—	
Steering Type—Worm & Sector?	Yes	Yes
Tire Size—Standard Rear—Inches	11x38	11x38
Tire Size—Standard Front—Inches	5.5x16	5.5x16

Transmission of Power

	"30BD"	"30CK"
Clutch—Dry, Single Plate?	Yes	Yes
Clutch—Spring Loaded?	Yes	Yes
Final Drive—Bevel, Spur	Spur	Spur
High Gear Ratio	24.2	24.2
Low Gear Ratio	96.0	96.0
Speeds—Number Forward	4	4
Speeds—Number Reverse	1	1

Advertised Speeds, mph, With Standard Transmission and Standard Tires—All Models: 2.7, 4.2, 5.9, 11.9; reverse 3.5.

*The Mercer 30BD was tested as the Farmaster FD33 and the Mercer 30CK as the Farmaster FG33.

Mercer "30BD"

("30CK" is similar)

MERCER ROBINSON CO., INC.
New York 7, N. Y.

MINNEAPOLIS-MOLINE CO.
Minneapolis, Minnesota

Minneapolis-Moline "BF"   1952
"Uni-Tractor L"   1952

General

Minneapolis-Moline "BF"

Number and Size Plows	2-14
Type—Axle, Tricycle, Adj. Axle	AA&T
Shipping Wt., Max., on Rubber—Lbs.	2900
Nebraska Test Number	469
Observed Drawbar Horsepower	24.12
Observed Belt Horsepower	27.12
Corrected Drawbar Horsepower	25.11
Corrected Belt Horsepower	27.64
Maximum Pull—Lbs.	2725
Speed @ Maximum Pull—mph	2.10
Weight @ Maximum Pull—Lbs.	4636
Front Tread, Adj. Range—In...(A.A.)	52-72
Rear Tread, Adj. Range—In...(A.A.)	52-76
Height Overall—Inches	76
Length Overall—Inches (Axle)	118⅛
(Tri.)	116¾
Wheelbase—Inches (Axle)	82½
(Tri.)	79¾
Cultivating Clearance—Inches (Axle)	22
(Tri.)	26
Hydraulic Power Unit	Std.

Belt Pulley—P.T.O.—Engine

Pulley Diameter, Standard—Inches	10
Pulley Face Width—Inches	6½
Pulley Speed, Loaded—rpm	1098
Pulley Speed, Loaded—fpm	3037
Power Take-Off—Std., Optional	Opt.
Is Power to P.T.O. Continuous?	No
Engine—Make	Herc.
Engine—Model	IXB3SL
Displacement—Cubic Inches	133
Compression Ratio, Standard	6.5
Rated rpm	1800
Piston Speed fpm @ Rated rpm	1200

Brakes—Steering—Tires

Brakes, Type—Contracting Band?	Yes
Brakes, Location—Bull Pinion Shafts?	Yes
Steering Make	Own
Steering, Type—Cam & Lever, Worm & Gear	W&G
Tire Size—Standard Rear—Inches	10x28
Tire Size—Std. Front—Inches (Axle)	5x15
(Tri. Single)	6x15
(Tri. Dual)	5x15

Minneapolis-Moline "BF"

Transmission of Power

Clutch—Dry Disc Spring Loaded?	Yes
Final Drive—Spur, Chain	Spur
High Gear Ratio	17.87
Low Gear Ratio	97.22
Speeds—Number Forward	4
Speeds—Number Reverse	1

General

	Minneapolis-Moline Uni-Tractor "L"
Number and Size Plows...............	*———
Type—Axle, Tricycle	Tri.
Shipping Weight on Rubber—Lbs......	3610
Nebraska Test Number.............	None
Rear Tread, Adj. Range—Inches....**———	
Front Tread, Min. & Max.—Inches....	83¼
Length Overall, Maximum—Inches....	142½
Wheelbase—Inches	104½
Cultivating Clearance—Inches	11½
Hydraulic Power Unit..............	Std.

Belt Pulley—P.T.O.—Engine

Pulley Diameter, Standard—Inches...	None
Power Take-Off—Standard, Optional.	Std.
Is Power to P.T.O. Continuous?.....	Yes
Engine—Make	Own
Engine—Model	V-206
Displacement—Cubic Inches	206
Compression Ratio, Standard........	6.1
Rated rpm	1375
Piston Speed fpm @ Rated rpm.....	1142

Brakes—Steering—Tires

Brakes, Type—Internal Expanding?..	Yes
Brakes, Location—Bull Pinion Shafts, Front Wheel Axle Shafts.........	FWAS
Steering Make	Own
Steering, Type—Cam & Lever, Worm & Sector..................	W&S
Tire Size—Standard Rear—Inches...	7.5x18
Tire Size—Standard Front—Inches..	†10x24

Transmission of Power

Clutch—Dry, Single Plate, Spring Idler & Flat Belt................	SI&FB
Final Drive—Spur, Chain............	Spur
High Gear Ratio....................	17.32
Low Gear Ratio....................	174.42
Sliding Gear Speed Change?.........	Yes
Variable Dia. V-Belt Pulley In Drive?	Yes
Gearset Speeds—Number Forward...	3
Gearset Speeds—Number Reverse...	1

"Uni-Tractor L"

MINNEAPOLIS-MOLINE COMPANY
Minneapolis, Minnesota

*Not used for plowing; designed as power and propelling unit for direct attachment of special MM harvesting, and corn husking, snapper and picker-sheller machines. **Single wheel. †Driving wheels.

THE OLIVER CORP.
Chicago, Illinois

Oliver "66D" Row Crop	1952-1954
Oliver "66D" Standard	1952-1954
Oliver "66HC" Standard	1952-1954
Oliver "77D" Row Crop	1952-1954
Oliver "77D" Standard	1952-1954
Oliver "77HC" Standard	1952-1954
Oliver "88D" Row Crop	1952-1954
Oliver "88D" Standard	1952-1954
Oliver "88HC" Standard	1952-1954
Oliver Crawler "OC-3"	1952-1957

Flexible POWER
for Every Farm... and Operation!

Row Crop "88" with LP-gas engine.

There's an Oliver to match any size of farm, any practice, any crop, any soil condition.

With Oliver, the farmer can choose the kind of tractor, wheel or crawler, that best meets his needs. He has a range of sizes in each, from the 2-plow, "66" wheel tractor or the OC-3 Crawler, to the big 4-5 plow "99" on wheels and the mighty Model "D" on crawlers. There is a choice in wheel tractors of row-crop, standard, or adjustable front axle types and the OC-3 crawler can be obtained in several tread widths.

All fuel requirements can also be met with these tractors.

- The "66"—Diesel or Gasoline
- The "77"—Diesel, Gasoline or LP-gas
- The "88"—Diesel, Gasoline or LP-gas
- The "99"—Gasoline
- The "OC-3"—Gasoline   The "D"—Diesel
- The "A"—Diesel or Gasoline
- The "B"—Diesel or Gasoline

Full 2-plow Row Crop "66".

Nowhere can the farmer find a combination like this —power of any size or type, plus *farm-versatility* features that bring real savings in any farm operation. It's a combination that leads to *extra* sales . . . and greater profits for Oliver dealers. The OLIVER Corporation, 400 West Madison Street, Chicago 6, Ill.

Model "OC-3" Crawler.

Diesel-powered Row Crop "77" with Adjustable Front Axle.

OLIVER

"FINEST IN FARM MACHINERY"

General

	Oliver **Standard "66HC" "66D"**	Row Crop "66D"
Number and Size Plows	2-14	2-14
Type—Axle, Adj. Axle, Tricycle	Axle	AA&T
Shipping Wt., Maximum—Lbs.	3185	2600
Nebraska Test Number....(HC Gas.)	413	412
Observed Drawbar Horsepower	21.52	21.03
Observed Belt Horsepower	24.90	24.91
Corrected Drawbar Horsepower	22.61	22.30
Corrected Belt Horsepower	26.21	26.05
Maximum Pull—Lbs.	3065	3207
Speed @ Maximum Pull	2.40	2.25
Weight @ Maximum Pull—Lbs.	5602	5563
Rear Tread, Adj. Range—Inches	50-58¾	60-88
(Orchard Models)	47½	
Front Tread, Adj. Range—In...(Tri.)	46-51⅛	6⅜-11½
(Adj. Axle)		50¾-87¾
(Orchard Models)	46	
Height Overall—Inches	78⅞	85¼
(Orchard Models)	59½	
Length Overall—Inches	123⅞	134⅞
Wheelbase—Inches	73⅜	86¾
Cultivating Clearance—Inches	11¾	24⅜
(Orchard Models)	11	
Hydraulic Power Unit	Opt.	Opt.

Belt Pulley—P.T.O.—Engine

Pulley Diameter, Standard—Inches	11⅞	11⅞
Pulley Face Width—Inches	7¼	7¼
Pulley Speed, Loaded—rpm	987	987
Pulley Speed, Loaded—fpm	3065	3065
Power Take-Off—Standard, Optional	Opt.	Opt.
Is Power to P.T.O. Continuous?	Yes	Yes
Engine—Make	Own	Own
Displacement—Cubic Inches (HC & D)	129.3	129.3
Compression Ratio, Standard...(HC)	6.75	6.75
(D)	15.5	15.5
Rated rpm	1600	1600
Piston Speed fpm @ Rated rpm	1000	1000

Brakes—Steering—Tires

Brakes, Type—Double Disc?	Yes	Yes
Brakes, Location—Bull Gear Pinions?	Yes	Yes
Steering, Type—Worm & Sector, Circulating Ball ....(Tricycle)	CB	W&S
(Adj. Axle)		CB
Tire Size—Standard Rear—Inches	10x24	9x38
(Orchard Models)	12x26	
Tire Size—Standard Front—Inches	5x15	5x15
(Orchard Models)	6x16	

Transmission of Power

Clutch—Dry Disc Spring Loaded?	Yes	Yes
Final Drive—Spur, Chain	Spur	Spur
High Gear Ratio	16.29	21.65

Oliver "66" Standard

Oliver "66" Row Crop

THE OLIVER CORPORATION
Chicago, Ill.

	Standard	Row Crop
Low Gear Ratio	75.41	100.39
Speeds—Number Forward	6	6
Speeds—Number Reverse	2	2

**Also available as orchard & grove tractors.

General

	Oliver	
	Standard "77HC" "77D"	**Row Crop** "77KD"
Number and Size Plows...............	2, 3-14	2, 3-14
Type—Axle, Adj. Axle, Tricycle......	Axle	T&AA
Shipping Weight, Maximum—Lbs......	4545	3801
Nebraska Test Number.............	405	425
Observed Drawbar Horsepower....	28.48	32.89
Observed Belt Horsepower........	33.56	37.17
Corrected Drawbar Horsepower...	29.78	34.20
Corrected Belt Horsepower.......	35.28	38.82
Maximum Pull—Lbs.	3802	4714
Speed @ Maximum Pull...........	2.61	2.29
Weight @ Maximum Pull—Lbs.....	7418	8023
Rear Tread, Adj. Range—Inches.....	47-52½	60-92½
(Orchard Models)	49	
Front Tread, Adj. Range—In. (A, Tri.)	49-54¾	8-12⅛
(Orchard Models & Adj. Axle)	48¾	60-89¾
Height Overall—Inches	*69½	*75
(Orchard Models)	59½	
Length Overall—Inches	129¾	139¼
Wheelbase—Inches	78¼	90¾
Cultivating Clearance—Inches	11¾	24⅞
(Orchard Models)	10	
Hydraulic Power Unit...............	Opt.	Opt.

Belt Pulley—P.T.O.—Engine

Pulley Diameter, Standard—Inches...	11⅞	11⅞
Pulley Face Width—Inches..........	7¼	7¼
Pulley Speed, Loaded—rpm..........	992	992
Pulley Speed, Loaded—fpm..........	3080	3080
Power Take-Off, Standard, Optional.	Opt.	Opt.
Is Power to P.T.O. Continuous?.....	Yes	Yes
Engine—Make	Own	Own
Displacement—Cu. In. ..(HC, LP, D)	193.9	193.9
Compression Ratio, Standard... (HC)	6.75	
Rated rpm	1600	1600
Piston Speed fpm @ Rated rpm......	1000	1000

Brakes—Steering—Tires

Brakes, Type—Double Disc?.........	Yes	Yes
Brakes, Location—Bull Gear Pinions?	Yes	Yes
Steering, Type—Worm & Sector,		
Circulating Ball ....(Tricycle)	CB	W&S
(Adj. Axle)		CB
Tire Size—Standard Rear—Inches...	12x26	11x38
Tire Size—Standard Front—Inches..	5.5x16	5.5x16
(Orchard Models)	6x16	

Transmission of Power

Clutch—Dry Disc Spring Loaded?....	Yes	Yes
Final Drive—Spur, Chain..........	Spur	Spur
High Gear Ratio...................	18.64	22.94
Low Gear Ratio...................	87.05	107.17
Speeds—Number Forward ....‡6	‡6	
Speeds—Number Reverse ....‡2	‡2	

Oliver "77" Orchard

**(Similar Cowling and Fenders on
"66" and "88" Orchard Types)**

Oliver "77" Row Crop

THE OLIVER CORPORATION
Chicago, Illinois

Advertised Speeds, mph, With Standard Transmission & Standard Tires—Standard & Orchard Models:
2½, 3¼, 4⅓, 5¾, 6⅝, 11⅝; reverse 2⅝ and 4½.
Row Crop Models: Within ⅛ mph of Standard Models.
*To top of steering wheel.

**Also available as orchard & grove tractors.

‡Also available with 4 forward and 4 reserve
speeds.

General	Oliver **Standard "88HC" "88D"	Row Crop "88D"
Number and Size Plows	3, 4-14	3, 4-14
Type—Axle, Adj. Axle, Tricycle	Axle	T&AA
Shipping Weight, Maximum—Lbs.	5285	5025
Nebraska Test Number	†391	388
Observed Drawbar Horsepower	37.27	36.97
Observed Belt Horsepower	43.15	41.99
Corrected Drawbar Horsepower	38.56	38.40
Corrected Belt Horsepower	44.96	44.66
Maximum Pull—Lbs.	5270	5173
Speed @ Maximum Pull	2.26	2.51
Weight @ Maximum Pull—Lbs.	7804	8484
Rear Tread, Adj. Range—Inches	54-62	60-92½
(Orchard Models)	49	
Front Tread, Adj. Range—In. (A, Tri.)	49-54¾	8-12⅛
(Orchard Models & Adj. Axle)	48¾	60-89¾
Height Overall—Inches	*69⅝	*75
(Orchard Models)	61½	
Length Overall—Inches	133¾	143⅝
Wheelbase—Inches	79¼	93¾
Cultivating Clearance—Inches	12	25⅝
(Orchard Models)	10	
Hydraulic Power Unit	Opt.	Opt.

Oliver "88" Standard

Belt Pulley—P.T.O.—Engine

Pulley Diameter, Standard—Inches	11⅞	11⅞
Pulley Face Width—Inches	7¼	7¼
Pulley Speed, Loaded—rpm	992	992
Pulley Speed, Loaded—fpm	3080	3080
Power Take-Off—Standard, Optional	Opt.	Opt.
Is Power to P.T.O. Continuous?	Yes	Yes
Engine—Make	Own	Own
Displacement—Cu. In.	230.9	230.9
Compression Ratio, Standard	4.75	4.75
(HC)	6.75	
(D)	15.5	15.5
Rated rpm	1600	1600
Piston Speed fpm @ Rated rpm	1067	1067

Brakes—Steering—Tires

Brakes, Type—Double Disc?	Yes	Yes
Brakes, Location—Bull Gear Pinions?	Yes	Yes
Steering, Type—Worm & Sector, Circulating Ball (Tricycle)	CB	W&S
(Adj. Axle)		CB
Tire Size—Standard Rear—Inches	13x26	12x38
Tire Size—Standard Front—Inches	6x16	6x16

Transmission of Power

Clutch—Dry Disc Spring Loaded?	Yes	Yes
Final Drive—Spur, Chain	Spur	Spur
High Gear Ratio	19.21	23.05
Low Gear Ratio	90.46	108.55
Speeds—Number Forward	‡6	‡6
Speeds—Number Reverse	‡2	‡2

Oliver "88" Row Crop

THE OLIVER CORPORATION
Chicago, Illinois

Advertised Speeds, mph, With Standard Transmission and Tires—All Models: 2½, 3¼, 4¼, 5½, 6¾, 11¾; reverse 2½ and 4⅜.

*To top of steering wheel.

**Also available as orchard & grove tractors. ‡Also available with 4 forward and 4 reverse speeds.

General

	Oliver Crawler "OC-3"
Number and Size Plows	2-14
Type—Axle, Track	Track
Shipping Weight—Lbs.	3163
Nebraska Test Number	*434
Observed Drawbar Horsepower	21.30
Observed Belt Horsepower	25.30
Corrected Drawbar Horsepower	21.85
Corrected Belt Horsepower	26.36
Maximum Pull—Lbs.	3940
Speed @ Maximum Pull—mph	1.87
Weight @ Maximum Pull—Lbs.	4183
Crawler Tread, Minimum—Inches	31
Crawler Tread, Maximum—Inches	68
Height Overall—Inches	**50
Length Overall—Inches	100⅛
Cultivating Clearance—Inches	18¾
Hydraulic Power Unit	Opt.

Belt Pulley—P.T.O.—Engine

Pulley Diameter, Standard—Inches	8½
Pulley Face Width—Inches	6½
Pulley Speed, Loaded—rpm	1030
Pulley Speed, Loaded—fpm	2300
Power Take-Off—Standard, Optional	Opt.
Is Power to P.T.O. Continuous?	No
Engine—Make	Herc.
Engine—Model	IXB3
Displacement—Cubic Inches	132.7
Compression Ratio, Standard	6.66
Rated rpm	1700
Piston Speed fpm @ Rated rpm	1133

Steering—Brakes—Tracks—Tires

Steering, Type—Planetary Diff., Cam & Lever	PD
Steering, Location—In Final Drive?	Yes
Brakes, Actuation—Hydraulic, Mech.	Mech.
Brakes, Type—Contracting Band?	Yes
Brakes, Location—Steering Diff., Bull Pinion Shafts	SD
Track Face Width, Standard—Inches	6
Ground Contacting Area of Tracks—Square Inches	600

Transmission of Power

Clutch—Dry Disc Spring Loaded?	Yes
Clutch—Dry Disc Overcenter?	No
Clutch—Semi-Centrifugal?	Yes
Separate Clutch for P.T.O. & B.P.?	Yes
Final Drive—Spur, Chain	Spur
High Gear Ratio	24.36
Low Gear Ratio	63.43
Speeds—Number Forward	3
Speeds—Number Reverse	1

Oliver Crawler "OC-3"

THE OLIVER CORPORATION
Chicago, Illinois

*Tested as Model "HG". **Excluding air intake and exhaust pipes.

1953

In 1953, eight tractor manufacturers introduced 23 tractor models. Cockshutt Farm Equipment, Ltd. of Brantford, Ontario, Canada, introduced the Cockshutt "20" to the U.S. market.

AMERICAN TRACTOR CORP.

Churubusco, Indiana

Terratrac "DT-34"   1953-1955

Terratrac "DT-34"

General

	American Tractor Terratrac "DT-34"
Number and Size Plows	3-14
Shipping Weight—Lbs.	4750
Nebraska Test Number	None
Tread, Minimum—Inches	42
Tread, Maximum—Inches	72
Height Overall—Inches	*54
Length, Overall—Inches	96
Cultivating Clearance—Inches	18
Hydraulic Power Unit	Opt.

Belt Pulley—P.T.O.—Engine

Pulley Diameter, Standard—Inches	8½
Pulley Face Width—Inches	6½
Pulley Speed, Loaded—rpm	1130
Pulley Speed, Loaded—fpm	2514
Power Take-Off—Standard, Optional.	Opt.
Is Power to P.T.O. Continuous?	No
Engine—Make	Cont'l
Engine—Model	GD-157
Number Cylinders & Displacement	4-157
Rated rpm	1850

Steering Brakes—Tracks

Steering Brakes Type—Contracting Wet Band?	Yes
Steering Brakes Location—Diff.?	Yes
Track Face Width—Inches	12
Ground Contacting Area of Tracks—Square Inches	1358

AMERICAN TRACTOR CORP.

Churubusco, Indiana

Transmission of Power

Clutch—Dry Disc Spring Loaded?	Yes
Final Drive—Spur, Chain	Spur
High Gear Ratio	26.21
Low Gear Ratio	68.27
Speeds—Number Forward	3
Speeds—Number Reverse	1

*To top of cowling.

J. I. CASE CO.
Racine, Wisconsin

Case "DC-3"   1953-1955
Case "DC-4"   1953-1955
Case "DV"   1953-1955
Case "VAS"   1953-1956

General	J. I. Case "DC-3" "DC-4"	"DV"
Number and Size Plows..............	3-14	3-14
Type—Axle, Adj. Axle, Tricycle...(3)	AA&T	Axle
(4)	Axle	
Approximate Max. Weight, Std. Equip..	RNA	RNA
Nebraska Test Number.........(3)	340	None
Rear Tread, Adj. Range—Inches.....	48-*84	43
Front Tread, Adj. Range—In...(Tri.)	9-14½	
(Axle)	48	47½
(Adj. Axle)	56-80	
Height Overall—Inches ....(Tri.)	58	
(Adj. Axle-Axle)	56⅛	50⅝
Length Overall—Inches ......(Tri.)	140	119
Wheelbase—Inches ....(Tri.)	88⅞	
(Adj. Axle-Axle)	74.5	66.3
Electric Starting—Standard, Optional.	Opt.	Opt.
Cultivating Clearance—Inches..(Tri.)	24.6	
Hydraulic Power Unit.........(Tri.)	Std.	
(Adj. Axle-Axle)	Opt.	Opt.

Case "DC-3"

(Non-adjustable axle type "DC-4" is similar)

Belt Pulley—P.T.O.—Engine		
Pulley Diameter, Standard—Inches...	12¼	12¼
Pulley Face Width—Inches.........	7¼	7¼
Pulley Speed, Loaded—rpm.........	818	818
Pulley Speed, Loaded—fpm.........	2620	2620
Power Take-off—Std., Opt.......(3)	Std.	Opt.
(4)	Opt.	
Is Power to P.T.O. Continuous?.....	Yes	Yes
P.T.O. Cont. When Gearshifting?....	Yes	Yes
Engine—Make and Model............	Own D	Own D
Number Cylinders & Displacement....	4-260	4-260
Rated rpm	1200	1200

J. I. CASE CO.

Racine, Wisconsin

Brakes—Steering—Tires		
Brakes Type—Double Disc?........	Yes	Yes
Brakes Location—Diff. Side Gears?.	Yes	Yes
Steering Type—Worm & Wheel?.....	Yes	Yes
Tire Size—Standard Rear—Inches....	11x38	13x26
Tire Size—Std. Front—Inches....(3)	5.5x16	6.00x16
(4)	6x16	

Case "DV"

Transmission of Power		
Clutch—Wet Single Plate?.........	Yes	Yes
Clutch—O'center, Spring Loaded.....	SL	SL
Final Drive—Spur, Chain..........	Chain	Chain
High Gear Ratio....................	RNA	RNA
Low Gear Ratio....................	RNA	RNA
Speeds—Number Forward	4	4
Speeds—Number Reverse	1	1

J. I. CASE CO.

Racine, Wisconsin

Advertised Speeds, mph, With Std. Transmission & Std. Tires—Models DC-3, DC4 & DV: 2.2, 3.8, 5.2, 10.4; reverse, 3.0.

*96" available on order for DC-3.   RNA—Manufacturer declines to release the information.

General

	J. I. Case VAS
Number and Size Plows	1, 2-14
Type—Axle, Adjustable Axle	AA
Shipping Weight on Rubber—Lbs	RNA
Nebraska Test Number	None
Rear Tread—Adj. Range—Inches	42-70
Front Tread—Adj. Range—Inches	42-58
Height Overall—Inches	62.5
Length Overall—Inches	106.5
Wheelbase—Inches	69.5
Cultivating Clearance—Inches	23.7
Hydraulic Power Unit	Std.

Belt Pulley—P.T.O.—Engine

Pulley Diameter, Standard—Inches	10¼
Pulley Face Width—Inches	6
Pulley Speed, Loaded—rpm @ 1425 rpm	969
(@ 1650 rpm)	1120
Pulley Speed, Loaded—fpm @ 1425 rpm	2600
(@ 1650 rpm)	3005
Power Take-off—Standard, Optional	Std.
Is Power to P.T.O. Continuous?	No
Engine—Make	Own
Engine—Model	VA
Number Cylinders & Displacement	4-124
Rated rpm	1425 & 1650

Brakes—Steering—Tires

Brakes, Type—Disc?	Yes
Brakes, Location—Diff. Side Gears?	Yes
Steering Type—Worm & Sector?	Yes
Tire Size—Standard Rear—Inches	10x28
Tire Size—Standard Front—Inches	5x15

Transmission of Power

Clutch—Dry Single Plate?	Yes
Clutch—Spring Loaded?	Yes
Final Drive—Spur, Bevel & Spur	Spur
High Gear Ratio	RNA
Low Gear Ratio	RNA
Speeds—Number Forward	4
Speeds—Number Reverse	1

RNA—Manufacturer declines to release the information.

Case "VAS"

J. I. CASE CO.
Racine, Wisconsin

CATERPILLAR TRACTOR CO.
Peoria, Illinois

Caterpillar "DW10"   1953-1954

General

Caterpillar "DW10"

Type—Axle, Adjustable Axle........	Axle
Shipping Weight on Rubber—Lbs.....	16640
Nebraska Test Number.............	None
Rear Tread—Inches	69½
Front Tread—Inches	70½
Height Overall—Inches	76.7
Length Overall—Inches	185
Wheelbase—Inches	112.1
Hydraulic Power Unit..............	None

Belt Pulley—P.T.O.—Engine

Pulley Diameter, Standard—Inches...	None
Power Take-off—Standard, Optional.	None
Engine—Make	Own
Engine—Model	DW10
Number Cylinders & Displacement....	6-525
Rated rpm	1800

Brakes—Steering—Tires

Brakes, Type—Expanding Band?.....	Yes
Brakes, Location—Wheels?	Yes
Steering Type—Worm & Sector, Worm & Circulating Ball..........	W&CB
Tire Size—Standard Rear—Inches...	21x25
Tire Size—Standard Front—Inches..	12x20

Transmission of Power

Clutch—Dry Double Plate?........	Yes
Clutch—Spring Loaded?	Yes
Final Drive—Spur, Bevel & Spur.....	B&S
High Gear Ratio...................	17.8
Low Gear Ratio...................	142.4
Speeds—Number Forward	5
Speeds—Number Reverse	1

Caterpillar "DW10"

CATERPILLAR TRACTOR CO.
Peoria, Illinois

COCKSHUTT FARM EQUIPMENT, LTD.
Brantford, Ontario, Canada

Cockshutt "20"   1953

General	Cockshutt "20"
Number and Size Plows	1, 2-14
Type—Axle, Adj. Axle, Tricycle	AA&T
Shipping Wt. on Rubber—Lbs...(Axle)	2080
Nebraska Test Number....(Gasoline)	474
Rear Tread, Adj. Range—In.	48-76
Front Tread, Adj. Range—In... (Tri.)	7-12
(Adj. Axle)	48-76
Height Overall—Inches	76
Length Overall—Inches	115
Wheelbase—Inches	79
Cultivating Clearance—Inches	
(Adj. Axle)	21.8
(Tri.)	24.3
Hydraulic Power Unit	Opt.

Belt Pulley—P.T.O.—Engine

Pulley Diameter, Standard—Inches	10
Pulley Face Width—Inches	6½
Pulley Speed, Loaded—rpm	1160
Pulley Speed, Loaded—fpm	3040
Power Take-off—Standard, Optional	Opt.
Is Non Continuous P.T.O. Available?	Yes
Is Continuous P.T.O. Available?	No
P.T.O. Cont. When Gearshifting	Yes
Engine—Make	Cont'l.
Engine—Model ....(Diesel)	None
(Gasoline)	F140
Number Cylinders & Displacement	4-140
Rated rpm	1800

Brakes—Steering—Tires

Brakes, Type—Clamping Shoes?	Yes
Location—Differential Shafts?	Yes
Steering—Make	Own
Type—Cam & Lever, Worm & Gear	W&G
Tire Size—Standard Rear—Inches	10x24
Tire Size—Standard Front—Inches	5.0x15

Transmission of Power

Clutch—Dry Disc Spring Loaded?	Yes
Final Drive—Bevel, Chain, Spur	Spur
High Gear Ratio	16.7
Low Gear Ratio	89.2
Speeds—Number Forward	4
Speeds—Number Reverse	1

Cockshutt "20"

COCKSHUTT FARM EQUIP., LTD.
Brantford, Canada

DEERE & CO.
Moline, Illinois

John Deere "50"	1953-1956
John Deere "60"	1953-1956
John Deere "60" Hi-Crop	1953-1956

General

John Deere "50"

Number and Size Plows 2-14
Type—Track, Tricycle, Adj. Axle . . . . T&AA
Shipping Weight on Rubber—Lbs 4435
Nebraska Test Number . . . . (Gasoline) 486
Rear Tread, Adj. Range—Inches 56-88
Front Tread, Adj. Range—In . . . (Tri.) 7.3-11.1
                    (Adj. Axle) 56-80
Height Overall—Inches . . . . (Tri.) *82.1
                    (Adj. Axle) *83.7
Length Overall—Inches 132.7
Wheelbase—Inches 90
Standard Starting—Electric? . . . . Yes
Cultivating Clearance—In. . . . . (Tri.) 24.1
                    (Adj. Axle) 2
Hydraulic Power Unit . . . . Opt.

Belt Pulley—P.T.O.—Engine

Pulley Diameter, Standard—Inches . . . $9\frac{11}{16}$
Pulley Face Width—Inches . . . . $7\frac{1}{4}$
Pulley Speed, Loaded—rpm 1250
Pulley Speed, Loaded—fpm 3170
Power Take-off—Standard, Optional . Std.
Is Standard P.T.O. Continuous? . . . . . No
Is Continuous P.T.O. Available? . . . . . Yes
P.T.O. Cont. When Gearshifting? . . . . Yes
Engine—Make . . . . Own
Number Cylinders & Displacement 2-190.4
Rated rpm 1250

Brakes

Type—Int. Expanding, Contracting . . . IE
Location—Steering Clutches, Sep.
   Shafts Driven by Bull Gears . . . . . . SS

Steering—Tires—Tracks

Steering Type—Worm & Gear . . . . W&G
Tire Size—Standard Rear—Inches . . . 10x38
Tire Size—Standard Front—Inches . . 5.5x16

Transmission of Power

Clutch—Single Plate, Multiple Disc . . . MD
Clutch—Dry, Wet . . . . Dry
Clutch—Spring Loaded, Overcenter . . OC
Final Drive—Spur, Chain . . . . Spur
High Gear Ratio 19.6
Low Gear Ratio 128.1
Speeds—Number Forward 6
Speeds—Number Reverse 1

John Deere "50"

DEERE & COMPANY
Moline, Illinois

*Including stacks.

General

	John Deere "60"	"60" Hi-Crop
Number and Size Plows...............	3-14	3-14
Type—Adjustable Axle, Tricycle.....	A.A.,T.	A.A.
Shipping Weight on Rubber—Lbs......	5300	6685
Nebraska Test Number...(Gasoline)	472,490	None
Rear Tread, Adj. Range—Inches.....	56-88	60-90
Front Tread, Min.—Inches....(A.A.)	56	60
(Tri.)	$8\frac{5}{16}$	
Front Tread, Max.—Inches....(A.A.)	80	84
(Tri.)	$12\frac{1}{16}$	
Height Overall—Inches ....(Tri.)	84.1	
(A.A.)	$85\frac{1}{4}$	93
Length Overall—Inches	139	$152\frac{1}{2}$
Wheelbase—Inches	90	$98\frac{13}{16}$
Cultivating Clearance—Inches (A.A.)	27.3	$30\frac{7}{8}$
(Tri.)	25.3	
Hydraulic Power Unit—Std., Optional.	Opt.	Opt.

Belt Pulley—P.T.O.—Engine

Pulley Diameter, Standard—Inches...	$12\frac{13}{16}$	$12\frac{13}{16}$
Pulley Face Width—Inches..........	$7\frac{3}{8}$	$7\frac{3}{8}$
Pulley Speed, Loaded—rpm..........	975	975
Pulley Speed, Loaded—fpm..........	3270	3270
Power Take-off—Standard, Optional.	Std.	Std.
Is Standard P.T.O. Continuous?......	No	No
Is Continuous P.T.O. Available?......	Yes	Yes
P.T.O. Cont. When Gearshifting?....	Yes	Yes
Engine—Make	Own	Own
Engine—Model	60	60
Number Cylinders & Displacement...	2-321	2-321
Rated rpm	975	975

Brakes—Steering—Tires

Brakes, Type—Internal Expanding?..	Yes	Yes
Brakes, Location—Separate Shaft?..	Yes	Yes
Steering Type—Worm & Gear?......	Yes	Yes
Tire Size—Standard Rear—Inches....	11x38	11x38
Tire Size—Standard Front—Inches...	6.0x16	7.5x20

Transmission of Power

Clutch—Multiple Dry Disc O'center?.	Yes	Yes
Final Drive—Bevel, Chain, Spur......	Spur	Chain
High Gear Ratio...................	14.53	14.25
Low Gear Ratio...................	113.9	111.2
Speeds—Number Forward	6	6
Speeds—Number Reverse	1	1

Advertised Speeds, mph, With Std. Transmission &
Std. Tires—Model 60: 1.5, 2.5, 3.5, 4.5, 6.25, 11.0;
reverse, 3.0.

John Deere "60"

John Deere "60" Hi-Crop

DEERE & COMPANY
Moline, Illinois

1953

INTERNATIONAL HARVESTER CO.
Chicago, Illinois

International Crawler "TD-24"	1953
McCormick Farmall "Super H"	1953-1954
McCormick Farmall "Super HV"	1953-1954
McCormick Farmall "Super M"	1953-1954
McCormick Farmall "Super MD"	1953-1954
McCormick Farmall "Super MV"	1953-1954
McCormick Farmall "Super MDV"	1953-1954
McCormick "Super W6"	1953-1954
McCormick "Super WD6"	1953-1954
McCormick "Super WD9" Diesel	1953-1954

General	International "TD-24"
Engine Type—Diesel, Non-Diesel.....	Diesel
Number and Size Plows..............	**___
Shipping Weight—Lbs.	38350
Nebraska Test Number	447
Tread, Standard—Inches	80
Height Overall—Inches	102¾
Length Overall—Inches	182¼
Ground Clearance—Inches	13⅞
Electric Starting—Std. or Opt......	Std.
Hydraulic Power Unit..............	None

Belt Pulley—P.T.O.—Engine

Pulley Diameter, Standard—Inches...	None
Power Take-Off—Standard, Optional.	None
Engine—Make	Own
Engine—Model	D24
Number Cylinders & Displacement...	6-1091
Rated rpm	1375

Steering—Brakes—Tracks

Steering Type—Track Clutches?.....	Yes
Steering Clutches, Type—Multiple Disc Spring Loaded?.............	Yes
Steering Clutch Actuation—Manual, Hydraulic Power	†HP
Brakes, Type—Contracting Band, Disc	Disc
Brakes Actuation—Manual, Hydraulic Power	M&HP
Track Face Width, Standard—Inches.	22
Ground Contacting Area of Standard Tracks—Square Inches	4598
(Optional)	5159

Transmission of Power

Clutch—Single or Double Plate?	DP
Clutch—Overcenter and Dry?........	Yes
Final Drive	Spur
High Gear Ratio	20.49
Low Gear Ratio	100.61
Speeds—Number Forward	8
Speeds—Number Reverse	8
Speed Change—Sliding Gear or Syncro Mesh & Planetary	SM&P

International Crawler "TD-24"

INTERNATIONAL HARVESTER CO.
Chicago, Illinois

†Two range power actuated planetary gearset provides gradual turns (27%-73% tracks speed relationship) with power applied to both tracks or pivot turns with all power applied to outside track. **6 to 13 deep tillage plows.

General

	McCormick Farmall Super "H"	Super "HV"
Number and Size Plows............	2, 3-14	2, 3-14
Type—Axle, Tricycle, Adj. Axle......	T&AA	Axle
Shipping Weight, Max., on Rubber.....	4100	5070
Nebraska Test Number.............	492	
Rear Tread, Adj. Range—Inches.....	48-88	60-72
Front Tread, Adj. Range—In..(Axle)	56¾-89½	60-66
(Tri.)	8⅛-16¾	
Height Overall—Inches ......(Axle)	85½	95⅜
(Tri.)	85	
Length Overall—Inches ......(Axle)	144⅝	146½
(Tri.)	133	
Wheelbase—Inches ....(Axle)	100¾	91½
(Tri.)	89¼	
Cultivating Clearance—Inches (Axle)	19	30¼
(Tri.)	25½	
Hydraulic Power Unit..............	Opt.	Opt.

Belt Pulley—P.T.O.—Engine

Pulley Diameter, Standard—Inches...	9¾	9¾
Pulley Face Width—Inches..........	7½	7½
Pulley Speed, Loaded—rpm.........	1019	1019
Pulley Speed, Loaded—fpm.........	2601	2601
Power Take-Off—Standard, Optional.	Opt.	Opt.
Is Power to P.T.O. Continuous?.....	No	No
Engine—Make	Own	Own
Engine—Model	C-164	C-164
Number Cylinders & Displacement...	4-164	4-164
Rated rpm	1650	1650

Brakes—Steering—Tires

Brakes, Type—Disc?	Yes	Yes
Brakes, Location—Bull Pinion Shafts?	Yes	Yes
Steering, Type—Worm & Gear?......	Yes	Yes
Tire Size—Standard Rear—Inches...	11x38	12x36
Tire Size—Standard Front—Inches..	5.5x16	6x20

Transmission of Power

Clutch—Dry Disc Spring Loaded?....	Yes	Yes
Final Drive—Spur, Chain............	Spur	Chain
High Gear Ratio	RNA	RNA
Low Gear Ratio	RNA	RNA
Speeds—Number Forward	5	5
Speeds—Number Reverse	1	1

Advertised Speeds, mph, With Std. Transmission & Std. Tires—Model Super H: 2.59, 3.75, 5.01, 6.67, 16.20; reverse, 3.27. Model Super HV: 2.46, 3.56, 4.75, 6.32, 15.36; reverse, 3.10.

RNA—Manufacturer declines to release the information.

McCormick Farmall "Super H"

McCormick Farmall "Super HV"

INTERNATIONAL HARVESTER CO.
Chicago, Illinois

General	McCormick Farmall Super "M" "MD"	Super "MV" "MDV"
Number and Size Plows..............	4-14	4-14
Type—Axle or Tricycle or Adj. Axle..	T&AA	Axle
Shipping Weight, Max., on Rubber.....	5725	6075
Nebraska Test Number.............	475, 477, 484	
Rear Tread, Adj. Range—Inches......	52-88	60-72
Front Tread, Adj. Range—In...(A.A.)	56¾-89½	60-66
(Tri.)	8⅜-17½	
Height Overall—Inches	*_____	*_____
Length Overall—Inches (M, MV-Axle)	146	146½
(MD, MDV-Axle)	147½	148
(M-Tri.)	134⅝	
(MD-Tri.)	136⅛	
Wheelbase—Inches ....(M, MV-Axle)	100⅝	91½
(MD, MDV-Axle)	102⅛	93
(M-Tri.)	89¼	
(MD-Tri.)	90¾	
Cultivating Clearance—Inches (Axle)	19⅜	30¼
(Tri.)	26¼	
Hydraulic Power Unit..............	Opt.	Opt.

McCormick Farmall "Super M"

Belt Pulley—P.T.O.—Engine

Pulley Diameter, Standard—Inches...	11	11
Pulley Face Width—Inches.........	7½	7½
Pulley Speed, Loaded—rpm.........	899	899
Pulley Speed, Loaded—fpm.........	2588	2588
Power Take-Off—Standard, Optional.	Opt.	Opt.
Is Power to P.T.O. Continuous?.....	No	No
Engine—Make	Own	Own
Engine—Model..(Gasoline & LP-Gas)	C-264	C-264
(Diesel)	D-264	D-264
Number Cylinders & Displacement...	4-264	4-264
Rated rpm	1450	1450

Brakes—Steering—Tires

Brakes, Type—Disc?	Yes	Yes
Brakes, Location—Bull Pinion Shafts?	Yes	Yes
Steering, Type—Worm & Gear?......	Yes	Yes
Tire Size—Standard Rear—Inches...	12x38	13x36
Tire Size—Standard Front—Inches..	6x16	6x20

Transmission of Power

Clutch—Dry Disc Spring Loaded?....	Yes	Yes
Final Drive—Spur, Chain............	Spur	Chain
High Gear Ratio....................	14.77	15.64
Low Gear Ratio	92.39	97.83
Speeds—Number Forward	5	5
Speeds—Number Reverse	1	1

Advertised Speeds, mph, With Standard Transmission and Standard Tires—Models Super M, MD: 2.67, 3.81, 4.95, 6.80, 16.70; reverse, 3.57. Models Super MV, MDV: 2.69, 3.84, 4.99, 6.86, 16.84; reverse, 3.60.

*Adjustable Axle: M 95⅛, MD 94. Standard Axle: MV 94⅜, MDV 93¼. Tricycle: M 94¼, MD 93.

McCormick Farmall "Super MV"

INTERNATIONAL HARVESTER CO.
Chicago, Illinois

General

	McCormick Super "W6" "WD6"
Number and Size Plows.............	4-14
Type—Axle, Tricycle	Axle
Shipping Wt., Max., on Rubber—Lbs...	5490
Nebraska Test Number	476, 378, 485
Rear Tread, Min. & Max.—Inches.....	55
Front Tread, Min. & Max.—Inches....	46.6
Height Overall—Inches ....(W6)	90⅞
(WD6)	89⅜
Length Overall—Inches	125
Wheelbase—Inches	75⅞
Cultivating Clearance—Inches	15¼
Hydraulic Power Unit..............	Opt.

Belt Pulley—P.T.O.—Engine

Pulley Diameter, Standard—Inches...	11
Pulley Face Width—Inches..........	7½
Pulley Speed, Loaded—rpm..........	899
Pulley Speed, Loaded—fpm..........	2588
Power Take-off—Standard, Optional.	Opt.
Is Power to P.T.O. Continuous?.....	No
Engine—Make	Own
Engine—Model ....(Gasoline)	C-264
(Diesel)	D-264
Number Cylinders & Displacement...	4-264
Rated rpm	1450

Brakes—Steering—Tires

Brakes, Type—Disc?	Yes
Brakes, Location—Bull Pinion Shafts?	Yes
Steering, Type—Worm & Gear?.....	Yes
Tire Size—Standard Rear—Inches...	14x30
Tire Size—Standard Front—Inches..	6x16

Transmission of Power

Clutch—Dry Disc Spring Loaded?....	Yes
Final Drive—Spur, Chain	Spur
High Gear Ratio	13.89
Low Gear Ratio	93.76
Speeds—Number Forward	5
Speeds—Number Reverse	1

McCormick "Super W6"

INTERNATIONAL HARVESTER CO.
Chicago, Illinois

442

1953

General

	McCormick Super "WD9"
Number and Size Plows	5-14
Type—Axle, Tricycle	Axle
Shipping Wt., Max., on Rubber—Lbs.	6890
Nebraska Test Number	None
Rear Tread, Adj. Range—Inches	60
Front Tread—Inches	52
Height Overall—Inches	81⅞
Length Overall—Inches	134¼
Wheelbase—Inches	83½
Cultivating Clearance—Inches	15
Hydraulic Power Unit	Opt.

Belt Pulley—P.T.O.—Engine

Pulley Diameter, Standard—Inches	14
Pulley Face Width—Inches	8½
Pulley Speed, Loaded—rpm	707
Pulley Speed, Loaded—fpm	2593
Power Take-Off—Standard, Optional	Opt.
Is Power to P.T.O. Continuous?	No
Engine—Make	Own
Engine—Model	D-350
Number Cylinders & Displacement	4-350
Rated rpm	1500

Brakes—Steering—Tires

Brakes, Type—Cont. Band, Disc	Disc
Brakes, Location—Bull Pinion Shafts?	Yes
Steering Make	Ross
Steering Type—Cam & Lever?	Yes
Tire Size—Rubber Rear—Inches	14x34
Tire Size—Rubber Front—Inches	7.5x18

Transmission of Power

Clutch—Dry, Single Plate?	Yes
Clutch—Spring Loaded, Overcenter	SL
Final Drive—Spur, Chain	Spur
High Gear Ratio	15.86
Low Gear Ratio	105.73
Speeds—Number Forward	5
Speeds—Number Reverse	1

McCormick "Super WD9" Diesel

INTERNATIONAL HARVESTER CO.
Chicago, Illinois

MINNEAPOLIS-MOLINE CO.
Minneapolis, Minnesota

Minneapolis-Moline "BF"　　　　　　1953-1957
Minneapolis-Moline "V"　　　　　　　1953-1954

General

	Minneapolis-Moline "BF"
Number and Size Plows	2-14
Type—Axle, Tricycle, Adj. Axle	AA&T
Shipping Wt., Max., on Rubber—Lbs.	2900
Nebraska Test Number	469
Front Tread, Adj. Range—In. (A.A.)	52-72
(Tri.)	6.8-13.6
Rear Tread, Adj. Range—In. (A.A.)	52-76
Height Overall—Inches	76
Length Overall—Inches (A.A.)	119
(Tri.)	116
Wheelbase—Inches (A.A.)	81.6
(Dual Wheel Tri.)	79.0
(Single Wheel Tri.)	78.6
Cultivating Clearance—Inches (A.A.)	22
(Tri.)	26
Hydraulic Power Unit	Std.

Belt Pulley—P.T.O.—Engine

Pulley Diameter, Standard—Inches	10
Pulley Face Width——Inches	6½
Pulley Speed, Loaded—rpm	1098
Pulley Speed, Loaded—fpm	3037
Power Take-off—Standard, Optional	Opt.
Is Power to P.T.O. Continuous?	No
Engine—Make	Herc.
Engine—Model	IXB3SL
Number Cylinders & Displacement	4-133
Rated rpm	1800

Brakes—Steering—Tires

Brakes, Type—Contracting Band?	Yes
Brakes, Location—Bull Pinion Shafts?	Yes
Steering Make	Own
Steering, Type—Cam & Lever, Worm & Gear	W&G
Tire Size—Standard Rear—Inches	10x28
Tire Size—Std. Front—Inches (A.A.)	5x15
(Tri. Single)	6x16
(Tri. Dual)	5x15

Transmission of Power

Clutch—Dry Disc Spring Loaded?	Yes
Final Drive—Spur, Chain	Spur
High Gear Ratio	17.87
Low Gear Ratio	97.22
Speeds—Number Forward	4
Speeds—Number Reverse	1

Minneapolis-Moline "BF" Dual Wheel Tricycle

MINNEAPOLIS-MOLINE COMPANY
Minneapolis, Minnesota

General   "V"

Number and Size Plows............. 1-14
Type—Axle, Adj. Axle .... AA
Shipping Weight on Rubber—Lbs..... 1612
Nebraska Test Number............. None
Rear Tread, Adj. Range—Inches..... 42-60
Front Tread, Adj. Range—Inches.... 42-60
Height Overall—Inches 61.2
Length Overall, Maximum—Inches... 105
Wheelbase—Inches 74
Cultivating Clearance—Inches 23
Hydraulic Power Unit .... Std.

Belt Pulley—P.T.O.—Engine

Pulley Diameter, Standard—Inches... 6
Pulley Face Width—Inches 5.5
Pulley Speed, Loaded—rpm......... 1990
Pulley Speed, Loaded—fpm......... 3100
Power Take-Off—Standard, Optional. Opt.
Is Non Continuous P.T.O. Available?. Yes
Is Continuous P.T.O. Available?..... No
P.T.O. Cont. When Gearshifting?.... No
Engine—Make .... Herc.
Engine—Model ZXB3
Number Cylinders & Displacement... 4-65
Rated rpm 1800

Brakes—Steering—Tires

Brakes, Type—Int. Exp., Cont. Band. CB
Brakes, Location—Bull Pin. Shafts?. Yes
Steering Make .... Ross
Steering, Type—Cam & Lever?...... Yes
Tire Size—Standard Rear—Inches... 8x24
Tire Size—Standard Front—Inches.. 4x15

Transmission of Power

Clutch—Dry Single Plate?.......... Yes
Clutch—Overcenter, Spring Loaded.. SL
Final Drive—Spur, Chain........... Spur
High Gear Ratio 26.2
Low Gear Ratio 70.2
Gearset Speeds—Number Forward .. 3
Gearset Speeds—Number Reverse .. 1

Minneapolis-Moline "V"

MINNEAPOLIS-MOLINE COMPANY
Minneapolis, Minnesota

SHAW MANUFACTURING CO.
Galesburg, Kansas

Shaw Du-All "R12T"

General

	Shaw "R12T"
Number and Size Plows	1-14
Type—Axle, Track	Axle
Shipping Weight—Lbs.	1150
Nebraska Test Number	None
Rear Tread—Adj. Range—Inches	28-44
Front Tread—Inches	31
Height Overall—Inches	61
Length Overall—Inches	85
Wheelbase—Inches	60
Cultivating Clearance—Inches	24
Hydraulic Power Unit	Opt.

Belt Pulley—P.T.O.—Engine

Pulley Diameter, Standard—Inches	4
Pulley Face Width—Inches	4
Pulley Speed, Loaded—rpm	2000
Pulley Speed, Loaded—fpm	2094
Power Take-Off—Standard, Optional	Opt.
Is Power to P.T.O. Continuous?	†Yes
Engine—Make	Wis.
Engine—Model	TF
Displacement—Cubic Inches	53.9
Compression Ratio, Standard	4.67
Rated rpm	2000
Piston Speed fpm @ Rated rpm	1083

Steering—Brakes—Tracks—Tires

Steering, Type—Planetary Diff., Cam & Lever	C&L
Brakes, Actuation—Hydraulic, Mech.	Mech.
Brakes, Type—Contracting Band?	Yes
Brakes, Location—Steering Diff., Bull Pinion Shafts	BPS
Tire Size—Standard Rear—Inches	6x24
Tire Size—Standard Front—Inches	3x12

Transmission of Power

Clutch—Dry Disc Spring Loaded?	No
Clutch—Dry Disc Overcenter?	Yes
Separate Clutch for P.T.O. & B.P.?	No
Final Drive—Spur, Chain	Spur
Speeds—Number Forward	3
Speeds—Number Reverse	1

Shaw Du-All "R12T"

SHAW MANUFACTURING COMPANY
Galesburg, Kansas

†PTO located on forward end of engine with optional Flat or Vee pulley attachmaent.

Double-Disc Brakes Make Farming Safer

Double-Disc Brakes Are:

SAFER for hillside farming with a heavy load

SAFER going backwards as well as forwards

SAFER in loose soil

SAFER at road speeds

SAFER for short, sharp turning

SAFER for "jockeying" in close quarters

Farmers wanted safer tractor brakes. They wanted Double-Disc Brakes. They got them. Today, more than 60 models of most popular makes of farm tractors and self-propelled farm machines are equipped with safer Ausco Double-Disc Brakes.

Make sure your tractors are equipped with Auto Specialties Double-Disc Brakes which are in great demand by farmers.

AUTO SPECIALTIES MFG. CO., INC.

SAINT JOSEPH, MICHIGAN

Plants also at Benton Harbor and Hartford, Michigan, and Windsor, Ontario, Canada.

Makers of Disc Brakes, Power Take-Off and other Clutches, Mechanical and Hydraulic Auto Jacks, Cast Alloy Steel Crankshafts, Malleable Iron and Steel Castings.

Suppliers to the agricultural and automotive industries since 1908.

1954

In 1954, 14 tractor manufacturers introduced 42 new models. Allis-Chalmers Manufacturing Company brought out the WD-45. The WD-45 was the first tractor with a live power take-off and was originally designed to mate with the A-C round baler. Ford Tractor Division brought out the NAA.

ALLIS-CHALMERS MANUFACTURING CO.
Milwaukee, Wisconsin

Allis-Chalmers "WD-45"   1954

General | Allis-Chalmers "WD-45"

General	Allis-Chalmers "WD-45"
Number and Size Plows	3-14
Type—Axle, Adj. Axle, Tricycle	All
Shipping Weight on Rubber—Lbs	4450
Nebraska Test Number (Gasoline)	499
Rear Tread, Adj. Range—Inches	56-90
Height Overall—Inches	81½
Length Overall—Inches	127.1
Wheelbase—Inches	88
Cultivating Clearance—Inches	29
Hydraulic Power Unit	Std.

Belt Pulley—P.T.O.—Engine

Pulley Diameter, Standard—Inches	9
Pulley Face Width—Inches	6½
Pulley Speed, Loaded—rpm	1260
Pulley Speed, Loaded—fpm	2960
Power Take-off—Standard, Optional	Std.
Is Power for P.T.O. Continuous?	Yes
P.T.O. Cont. When Gearshifting?	Yes
Engine—Make	Own
Engine—Model	W-45
Number Cylinders & Displacement	4-226
Rated rpm	1400

Brakes—Steering—Tires

Brakes Type	Shoe
Drums Location—Wheel Axle Shafts, Bull Pinion Shafts	BPS
Steering Type—Cam & Lever, Worm & Segment	W&S
Tire Size—Standard Rear—Inches	12x28
Tire Size—Standard Front—Inches	5.5x16

Allis-Chalmers "WD-45"

ALLIS-CHALMERS MFG. CO.

Milwaukee, Wisconsin

Transmission of Power

Clutch—Dry Disc Spring Loaded?	*
Final Drive—Bevel, Spur	Spur
High Gear Ratio	19.5
Low Gear Ratio	72.5
Speeds—Number Forward	4
Speeds—Number Reverse	1

*WD has two clutches. Engine clutch is single plate, spring loaded, dry type. Transmission clutch is multiple disc, overcenter, wet type.

J. I. CASE CO.
Racine, Wisconsin

Case "VAC-14"
Case "500 Diesel"

1954-1956
1954-1957

General	J. I. Case "VAC-14"
Number and Size Plows.............	1, 2-14
Type—Adjustable Axle, Tricycle.....	AA
Shipping Weight, With Std. Equip.....	RNA
Nebraska Test Number.............	None
Rear Tread, Adj. Range—Inches.....	44-88
Front Tread, Adj. Range—In........	52-76
Height Overall—Inches	58
Length Overall—Inches	114.7
Wheelbase—Inches	77
Cultivating Clearance—Inches	RNA
Hydraulic Power Unit..............	Std.

Belt Pulley—P.T.O.—Engine

Pulley Diameter, Standard—Inches...	10¼
Pulley Face Width—Inches..........	6
Pulley Speed, Loaded—rpm..........	969
Pulley Speed, Loaded—fpm..........	2600
Power Take-off—Standard, Optional.	Opt.
Is Power to P.T.O. Continuous?.....	No
Engine—Make	Own
Engine—Model	VA
Number Cylinders & Displacement...	4-124
Rated rpm	1425

Brakes—Steering—Tires

Brakes, Type—Internal Exp., Disc...	IE
Brakes, Location—Diff. Side Gears?.	Yes
Steering Type—Worm & Sector?....	Yes
Tire Size—Standard Rear—Inches...	11x28
Tire Size—Standard Front—Inches..	5x15

Transmission of Power

Clutch—Dry Disc Spring Loaded?....	Yes
Final Drive—Spur, Chain...........	Spur
High Gear Ratio...................	RNA
Low Gear Ratio...................	RNA
Speeds—Number Forward	4
Speeds—Number Reverse	1

Case "VAC-14"

J. I. CASE CO.
Racine, Wisconsin

General

Number and Size Plows	4, 5-14
Type—Track, Adj. Axle, Tricycle	Axle
Nebraska Test Number	None
Rear Tread—Inches	60.7
Front Tread—Inches	53.7
Height Overall—Inches	61.4
Length Overall—Inches	144.2
Wheelbase—Inches	87.7
Starting—Auxiliary Engine, Electric	Elec.
Cultivating Clearance—Inches	RNA
Hydraulic Power Unit—Std., Optional	Opt.

Belt Pulley—P.T.O.—Engine

Pulley Diameter, Standard—Inches	13
Pulley Face Width—Inches	8.75
Pulley Speed, Loaded—rpm	956
Pulley Speed, Loaded—fpm	3254
Power Take-off—Standard, Optional	Opt.
Is Power to P.T.O. Continuous?	Yes
P.T.O. Cont. When Gearshifting?	Yes
Engine—Make	Own
Engine—Model	500
Number Cylinders & Displacement	6-377
Rated rpm	1350

Brakes—Steering—Tires—Tracks

Brakes, Type—Cont. Band, Disc	Disc
Brakes, Location—Steering Clutches or Differential Shafts	DS
Steering Type—Multiple Disc Clutches or Worm & Gear	*W&G
Tire Size—Standard Rear—Inches	14x30
Tire Size—Standard Front—Inches	7.5x18

Transmission of Power

Clutch—Single Wet Plate, Double Dry Plate	SWP
Clutch—Overcenter?	Yes
Final Drive—Spur, Chain	Chain
High Gear Ratio	RNA
Low Gear Ratio	RNA
Speeds—Number Forward	4
Speeds—Number Reverse	1

Case "500 Diesel"

J. I. CASE CO.
Racine, Wisconsin

*Power steering available as optional.   RNA—Manufacturer declines to release the information.

CATERPILLAR TRACTOR CO.
Peoria, Illinois

Caterpillar "DW20"   1954

General	Caterpillar "DW20"
Type—Axle, Adjustable Axle........	Axle
Shipping Weight on Rubber—Lbs.....	24000
Nebraska Test Number.............	None
Rear Tread—Inches	84
Front Tread—Inches	88
Height Overall—Inches	95
Length Overall—Inches	212
Wheelbase—Inches	128
Hydraulic Power Unit..............	None

Belt Pulley—P.T.O.—Engine

Pulley Diameter, Standard—Inches...	None
Power Take-off—Standard, Optional.	None
Engine—Make	Own
Engine—Model	DW20
Number Cylinders & Displacement....	6-743
Rated rpm	1900

Brakes—Steering—Tires

Brakes, Type—Expanding Band?.....	Yes
Brakes, Location—Wheels?	Yes
Steering Type—Worm & Sector, Worm & Circulating Ball..........	W&CB
Tire Size—Standard Rear—Inches...	24x29
Tire Size—Standard Front—Inches..	14x24

Transmission of Power

Clutch—Dry Double Plate?........	Yes
Clutch—Spring Loaded?	Yes
Final Drive—Spur, Bevel & Spur.....	B&S
High Gear Ratio..................	15.75
Low Gear Ratio..................	139.2
Speeds—Number Forward	5
Speeds—Number Reverse	1

Caterpillar "DW20"

CATERPILLAR TRACTOR CO.
Peoria, Illinois

CUSTOM TRACTOR MANUFACTURING CO., INC.

Hustisford, Wisconsin

Custom "96R"	1954
Custom "96W"	1954
Custom "98R"	1954
Custom "98W"	1954

General

	Custom "98"	"96"
Number and Size Plows	3, 4-14	3-14
Type—Axle, Tricycle .....(98R-96R)	Tri.	Tri.
(98W-96W)	Axle	Axle
Shipping Weight on Rubber—		
Lbs. ....(98R-96R)	4436	4136
(98W-96W)	4696	4296
Nebraska Test Number	None	None
Rear Tread, Minimum—Inches.(Axle)	66½	66½
(Tri.)	56	56
Rear Tread, Maximum—Inches.(Axle)	78½	78½
(Tri.)	84	84
Front Tread, Minimum—In....(Axle)	55½	55½
(Tri.)	8	8
Front Tread, Maximum—In....(Axle)	61½	61½
(Tri.)	14	14
Height Overall—Inches ......(Axle)	78	78
(Tri.)	80	80
Length Overall—Inches ......(Axle)	137⅛	134⅞
(Tri.)	139⅛	136⅞
Wheelbase—Inches ....(Axle)	93⅝	91⅜
(Tri.)	93¾	91½
Cultivating Clearance—Inches.(Axle)	17	17
(Tri.)	25	25
Hydraulic Power Unit	Std.	Std.

Belt Pulley—P.T.O.—Engine

Pulley Diameter, Standard—Inches	11	11
Pulley Face Width—Inches	7½	7½
Pulley Speed Loaded—rpm	1011	1011
Pulley Speed Loaded—fpm	2911	2911
Power Take-Off—Std., Opt., None	Std.	Std.
Is Power for P.T.O. Continuous?	No	No
Engine—Make	Chry.	Chry.
Engine—Model	*Ind.8A	*Ind.6A
Number Cylinders & Displacement	6-250	6-230
Rated rpm	1800	1800

Brakes—Steering—Tires

Brakes, Type—Internal Expanding?	Yes	Yes
Brakes, Location—Rear Wheel Axle Shafts & Transmission?	Yes	Yes
Brakes, Actuation—Hydraulic, Mechanical	H&M	H&M
Steering—Make	Ross	Ross
Type—Cam & Lever, Worm & Sector	C&L	C&L
Tire Size—Std. Rear—Inches..(Axle)	14x30	14x30
(Tri.)	12x38	12x38
Tire Size—Std. Front—Inches	6x16	6x16

Transmission of Power

	"98"	"96"
Clutch—Dry Disc Spring Loaded?	Yes	Yes
Final Drive—Bevel, Chain, Spur	Spur	Spur
High Gear Ratio......(98R-96R&W)	15.93	15.93
(98W)	17.35	
Low Gear Ratio......(98R-96R&W)	120.7	120.7
(98W)	131.66	
Speeds—Number Forward	5	5
Speeds—Number Reverse	1	1

Advertised Speeds, mph, With Std. Transmission & Std. Tires, at 1500 engine rpm—Models 96R-96W-98R: 2.06, 3.56, 5.13, 9.11, 15.64; reverse, 2.08. Model 98W: 1.73, 3.00, 4.31, 7.66, 13.15; reverse, 1.75.
*Engines are equipped with Fluid Drive drive coupling.

Custom "96W" & "98W"

Custom "96R" & "98R"

CUSTOM TRACTOR MFG. CO., INC.
Hustisford, Wisconsin

DEERE & CO.
Moline, Illinois

John Deere "40" Crawler	1954-1955
John Deere "40" Standard	1954-1955
John Deere "40" Tricycle	1954-1955
John Deere "60 O"	1954-1956
John Deere "60 S"	1954-1956
John Deere "70"	1954
John Deere "70 Non Diesel Hi-Crop"	1954-1956

General

John Deere "40" Crawler

Number and Size Plows	3-14
Type—Track, Tricycle, Adj. Axle	Track
Shipping Weight on Rubber—Lbs	3875
Tread, Standard—Inches	36 & 46
Tread, Optional—Inches	38 & 44
Height Overall—Inches	*65.6
Length Overall—Inches	102
Standard Starting—Electric?	Yes
Hydraulic Power Unit	Opt.

Belt Pulley—P.T.O.—Engine

Pulley Diameter, Standard—Inches	9
Pulley Face Width—Inches	6
Pulley Speed, Loaded—rpm	1270
Pulley Speed, Loaded—fpm	3000
Power Take-off—Standard, Optional	Std.
Is Standard P.T.O. Continuous?	No
Is Continuous P.T.O. Available?	No
Engine—Make	Own
Number Cylinders & Displacement	2-100.5
Rated rpm	1850

Brakes

Type—Int. Expanding, Contracting	Con.
Location—Steering Clutches, Sep. Shafts Driven by Bull Gears	SC

Steering—Tires—Tracks

Steering Type—Worm & Gear	
Steering Clutches Type—Mult. Disc?	Yes
Track Face Width, Standard—Inches	10, 12
Tire Size—Standard Rear—Inches	Track
Tire Size—Standard Front—Inches	Track

Transmission of Power

Clutch—Single Plate, Multiple Disc	SP
Clutch—Dry, Wet	Dry
Clutch—Spring Loaded, Overcenter	SL
Final Drive—Spur, Chain	Spur
High Gear Ratio	21.9
Low Gear Ratio	141.0
Speeds—Number Forward	4
Speeds—Number Reverse	1

John Deere "40" Crawler

DEERE & COMPANY
Moline, Illinois

*Including stacks.

General	John Deere "40" Std.	"40" Tri.
Number and Size Plows	1-16 or	2-14
Type—Axle, Tricycle, Adj. Axle	AA	T&AA
Shipping Weight on Rubber—Lbs	2750	3000
Rear Tread, Adj. Range—Inches	38.5-54	48-96
Front Tread, Minimum—Inches (Tri.)		6.7
(Adj. Axle)	39	48
Front Tread, Maximum—Inches (Tri.)		11.7
(Adj. Axle)	54	88
Height Overall—Inches	*71	*73.7
Length Overall—Inches	114.7	130.6
Wheelbase—Inches	70	82¼
Cultivating Clearance—Inches	21	21
Hydraulic Power Unit	Std.	Std.

Belt Pulley—P.T.O.—Engine

Pulley Diameter, Standard—Inches	9	9
Pulley Face Width—Inches	6	6
Pulley Speed, Loaded—rpm	1270	1270
Pulley Speed, Loaded—fpm	3000	3000
Power Take-Off—Standard, Optional	Std.	Std.
Is Power to P.T.O. Continuous?	No	No
Engine—Make	Own	Own
Number Cylinders & Displacement	2-100.5	2-100.5
Rated rpm	1850	1850

Brakes—Steering—Tires

Brakes, Type—Double Disc?	Yes	Yes
Brakes, Location—Bull Pinion Shaft?	Yes	Yes
Steering Make	Ross	Ross
Steering Type—Cam & Lever?	Yes	Yes
Tire Size—Standard Rear—Inches	9x24	9x34
Tire Size—Standard Front—Inches	5x15	5x15

Transmission of Power

Clutch—Dry Disc Spring Loaded?	Yes	Yes
Final Drive—Spur, Chain	Spur	Spur
High Gear Ratio	18.3	23.1
Low Gear Ratio	116.2	147.0
Speeds—Number Forward	4	4
Speeds—Number Reverse	1	1

Advertised Speeds, mph, With Std. Transmission & Std. Tires—Models "40" Standard & "40" Tricycle: 1.6, 3.1, 4.2, 12.0; reverse, 2.5.
*Including stacks.

John Deere "40" Standard

John Deere "40" Tricycle

DEERE & COMPANY
Moline, Illinois

John Deere "60 O"

General	John Deere "60O" "60S"	"70"
Number and Size Plows............	3-14	4-14
Type—Axle, Adj. Axle, Tricycle......	Axle	T&AA
Shipping Weight on Rubber—Lbs.....	5347	6035
Nebraska Test Number....(Gasoline)		493
Rear Tread, Minimum—Inches..(60O)	54.4	60.0
(60S)	58.0	
Rear Tread, Maximum—Inches.(60O)	58.4	88.0
(60S)	62.0	
Front Tread, Min.—In...(60O & 70T)	47.2	8.3
(60S & 70AA)	50.0	56.0
Front Tread, Max.—In...(60O & 70T)	47.2	12.1
(60O & 70T)	50.0	80.0
Height Overall—In. .....(60O & 70T)	*58.7	*88.1
(60S & 70AA)	*71.0	*89.3
Length Overall—Inches		136.2
Wheelbase—Inches	75.7	90.0
Cultivating Clear.—In. ..(60O & 70T)		25.4
(60S & 70AA)		26.1
Hydraulic Power Unit—Std., Optional.	Opt.	Opt.

Belt Pulley—P.T.O.—Engine

Pulley Diameter, Standard—Inches...	12¹³⁄₁₆	12⅞
Pulley Face Width—Inches..........	7⅜	7⅜
Pulley Speed, Loaded—rpm.........	975	975
Pulley Speed, Loaded—fpm.........	3270	3285
Power Take-off—Standard, Optional.	Std.	Std.
Is Standard P.T.O. Continuous?.....	No	No
Is Continuous P.T.O. Available?.....	Yes	Yes
P.T.O. Cont. When Gearshifting?....	Yes	Yes
Engine—Make	Own	Own
Engine—Model	60	70
No. Cylinders & Displacement (Gas.).	2-321	2-380
No. Cyl. & Displacement (LP-Gas)..	2-321	2-413
Rated rpm	975	975

John Deere "60 S"

Brakes—Steering—Tires

Brakes, Type—Internal Expanding?..	Yes	Yes
Brakes, Location—Separate Shaft?..	Yes	Yes
Steering Type—Worm & Gear?......	Yes	Yes
Tire Size—Std. Rear—Inches..(60O)	13x26	12x38
(60S)	13x30	
Tire Size—Standard Front—Inches..	6x16	6x16

Transmission of Power

Clutch—Multiple Dry Disc O'center?.	Yes	Yes
Final Drive—Bevel, Chain, Spur......	Spur	Spur
Speeds—Number Forward	6	6
Speeds—Number Reverse	1	1

Advertised Speeds, mph, With Std. Transmission & Std. Tires—Models 60O & 60S: 1.5, 2.5, 3.5, 4.5, 6.5, 11.5; reverse, 3.0 on 60S or 2.75 on 60O. Model 70: 2.5, 3.5, 4.5, 6.5, 8.75, 12.5; reverse, 3.25.
*Including stacks.

John Deere "70"

DEERE & COMPANY
Moline, Illinois

The rung of a ladder...

"The rung of a ladder was never meant to rest upon, but only to hold a man's foot long enough to enable him to put the other somewhat higher."

Thomas Huxley

Those eloquent lines embody a principle that has been followed at John Deere for more than a century of manufacturing quality farm equipment.

Pausing on each rung just long enough to make sure of their footing, John Deere engineers, for instance, are climbing ever upward, finding new ways to speed up crop production . . . to lighten the farmer's work . . . to increase his profits.

The results, of course, are manifold. But none are more valued than farmer respect and enthusiasm for John Deere products, which—in 116 years of service to American agriculture—have never been higher than they are today. And by

this very measure, recent progress in the design, development, and manufacture of John Deere farm equipment has been particularly outstanding.

The latest "rung of achievement" is the introduction of the Model "70" Tractor, shown below. An important new member of a famous family, the John Deere Model "70" is a powerful tractor, with feature after feature that proclaim it the modern tractor for the large row-crop farm . . . a tractor that continues and accentuates the famed John Deere policy of offering farmers across the nation the utmost in modern design and proved performance . . . in quality farm equipment.

J O H N   D E E R E **M O L I N E ,   I L L .**

General

	John Deere 70 Hi-Crop
Number and Size Plows	5-14
Type—Axle, Adj. Axle, Tricycle	AA
Shipping Weight—Lbs.	7410
Rear Tread, Adj. Range—Inches	60-90
Front Tread, Adj. Range—In.	60-84
Height Overall—Inches	101
Length Overall—Inches	153
Wheelbase—Inches	98.8
Cultivating Clear.—Inches	30.8
Hydraulic Power Unit—Std., Opt.	Opt.

Belt Pulley—P.T.O.—Engine

Pulley Diameter, Standard—Inches.	12⅞
Pulley Face Width—Inches	7⅜
Pulley Speed, Loaded—rpm	975
Pulley Speed, Loaded—fpm	3285
Power Take-off—Standard, Opt.	Std.
Is Standard P.T.O. Continuous?	No
Is Continuous P.T.O. Available?	Yes
P.T.O. Cont. When Gearshifting?	Yes
Engine—Make	Own
Engine—Model	70
No. Cylinders & Displacement (Gas & LP-Gas)	2-380
(All Fuel)	2-413
Rated rpm	975

Brakes—Steering—Tires

Brakes, Type—Internal Expanding?	Yes
Brakes, Location—Separate Shaft?	Yes
Steering Type—Worm & Gear?	Yes
Power Steering—Standard, Optional.	Opt.
Tire Size, Std. Front—In	12x38
Tire Size—Std. Front—Inches	7.5x20

Transmission of Power

Clutch—Multiple Dry Disc O'center?	Yes
Final Drive—Bevel, Chain, Spur	Chain
Speeds—Number Forward	6
Speeds—Number Reverse	1

John Deere "70 Non Diesel Hi-Crop"

DEERE & COMPANY
Moline, Illinois

FORD MOTOR CO.
Ford Tractor Division
Birmingham, Michigan

Ford "NAA"   1954

General

	Ford "NAA"
Number and Size Plows	2-14
Type—Axle, Adjustable Axle	AA
Shipping Weight on Rubber—Lbs	2600
Nebraska Test Number....(Gasoline)	494
Rear Tread, Adj. Range—Inches	48-76
Front Tread, Adj. Range—Inches	48-76
Height Overall—Inches	57.5
Length Overall—Inches	118.8
Wheelbase—Inches	73.8
Cultivating Clearance—Inches	21
Hydraulic Power Unit	Std.

Belt Pulley—P.T.O.—Engine

Pulley Diameter, Standard—Inches	9
Pulley Face Width—Inches	6½
Pulley Speed, Loaded—rpm	1358
Pulley Speed, Loaded—fpm	3199
Power Take-off—Standard, Optional	Opt.
Is Non Continuous P.T.O. Available?	Yes
Is Continuous P.T.O. Available?	Yes
P.T.O. Cont. When Gearshifting?	No
Engine—Make	Own
Engine—Model	NAA
Number Cylinders & Displacement	4-134
Rated rpm—Belt	2000
Drawbar	1750

Brakes—Steering—Tires

Brakes, Type—Internal Expanding Shoes, Contracting Band	IES
Brakes, Location—Wheel Axle Shafts, On Bull Pinion Shaft	WAS
Brake Units per Tractor	2
Steering Type—Worm & Ball Nut, Steering Clutches & Brakes	W&B
Tire Size—Standard Rear—Inches	10x28
Tire Size—Standard Front—Inches	4x19

Transmission of Power

Clutch—Single Plate, Double Plate	SP
Clutch—Spring Loaded?	Yes
Final Drive—Bevel, Spur Gear, Chain— (Rear Wheels)	Bevel
High Gear Ratio	19.86
Low Gear Ratio	73.33
Speeds—Number Forward	4
Speeds—Number Reverse	1
Speed Change—Constant Mesh, Sliding Gear	CM

Ford "NAA"

**FORD TRACTOR DIVISION
FORD MOTOR CO.
Birmingham, Michigan**

HARRIS MANUFACTURING CO.
Stockton, California

Harris "F8W"   1954-1956
Harris "F8WC"   1954-1956

General

	Harris "F8W" "F8WC"
Number and Size Plows	3-14
Type—Axle, Adjustable Axle	Axle
Shipping Weight on Rubber—Lbs.	4860
Nebraska Test Number.... (Gasoline)	†479
Rear Tread, Adj. Range—Inches	48-76
Front Tread, Adj. Range—Inches	48-76
Height Overall—Inches	65
Length Overall—Inches	††99.5
Wheelbase—Inches	54
Cultivating Clearance—Inches	18
Hydraulic Power Unit	Opt.

Belt Pulley—P.T.O.—Engine

Pulley Diameter, Standard—Inches	None
Pulley Face Width—Inches	None
Pulley Speed, Loaded—rpm	None
Pulley Speed, Loaded—fpm	None
Power Take-off—Standard, Optional	Opt.
Is Non Continuous P.T.O. Available?	No
Is Continuous P.T.O. Available?	No
Engine—Make	Chry.
Engine—Model	Ind.8A
Number Cylinders & Displacement	6-250.6
Rated rpm—Belt	
Drawbar	2000

Brakes—Steering—Tires

Brakes, Type—Internal Expanding Shoes, Contracting Band	CB
Brakes, Location—Wheel Axle Shafts, On Bull Pinion Shaft	BPS
Brake Units per Tractor	*4
Steering Type—Worm & Ball Nut, Steering Clutches & Brakes	SC&B
Tire Size—Standard Rear—Inches	13x24
Tire Size—Standard Front—Inches	13x24

*Two on planetary drum and two on the bull pinion shafts. †Tested as the Harris "PH53". ††Less drawbar.

Harris "F8W"

("F8WC" is similar)

HARRIS MFG. CO.
Stockton, California

Transmission of Power

Clutch—Single Plate, Double Plate	DP
Clutch—Spring Loaded?	Yes
Final Drive—Bevel, Spur Gear, Chain—	
(Rear Wheels)	S.Gear
(Front Wheels)	Chain
High Gear Ratio	18.5
Low Gear Ratio	117.2
Speeds—Number Forward	8
Speeds—Number Reverse	2
Speed Change—Constant Mesh, Sliding Gear	SG

INTERNATIONAL HARVESTER CO.
Chicago, Illinois

McCormick ''Super W4''   1954

General

	McCormick Super "W4"
Number and Size Plows..............	2, 3-14
Type—Axle, Tricycle	Axle
Shipping Wt., Max., on Rubber—Lbs...	3915
Nebraska Test Number	491
Rear Tread, Min. & Max.—Inches.....	52
Front Tread, Min. & Max.—Inches....	45.8
Height Overall—Inches	80½
Length Overall—Inches	114
Wheelbase—Inches	66⅝
Cultivating Clearance—Inches	15⅛
Hydraulic Power Unit..............	Opt.

Belt Pulley—P.T.O.—Engine

Pulley Diameter, Standard—Inches...	9¾
Pulley Face Width—Inches.........	7½
Pulley Speed, Loaded—rpm.........	1019
Pulley Speed, Loaded—fpm.........	2601
Power Take-off—Standard, Optional.	Opt.
Is Power to P.T.O. Continuous?.....	No
Engine—Make	Own
Engine—Model	C-164
Number Cylinders & Displacement...	4-164
Rated rpm	1650

Brakes—Steering—Tires

Brakes, Type—Disc?	Yes
Brakes, Location—Bull Pinion Shafts?	Yes
Steering, Type—Worm & Gear?.....	Yes
Tire Size—Standard Rear—Inches...	13x26
Tire Size—Standard Front—Inches..	5.5x16

Transmission of Power

Clutch—Dry Disc Spring Loaded?....	Yes
Final Drive—Spur, Chain	Spur
High Gear Ratio	15.27
Low Gear Ratio	95.39
Speeds—Number Forward	5
Speeds—Number Reverse	1

McCormick "Super W4"

INTERNATIONAL HARVESTER CO.
Chicago, Illinois

MASSEY-HARRIS CO.

Racine, Wisconsin

Massey-Harris "Colt"	1954-1956
Massey-Harris "Mustang"	1954-1956
Massey-Harris "Pacer"	1954
Massey-Harris "33" Tricycle	1954-1955
Massey-Harris "33" Adjustable Axle	1954-1955

General

	Massey-Harris "Pacer"	"Colt"
Number and Size Plows	2-12	2-14
Type—Axle, Adj. Axle, Tricycle	AA	All
Shipping Weight, Maximum—Lbs.	1980	2745
Nebraska Test Number	None	None
Rear Tread, Adj. Range—In...(A.A.)	41-69	52-80
(Axle)		52
(Tri.)		52-80
Front Tread, Adj. Range—In..(A.A.)	44-68	52-74
(Axle)		45.7
(Tri.)		6.7-12.3
Height Overall, Maximum—Inches	62.6	65.8
Length Overall—Inches ......(A.A.)	103.6	126.1
(Axle)		122.5
(Tri.)		123.3
Wheelbase—Inches ....(A.A.)	72.2	87.0
(Axle)		76.0
(Tri.)		82.7
Cultivating Clearance—Inches	20.5	19.3
Hydraulic Power Unit—Std., Optional	Opt.	Opt.

Belt Pulley—P.T.O.—Engine

Pulley Diameter, Standard—Inches	6	9.5
Pulley Face Width—Inches	5.5	6.25
Pulley Speed, Loaded—rpm	1990	1224
Pulley Speed, Loaded—fpm	3125	3044
Power Take-off—Standard, Optional	Opt.	Opt.
Is Power to P.T.O. Continuous?	No	No
Engine—Make	Cont'l.	Cont'l.
Engine—Model	Y91	F124
Number Cylinders & Displacement	4-91	4-124
Rated rpm	1800	1800

Brakes—Steering—Tires

Brakes, Type—Contracting Band, Disc	CB	Disc
Brakes, Location—Bull Pinion Shafts, Wheel Axle Shafts	BPS	WAS
Steering Make	Ross	Saginaw
Steering Type—Cam & Lever, Worm & Sector	C&L	W&S
Tire Size—Standard Rear—Inches	9x24	10x28
Tire Size—Std. Front—In.....(A.A.)	4x15	4x15
(Axle)		5x15
(Dual Wheel Tricycle)		4x15
(Single Wheel Tricycle)		6x12

Transmission of Power

Clutch—Dry Disc Spring Loaded?	Yes	Yes
Final Drive—Spur, Bevel Gear	Spur	BG
High Gear Ratio	27.4	15.03
Low Gear Ratio	70.2	79.6
Speeds—Number Forward	3	4
Speeds—Number Reverse	1	1

Massey-Harris "Pacer"

Massey-Harris "Colt"

MASSEY-HARRIS COMPANY
Racine, Wisconsin

Advertised Speeds, mph, With Std. Transmission & Std. Tires—Model Pacer: 2.9, 3.8, 7.4; reverse, 3.4. Model Colt: 2.5, 3.5, 4.6, 13.0; reverse, 2.5,

General	Massey-Harris "Mustang"	"33"
Number and Size Plows.............	2-14	2, 3-14
Type—Axle, Adj. Axle, Tricycle......	All	All
Shipping Wt., Max., on Rubber—Lbs...	2770	4030
Nebraska Test Number...(Gasoline)	None	None
Rear Tread, Adj. Range—In...(Axle)	52	52.1
(Adj. Axle & Tri.)	52-80	52.7-88.6
Front Tread, Adj. Range—In..(Axle)	45.7	47.6
(Adj. Axle)	52-74	58.2-84.2
(Tri.)	6.7-12.3	8.5
Height Overall, Maximum—Inches....	66.6	80.7
Length Overall—Inches ......(Axle)	121	129
(Dual Wheel Tri.)	122.5	137
(Single Wheel Tri.)	123.3	137
(Adj. Axle)	128	149
Wheelbase—Inches ....(Axle)	75.7	79.6
(Adj. Axle)	87	100.6
(Dual Wheel Tri.)	82.5	88.1
(Single Wheel Tri.)	82.5	88.8
Cultivating Clearance—Inches (Axle)	20.3	19.6
(Tri.)	20.3	24.5
Hydraulic Power Unit..............	Opt.	Opt.

Massey-Harris "Mustang"

Belt Pulley—P.T.O.—Engine

Pulley Diameter, Standard—Inches..	9.5	13.5
Pulley Face Width—Inches.........	6.25	6.5
Pulley Speed, Loaded—rpm.........	1224	890
Pulley Speed, Loaded—fpm.........	3044	3146
Power Take-off—Standard, Optional.	Opt.	Opt.
Is Non Continuous P.T.O. Available?.	Yes	Yes
Is Continuous P.T.O. Available?.....	No	Yes
P.T.O. Cont. When Gearshifting?....		No
Engine—Make	Cont'l.	Own
Engine—Model	F140	E201
Number Cylinders & Displacement...	4-140	4-201
Rated rpm	1800	1500

Massey-Harris "33" (Tricycle)

Brakes—Steering—Tires

Brakes, Type—Int. Exp. Shoe, Disc..	Disc	Either
Brakes, Location—Wheel Axle Shafts, Differential Shafts	WAS	DS
Steering Make	Saginaw	Saginaw
Steering Type—Worm & Sector?....	W&S	W&S
Tire Size—Std. Rear—Inches..(Axle)	11x28	12x28
(Adj. Axle & Tri.)	11x28	11x38
Tire Size—Std. Front—Inches.(Axle)	5x15	5.5x16
(Adj. Axle)	5x15	5.5x16
(Dual Wheel Tri.)	4x15	5.5x16
(Single Wheel Tri.)	6x12	9x10

Transmission of Power

Clutch—Dry Disc Spring Loaded?....	Yes	
Final Drive—Bevel Gear, Spur......	BG	Spur
High Gear Ratio...................	15.03	19.0
Low Gear Ratio...................	79.6	92.9
Speeds—Number Forward	4	5
Speeds—Number Reverse	1	1

Advertised Speeds, mph, With Std. Transmission & Std. Tires—Model Mustang: 2.6, 3.7, 4.8, 13.5; reverse, 2.6. Model 33 Axle: 2.3, 3.2, 4.0, 5.6, 11.1; reverse, 2.6. Model 33 Adj. Axle & Tricycle: 2.7, 3.7, 4.7, 6.5, 13.1; reverse, 3.0.

Massey-Harris "33" (Adj. Axle)

MASSEY-HARRIS COMPANY
Racine, Wisconsin

MINNEAPOLIS-MOLINE CO.
Minneapolis, Minnesota

Minneapolis-Moline "BG"	1954-1957
Minneapolis-Moline "G" Non Diesel	1954-1955
Minneapolis-Moline "G" Diesel	1954-1955
Minneapolis-Moline "UB" Type E	1954
Minneapolis-Moline "UB" Type N	1954
Minneapolis-Moline "UB" Type U	1954
Minneapolis-Moline "ZB" Type E	1954-1957
Minneapolis-Moline "ZB" Type N	1954-1957
Minneapolis-Moline "ZB" Type U	1954-1957

General — Minneapolis-Moline "BG"

Number and Size Plows	2-14
Type—Axle, Tricycle, Adj. Axle	AA
Shipping Wt., Max., on Rubber—Lbs.	2880
Nebraska Test Number	None
Front Tread, Adj. Range—In.	41-58
Rear Tread, Adj. Range—In.	40-68
Height Overall—Inches	76
Length Overall—Inches	110
Wheelbase—Inches	75
Cultivating Clearance—Inches	20.5
Hydraulic Power Unit	Std.

Belt Pulley—P.T.O.—Engine

Pulley Diameter, Standard—Inches	8.5
Pulley Face Width——Inches	6.5
Pulley Speed, Loaded—rpm	1160
Pulley Speed, Loaded—fpm	2580
Power Take-off—Standard, Optional.	Opt.
Is Power to P.T.O. Continuous?	No
Engine—Make	Herc.
Engine—Model	IXB3SL
Number Cylinders & Displacement	4-133
Rated rpm	1800

Brakes—Steering—Tires

Brakes, Type—Contracting Band?	Yes
Brakes, Location—Bull Pinion Shafts?	Yes
Steering Make	Ross
Steering, Type—Cam & Lever, Worm & Gear	C&L
Tire Size—Standard Rear—Inches	11x24
Tire Size—Std. Front—Inches	5x15

Transmission of Power

Clutch—Dry Disc Spring Loaded?	Yes
Final Drive—Spur, Chain	Spur
High Gear Ratio	RNA
Low Gear Ratio	RNA
Speeds—Number Forward	4
Speeds—Number Reverse	1

RNA—Manufacturer declines to release the information.

Minneapolis-Moline "BG"

MINNEAPOLIS-MOLINE COMPANY
Minneapolis, Minnesota

General

	Minneapolis-Moline "G" Non Diesel	"G" Diesel
Number and Size Plows.............	4, 5-14	4, 5-14
Type—Axle, Adjustable Axle	Axle	Axle
Shipping Wt., Max., on Rubber—Lbs...	6500	7200
Nebraska Test Number...(Gasoline)	437	None
Rear Tread—Inches	62	62
Front Tread—Inches	54.2	54.2
Height Overall—Inches	71	71
Length Overall, Maximum—Inches....	135.3	149.3
Wheelbase—Inches	82.5	96.1
Cultivating Clearance—Inches	14	14
Hydraulic Power Unit..............	Opt.	Opt.

Belt Pulley—P.T.O.—Engine

Pulley Diameter, Standard—Inches...	16	16
Pulley Face Width—Inches.........	7	7
Pulley Speed, Loaded—rpm.........	627	641
Pulley Speed, Loaded—fpm.........	2630	3110
Power Take-off—Standard, Optional.	Opt.	Opt.
Is Non Continuous P.T.O. Available?.	Yes	Yes
Is Continuous P.T.O. Available?.....	Yes	No
P.T.O. Cont. When Gearshifting?....	No	
Engine—Make	Own	Own
Engine—Model ....(Gasoline)	403C	D425
(LP-Gas)	340A	
No. Cyl. & Displacement...(Gasoline)	4-403	6-425
(LP-Gas)	4-340	
Rated rpm	1100	1300

Brakes—Steering—Tires

Brakes, Type—Disc?	Yes	Yes
Brakes, Location—Bull Pin. Shafts?.	Yes	Yes
Steering Make	Ross	Ross
Steering, Type—Cam & Lever, Worm & Sector?................	C&L	C&L
Tire Size—Standard Rear—Inches...	14x34	14x34
Tire Size—Standard Front—Inches..	7.5x18	7.5x18

Transmission of Power

Clutch—Dry Disc Overcenter?......	Yes	Yes
Final Drive—Spur, Bevel Gear.......	Spur	Spur
High Gear Ratio	13.33	14.52
Low Gear Ratio	73.83	80.42
Speeds—Number Forward	5	5
Speeds—Number Reverse	1	1

Advertised Speeds, mph, With Std. Tires & Std. Transmission—Model G Non Diesel: 2.5, 3.5, 4.1, 6.0, 13.8; reverse, 2.0. Model G Diesel: 2.7, 3.8, 4.5, 6.5, 15.0; reverse, 2.1.

Minneapolis-Moline "G" Non Diesel

("G" Diesel is similar)

MINNEAPOLIS-MOLINE COMPANY
Minneapolis, Minnesota

General

	Minneapolis-Moline "UB" Types E, N&U
Number and Size Plows.............	3, 4-14
Type—Axle, Tri., Adj. Axle (N&U)...	Tri.
(Type E)	AA
Shipping Wt., Max., on Rubber—Lbs...	5700
Nebraska Test Number	None
Rear Tread, Minimum—Inches.......	54.5
Rear Tread, Maximum—In.....(E&U)	84½
(N)	96
Front Tread, Adj. Range—In.....(U)	8⅜-13
(E)	56-84
Height Overall—Inches ....(U)	78.5
Length Overall—Inches .....(N&U)	133
(E)	141
Wheelbase—Inches ....(N&U)	88
(E)	96
Cultivating Clearance—In. ...(N&U)	25
(E)	20
Hydraulic Power Unit..............	Opt.

Belt Pulley—P.T.O.—Engine

Pulley Diameter, Standard—Inches...	16
Pulley Face Width—Inches.........	7
Pulley Speed, Loaded—rpm.........	741
Pulley Speed, Loaded—fpm.........	3110
Power Take-Off—Standard, Optional.	Opt.
Is Non Continuous P.T.O. Available?.	Yes
Is Continuous P.T.O. Available?.....	Yes
P.T.O. Cont. When Gearshifting?....	No
Engine—Make	Own
Engine—Model ....(Gasoline & LPG)	283B
(Diesel)	D283
Number Cylinders & Displacement...	4-283
Rated rpm	1300

Brakes—Steering—Tires

Brakes, Type—Disc?	Yes
Brakes, Location—Bull Pin. Shafts?.	Yes
Steering Make	Own
Type—Cam & Lever, Worm & Sector?	W&S
Tire Size—Standard Rear—Inches...	12x38
Tire Size—Std. Front—In. ...(E&U)	6x16
(N)	9x10

Transmission of Power

Clutch—Dry Single Disc?..........	Yes
Clutch—Spring Loaded, Overcenter..	SL
Final Drive—Spur, Chain..........	Spur
High Gear Ratio	14.52
Low Gear Ratio	80.42
Speeds—Number Forward	5
Speeds—Number Reverse	1

Minneapolis-Moline "UB" Type U

(Single wheel "UB" Type N and adjustable axle "UB" Type E models are similar)

MINNEAPOLIS-MOLINE COMPANY
Minneapolis, Minnesota

General	Minneapolis-Moline "ZB" Type E	"ZB" Types N&U
Number and Size Plows	3-14	3-14
Type—Adjustable Axle, Tricycle	AA	Tri.
Shipping Weight on Rubber—Lbs	3900	3750
Nebraska Test Number	None	None
Rear Tread, Adj. Range—Inches (U)	54-88	54-88
(N)		54-96
Front Tread, Adj. Range—Inches (U)	56-84	7¾-12⅞
Height Overall—Inches	74	74
Length Overall—Inches (U)	134.3	126.2
(N)		124.7
Wheelbase—Inches (U)	90⅛	82
(N)		82⅜
Cultivating Clearance—Inches	19.8	25
Hydraulic Power Unit	Opt.	Opt.

Belt Pulley—P.T.O.—Engine

Pulley Diameter, Standard—Inches	15⅛	15⅛
Pulley Face Width—Inches	7	7
Pulley Speed, Loaded—rpm	786	786
Pulley Speed, Loaded—fpm	3110	
Power Take-off—Standard, Optional	Opt.	Opt.
Is Non Continuous P.T.O. Available?	Yes	Yes
Is Continuous P.T.O. Available?	Yes	Yes
P.T.O. Cont. When Gearshifting?	No	No
Engine—Make	Own	Own
Engine—Model	206G	206G
Number Cylinders & Displacement	4-206	4-206
Rated rpm	1500	1500

Brakes—Steering—Tires

Brakes, Type—Disc?	Yes	Yes
Brakes, Location—Bull Pinion Shaft?	Yes	Yes
Steering, Type—Worm & Sector?	Yes	Yes
Tire Size—Standard Rear—Inches	11x38	11x38
Tire Size—Std. Front—In... (Type N)	5.5x16	7.5x10
(Type U)		5.5x16

Transmission of Power

Clutch—Dry Single Disc?	Yes	Yes
Clutch—Spring Loaded?	Yes	Yes
Final Drive—Spur, Chain	Spur	Spur
High Gear Ratio	18.77	18.77
Low Gear Ratio	100.89	100.89
Speeds—Number Forward	5	5
Speeds—Number Reverse	1	1

Advertised Speeds, mph, With Std. Tires & Std. Transmission—All 3 Models: 2.4, 4.6, 3.6, 6.3, 13.1; reverse, 2.2.

Minneapolis-Moline "ZB" Type N

Minneapolis-Moline "ZB" Type U

(Adjustable axle "ZB" Type E Model is similar)

MINNEAPOLIS-MOLINE COMPANY
Minneapolis, Minnesota

And then he said:

"LOOK, MISTER, ALL I WANT TO KNOW IS— DOES THIS TRACTOR LAST LONGER?"

The answer is, "Yes!" if the vital, heavy-duty parts are made with U·S·S Carilloy steel. Here's why.

U·S·S CARILLOY STEELS ARE STRONGER

We can pack much more strength into a pound of Carilloy steel than we could ever get in carbon steel. Just a pinch of nickel, chromium, molybdenum, and other alloying elements greatly improves the physical properties of the steel . . . and the strength and durability of the parts made from it.

U·S·S CARILLOY STEELS REDUCE WEIGHT

When heavily-stressed gears, pinions, and axles on farm equipment are made of U·S·S Carilloy steel, they can be made much stronger without increasing their weight. Or, their size and weight can be decreased *without* reducing strength of the finished part.

U·S·S CARILLOY STEELS MEET EVERY REQUIREMENT

With Carilloy steels, you can get any combination of physical properties you need: great tensile strength, hardenability, toughness, or ductility—in a wide range of forms, sizes and shapes. They are available in the hot rolled quenched and tempered, annealed, or normalized conditions, any of which can be furnished to quality standards suitable for any application.

Get in touch with our nearest District Office for complete information. Or, write to United States Steel, 525 William Penn Place, Pittsburgh 30, Pennsylvania.

UNITED STATES STEEL CORPORATION, PITTSBURGH • COLUMBIA-GENEVA STEEL DIVISION, SAN FRANCISCO
TENNESSEE COAL & IRON DIVISION, FAIRFIELD, ALA. • UNITED STATES STEEL SUPPLY DIVISION, WAREHOUSE DISTRIBUTORS
UNITED STATES STEEL EXPORT COMPANY, NEW YORK

U·S·S Carilloy Steels

ELECTRIC FURNACE OR OPEN HEARTH   COMPLETE PRODUCTION FACILITIES IN CHICAGO OR PITTSBURGH

1954

469

THE OLIVER CORP.
Chicago, Illinois

Oliver Crawler "OC-6" Diesel	1954
Oliver Crawler "OC-6" HC	1954
Oliver Crawler "OC-18"	1954
Oliver "99" Diesel	1954
Oliver "99" HC	1954

General

	Oliver Crawler "OC-6" HC&D"
Number and Size Plows	3-14
Shipping Weight, Maximum—Lbs	5425
Nebraska Test Number	None
Tread, Minimum—Inches	42
Tread, Maximum—Inches	60, 68
Height Overall—Inches	**58.7
Length Overall—Inches	121.5
Wheelbase—Inches	54.2
Cultivating Clearance—Inches	22.5
Hydraulic Power Unit	Opt.

Belt Pulley—P.T.O.—Engine

Pulley Diameter, Standard—Inches	10
Pulley Face Width—Inches	6.75
Pulley Speed, Loaded—rpm	11.84
Pulley Speed, Loaded—fpm	3100
Power Take-Off—Standard, Optional	Opt.
Is Power to P.T.O. Continuous?	Yes
P.T.O. Cont. When Gearshifting?	Yes
Engine—Make	Own
Number Cylinders & Displacement	6-194
Rated rpm	1600

Steering—Brakes—Tracks

Steering, Type—Planetary Diff.?	Yes
Steering, Location—In Final Drive?	Yes
Brakes, Actuation—Hydraulic, Mech.	Mech.
Brakes, Type—Contracting Band?	Yes
Brakes, Location—Steering Diff.	SD
Track Face Width, Std.—Inches	8
Ground Contacting Area of Tracks—Square Inches	866

Transmission of Power

Clutch—Dry Disc Spring Loaded?	Yes
Clutch—Semi-Centrifugal?	Yes
Separate Clutch for P.T.O. & B.P.?	Yes
Final Drive—Spur, Chain	Spur
High Gear Ratio	14.6
Low Gear Ratio	68.6
Speeds—Number Forward	6
Speeds—Number Reverse	2

**Excluding air intake and exhaust pipes.

Oliver Crawler "OC-6" Diesel

("OC-6" HC is similar)

THE OLIVER CORPORATION
Chicago, Illinois

General

	Oliver Crawler "OC-18"
Number and Size Plows	12,18-14
Type—Axle, Track	Track
Shipping Weight—Lbs.	31915
Nebraska Test Number	489
Track Tread—Inches	78
Height Overall—Inches	**82.7
Length Overall—Inches	167.1
Wheelbase—Inches	99.3
Cultivating Clearance—Inches	16.3
Hydraulic Power Unit	Opt.

Belt Pulley—P.T.O.—Engine

Pulley Diameter, Standard—Inches	None
Power Take-Off—Standard, Optional	Opt.
Is Power to P.T.O. Continuous?	No
Engine—Make	Herc.
Engine—Model	DFXE
Number Cylinders & Displacement	6-895
Rated rpm	1500

Steering—Brakes—Tracks—Tires

Steering, Type—Planetary Diff., Cam & Lever	†PD
Steering, Location—In Final Drive?	Yes
Brakes, Actuation—Hyd., Mech.	†Hyd.
Brakes, Type—Contracting Band?	Yes
Brakes, Location—Steering Diff., Bull Pinion Shafts	SD
Track Face Width, Std.—Inches	22
(Optional)	24, 26
Ground Contacting Area of Tracks—Square Inches	4411

Transmission of Power

Clutch—Single or Double Disc	DD
Clutch—Dry Disc Overcenter?	Yes
Separate Clutch for P.T.O. & B.P.?	None
Final Drive—Spur, Chain	Spur
High Gear Ratio	24.13
Low Gear Ratio	87.27
Speeds—Number Forward	4
Speeds—Number Reverse	2

Oliver Crawler "OC-18"

THE OLIVER CORPORATION
Chicago, Illinois

**Excluding air intake and exhaust pipes.
†Air operated is optional.

General

	Oliver "99 HC&D"
Number and Size Plows	4, 5-14
Type—Axle, Track	Axle
Shipping Weight—Lbs.	7000
Rear Wheel Tread—Inches	57.8
Front Wheel Tread—Inches	53¼
Height Overall—Inches	83.8
Length Overall—Inches	139.5
Wheelbase—Inches	85
Cultivating Clearance—Inches	12
Hydraulic Power Unit	Opt.

Belt Pulley—P.T.O.—Engine

Pulley Diameter, Standard—Inches	13.5
Pulley Face Width—Inches	8¼
Pulley Speed, Loaded—rpm	596
Pulley Speed, Loaded—fpm	3136
Power Take-Off—Standard, Optional.	Opt.
Is Power to P.T.O. Continuous?	No
Engine—Make	Own
Engine—Model (Diesel)	99D
(Gasoline)	99HC
Number Cyl. & Displacement (Diesel)	6-302
(Gasoline)	6-302
Rated rpm	1675

Brakes—Steering—Tires—Tracks

Brakes, Type—Contracting Band, Disc	Disc
Brakes, Location—Wheel Axle Shafts, Steering Differential	WAS
Steering Make—Own, Saginaw	Sag.
Steering Type—Circulating Ball, Planetary Differential	CB
Tire Size—Standard Rear—Inches	14x30
Tire Size—Standard Front—Inches	7.5x18

Transmission of Power

Clutch—Single or Double Plate?	SP
Clutch—Spring Loaded?	Yes
Clutch—Semi Centrifugal?	No
Final Drive—Spur, Chain	Spur
Speeds—Number Forward	4
Speeds—Number Reverse	1

Oliver "99" Diesel

("99" HC is similar)

THE OLIVER CORPORATION
Chicago, Illinois

R. H. SHEPPARD CO., INC.
Hanover, Pennsylvania

Sheppard Diesel "SD4"   1954

General

	Sheppard Diesel "SD4"
Type—Axle, Tricycle, Adj. Axle	T&AA
Shipping Weight, Maximum—Lbs	6250
Nebraska Test Number	None
Rear Tread, Adj. Range—Inches	56-84
Front Tread, Adj. Range—In...(Tri.)	9.2-12.7
(Adj. Axle)	56-80
Height Overall—Inches	83.5
Length Overall—Inches ......(Tri.)	138.2
(Adj. Axel)	140.7
Wheelbase—Inches	91.5
Cultivating Clearance—In. ....(Tri.)	26
(Adj. Axle)	22
Hydraulic Power Unit	Opt.

Belt Pulley—P.T.O.—Engine

Pulley Diameter, Standard—Inches	10
Pulley Face Width—Inches	$7\frac{7}{16}$
Pulley Speed, Loaded—rpm	1150
Pulley Speed, Loaded—fpm	3010
Power Take-Off—Standard, Optional	Opt.
Is Power to P.T.O. Continuous?	Yes
P.T.O. Cont. When Gearshifting?	Yes
Engine—Make	Own
Engine—Model	16
Number Cylinders & Displacement	4-319
Rated rpm ....(Drawbar)	1650
(Belt)	1650

Brakes—Steering—Tires

Brakes, Type—Disc, Int. Expanding	Disc
Brakes, Location—Bull Pinion Shafts, Wheel Shafts	BPS
Brake Units per Tractor	2
Steering Make	Ross
Steering Type—Cam & Lever?	Yes
Tire Size—Standard Rear—Inches	13x38
Tire Size—Standard Front—Inches	6x16

Transmission of Power

Clutch—Dry Disc Spring Loaded?	Yes
Final Drive—Spur, Bevel	Spur
Speeds—Number Forward	10
Speeds—Number Reverse	2

Sheppard Diesel "SD4"

R. H. SHEPPARD CO., INC.
Hanover, Pennsylvania

WILLYS MOTORS, INC.
Toledo, Ohio

Willys Farm Jeep "CJ3B"   1954

General

	Willys Farm Jeep "CJ3B"
Number and Size Plows.............	2-12
Type—Axle, Tricycle, Adj. Axle......	Axle
Shipping Weight, Maximum—Lbs......	2160
Nebraska Test Number.............	502
Rear Tread, Adj. Range—Inches.....	48.2
Front Tread, Adj. Range—In.......	48.2
Height Overall—Inches	66.7
Length Overall—Inches	130
Wheelbase—Inches	80
Cultivating Clearance—In.	8.2
Hydraulic Power Unit..............	Opt.

Belt Pulley—P.T.O.—Engine

Pulley Diameter, Standard—Inches...	8
Pulley Face Width—Inches..........	8
Pulley Speed, Loaded—rpm.........	1714
Pulley Speed, Loaded—fpm.........	3599
Power Take-Off—Standard, Optional.	Opt.
Is Power to P.T.O. Continuous?.....	No
Engine—Make	Own
Engine—Model	CJ3B
Number Cylinders & Displacement...	4-134
Rated rpm ....(Drawbar)	2000
(Belt)	2400

Brakes—Steering—Tires

Brakes, Type—Disc, Int. Expanding..	IE
Brakes, Location—Bull Pinion Shafts, Wheel Shafts	WS
Brake Units per Tractor...........	*4
Steering Make	Ross
Steering Type—Cam & Lever?......	Yes
Tire Size—Standard Rear—Inches...	6x16
Tire Size—Standard Front—Inches..	6x16

Transmission of Power

Clutch—Dry Disc Spring Loaded?....	Yes
Final Drive—Spur, Bevel	Bevel
High Gear Ratio	5.38
Low Gear Ratio	36.57
Speeds—Number Forward	6
Speeds—Number Reverse	2

*Plus mechanically operated hand brake located on propeller shaft.

Willys Farm Jeep "CJ3B"

WILLYS MOTORS, INC.
Toledo, Ohio

Here's Year-Round
FARM POWER...

4-WHEEL-DRIVE
Farm 'Jeep'

REG. U.S. PAT. OFF.

The Farm 'Jeep' is a new development of the famous Universal 'Jeep', designed especially for 365-day-a-year farm use. Four-wheel drive and speed range make possible the wider use of the Farm 'Jeep'. It has 6 forward speeds and selective 2- and 4-wheel drive, thus providing correct speeds for field work and in addition normal highway speeds for hauling. Its 4-wheel drive traction, wide speed range, hydraulic lift and drawbar fit the Farm 'Jeep' for hard, all-year use in the field and around the farm. Power take-off is optional at extra cost.

EXTRA TRACTION
Dependable 4-wheel drive provides the extra traction so often needed for slippery fields and heavy pulling —traction for any work or travel need.

SPEED FOR EVERY NEED
The new Farm 'Jeep' operates at tractor speeds; provides high speed for operating implements such as rotary hoes. Normal road speeds for highway travel.

COMFORT
Heavy-duty springs and folding windshield offer greater comfort, in the field or on the highway. Closed cab, for bad weather, optional at extra cost.

ECONOMY
The Farm 'Jeep' spreads its cost over many kinds of jobs—the year round. It operates under conditions that would stop other power units—saves time. Operating cost is low.

EASE OF OPERATION
Hydraulic lift makes operation of three-point attachment implements easy. Drawbar for use with trailers, wagons or pull type implements.

SAFETY
A low center of gravity and 4-wheel-drive stability mean greater safety on the highway and in the field. Automotive type brakes provide further safety.

WILLYS-OVERLAND MOTORS, TOLEDO 1, OHIO
Makers of America's Most Useful Vehicles

1954

475

1955

In 1955, 14 tractor manufacturers brought out 60 new tractor models. Massey-Harris-Ferguson, Ferguson Division, introduced the TO-35 Standard and Deluxe. Ford Motor Company introduced Models 640, 650, 660, 850 and 860, and the Fordson Major Diesel.

AMERICAN TRACTOR CORP.

Churubusco, Indiana

Terratrac "GT-28"	1955
Terratrac "GT-32"	1955

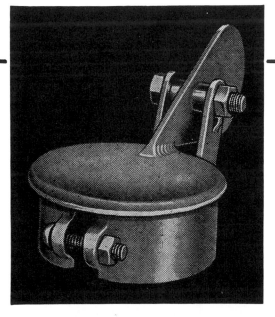

"WEATHERCAP"

Protect your engines all year 'round with "Weathercap", the automatic exhaust pipe cover. "Weathercap" opens and closes instantly by means of engine exhaust. Now used as standard equipment on well known trucks, tractors, combines. Sizes available to fit from 1" to 6-3/16" O.D. exhausts without shimming. Saves cost many times over. Immediate delivery.

ANTHES FORCE OILER COMPANY
Fort Madison, Iowa

Sell your customers tractor driving comfort on the coldest winter days

TRACTOR WARMSEAT

Gives warmth with safety

Your customers are interested in warm, safe tractor driving in winter. TRACTOR WARMSEAT gives them warmth for the entire body, helping to prevent winter colds and body stiffness. Takes heat from the tractor's water system . . . gives comfort with SAFETY because it provides warmth without the danger of engine fumes. DOES NOT INTERFERE WITH MOUNTED EQUIPMENT . . . quickly and easily mounted on any tractor. Heat control standard equipment. Covered by patents.

• Fully guaranteed . . . low in price . . . liberal dealer discounts. WRITE for COMPLETE INFORMATION.

TRACTOR WARMSEAT CO., Hopedale, Ill.

General

	American Tractor Terratrac	
	GT-28	GT-32
Number and Size Plows...............	3-14	3-14
Shipping Weight—Lbs.	3671	4504
Nebraska Test Number, GT 30.......	None	None
Tread, Minimum—Inches	36	36
Tread, Maximum—Inches	72	72
Height, Overall—Inches	65	65
Length, Overall—Inches	98	98
Cultivating Clearance—Inches	18	18
Hydraulic Power Unit.................	Opt.	Opt.

Belt Pulley—P.T.O.—Engine

Pulley Diameter, Standard—Inches...	6	6
Pulley Face Width—Inches..........	7	7
Pulley Speed, Loaded—rpm..........	664	664
Pulley Speed, Loaded—fpm..........	1043	1043
Power Take-Off—Standard, Optional	Opt.	Opt.
Is Power to P.T.O. Continuous?....	No	No
Engine—Make	Cont'l	Cont'l
Engine—Model	F-140	F-140
Number Cylinders & Displacement....	4-140	4-140
Rated rpm	1850	1850

Steering Brakes—Tracks

Steering Brakes Type—Contracting Wet Band?	Yes	Yes
Steering Brakes Location—Diff.?...	Yes	Yes
Track Face Std. Width—In..........	7½	11
Ground Contacting Area of Standard Tracks—Sq. In.	770	1248

Transmission of Power

Clutch—Dry Disc Spring Loaded?....	Yes	Yes
Final Drive—Spur, Chain	Spur	Spur
High Gear Ratio...................	26.21	26.2
Low Gear Ratio	68.27	81.3
Speeds—Number Forward	3	3
Speeds—Number Reverse	1	1

Terratrac "GT-28"

Terratrac "GT-32"

AMERICAN TRACTOR CORP.
Churubusco, Indiana

J. I. CASE CO.
Racine, Wisconsin

Case "DCS"   1955
Case "SC-3"   1955

	J. I. Case **DCS**
General	
Number and Size Plows	3-14
Type—Axle, Tricycle	Axle
Approximate Max. Weight, Std. Equip.	RNA
Nebraska Test Number	None
Rear Tread, Min. & Max.—Inches	70
Front Tread, Min. & Max.—Inches	69½
Height Overall—Inches	70.6
Length Overall—Inches	135¼
Wheelbase—Inches	87¼
Electric Starting—Standard, Optional	Opt.
Cultivating Clearance—Inches	31.0
Hydraulic Power Unit	Std.
Belt Pulley—P.T.O.—Engine	
Pulley Diameter, Standard—Inches	12¼
Pulley Face Width—Inches	7¼
Pulley Speed, Loaded—rpm	818
Pulley Speed, Loaded—fpm	2620
Power Take-off—Standard, Optional	Std.
Is Power to P.T.O. Continuous?	Yes
P.T.O. Cont. When Gearshifting?	Yes
Engine—Make and Model	Own D
Number Cylinders & Displacement	4-276
Rated rpm	1200
Brakes—Steering—Tires	
Brakes Type—Double Disc?	Yes
Brakes Location—Diff. Side Gears?	Yes
Steering Type—Worm & Wheel?	Yes
Tire Size—Std. Rear—Inches	12x38
Tire Size—Standard Front—Inches	7.50x18
Transmission of Power	
Clutch—Wet Single Plate?	Yes
Clutch—O'center, Spg. Loaded	SL
Final Drive—Spur, Chain	Chain
High Gear Ratio	RNA
Low Gear Ratio	RNA
Speeds—Number Forward	4
Speeds—Number Reverse	1

Case "DCS"

J. I. CASE CO.
Racine, Wisconsin

RNA—Manufacturer declines to release the information.

General

	J. I. Case SC-3
Number and Size Plows	2-14
Type—Axle, Tricycle, Adj. Axle	AA&T
Shipping Wt. Max., Std. Equip.—Lbs.	RNA
Nebraska Test Number	496,497
Rear Tread, Adj. Range—Inches	44-80
Front Tread, Adj. Range—In. . (Tri.)	6-13⅛
(Adj. Axle)	56-80
Height Overall—Inches	56.5
Length Overall—Inches	133
Wheelbase—Inches	83.2
Electric Starting—Std., Optional	Opt.
Cultivating Clearance—Inches	23.7
Hydraulic Power Unit	Opt.

Belt Pulley—P.T.O.—Engine

Pulley Diameter, Standard—Inches	9¼
Pulley Face Width—Inches	6⅜
Pulley Speed, Loaded—rpm	1078
Pulley Speed, Loaded—fpm	2600
Power Take-off—Standard, Optional.	Std.
Is Power to P.T.O. Continuous?	Yes
P.T.O. Cont. When Gearshifting?	Yes
Engine—Make	Own
Engine—Model	S
Number Cylinders & Displacement	4-165
Rated rpm	1600

Case "SC-3"

J. I. CASE CO.
Racine, Wisconsin

Brakes—Steering—Tires

Brakes, Type—Disc, Internal Exp.	Disc
Brakes, Location—Diff. Side Gears?	Yes
Steering Type—Worm & Wheel?	Yes
Tire Size—Standard Rear—Inches	10x38
Tire Size—Std. Front—Inches	5x15

Transmission of Power

Clutch—Spring Loaded Single Plate?	Yes
Clutch—Dry, Wet	Wet
Final Drive—Spur, Chain	Chain
High Gear Ratio	RNA
Low Gear Ratio	RNA
Speeds—Number Forward	4
Speeds—Number Reverse	1

RNA—Manufacturer declines to release the information.

DEERE & CO.
Moline, Illinois

John Deere "40" Utility   1955
John Deere "70 Diesel Standard"   1955
John Deere "70 Non Diesel Standard"   1955-1956

General

	John Deere 40 Utility
Type—Track, Tricycle, Adj. Axle....	AA
Shipping Weight on Rubber—Lbs.	2850
Rear Tread, Adj. Range—Inches....	¹41-68.5
Front Tread, Adj. Range—Inches....	55
Height Overall—Inches	64.5
Length Overall—Inches	125.5
Wheelbase—Inches	78.7
Standard Starting—Electric?	Yes
Cultivating Clearance—Inches.......	11.0

Belt Pulley—P.T.O.—Engine

Pulley Diameter, Standard—Inches...	9
Pulley Face Width—Inches..........	6
Pulley Speed, Loaded—rpm..........	1270
Pulley Speed, Loaded—fpm........	3000
Power Take-off—Standard, Optional.	Opt.
Is Standard P.T.O. Continuous?.....	No
Is Continuous P.T.O. Available?.....	No
P.T.O. Cont. When Gearshifting?....	No
Engine—Make	Own
Number Cylinders & Displacement...	2-100.5
Rated rpm	1850

John Deere "40" Utility

DEERE & COMPANY
Moline, Illinois

Brakes—Steering—Tires—Tracks

Brakes, Type—Disc, Contracting....	Disc
Brakes, Location—Steering Clutches, Bull Pinion Shafts	BPS
Steering Type—Cam & Lever.......	C & L
Steering Clutches Type—Mult. Disc?.	None
Track Face Width, Standard—In. ...	None
Tire Size—Standard Rear—Inches...	10x24
Tire Size—Standard Front—Inches..	5x15

Transmission of Power

Clutch—Single Plate	SP
Clutch—Dry, Wet	Dry
Clutch—Spring Loaded, Overcenter..	SL
Final Drive—Spur, Chain...........	Spur
High Gear Ratio..................	18.3
Low Gear Ratio	116.2
Speeds—Number Forward	4
Speeds—Number Reverse	1

¹With power adjusted wheels.

General

	John Deere 70 Std. Non Diesel, Diesel
Number and Size Plows	5-14
Type—Axle, Adj. Axle, Tricycle	Axle
Shipping Weight—Lbs. ..(Non Diesel)	6815
(Diesel)	7140
Nebraska Test Number	None
Rear Tread, Adj. Range—Inches	62-80
Front Tread, Adj. Range—In.	55.5
Height Overall—In.	87.7
Length Overall—Inches	129.8
Wheelbase—Inches	82.0
Hydraulic Power Unit—Std., Optional	Opt.

Belt Pulley—P.T.O.—Engine

Pulley Diameter, Standard—Inches	12⅞
Pulley Speed, Loaded—rpm..(Diesel)	1125
(Non Diesel)	975
Pulley Speed, Loaded—fpm..(Diesel)	3790
(Non Diesel)	3270
Power Take-Off—Standard, Optional.	Std.
Is Standard P.T.O. Continuous?	No
Is Continuous P.T.O. Available?	Yes
P.T.O. Cont. When Gearshifting?	Yes
Engine—Make	Own
Engine—Model	70
No. Cylinders & Displacement	
(Gas & LP-Gas)	2-380
(All Fuel)	2-413
(Diesel)	2-376
Rated rpm ....(Non Diesel)	975
(Diesel)	1125

Brakes—Steering—Tires

Brakes, Type—Internal Expanding?	Yes
Brakes, Location—Separate Shaft?	Yes
Steering Type—Worm & Gear?	Yes
Power Steering—Standard, Optional.	Opt.
Tire Size, Std. Rear—In. (Non Diesel)	14x30
(Diesel)	15x30
Tire Size—Standard Front—Inches	6.5x18

Transmission of Power

Clutch—Multiple Dry Disc O'center?..	Yes
Final Drive—Bevel, Chain, Spur	Spur
High Gear Ratio ....(Diesel)	15.32
Low Gear Ratio ....(Diesel)	77.2
Speeds—Number Forward	6
Speeds—Number Reverse	1

John Deere "70 Non Diesel Std."

John Deere "70 Diesel Std."

DEERE & COMPANY
Moline, Illinois

1955

MASSEY-HARRIS-FERGUSON INC.
Ferguson Division
Racine, Wisconsin

Ferguson "TO-35" Deluxe   1955-1957
Ferguson "TO-35" Standard   1955-1957

	Ferguson TO-35 Standard Deluxe

General

Number and Size Plows............	3-12
Type—Adjustable Axle, Tricycle....	AA
Shipping Weight, Max., ...(Standard)	2850
	2910
Rear Tread, Adj. Range—Inches....	48-76
Front Tread, Adj. Range—Inches..	48-80
Height Overall—Inches	57.0
Length Overall—Inches	116.75
Wheelbase—Inches	72
Cultivating Clearance—Inches	19.75
Hydraulic Power Unit.............	Std.

Belt Pulley—P.T.O.—Engine

Pulley Diameter, Standard—Inches..	9
Pulley Face Width—Inches........	6½
Pulley Speed, Loaded—rpm.........	1316
Pulley Speed, Loaded—fpm........	3100
Power Take-off—Standard, Opt. ..	Std.
Is Power to PTO Cont.? .(Standard)	No
(Deluxe)	Yes
P.T.O. Continuous When Gearshifting?.....(Deluxe)	Yes
Engine—Make	Cont'l
Engine—Model	Z134
Number Cylinders & Displacement...	4-134
Rated rpm	2000

Brakes—Steering—Tires

Brakes, Type—Contracting Band, Internal Expanding Shoes........	IES
Brakes, Location—Bull Pinion Shafts, Wheel Axle Shafts..............	WAS
Steering Make	Saginaw
Steering Type—Cam & Lever, Worm & Ball Nut..............	W&BN
Tire Size—Std. Rear—Inches.......	10x28
Tire Size—Standard Front—Inches.	4x19

Transmission of Power

Clutch—Single or Double Disc. .(Std.)	SD
(Deluxe)	DD
Clutch—Spring Loaded?	Yes
Final Drive—Spur, Bevel..........	Bevel
High Gear Ratio	20.2
Low Gear Ratio	222.22
Speeds—Number Forward	6
Speeds—Number Reverse	2

Ferguson "TO-35"

FERGUSON DIV.
MASSEY-HARRIS-FERGUSON INC.
Racine, Wisconsin

PROOF of the power in a name

You've undoubtedly heard about it . . . the new Ferguson Tractor-Mate Baler. *It's side-mounted,* a bold new concept in baler design.

This revolutionary new harvesting machine is typically *Ferguson* . . . still another startling example of the fresh, uninhibited design approach for which Ferguson is justly famous.

And this sensational, new side-mounted baler is only one of *many* remarkable new things to come, bearing the *Ferguson* name.

It points the way to the profit opportunity of a lifetime for the alert, eyes-to-the-future dealer who has a Ferguson Franchise.

But we can't possibly answer all your questions here.

The thing to do is to find out right now how you can qualify for one of the new Ferguson Franchises.

No matter what line you carry now, wire or write us today for complete details of this outstanding sales opportunity.

Our address is: Ferguson, Racine, Wisc.

YOU'LL SEE MORE AND MORE OF **Ferguson**

FORD MOTOR CO.
Tractor & Implement Division
Birmingham, Michigan

Ford "640"	1955-1957
Ford "650"	1955-1957
Ford "660"	1955-1957
Ford "850"	1955-1957
Ford "860"	1955-1957

	Ford	
	640 650 660	850 860
General		
Number and Size Plows.............	2-14	3-14
Type—Axle, Adjustable Axle........	AA	AA
Shipping Weight on Rubber—Lbs.	2800	2960
Nebraska Test Number............	None	None
Rear Tread, Adj. Range—Inches.....	52-76	52-76
Front Tread, Adj. Range—Inches....	52-76	52-76
Height Overall—Inches	58.7	59.3
Length Overall—Inches	121.4	121.8
Wheelbase—Inches	75.18	75.18
Cultivating Clearance—Inches	21.0	21.0
Hydraulic Power Unit	Std.	Std.

Belt Pulley—P.T.O.—Engine

Pulley Diameter, Standard—Inches...	9	9
Pulley Face Width—Inches.........	6½	6½
Pulley Speed Loaded—rpm...........	1366	1366
Pulley Speed, Loaded—fpm.........	3218	3218
Power Take-Off—Standard, Opt. ...	Std.	Std.
Is Std. PTO Continuous?...(660, 860)	Yes	Yes
(640, 650, 850)	No	No
PTO Cont. When Gearshifting?.....	Yes	Yes
Engine—Make	Own	Own
Engine—Model	EAE	EAF
Number Cylinders & Displacement...	4-134	4-172
Rated rpm	2000	2000

Brakes—Steering—Tires

Brakes, Type—Internal Expanding Shoes, Contracting Band..........	IES	IES
Brakes, Location—Wheel Axle Shafts.	WAS	WAS
Brake Units per Tractor...........	2	2
Steering Type—Worm & Ball Nut.....	W&BN	W&BN
Tire Size—Standard Rear—Inches...	11x28	12x28
Tire Size—Standard Front—Inches...	5.5x16	6x16

Transmission of Power

Clutch—Dry Single Disc, Dry Double Disc......(640, 650, 850)	DSD	DSD
(660, 860)	DDD	DDD
Clutch—Spring Loaded?	Yes	Yes
Final Drive—Bevel, Spur Gear.......	Bevel	Bevel
High Gear Ratio...............(640)	19.85	19.79
Low Gear Ratio...............(640)	73.26	125.8
Speeds—Number Forward .....(640)	4	5
(650, 660)	5	....
Speeds—Number Reverse	1	1

Ford "640, 650 & 660"

Ford "850 & 860"

**TRACTOR & IMPLEMENT DIVISION
FORD MOTOR CO.
Birmingham, Michigan**

Advertised Speeds, mph, With Std. Transmission & Std. Tires—Model 640: 3.7, 4.76, 6.56, 13.67; reverse, 4.28. Models 650 & 660: 2.31, 3.67, 4.95, 6.77, 14.73; reverse, 3.95. Models 850 & 860: 2.22, 3.52, 4.72, 6.48, 14.10; reverse, 3.80.

FORD MOTOR CO.
Dagenham, England

Fordson Major Diesel   1955

General

	Fordson Major Diesel
Type—Axle, Adjustable Axle.........	Axle
Shipping Weight on Rubber—Lbs.	5250
Nebraska Test Number.............	500
Rear Tread, Adj. Range—Inches.....	52-72
Front Tread, Adj. Range—Inches....	50.5-74
Height Overall—Inches	63.0
Length Overall—Inches	130.5
Wheelbase—Inches	80.0
Cultivating Clearance—Inches	19.5
Hydraulic Power Unit..............	Std.

Belt Pulley—P.T.O.—Engine

Belt Pulley—Standard, Optional.....	8.5
Pulley Diameter, Standard—Inches...	6.375
Power Take-Off—Standard, Opt. ...	Std.
Is Power to P.T.O. Continuous?.....	No
Engine—Make	Own
Engine—Model	E1A-DDN
No. Cyl. & Displ.	4-220
Rated rpm	1400

Brakes—Steering—Tires

Brakes, Type—Contracting Band, Internal Expanding Shoes.........	IES
Brakes, Location—Planetary Drum & On Bull Pinion Shaft, Wheel Axle Shafts	WAS
Brake Units per Tractor...........	2
Steering Type—Steering Clutches & Brake, Worm & Ball Nut.........	W&BN
Tire Size—Standard Rear—Inches....	14x30
Tire Size—Standard Front—Inches..	7.5x16

Transmission of Power

Clutch—Spring Loaded Double Plate, Spring Loaded Single Plate.......	SLSP
Final Drive—Bevel, Spur Gear, Chain (Rear Wheels)	SG
(Front Wheels)	None
High Gear Ratio	19.4
Low Gear Ratio...................	123.0
Speeds—Number Forward	6
Speeds—Number Reverse	2

Fordson Major Diesel

HARRIS MANUFACTURING CO.
Stockton, California

Harris "F8WC"   1955-1956

General	Harris F8WC
Number and Size Plows	2, 3-14
Type—Axle, Adjustable Axle	Axle
Shipping Weight on Rubber—Lbs.	5200
Nebraska Test Number	479, 519 523
Rear Tread, Adj. Range—Inches	48-76
Front Tread, Adj. Range—Inches	48-76
Height Overall—Inches	66.0
Length Overall—Inches	99.5
Wheelbase—Inches	54.0
Cultivating Clearance—Inches	18.0
Hydraulic Power Unit	Opt.

Belt Pulley—P.T.O.—Engine

Belt Pulley—Standard, Optional	None
Pulley Diameter, Standard—Inches	None
Power Take-Off—Standard, Opt.	Std.
Is Power to P.T.O. Continuous?	No
Engine—Make	Chry.
Engine—Model	Ind. 8
No. Cyl. & Displ.	6-250
Rated rpm	2000

Brakes—Steering—Tires

Brakes, Type—Contracting Band, Internal Expanding Shoes	CB
Brakes, Location—Planetary Drum & On Bull Pinion Shaft, Wheel Axle Shafts	PD & BPS
Brake Units per Tractor	[1]4
Steering Type—Steering Clutches & Brake, Worm & Ball Nut	SC&B
Tire Size—Standard Rear—Inches	13x24
Tire Size—Standard Front—Inches	13x24

Transmission of Power

Clutch—Spring Loaded Double Plate, Spring Loaded Single Plate	SLDP
Final Drive—Bevel, Spur Gear, Chain (Rear Wheels)	SG
(Front Wheels)	Chain
High Gear Ratio	18.5
Low Gear Ratio	117.2
Speeds—Number Forward	8
Speeds—Number Reverse	2

[1]Two on planetary drum and two on the bull pinion shafts.

Harris "F8W"
(F8WC is similar)

HARRIS MFG. CO.
Stockton, California

INTERNATIONAL HARVESTER CO.

Chicago, Illinois

International "400"	1955
International "400D"	1955
McCormick Farmall "100"	1955-1957
McCormick Farmall "100" High Clearance	1955-1957
McCormick Farmall "200"	1955-1957
McCormick Farmall "300"	1955-1957
McCormick Farmall "300" High Clearance	1955-1957
McCormick Farmall "400"	1955-1957
McCormick Farmall "400 Diesel"	1955-1957
McCormick "Super WD9" Diesel	1955-1956
McCormick "Super WDR9"	1955-1956
McCormick "WR9S"	1955-1956

General	International 400	400 Diesel
Number and Size Plows	4-14	4-14
Type—Axle, Tricycle	Axle	Axle
Shipping Wt., Max., on Rubber	5680	6000
Nebraska Test Number	None	None
Rear Tread, Min. & Max.—In.	60	60
Front Tread, Min. & Max.—In.	51	51
Height Overall—Inches	93	92
Length Overall—Inches	130	130
Wheelbase—Inches	82	82
Hydraulic Power Unit	Opt.	Opt.

International "400"

Belt Pulley—P.T.O.—Engine

Pulley Diameter, Standard—Inches	11	11
Pulley Face Width—Inches	7½	7½
Pulley Speed, Loaded—rpm	899	899
Pulley Speed, Loaded—fpm	2588	2588
Power Take-Off—Std., Opt.	Opt.	Opt.
Is Power for P.T.O. Continuous?	Yes	Yes
P.T.O. Cont. When Gearshifting?	Yes	Yes
Engine—Make	Own	Own
Engine—Model	C-264	D-264
Number Cylinders & Displacement	4-264	4-264
Rated rpm	1450	1450

Brakes—Steering—Tires

Brakes, Type—Disc.?	Yes	Yes
Brakes, Location—Bull Pinion Shafts?	Yes	Yes
Steering, Type—Worm & Gear?	Yes	Yes
Tire Size—Standard Rear—Inches	14x30	14x30
Tire Size—Standard Front—Inches	6.5x18	6.5x18

International "400D"

Transmission of Power

Clutch—Dry Disc Spring Loaded?	Yes	Yes
Final Drive—Spur, Chain	Spur	Spur
High Gear Ratio	13.89	13.89
Low Gear Ratio	137.6	137.6
Speeds—Number Forward	10	10
Speeds—Number Reverse	2	2

Advertised Speeds, mph, With Std. Tires & Std. Transmission—Models International 400 & 400 Diesel: 1.63 & 2.42, 2.51 & 3.72, 3.15 & 4.67, 4.38 & 6.49, 10.9 & 16.15; reverse, 2.17 & 3.22.

INTERNATIONAL HARVESTER CO.
Chicago, Illinois

	I-H McCormick Farmall 100	100 High Clear.

General

Number and Size Plows	–1-16 or 2-12–	
Type—Axle, Adjustable Axle	AA	AA
Shipping Weight on Rubber—Lbs.	2600	3020
Nebraska Test Number	None	None
Rear Tread, Adj. Range—Inches	40-68	48-68
Front Tread, Adj. Range—Inches	44-70	44-68
Height Overall—Inches	82	88
Length Overall—Inches	107	115
Wheelbase—Inches	71	71
Cultivating Clearance—Inches	22	27
Hydraulic Power Unit, Std., Optional.	Std.	Std.

Belt Pulley—P.T.O.—Engine

Pulley Diameter, Standard—Inches	8.5	8.5
Pulley Face Width—Inches	6	6
Pulley Speed, Loaded—rpm	1157	1157
Pulley Speed, Loaded—fpm	2574	2574
Power Take-off—Standard, Optional.	Opt.	Opt.
Is Power to P.T.O. Continuous?	No	No
Engine—Make	Own	Own
Engine—Model	C-123	C-123
Number Cylinders & Displacement	4-123	4-123
Rated rpm	1400	1400

Brakes—Steering—Tires

Brakes, Type—Contracting Band?	Yes	Yes
Brakes, Location—Bull Pinion Shafts	BPS	BPS
Steering Make	Own	Own
Steering Type—Worm & Sector?	Yes	Yes
Tire Size—Standard Rear—Inches	9x24	9x36
Tire Size—Standard Front—Inches	5x15	4x19

Transmission of Power

Clutch—Dry Disc Spring Loaded?	Yes	Yes
Final Drive—Spur, Chain	Spur	Spur
High Gear Ratio	15.8	15.8
Low Gear Ratio	68.3	68.3
Speeds—Number Forward	4	4
Speeds—Number Reverse	1	1

Advertised Speeds, mph, With Std. Transmission & Std. Tires—Model 100: 2.32, 3.68, 4.87, 10.0; reverse, 2.87. Model 100 High Clearance: 3.0, 4.87, 6.37, 13.25; reverse, 3.75.

Farmall "100"

INTERNATIONAL HARVESTER CO.
Chicago, Illinois

General

	I-H McCormick Farmall 200
Number and Size Plows	2-14
Type—Adj. Axle, Axle, Tricycle	T&AA
Shipping Wt., Max., on Rubber—Lbs.	3310
Nebraska Test Number	None
Rear Tread, Adj. Range—Inches	48-80
Front Tread, Min.—Inches (A.A.)	59
(Tri.)	6.5
Front Tread, Max.—Inches (Tri.)	12.5
(Adj. Axle)	89
Height Overall—Inches	85
Length Overall—Inches	123
Wheelbase—Inches	82
Electric Starting—Std. or Opt.	Std.
Cultivating Clearance—Inches (A.A.)	23
(Tri.)	23.5
Hydraulic Power Unit	Std.

Belt Pulley—P.T.O.—Engine

Pulley Diameter, Standard—Inches	8½
Pulley Face Width—Inches	6
Pulley Speed, Loaded—rpm	1363
Pulley Speed, Loaded—fpm	3033
Power Take-Off—Standard, Optional.	Opt.
Is Power to P.T.O. Continuous?	No
Engine—Make	Own
Engine—Model	C-123
Number Cylinders & Displacement	4-123
Rated rpm	1650

Brakes—Steering—Tires

Brakes, Type—Contracting Band, Disc	Disc
Brakes, Location—Bull Pinion Shafts?	Yes
Steering, Type—Worm & Gear?	Yes
Tire Size—Std. Rear—Inches	10x36
Tire Size—Std. Front—Inches	5x15

Transmission of Power

Clutch—Dry Disc Spring Loaded?	Yes
Final Drive—Spur, Chain	Spur
High Gear Ratio	23.8
Low Gear Ratio	103.3
Speeds—Number Forward	4
Speeds—Number Reverse	1

Farmall "200"

INTERNATIONAL HARVESTER CO.
Chicago, Illinois

	I-H McCormick Farmall	
General	**300**	**300 High Clear.**
Number and Size Plows..............	3-14	3-14
Type—Axle, Tricycle, Adj. Axle......	T&AA	AA
Shipping Wt., Max., on Rubber...(AA)	5040	5720
(Tricycle)	4800	....
Nebraska Test Number.............	None	None
Rear Tread, Adj. Range—Inches.....	48-93	62-74
Front Tread, Adj. Range—In. ..(AA)	57-90	60-84
(Tri.)	8-17	....
Height Overall—Inches	85	95
Length Overall—Inches	136	149
Wheelbase—Inches	92	94
Cultivating Clearance—Inches..(AA)	19	30
(Tri.)	25½	....
Hydraulic Power Unit..............	Opt.	Opt.

Belt Pulley—P.T.O.—Engine

Pulley Diameter, Standard—Inches...	9¾	9¾
Pulley Face Width—Inches..........	7½	7½
Pulley Speed, Loaded—rpm..........	1081	1081
Pulley Speed, Loaded—fpm..........	2759	2759
Power Take-Off—Standard, Optional.	Opt.	Opt.
Is Power to P.T.O. Continuous?.....	Yes	Yes
P.T.O. Cont. When Gearshifting?....	Yes	Yes
Engine—Make	Own	Own
Engine—Model	C-169	C-169
Number Cylinders & Displacement....	4-169	4-169
Rated—rpm	1750	1750

Farmall "300"

INTERNATIONAL HARVESTER CO.
Chicago, Illinois

Brakes—Steering—Tires

Brakes, Type—Disc.?	Yes	Yes
Brakes, Location—Bull Pinion Shafts?	Yes	Yes
Steering, Type—Worm & Gear?......	Yes	Yes
Tire Size—Standard Rear—Inches...	11x38	11x38
Tire Size—Standard Front—Inches...	5.5x16	6x20

Transmission of Power

Clutch—Dry Disc Spring Loaded?....	Yes	Yes
Final Drive—Spur, Chain...........	Spur	Chain
High Gear Ratio....................	17.97	19.02
Low Gear Ratio	171.8	181.9
Speeds—Number Forward	10	10
Speeds—Number Reverse	2	2

Advertised Speeds, mph, With Std. Transmission & Std. Tires—Model 300: 1.68 & 2.5, 2.58 & 3.82, 3.48 & 5.15, 4.46 & 6.60, 10.87 & 16.11; reverse, 2.1 & 3.12. Model 300 High Clearance: 1.62 & 2.40, 2.48 & 3.67, 3.34 & 4.96, 4.28 & 6.35, 10.45 & 15.49, reverse, 2.02 & 3.0.

General	I-H McCormick Farmall 400	400D
Number and Size Plows	4-14	4-14
Type—Axle or Tricycle or Adj. Axle	T&AA	T&AA
Shipping Wt., Max., on Rubber..(AA)	6190	6615
(Tricycle)	5950	6365
Nebraska Test Number	None	None
Rear Tread, Adj. Range—Inches	50-94	50-94
Front Tread, Adj. Range—In. .(A.A.)	57-90	57-90
(Tricycle)	——8.5-17.5——	
Height Overall—Inches	95	94
Length Overall—Inches	141	141
Wheelbase—Inches	96	96
Cultivating Clearance—In. ....(A.A.)	22.5	22.5
(Tricycle)	26	26
Hydraulic Power Unit	Opt.	Opt.

Belt Pulley—P.T.O.—Engine

Pulley Diameter, Standard—Inches	11	11
Pulley Face Width—Inches	7½	7½
Pulley Speed, Loaded—rpm	899	899
Pulley Speed, Loaded—fpm	2588	2588
Power Take-Off—Standard, Optional.	Opt.	Opt.
Is Power for P.T.O. Continuous?	Yes	Yes
P.T.O. Cont. When Gearshifting?	Yes	Yes
Engine—Make	Own	Own
Engine—Model	C-264	D-264
Number Cylinders & Displacement	4-264	4-264
Rated rpm	1450	1450

Brakes—Steering—Tires

Brakes, Type—Disc?	Yes	Yes
Brakes, Location—Bull Pinion Shafts?	Yes	Yes
Steering, Type—Worm & Gear?	Yes	Yes
Tire Size—Standard Rear—Inches	12x38	12x38
Tire Size—Standard Front—Inches	6x16	6x16

Transmission of Power

Clutch—Dry Disc Spring Loaded?	Yes	Yes
Final Drive—Spur, Chain	Spur	Spur
High Gear Ratio	14.78	14.78
Low Gear Ratio	146.4	146.4
Speeds—Number Forward	10	10
Speeds—Number Reverse	2	2

Advertised Speeds, mph, With Std. Transmission &
Std. Tires—Models 400 & 400D: 1.69 & 2.50, 2.60
& 3.85, 3.26 & 4.82, 4.53 & 6.71, 11.27 & 16.70;
reverse, 2.25 & 3.33.

Farmall "400"

Farmall "400 Diesel"

INTERNATIONAL HARVESTER CO.
Chicago, Illinois

	I-H McCormick Super WD9	McCormick WR-9S Super WDR9

General

	Super WD9	Super WDR9
Number and Size Plows	5-14	5-14
Type—Axle, Tricycle	Axle	Axle
Shipping Wt.—Lbs. ...(WD9, WDR9)	6630	7030
(WR-9S)	....	6700
Nebraska Test Number	518	....
Rear Tread—Inches	60	62
Front Tread—Inches	52	52
Height Overall—Inches	82	83
Length Overall—Inches	134	140
Wheelbase—Inches	83	83
Hydraulic Power Unit	Opt.	Opt.

Belt Pulley—P.T.O.—Engine

Pulley Diameter, Standard—Inches	14	14
Pulley Face Width—Inches	8½	8½
Pulley Speed, Loaded—rpm	707	707
Pulley Speed, Loaded—fpm	2593	2593
Power Take-Off—Standard, Optional	Opt.	Opt.
Is Power to P.T.O. Continuous?	No	No
Engine—Make	Own	Own
Engine—Model (Gasoline)	....	C-335
(Diesel)	D-350	D-350
No. Cylinders & Displacement.(Diesel)	4-350	4-350
(Gasoline)	....	4-335
Rated rpm	1500	1500

McCormick "Super WD 9" Diesel

Brakes—Steering—Tires

Brakes, Type—Cont. Band, Disc	Disc	Disc
Brakes, Location—Bull Pinion Shafts?	Yes	Yes
Steering Make	Ross	Ross
Steering Type—Cam & Lever?	Yes	Yes
Tire Size—Rubber Rear—Inches	14x34	15x34
Tire Size—Rubber Front—Inches	7.5x18	7.5x18

Transmission of Power

Clutch—Dry, Single Plate?	Yes	Yes
Clutch—Spring Loaded, Overcenter	SL	OC
Final Drive—Spur, Chain	Spur	Spur
High Gear Ratio	15.9	15.9
Low Gear Ratio	105.7	105.7
Speeds—Number Forward	5	5
Speeds—Number Reverse	1	1

Advertised Speeds, mph, With Std. Transmission & Std. Rubber Tires—Model Super WD9: 2.32, 3.12, 4.5, 5.5, 15.75; reverse, 2.87. Models WR9S & Super WDR9: 2.5, 3.32, 4.75, 5.80, 16.75; reverse, 3.12.

McCormick "WR9S"

INTERNATIONAL HARVESTER CO.
Chicago, Illinois

1955

493

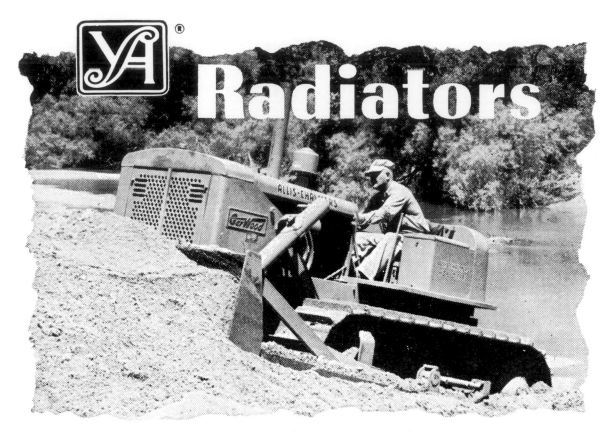

YA Radiators

. . . built rugged for rough going . . .

Where the going is rough and the job is tough, that's where you will find a quality YA Radiator on the job meeting the demands for efficient cooling. YA Radiators can take it. Illustrated is a crawler tractor feeding sand to a dragline from a river sand pit. The tractor is equipped with a YA Radiator that will stand up under the vibrations and stress of crawler tractor operation where load factor is very high. YA Radiators are used on this type of construction machinery the world over. Perhaps the equipment you manufacture calls for this type of radiator equipment . . . a letter from you will bring complete information on YA radiators.

Write Yates-American, Beloit, Wis., U.S.A.

California Representative E E Richter & Son, Emeryville, California

JENSEN TRACTOR MANUFACTURING CO.
Burbank, California

Jensen "Farmaster 150"   1955

General

	Jensen 150
Number and Size Plows	1-14
Type—Axle, Adjustable Axle	Axle
Nebraska Test Number	None
Rear Tread, Adj. Range—Inches	33-48
Front Tread, Adj. Range—Inches	34.5
Height Overall—Inches	58.0
Length Overall—Inches	91.0
Wheelbase—Inches	62
Cultivating Clearance—Inches	19.5
Hydraulic Power Unit	Opt.

Belt Pulley—P.T.O.—Engine

Pulley Diameter, Standard—Inches	4
Pulley Face Width—Inches	4
Pulley Speed, Loaded—rpm	2200
Pulley Speed, Loaded—fpm	2300
Power Take-Off—Standard, Optional	Opt.
Is Power to P.T.O. Continuous?	Yes
Engine—Make	Wis.
Engine—Model	TFU
No. Cylinders & Displacement	2-54

Brakes—Steering—Tires

Brakes, Type—Internal Expanding, Contracting Band	CB
Brakes, Location—Rear Wheels, Bull Pinion Shafts	BPS
Steering, Type, Cam & Lever, Worm & Gear	W&G
Tire Size—Standard Rear—Inches	7x24
Tire Size—Standard Front—Inches	4x12

Transmission of Power

Clutch—Single Plate?	Yes
Final Drive—Spur, Bevel Gears	Spur
High Gear Ratio	39.45
Low Gear Ratio	102.78
Speeds—Number Forward	3
Speeds—Number Reverse	1

Jensen "Farmaster 150"

JENSEN TRACTOR MFG. CO.
Burbank, California

MASSEY-HARRIS-FERGUSON INC.
Massey-Harris Division

Racine, Wisconsin

Massey-Harris "44D" Special (Row Crop)   1955
Massey-Harris "44D" Special (Standard)   1955
Massey-Harris "44" Special Non Diesel (Row Crop) 1955
Massey-Harris "44" Special Non Diesel (Standard) 1955

General

	Massey-Harris 44 Special Diesel	
	RC	Std.
Number and Size Plows	3, 4-14	3, 4-14
Type—Axle, Adj. Axle, Tricycle	AA&T	Axle
Shipping Weight, Maximum—Lbs.	5160	5275
Nebraska Test Number	....	426
Rear Tread, Adj. Range—In	57-88.2	58-62
Front Tread, Adj. Range—In ... (Tri.)	8.5-14.5	52.1
(Adj. Axle)	52-72.2	....
Height Overall—Inches (Tri.)	80.2	75.5
(Adj. Axle)	79.2	....
Length Overall—Inches	134.5	136.6
Wheelbase—Inches	88	88
Cultivating Clearance—Inches	25	22.6
Hydraulic Power Unit	Opt.	Opt.

Belt Pulley—P.T.O.—Engine

	RC	Std.
Pulley Diameter, Standard—Inches	13½	13½
Pulley Face Width—Inches	6.5	6.5
Pulley Speed, Loaded—rpm	890	890
Pulley Speed, Loaded—fpm	3146	3146
Power Take-Off—Standard, Optional	Opt.	Opt.
Is Power to P.T.O. Continuous?	No	No
Is Non Continuous P.T.O. Available?	Yes	Yes
Is Continuous P.T.O. Available?	Yes	Yes
P.T.O. Cont. When Gearshifting?	No	No
Engine—Make	Own	Own
Engine—Model	HD-260	HD-260
Number Cylinders & Displacement	4-260	4-260
Rated rpm	1350	1350

Brakes—Steering—Tires

	RC	Std.
Brakes, Type—Int. Exp. Shoe, Disc	Either	Either
Brakes, Location—Diff. Shafts?	Yes	Yes
Steering Type—Worm & Sector?	Yes	Yes
Tire Size—Std. Rear—Inches	13x38	13x30
Tire Size—Std. Front—Inches (AA)	6.5x16	7.5x16
(Dual Wheel Tri.)	6.5x16	....
(Single Wheel Tri.)	9x10	....

Transmission of Power

	RC	Std.
Clutch—Dry Disc Spring Loaded?	[1]Yes	[1]Yes
Final Drive—Spur, Chain	Spur	Spur
Speeds—Number Forward	5	5
Speeds—Number Reverse	1	1

Advertised Speeds, mph, With Std. Transmission & Std. Tires. Tricycle and Adj. Axle Models: 2.6, 2.74, 4.66, 6.52, 13.07; reverse, 3.02.

[1]Orchard and vineyard models have a Rockford over-center type.

Massey-Harris "44D" Special (RC)

**MASSEY-HARRIS DIV.
MASSEY-HARRIS-FERGUSON INC.
Racine, Wisconsin**

General

	Massey-Harris 44 Special Non Diesel	
	RC	Std.
Number and Size Plows..............	3, 4-14	3, 4-14
Type—Axle, Adj. Axle, Tricycle	AA&T	Axle
Shipping Weight, Maximum—Lbs.....	5210	5185
Nebraska Test Number..............	....	427
	....	510
Rear Tread, Adj. Range—In........	57-88.2	58-62
Front Tread, Adj. Range—In. (Tri.)	8.5-14.5	52.1
(Adj. Axle)	52-72.2	....
Height Overall—Inches ....(Tri.)	80.2	75.5
(Adj. Axle)	79.2	....
Length Overall—Inches	134.5	136.6
Wheelbase—Inches	88	88
Cultivating Clearance—Inches	25	22.6
Hydraulic Power Unit	Opt.	Opt.

Belt Pulley—P.T.O.—Engine

Pulley Diameter, Standard—Inches...	13½	13½
Pulley Face Width—Inches	6.5	6.5
Pulley Speed, Loaded—rpm..........	890	890
Pulley Speed, Loaded—fpm..........	3146	3146
Power Take-Off—Standard, Optional	Opt.	Opt.
Is Power to P.T.O. Continuous?....	No	No
Is Non Continuous P.T.O. Available?	Yes	Yes
Is Continuous P.T.O. Available?.....	Yes	Yes
P.T.O. Cont. When Gearshifting?....	No	No
Engine—Make	Own	Own
Engine—Model ....(44K, 44LP)	H-260	H-260
(44G)	H-277	H-277
No. Cyl. & Displacement (44K, 44LP)	4-260	4-260
(44G)	4-277	4-277
Rated rpm	1350	1350

Brakes—Steering—Tires

Brakes, Type—Int. Exp. Shoe, Disc.	Either	Either
Brakes,Location—Diff. Shafts?......	Yes	Yes
Steering Type—Worm & Sector?....	Yes	Yes
Tire Size—Std. Rear—Inches	13x38	13x30
Tire Size—Std. Front—Inches..(AA)	6.5x16	7.5x16
(Dual Wheel Tri.)	6.5x16	....
(Single Wheel Tri.)	9x10	....

Transmission of Power

Clutch—Dry Disc Spring Loaded?....	[1]Yes	[1]Yes
Final Drive—Spur, Chain	Spur	Spur
Speeds—Number Forward	5	5
Speeds—Number Reverse	1	1

Advertised Speeds, mph, With Std. Transmission & Std. Tires—Tricycle and Adj. Axle Models: 2.4, 3.6, 4.8, 6.25, 13.38; reverse, 3.16.

[1]Orchard and vineyard models have a Rockford over-center type.

Massey-Harris "44LP" Special

Massey-Harris "44" Special (RC)

MASSEY-HARRIS DIV.
MASSEY-HARRIS-FERGUSON INC.
Racine, Wisconsin

From planting time

Massey-Harris 44 Diesel Tractor and 22 Spring Tooth Harrow

to harvest time

Massey-Harris 33 Tractor and Number 20 Forage Clipper

...he deserves the best!

Caution!

Full-flow lubrication systems require oil filters that have very high oil flow rates, *plus* ultra-fine particle filtration. In by far the majority of Diesel engines, the manufacturer has specified a Purolator Micronic* Filter.

When some substitute filter refills are used in a full-flow system, they cannot handle sufficient volume of oil. The by-pass valve will open and allow dangerous unfiltered oil to reach the engine.

Play it safe! Sell only the oil filter refill recommended by the machine manufacturer . . . in most cases, Purolator!

YOUR customers look to you for helpful advice on equipment maintenance. One of the best ways to help insure them of dependable service is by stressing the importance of using only manufacturer-approved replacement parts.

Take oil filters for example. The filter that you supply is the right one for the job . . . your manufacturer's research and development prove this. However, a filter that does not adequately meet your customer's needs can ruin his engine in hours.

You can help your customers and build your reputation as well, by explaining the risk involved when substitute filter refills are used. *Stock and sell only manufacturer-approved oil filter refills.*

Nine times out of ten you'll find that Purolator* is the right filter refill. Why? Because by far the majority of farm tractor manufacturers supply Purolators as original equipment! *Reg. U. S. Pat. Off.

Purolator Products, Inc., Rahway, New Jersey, and Toronto, Ontario, Canada

MINNEAPOLIS-MOLINE CO.
Minneapolis, Minnesota

Minneapolis-Moline "BFH"	1955-1957
Minneapolis-Moline "GB" Non Diesel	1955
Minneapolis-Moline "GB" Diesel	1955
Minneapolis-Moline "UB" Type E	1955-1957
Minneapolis-Moline "UB" Type N	1955-1957
Minneapolis-Moline "UB" Type U	1955

General

Minneapolis-Moline BFH

Number and Size Plows	2-14
Type—Axle, Tricycle, Adj. Axle	AA&T
Shipping Wt., Max., on Rubber—Lbs.	2900
Nebraska Test Number	469
Front Tread, Adj. Range—In. (A.A.)	52-76
(Tri.)	6.8-13.6
Rear Tread, Adj. Range—In. (A.A.)	52-76
Height Overall—Inches	76
Length Overall—Inches (A.A.)	119
(Tri.)	116
Wheelbase—Inches (A.A.)	81.6
(Dual Wheel Tri.)	79.0
(Single Wheel Tri.)	78.6
Cultivating Clearance—Inches (A.A.)	22
(Tri.)	26
Hydraulic Power Unit	Std.

Belt Pulley—P.T.O.—Engine

Pulley Diameter, Standard—Inches	10
Pulley Face Width—Inches	6.5
Pulley Speed, Loaded—rpm	1160
Pulley Speed, Loaded—fpm	3037
Power Take-off—Standard, Optional	Opt.
Is Power to P.T.O. Continuous?	No
Engine—Make	Herc.
Engine—Model	IXB3SL
Number Cylinders & Displacement	4-133
Rated rpm	1800

Brakes—Steering—Tires

Brakes, Type—Contracting Band?	Yes
Brakes, Location—Bull Pinion Shafts?	Yes
Steering Make	Own
Steering, Type—Cam & Lever, Worm & Gear	W&G
Tire Size—Standard Rear—Inches	10x28
Tire Size—Std. Front—Inches (A.A.)	5x15
(Tri. Single)	6x16
(Tri. Dual)	5x15

Transmission of Power

Clutch—Dry Disc Spring Loaded?	Yes
Final Drive—Spur, Chain	Spur
High Gear Ratio	17.87
Low Gear Ratio	97.22
Speeds—Number Forward	4
Speeds—Number Reverse	1

Minneapolis-Moline "BFH"

MINNEAPOLIS-MOLINE COMPANY
Minneapolis, Minnesota

General

	Minneapolis-Moline	
	GB Non Diesel	GB Diesel
Number and Size Plows	5-14	5-14
Type—Axle, Adjustable Axle	Axle	Axle
Shipping Wt., Max.,	6600	7400
Nebraska Test Number	None	None
Rear Tread—Inches	66	66
Front Tread—Inches	54.2	54.2
Height Overall—Inches	72.5	72.5
Length Overall, Max.—In.	137.5	151.3
Wheelbase—Inches	82.5	96.1
Cultivating Clearance—In.	14.75	14.75
Hydraulic Power Unit	Opt.	Opt.

Belt Pulley—P.T.O.—Engine

Pulley Diameter, Standard—Inches	16	16
Pulley Face Width—Inches	7	7
Pulley Speed, Loaded—rpm	741	741
Pulley Speed, Loaded—fpm	3110	3110
Power Take-off—Standard, Optional.	Opt.	Opt.
Is Non Continuous P.T.O. Available?.	Yes	Yes
Is Cont. P.T.O. Avaliable?	Yes	Yes
P.T.O. Cont. When Gearshifting?	No	No
Engine—Make	Own	Own
Engine—Model	403C	D425
No. Cyl. & Displacement	4-403	6-425
Rated rpm	1300	1300

Brakes—Steering—Tires

Brakes, Type—Disc?	Yes	Yes
Brakes, Location—Bull Pin. Shafts?.	Yes	Yes
Steering Make	Ross	Ross
Steering, Type—Cam & Lever, Worm & Sector?	C&L	C&L
Tire Size—Std. Rear—In.	15x34	15x34
Tire Size—Standard Front—Inches..	7.5x18	7.5x18

Transmission of Power

Clutch—Dry Disc Overcenter?	Yes	Yes
Final Drive—Spur, Bevel Gear	Spur	Spur
High Gear Ratio	13.33	14.52
Low Gear Ratio	73.83	80.42
Speeds—Number Forward	5	5
Speeds—Number Reverse	1	1

Minneapolis-Moline "GB"
(GB Diesel is similar)

MINNEAPOLIS-MOLINE COMPANY
Minneapolis, Minnesota

General

	Minneapolis-Moline UB Type E	Minneapolis-Moline UB Type N
Number and Size Plows	4-14	4-14
Type—Axle, Tri., Adj. Axle	AA	Tri.
Shipping Wt., Max., on Rubber—Lbs.	5700	5700
Nebraska Test Number	None	None
Rear Tread, Minimum—Inches	54.5	54.5
Rear Tread, Maximum—Inches	84.5	96
Front Tread, Adj. Range—Inches	56-84	....
Height Overall—Inches	78.5	78.5
Length Overall—Inches	133	141
Wheelbase—Inches	96	88
Cultivating Clearance—Inches	20	25
Hydraulic Power Unit	Opt.	Opt.

Belt Pulley—P.T.O.—Engine

Pulley Diameter, Standard—Inches	16	16
Pulley Face Width—Inches	7	7
Pulley Speed, Loaded—rpm	741	741
Pulley Speed, Loaded—fpm	3110	3110
Power Take-Off—Standard, Optional	Opt.	Opt.
Is Non Continuous P.T.O. Available?	Yes	Yes
Is Continuous P.T.O. Available?	Yes	Yes
P.T.O. Cont. When Gearshifting?	No	No
Engine—Make	Own	Own
Engine—Model .....(Gasoline & LPG)	283B	283B
(Diesel)	D283	D283
Number Cylinders & Displacement	4-283	4-283
Rated rpm	1300	1300

Minneapolis-Moline "UB" Type E

Brakes—Steering—Tires

Brakes, Type—Disc?	Yes	Yes
Brakes, Location—Bull Pin. Shafts?	Yes	Yes
Steering Make	Ross	Own
Type—Cam & Lever, Worm & Sector?	C&L	W&S
Tire Size—Standard Rear—Inches	12x38	12x38
Tire Size—Standard Front—Inches	6x16	9x10

Transmission of Power

Clutch—Dry Single Disc?	Yes	Yes
Clutch—Spring Loaded, Overcenter	OC	SL
Final Drive—Spur, Chain	Spur	Spur
High Gear Ratio	14.52	14.52
Low Gear Ratio	80.42	80.42
Speeds—Number Forward	5	5
Speeds—Number Reverse	1	1

Minneapolis-Moline "UB" Type N

Advertised Speeds, mph, With Standard Tires & Standard Transmission—All Models: 2.7, 3.9, 4.5, 6.5, 15.1; reverse, 2.1.

MINNEAPOLIS-MOLINE COMPANY
Minneapolis, Minnesota

General

	Minneapolis-Moline UB Type U
Number and Size Plows	4-14
Type—Axle, Tri., Adj. Axle	Tri.
Shipping Wt., Max., on Rubber—Lbs.	5700
Nebraska Test Number	520, 522
Rear Tread, Minimum—Inches	54.5
Rear Tread, Maximum—Inches	84½
Front Tread, Adj. Range—Inches	8⅜-13
Height Overall—Inches	78.5
Length Overall—Inches	133
Wheelbase—Inches	88
Hydraulic Power Unit	Opt.

Belt Pulley—P.T.O.—Engine

Pulley Diameter, Standard—Inches	16
Pulley Face Width—Inches	7
Pulley Speed, Loaded—rpm	741
Pulley Speed, Loaded—fpm	3110
Power Take-Off—Standard, Optional	Opt.
Is Non Continuous P.T.O. Available?	Yes
Is Continuous P.T.O. Available?	Yes
P.T.O. Cont. When Gearshifting?	No
Engine—Make	Own
Engine—Model ....(Gasoline & LPG)	283B
(Diesel)	D283
Number Cylinders & Displacement	4-283
Rated rpm	1300

Brakes—Steering—Tires

Brakes, Type—Disc?	Yes
Brakes, Location—Bull Pin. Shafts?	Yes
Steering Make	Own
Type—Cam & Lever, Worm & Sector?	W&S
Tire Size—Standard Rear—Inches	12x38
Tire Size—Standard Front—Inches	6x16

Transmission of Power

Clutch—Dry Single Disc?	Yes
Clutch—Spring Loaded, Overcenter	SL
Final Drive—Spur, Chain	Spur
High Gear Ratio	14.52
Low Gear Ratio	80.42
Speeds—Number Forward	5
Speeds—Number Reverse	1

Minneapolis-Moline "UB" Type U

MINNEAPOLIS-MOLINE COMPANY
Minneapolis, Minnesota

MOUNTAIN STATE FABRICATING CO.
Clarksburg, West Virginia

Silver King "370"   1955-1956
Silver King "371"   1955-1956

General

	Silver King 370
Number and Size Plows	2-14
Type—Axle, Tricycle, Adj. Axle	Tri.
Shipping Weight, Maximum—Lbs.	3550
Nebraska Test Number	[1]424
Rear Tread, Adj. Range—Inches	56-84
Height Overall—Inches	78
Length Overall—Inches	131
Wheelbase—Inches	83.75
Cultivating Clearance—In.	23
Hydraulic Power Unit	Opt.

Belt Pulley—P.T.O.—Engine

Pulley Diameter, Standard—Inches	6.6
Pulley Face Width—Inches	8
Pulley Speed, Loaded—rpm	1800
Pulley Speed, Loaded—fpm	3108
Power Take-Off—Standard, Opt.	Opt.
Is Power to P.T.O. Continuous?	No
P.T.O. Cont. When Gearshifting?	No
Engine—Make	Cont'l.
Engine—Model	F162
Number Cylinders & Displacement	4-162
Rated rpm	1800

Brakes—Steering—Tires

Brakes, Type—Disc, Cont. Band	CB
Brakes, Location—Bull Pinion Shafts.	BPS
Brake Units per Tractor	2
Steering Make	Ross
Steering Type—Cam & Lever?	Yes
Tire Size—Standard Rear—Inches	10x38
Tire Size—Standard Front—Inches	7.5x16

Transmission of Power

Clutch—Dry Disc Spring Loaded?	Yes
Final Drive—Spur, Bevel	Spur
High Gear Ratio	15.13
Low Gear Ratio	108.0
Speeds—Number Forward	4
Speeds—Number Reverse	1

[1]Tested as Silver King 3 Wheel Row Crop when Manufactured by the Fate-Root-Heath Co., Plymouth, Ohio.

Silver King "370"

MOUNTAIN STATE FABRICATING CO.
Clarksburg, West Virginia

General

	Silver King 371
Number and Size Plows	2-14
Type—Axle, Tricycle, Adj. Axle	Axle
Shipping Weight, Maximum—Lbs.	2910
Rear Tread, Adj. Range—Inches	44-72
Front Tread, Adj. Range—Inches	48
Height Overall—Inches	73
Length Overall—Inches	113.7
Wheelbase—Inches	66.31
Cultivating Clearance—Inches	16.5
Hydraulic Power Unit	Opt.

Belt Pulley—P.T.O.—Engine

Pulley Diameter, Standard—Inches	6.6
Pulley Face Width—Inches	8
Pulley Speed, Loaded—rpm	1800
Pulley Speed, Loaded—fpm	3108
Power Take-Off—Standard, Optional	Opt.
Is Power to P.T.O. Continuous?	No
P.T.O. Cont. When Gearshifting?	No
Engine—Make	Cont'l.
Engine—Model	F162
Number Cylinders & Displacement	4-162
Rated rpm (Drawbar)	1800
(Belt)	1800

Brakes—Steering—Tires

Brakes, Type—Internal Expanding, Contracting Band	CB
Brakes, Location—Bull Pinion Shafts, Wheel Shafts	BPS
Brake Units per Tractor	2
Steering Make	Ross
Steering Type—Cam & Lever?	Yes
Tire Size—Standard Rear—Inches	11x28
Tire Size—Standard Front—Inches	6.5x16

Transmission of Power

Clutch—Dry Disc Spring Loaded?	Yes
Final Drive—Spur, Bevel	Spur
High Gear Ratio	13.02
Low Gear Ratio	92.95
Speeds—Number Forward	4
Speeds—Number Reverse	1

Advertised Speeds, mph, With Std. Transmission & Std. Tires—Silver King 371: 2.6, 4.3, 5.77, 18.63; reverse, 1.92.

Silver King "371"

MOUNTAIN STATE FABRICATING CO.
Clarksburg, West Virginia

THE OLIVER CORP.
Chicago, Illinois

Oliver "Super 55" Diesel	1955
Oliver "Super 55" HC	1955
Oliver "Super 66" Row Crop Diesel	1955
Oliver "Super 66" Row Crop HC	1955
Oliver "Super 77" Row Crop Diesel	1955-1956
Oliver "Super 77" Row Crop HC	1955-1956
Oliver "Super 77" Standard Diesel	1955-1956
Oliver "Super 77" Standard HC	1955-1956
Oliver "Super 88" Row Crop Diesel	1955-1956
Oliver "Super 88" Row Crop HC	1955-1956
Oliver "Super 88" Standard Diesel	1955-1956
Oliver "Super 88" Standard HC	1955-1956
Oliver "Super 99" Diesel	1955
Oliver "Super 99" HC	1955
Oliver Crawler "OC-12" Diesel	1955
Oliver Crawler "OC-12" HC	1955

Power
...in any size
and type!

OLIVER dealers have a twofold advantage. For *only* Oliver builds a *full line of diesel-powered tractors,* from the 2-plow "66" to the 4-5 plow "99". Secondly, Oliver offers a full range of *crawler* tractors, from the 2-plow "OC-3" to the mighty Model "D".

The *complete* Oliver line provides more profit opportunities. There's a size and type that meets the farmer's *exact* needs —his acreage, his working conditions, his cropping practices.

Besides that, Oliver dealers handle the most *modern* tractors made. Six forward speeds, Direct Drive Power Take-Off, six cylinder engine, rubber spring seat, double-disc brakes, "Hydra-lectric" control system—all these advancements help clinch sales . . . bring bigger returns and assure a brighter business future. The OLIVER Corporation, 400 West Madison Street, Chicago 6, Illinois.

"Grow with OLIVER—the Business Builder"  **OLIVER**

General	Oliver Super 55 HC & Diesel	Oliver Super 66RC
Number and Size Plows	....	2-14
Type—Axle, Adj. Axle, Tricycle	AA	T&AA
Shipping Wt., Std. Equip.—Lbs. . . (HC)	2833	2548
(Diesel)	2933	2648
Nebraska Test Number	524, 526	....
Rear Tread, Adj. Range—Inches	48-76	60-68
Front Tread, Adj. Range—In. . . . (Tri.)	48-76	6.3-11.5
(Adj. Axle)	....	50.7-87
Height Overall—Inches	70.3	85.2
Length Overall—Inches	120	134.3
Wheelbase—Inches	73	86.7
Cultivating Clearance—Inches	20	24.3
Hydraulic Power Unit	Std.	Opt.

Oliver "Super 55"

Belt Pulley—P.T.O.—Engine

Pulley Diameter, Standard—Inches	9	9.5
Pulley Face Width—Inches	6.5	7.25
Pulley Speed, Loaded—rpm	1319	1234
Pulley Speed, Loaded—fpm	1450	3068
Power Take-Off—Standard, Optional.	Opt.	Opt.
Is Power to P.T.O. Continuous?	Yes	Yes
P.T.O. Cont. When Gearshifting?	Yes	Yes
Engine—Make	Own	Own
Number Cylinders & Displacement	4-144	4-144
Rated rpm	2000	2000

Brakes—Steering—Tires

Brakes, Type—Double Disc?	Yes	Yes
Brakes, Location—Bull Gear Pinions?.	Yes	Yes
Steering, Type—Worm & Sector, Circulating Ball . . . . (Tricycle)	....	W&S
(Adj. Axle)	CB	CB
Tire Size—Standard Rear—Inches	10x28	9x38
Tire Size—Standard Front—Inches	5.5x16	5x15

Oliver "Super 66" R. C.

Transmission of Power

Clutch—Dry Disc Spring Loaded?	Yes	Yes
Final Drive—Spur, Chain	Spur	Spur
High Gear Ratio	18.0	21.65
Low Gear Ratio	141.0	100.39
Speeds—Number Forward	6	6
Speeds—Number Reverse	2	2

Advertised Speeds, mph, With Standard Transmission and Standard Tires—Super 55@2000 rpm: 1.82, 2.80, 3.76, 5.78, 6.92, 14.25; reverse, 2.05, 4.23. Super 66@2000 rpm: 2.36, 3.4, 4.07, 5.87, 6.93, 11.94; reverse, 2.69, 4.63.

THE OLIVER CORPORATION
Chicago, Illinois

1955

General

	Oliver Super 77	
	Standard HC & Diesel	Row Crop
Number and Size Plows.............	2, 3-14	2, 3-14
Type—Axle, Adj. Axle, Tricycle......	Axle	T&AA
Shipping Wt., Std. Equip.—Lbs. ..(HC)	3169	3623
(Diesel)	3347	3801
Rear Tread, Adj. Range—Inches.....	47-52½	60-92½
Front Tread, Adj. Range—In. (A,Tri.)	49-54⅜	8-12½
(Adj. Axle)	....	60-89¾
Height Overall—Inches..............	[1]69.5	[1]75
Length Overall—Inches	129¾	139¼
Wheelbase—Inches	78¼	90¾
Cultivating Clearance—Inches	11¾	24⅞
Hydraulic Power Unit..............	Opt.	Opt.

Belt Pulley—P.T.O.—Engine

Pulley Diameter, Standard—Inches...	11⅞	11⅞
Pulley Face Width—Inches..........	7¼	7¼
Pulley Speed, Loaded—rpm..........	992	992
Pulley Speed, Loaded—fpm..........	3080	3080
Power Take-Off, Standard, Optional.	Opt.	Opt.
Is Power to P.T.O. Continuous?.....	Yes	Yes
P.T.O. Cont. When Gearshifting?....	Yes	Yes
Engine—Make	Own	Own
Number Cylinders & Displacement	6-216	6-216
Rated rpm	1600	1600

Brakes—Steering—Tires

Brakes, Type—Double Disc?........	Yes	Yes
Brakes, Location—Bull Gear Pinions?	Yes	Yes
Steering, Type—Worm & Sector, Circulating Ball ....(Tricycle)	CB	W&S
(Adj. Axle)		CB
Tire Size—Standard Rear—Inches...	12x26	11x38
Tire Size—Standard Front—Inches..	5.5x16	5.5x16

Transmission of Power

Clutch—Dry Disc Spring Loaded?....	Yes	Yes
Final Drive—Spur, Chain...........	Spur	Spur
High Gear Ratio...................	18.64	**22.94**
Low Gear Ratio...................	87.05	**107.17**
Speeds—Number Forward	[2]6	[2]6
Speeds—Number Reverse...........	[2]2	[2]2

Advertised Speeds, mph, With Standard Transmission and Standard Tires—All Models: 2.45, 3.22, 4.27, 5.62, 6.58, 11.47; reverse, 2.58, 4.5. [1]To top of steering wheel. [2]Also available with 4 forward and 4 reverse speeds.

Oliver "Super 77"

THE OLIVER CORPORATION
Chicago, Illinois

General

	Oliver Super 88	
	Standard HC & Diesel	Row Crop
Number and Size Plows..............	3, 4-14	3, 4-14
Type—Axle, Adj. Axle, Tricycle......	Axle	T&AA
Shipping Wt., Std. Equip.—Lbs...(HC)	4237	4597
(Diesel)	4452	4812
Nebraska Test Number..............	—525, 527—	
Rear Tread, Adj. Range—Inches.....	34-62	60-92½
Front Tread, Adj. Range—In. (A, Tri.)	49-54¾	8-12⅛
(Adj. Axle)	....	60-89¾
Height Overall—Inches..............	[1]69.6	[1]75
Length Overall—Inches	133¾	143⅝
Wheelbase—Inches	79¼	93¾
Cultivating Clearance—Inches	12	25⅝
Hydraulic Power Unit..............	Opt.	Opt.

Belt Pulley—P.T.O.—Engine

Pulley Diameter, Standard—Inches...	11⅞	11⅞
Pulley Face Width—Inches.........	7¼	7¼
Pulley Speed, Loaded—rpm.........	992	992
Pulley Speed, Loaded—fpm.........	3080	3080
Power Take-Off—Standard, Optional.	Opt.	Opt.
Is Power to P.T.O. Continuous?.....	Yes	Yes
Engine—Make	Own	Own
Number Cylinders & Displacement	6-265	6-265
Rated rpm	1600	1600

Brakes—Steering—Tires

Brakes, Type—Double Disc?........	Yes	Yes
Brakes, Location—Bull Gear Pinions?	Yes	Yes
Steering, Type—Worm & Sector, Circulating Ball ....(Tricycle)	CB	W&S
(Adj. Axle)	....	CB
Tire Size—Standard Rear—Inches...	13x26	12x38
Tire Size—Standard Front—Inches..	6x16	6x16

Oliver "Super 88" Row Crop

Transmission of Power

Clutch—Dry Disc Spring Loaded?....	Yes	Yes
Final Drive—Spur, Chain..........	Spur	Spur
High Gear Ratio..................	19.21	23.05
Low Gear Ratio..................	90.46	108.55
Speeds—Number Forward	[2]6	[2]6
Speeds—Number Reverse..........	[2]2	[2]2

Advertised Speeds, mph, With Standard Transmission and Tires—All Models: 2.49, 3.22, 4.28, 5.55, 6.82, 11.75; reverse, 2.55, 4.38. [1]To top of steering wheel. [2]Also available with 4 forward and 4 reverse speeds.

THE OLIVER CORPORATION
Chicago, Illinois

General

	Oliver Super 99 HC&D
Number and Size Plows	4, 5-14
Type—Axle, Track	Axle
Shipping Weight—Lbs.	7000
Rear Wheel Tread—Inches	62
Front Wheel Tread—Inches	59.8
Height Overall—Inches	90
Length Overall—Inches	136.8
Wheelbase—Inches	79.8
Cultivating Clearance—Inches	11.81
Hydraulic Power Unit	Opt.

Belt Pulley—P.T.O.—Engine

Pulley Diameter, Standard—Inches	12.25
Pulley Face Width—Inches	9
Pulley Speed, Loaded—rpm	980
Pulley Speed, Loaded—fpm	3142
Power Take-Off—Standard, Optional	Opt.
Is Power to P.T.O. Continuous?	No
Engine—Make	Own
Engine—Model (Diesel)	99D
(Gasoline)	99HC
Number Cyl. & Displacement (Diesel)	6-302
(Gasoline)	6-302
Rated rpm	1675

Brakes—Steering—Tires—Tracks

Brakes, Type—Contracting Band, Disc	Disc
Brakes, Location—Differential Shaft, Steering Differential	DS
Steering Make—Own, Saginaw	Sag.
Steering Type—Circulating Ball, Planetary Differential	CB
Tire Size—Standard Rear—Inches	14x34
Tire Size—Standard Front—Inches	7.5x18

Transmission of Power

Clutch—Single or Double Plate?	SP
Clutch—Spring Loaded?	Yes
Clutch—Semi Centrifugal?	No
Final Drive—Spur, Chain	Spur
High Gear Ratio	22.41
Low Gear Ratio	116.79
Speeds—Number Forward	6
Speeds—Number Reverse	2

Oliver "Super 99" Diesel
("Super 99" HC is similar)

THE OLIVER CORPORATION
Chicago, Illinois

NEW 2-3 Plow <u>Super</u> 55

NEW 2-3 Plow <u>Super</u> 66

All out for '55 Sales...
FIVE NEW
OLIVER SUPERS

NEW 3-4 Plow <u>Super</u> 77

NEW 4-Plow <u>Super</u> 88

NEW 4-5 Plow <u>Super</u> 99

Oliver's gone all the way—*five* brand-new Super tractors to give Oliver dealers a greater sales advantage than ever . . . in any size.

And, every one with the choice of the engines of tomorrow—efficient, overhead-valve gasoline engines with compression ratios up to 7.0 to 1 . . . or an easy-starting diesel.

All five tractors have the major advancements that farmers want—six forward speeds . . . independently controlled power take-off . . . depth-control hydraulic system . . . double-disc brakes . . . comfortable seat . . . light-handed steering.

That isn't all. Rounding out the Oliver power line-up is an entire fleet of crawler tractors. Yes, there are prospects galore for Oliver dealers in '55—splendid prospects to profit . . . bright prospects for the future. The OLIVER Corporation, 400 West Madison Street, Chicago 6, Illinois.

"Grow with OLIVER—the <u>Business Builder</u>"

OLIVER

General

	Oliver Crawler OC-12 HC&D
Type—Axle, Track	Track
Shipping Weight—Lbs. (Diesel)	10140
(HC)	9800
Track Tread—Inches	44
Height Overall—Inches	73.1
Length Overall—Inches	109.8
Wheelbase—Inches	71.06
Cultivating Clearance—Inches	13.43
Hydraulic Power Unit	None

Belt Pulley—P.T.O.—Engine

Pulley Diameter, Standard—Inches	12
Pulley Face Width—Inches	8.5
Pulley Speed, Loaded—rpm	1034
Pulley Speed, Loaded—fpm	3250
Power Take-Off—Standard, Opt.	Opt.
Is Power to P.T.O. Continuous?	No
Engine—Make	Herc.
Engine—Model (Diesel)	DJXC
(HC)	JXLD
No. Cyl. & Displacement (Diesel)	6-298
(HC)	6-339
Rated rpm	1750

Steering—Brakes—Tracks

Steering, Type—Planetary Diff. Differential Brakes	DB
Steering, Location—In Final Drive?	Yes
Brakes, Actuation—Hyd. Mech.	Mech.
Brakes, Type—Contracting Band?	Yes
Brakes, Location—Steering Diff., Differential Shafts	DS
Track Face Width, Std.—Inches	14
(Optional)	16, 18
Ground Contacting Area of Tracks—Square Inches	1990

Transmission of Power

Clutch—Single or Double Disc	DD
Clutch—Overcenter, Spring Loaded	SL
Final Drive—Spur, Chain	Spur
High Gear Ratio	24.0
Low Gear Ratio	78.9
Speeds—Number Forward	4
Speeds—Number Reverse	2

Oliver Crawler "OC-12"

THE OLIVER CORPORATION
Chicago, Illinois

SEAMAN MOTORS, INC.
Milwaukee, Wisconsin

Seaman "DS47"   1955-1956
Seaman "GS7C"   1955-1956
Seaman "GS7W"   1955-1956

	Seaman DS47 GS7C GS7W
General	
Number and Size Plows..............	None
Number and Width Rotary Tiller.....	1-84
Type—Wheel, Track	Wheel
Shipping Weight—Lbs. ....(DS47)	10000
(GS7C)	9200
(GS7W)	9400
Rear Wheel Tread, Adj. Range—In. ...	65-86
Front Wheel Tread—Inches........	69-80
Height Overall—Inches	84
Wheelbase—Inches	118
Hydraulic Power Unit..............	Opt.
Belt Pulley—P.T.O.—Engine	
Pulley Diameter, Standard—Inches...	None
Power Take-Off—Standard, Opt. ...	None
Engine—Make ....(DS47)	G.M.
(GS7C)	Cont'l.
(GS7W)	Wauk.
Engine—Model ....(DS47)	4-71
(GS7C)	B427
(GS7W)	135GZB
No. Cyl. & Displacement......(DS47)	4-284
(GS7C)	6-427
(GS7W)	6-451
Steering—Brakes—Tires	
Steering Make	Ross
Steering, Type—Cam & Lever.......	C&L
Brakes, Actuation—Hyd., Mech.	Hyd.
Brakes, Type—Contracting Band, Internal Expanding	IE
Brakes, Location—Rear Wheelbase Axle Shaft, Bull Pionion Shafts....	RWAS
Tire Size—Standard Rear—Inches...	13x38
Tire Size—Standard Front—Inches...	7.5x20
Transmission of Power	
Clutch—Single Dry Disc............	SD
Final Drive—Spur, Chain...........	Spur
Low Gear Ratio	176.0
Speeds—Number Forward	8
Speeds—Number Reverse	2

Seaman "DS47", "GS7C", "GS7W"

SEAMAN MOTORS, INC.
Milwaukee, Wisconsin

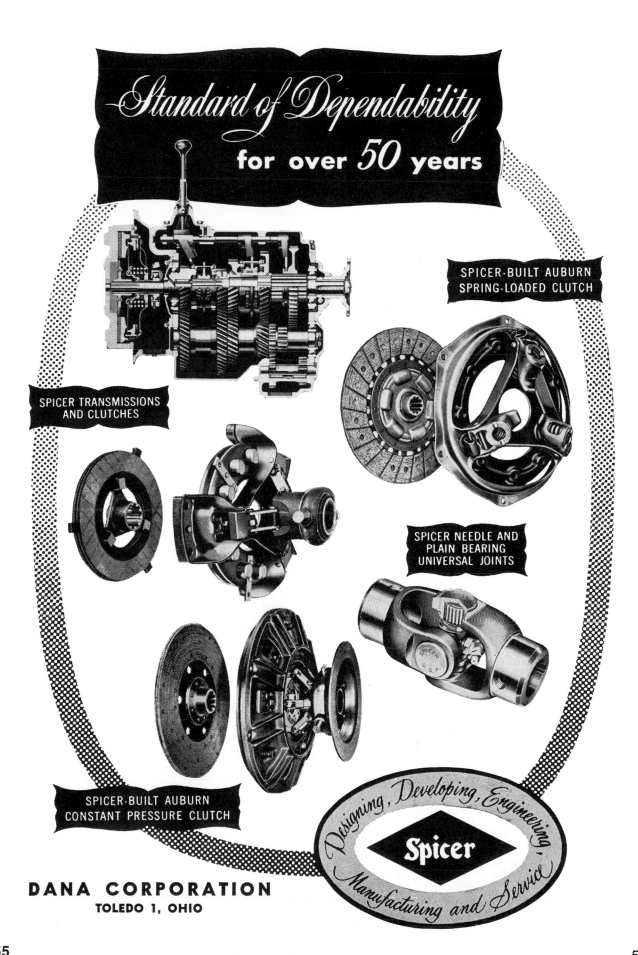

Standard of Dependability
for over 50 years

SPICER-BUILT AUBURN
SPRING-LOADED CLUTCH

SPICER TRANSMISSIONS
AND CLUTCHES

SPICER NEEDLE AND
PLAIN BEARING
UNIVERSAL JOINTS

SPICER-BUILT AUBURN
CONSTANT PRESSURE CLUTCH

Designing, Developing, Engineering, Manufacturing and Service

Spicer

DANA CORPORATION
TOLEDO 1, OHIO

1956

In 1956, ten tractor manufacturers introduced 54 new tractor models. Allis-Chalmers Manufacturing Company contributed six new models; American Tractor Corporation of Churubusco, Indiana, eight; J. I. Case Company, 12; Caterpillar Tractor Company, one; Deere & Company, seven; Ford Motor Company, eight; International Harvester Company, five; Massey-Harris-Ferguson, six; and Minneapolis-Moline Company, three.

ALLIS-CHALMERS MANUFACTURING CO.

Milwaukee, Wisconsin

Allis-Chalmers "HD6"	1956
Allis-Chalmers "HD11"	1956
Allis-Chalmers "HD16A"	1956
Allis-Chalmers "HD16AC"	1956
Allis-Chalmers "HD21"	1956
Allis-Chalmers "WD-45" Diesel	1956

Allis-Chalmers "WD-45"
Allis-Chalmers Mfg. Co., Milwaukee, Wis.

General	Allis-Chalmers WD-45 Diesel	HD6
Number and Size Plows	3-14	....
Type—Axle, Adj. Axle, Tricycle	All	Track
Shipping Weight—Lbs.	4730	12400
Nebraska Test Number	563	....
Track Tread—Inches	....	60
Rear Tread, Adj. Range—Inches	56-90	....
Front Tread, Adj. Range—In. .(A.A.)	52-84	....
Height Overall—Inches	69.8	65.6
Length Overall—Inches	128.4	127.1
Wheelbase—Inches	88.1	....
Starting—Electric, Sep. Engine	Elec.	Elec.
Cultivating Clearance—Inches	29.4	11.2
Hydraulic Power Unit	Std.	Opt.

Belt Pulley—P.T.O.—Engine

Pulley Diameter, Standard—Inches	9	....
Pulley Face Width—Inches	6.5	....
Pulley Speed, Loaded—rpm	1462	....
Pulley Speed, Loaded—fpm	3450	....
Power Take-off—Standard, Optional	Std.	Opt.
Is Power for P.T.O. Continuous?	Yes	No
P.T.O. Cont. When Gearshifting?	Yes	No
Engine—Make	Own	Own
Engine—Model	45D	HD344
Number Cylinders & Displacement	6-230	4-344
Rated rpm	1625	1800

Brakes—Steering—Tires—Tracks

Brakes Type	Shoe	Band
Brakes Location—Steering Clutch Compartment, Bull Pinion Shafts	BPS	SCC
Hydraulic or Mechanical Application	Mech.	Mech.
Steering Type— Worm & Segment, Clutches	W&S	Clutch
Steering Clutches Type— Spring Loaded Multiple Disc?	None	Yes
Track Face Standard Width—Inches	None	13
Track Face Width, Optional—Inches	None	....
Ground Contacting Area of Standard Tracks—Square Inches	None	1670.5
Tire Size—Standard Rear—Inches	12x28	....
Tire Size—Standard Front—Inches	5.5x16	....

Transmission of Power

Clutch—Dry Disc Overcenter?	[1]——	Yes
Final Drive—Spur, Chain	Spur	Spur
High Gear Ratio	21.1	RNA
Low Gear Ratio	98.3	RNA
Speeds—Number Forward	4	5
Speeds—Number Reverse	1	1 or 2

Advertised Speeds, mph, With Standard Transmission—Model WD-45 Diesel: 2.4, 3.75, 5.0, 11.25; reverse, 3.25. Model HD5: 1.5, 2.4, 3.3, 4.0, 5.5; reverse, 2.0; optional second reverse, 4.1.

[1]WD has two clutches. Engine clutch is single plate, spring loaded, dry type. Transmission clutch is multiple plate, overcenter, wet type. RNA= Manufacturer declines to release the information.

Allis-Chalmers "WD-45" Diesel

Allis-Chalmers "HD6"

ALLIS-CHALMERS MFG. CO.
Milwaukee, Wisconsin

	Allis-Chalmers	
General	**HD11**	**HD16A HD16AC**
Number and Size Plows.............	RNA	RNA
Shipping Weight—Lbs.	20500	31500
Nebraska Test Number	....	551,552
Tread—Inches	74	74
Height Overall—Inches	[1]84	[1]89.8
Length Overall—Inches	154	178
Starting—Electric, Sep. Engine......	Elec.	Elec.
Cultivating Clearance—Inches	13.3	14.3
Hydraulic Power Unit	Opt.	Opt.

Belt Pulley—P.T.O.—Engine

Pulley Diameter, Standard—Inches...	13.37	18
Pulley Face Width—Inches.........	10	15
Pulley Speed, Loaded—rpm.........	1045	786
Pulley Speed, Loaded—fpm.........	3540	3560
Power Take-off—Standard, Optional.	Opt.	Opt.
Is Power for P.T.O. Continuous?...	No	No
Engine—Make	Own	Own
Engine—Model	HD516	HD844
Number Cylinders & Displacement...	6-516	6-844
Rated rpm ....(HD16A)	1800	1600
(HD16AC)	....	1800

Brakes—Steering—Tracks

Brakes Type—Contracting Band.....	CB	CB
Brakes Location—Steering Clutch Compartment?	Yes	Yes
Hydraulic or Mechanical Application..	Mech.	Mech.
Steering Clutches Type—Multiple Disc Spring Loaded?..............	Yes	Yes
Track Face Standard Width—Inches.	16	20
Track Face Width, Optional—Inches.	Varies	Varies
Ground Contacting Area of Standard Track—Square Inches	2744	3853

Transmission of Power

Clutch—Dry Disc Overcenter?......	Yes	Yes
Final Drive—Spur, Chain	Spur	Spur
High Gear Ratio	RNA	RNA
Low Gear Ration	RNA	RNA
Speeds—Number Forward	6	[3]___
Speeds—Number Reverse	3	[3]___
Planetary Gearset	Yes	[3]___

Advertised Speeds, mph, With Std. Transmission—Model HD11: 1.4, 2.1, 2.9, 3.8, 4.4, 5.7; reverse 1.6, 3.5, 4.4. Model HD16A: 1.4, 2.1, 3.0, 3.9, 4.5, 5.8; reverse 1.5, 3.5 & 4.5. Model HD16AC: 0-2.5, 0-4.3, 0-7.2; reverse 0-3.2, 0-5.5.

[1]Without Stacks. [3]Model HD16AC has torque converter in series with clutch and 3 forward and 2 reverse speed gearset. Model HD16A has a 6 forward and 3 reverse speed planetary gearset. RNA =Manufacturer declines to release the information.

Allis-Chalmers "HD11"

Allis-Chalmers "HD16"

ALLIS-CHALMERS MFG. CO.
Milwaukee, Wisconsin

General

	Allis-Chalmers HD21
Number and Size Plows	RNA
Shipping Weight—Lbs.	44000
Nebraska Test Number	550
Tread—Inches	84
Height Overall—Inches	[1]98.8
Length Overall—Inches	194.7
Starting—Electric, Sep. Engine	Elect.
Cultivating Clearance—Inches	16.1
Hydraulic Power Unit	Opt.

Belt Pulley—P.T.O.—Engine

Pulley Diameter, Standard—Inches	20
Pulley Face Width—Inches	15
Pulley Speed, Loaded—rpm	825
Pulley Speed, Loaded—fpm	4440
Power Take-off—Std., Opt.	Opt.
Is Power for P.T.O. Continuous?	No
Engine—Make	Own
Engine—Model	HDS844
Number Cylinders & Displacement	6-844
Rated rpm	1800

Brakes—Steering—Tracks

Brakes, Type—Contracting Band?	Yes
Brakes, Location—Steering Clutch Compartment, Differential	SCC
Hydraulic or Mechanical Application.	Mech.
Steering Clutches Type—Multiple Disc Spring Loaded?	Yes
Track Face Standard Width Inches	24
Track Face Width, Opt.—Inches	Varies
Ground Contacting Area of Standard Track—Square Inches	5118

Transmission of Power

Clutch—Dry Disc Overcenter, Dry Disc Spring Loaded	DDO
Final Drive—Spur, Chain	Spur
High Gear Ratio	RNA
Low Gear Ratio	RNA
Speeds—Number Forward	[3]2
Speeds—Number Reverse	[3]1
Torque Converter?	[3]Yes

Advertised Speeds, mph, With Std. Transmission—
Model HD21: low, 0-3-0; high, 0-7-0; reverse,
4-5.5. Model 200: 1.74, 2.75, 4.52; reverse, 2.01.
[1]Without Stacks. [3]Has torque converter in series
with clutch and 2 speed gearset. RNA=Manu-
facturer declines to release the information.

Allis-Chalmers "HD-21"

ALLIS-CHALMERS MFG. CO.
Milwaukee, Wisconsin

AMERICAN TRACTOR CORP.
Churubusco, Indiana

TerraTrac "200"	1956-1957
TerraTrac "300"	1956-1957
TerraTrac "400"	1956-1957
TerraTrac "400D"	1956-1957
TerraTrac "500"	1956-1957
TerraTrac "500D"	1956-1957
TerraTrac "600"	1956-1957
TerraTrac "600D"	1956-1957

	American Tractor TerraTrac 200
General	
Number and Size Plows	3-14
Shipping Weight—Lbs.	4530
Tread—Inches	36-72
Height Overall—Inches	63.5
Length Overall—Inches	92.0
Starting—Electric, Sep. Engine	Elect.
Cultivating Clearance—Inches	16.0
Hydraulic Power Unit	Opt.
Belt Pulley—P.T.O.—Engine	
Pulley Diameter, Standard—Inches	6
Pulley Face Width—Inches	7
Pulley Speed, Loaded—rpm	664
Pulley Speed, Loaded—fpm	1043
Power Take-off—Std., Opt.	Opt.
Is Power for P.T.O. Continuous?	No
Engine—Make	Cont.
Engine—Model	F-140
Number Cylinders & Displacement	4-140
Rated rpm	1850
Brakes—Steering—Tracks	
Brakes, Type—Contracting Band?	Yes
Brakes, Location—Steering Clutch Compartment, Differential	Diff.
Hydraulic or Mechanical Application.	Mech.
Track Face Standard Width—Inches	10
Ground Contacting Area of Standard Track—Square Inches	1080
Transmission of Power	
Clutch—Dry Disc Overcenter, Dry Disc Spring Loaded	DDSL
Final Drive—Spur, Chain	Spur
High Gear Ratio	26.2
Low Gear Ratio	81.3
Speeds—Number Forward	3
Speeds—Number Reverse	1
Torque Converter?	No

TerraTrac "200"

AMERICAN TRACTOR CORP.
Churubusco, Indiana

General	American Tractor TerraTrac 300	400 400D
Number and Size Plows	3-14	....
Shipping Weight—Lbs.	4830	5125
Nebraska Test Number	None	None
Tread, Minimum—Inches	36	36
Tread, Maximum—Inches	72	72
Height, Overall—Inches	63.5	63.5
Length, Overall—Inches	92	101
Cultivating Clearance—Inches	16	16
Hydraulic Power Unit	Opt.	Opt.

TerraTrac "300"

Belt Pulley—P.T.O.—Engine

Pulley Diameter, Standard—Inches	6	6
Pulley Face Width—Inches	7	7
Pulley Speed, Loaded—rpm	664	664
Pulley Speed, Loaded—fpm	1043	1043
Power Take-off—Std., Opt.	Opt.	Opt.
Is Power to P.T.O. Continuous?	No	No
Engine—Make	Cont'l	Cont'l
Engine—Model	F-140	F-162
Number Cylinders & Displacement	4-140	4-162
Rated rpm	1850	1850

Brakes—Steering—Tracks

Steering Brakes, Type—Contracting Wet Band?	Yes	Yes
Steering Brakes Location—Diff.?	Yes	Yes
Track Face Std. Width—Inches	11	12
Ground Contacting Area Standard Tracks—Square Inches	1188	1368

TerraTrac "400"

Transmission of Power

Clutch—Dry Disc Spring Loaded?	Yes	Yes
Final Drive—Spur, Chain	Spur	Spur
High Gear Ratio	26.2	26.2
Low Gear Ratio	81.3	81.3
Speeds—Number Forward	3	3
Speeds—Number Reverse	1	1
Torque Converter?	No	No

Advertised Speeds, mph, With Std. Transmission—
Models 300 & 400: 1.74, 2.75, 4.52; reverse, 2.01.

AMERICAN TRACTOR CORP.
Churubusco, Indiana

General	American Tractor TerraTrac	
	500 500D	600 600D
Shipping Weight—Lbs. ..(500 & 600)	5310	7145
(500D & 600D)	5470	7205
Nebraska Test Number............	None	None
Tread, Minimum—Inches	36	....
Tread, Maximum—Inches	72	49
Height, Overall—Inches	63.5	65.0
Length, Overall—Inches	101	101
Cultivating Clearance—Inches	16	16
Hydraulic Power Unit.............	Opt.	Std.

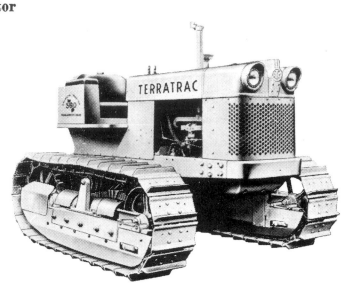

TerraTrac "500"

Belt Pulley—P.T.O.—Engine

Pulley Diameter, Std.—Inches......	6	....
Pulley Face Width—Inches.........	7	....
Pulley Speed, Loaded—rpm........	664	....
Pulley Speed, Loaded—fpm........	1042	....
Power Take-off—Std., Opt.	Opt.	Opt.
Is Power to P.T.O. Continuous?....	No	No
Engine—Make	Cont'l	Cont'l
Engine—Model ....(500 & 600)	FA-162	F-209
(500D & 600D)	GD-157	ED-208
Number Cyl. & Displ'm't .(500 & 600)	4-162	6-209
(500D & 600D)	4-157	4-208
Rated rpm	2250	2250

Brakes—Steering—Tracks

Steering Brakes Type—Contracting Wet Band, Hydraulic Clutches....	CWB	HC
Steering Brakes Location— Differential, Transmission	Diff.	Trans.
Track Face, Std. Width—Inches....	13	14
Ground Contacting Area of Standard Tracks—Square Inches..	1482	1760

TerraTrac "600"

Transmission of Power

Torque Converter?	Yes	Yes
Final Drive—Spur, Chain..........	Spur	Spur
High Gear Ratio..................	26.2	21.4
Low Gear Ratio..................	81.3	72.2
Speeds—Number Forward	3	4
Speeds—Number Reverse	1	4
Transmission—Sliding Gear, Constant Mesh Actuated by Hydraulic Clutches	SG	CMAHC

Advertised Speeds, mph, With Std. Transmission—
Models 500 & 500D: 0 to 1.88, 0 to 2.97, 0 to 4.88;
Reverse, 0 to 2.17. Models 600 & 600D: 0 to 1.58.
0 to 2.79, 0 to 3.23, 0 to 5.68; reverse, 0 to 1.71,
0 to 3.0, 0 to 3.5, 0 to 6.5.

AMERICAN TRACTOR CORP.
Churubusco, Indiana

J. I. CASE CO.
Racine, Wisconsin

Case "300" Utility	1956
Case "301" General Purpose	1956-1957
Case "310" Utility	1956
Case "311" General Purpose	1956-1957
Case "400" General Purpose	1956-1957
Case "401" General Purpose	1956-1957
Case "402" Orchard	1956-1957
Case "403" High Clearance	1956-1957
Case "410" General Purpose	1956-1957
Case "411" General Purpose	1956-1957
Case "412" Orchard	1956-1957
Case "413" High Clearance	1956-1957

CASE "400"
...The Tractor That's Thrilling the Whole Farm Market

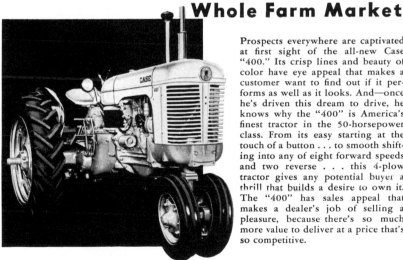

Prospects everywhere are captivated at first sight of the all-new Case "400." Its crisp lines and beauty of color have eye appeal that makes a customer want to find out if it performs as well as it looks. And—once he's driven this dream to drive, he knows why the "400" is America's finest tractor in the 50-horsepower class. From its easy starting at the touch of a button . . . to smooth shifting into any of eight forward speeds and two reverse . . . this 4-plow tractor gives any potential buyer a thrill that builds a desire to own it. The "400" has sales appeal that makes a dealer's job of selling a pleasure, because there's so much more value to deliver at a price that's so competitive.

Plus a New Line of Sales' Leaders...

★ **NEW FARM-SIZE AUTOMATIC BALER**

★ **NEW SEVEN-FOOT PULL-TYPE COMBINE**

★ **NEW SIX-HEAD FORAGE HARVESTER**

★ **NEW 125-BUSHEL PTO SPREADER**

★ **NEW TWO-ROW COTTON STRIPPER**

★ **NEW DRIVE-IN 4-ROW CULTIVATOR**

With fast-moving research Case is geared to give farmers exactly what they want in modern machinery for today's new ways of farming.

From new mounted, break-away, pivot-action plows for contour work . . . to big, self-propelled combines . . . Case provides dealers with a line of products that leads the way in unlimited opportunity to meet the farmers' needs . . . in making sales soar to new highs in profit. Now is your time to enjoy a solid selling edge. J. I. Case Co., Racine, Wis.

General

	J. I. Case 300 310
Engine Type ....(300)	Diesel
(310)	Non Die.
Number and Size Plows.............	3-14
Type—Axle, Tricycle	Axle
Shipping Wt., Max.—Lbs. ......(300)	3060
(310)	2920
Nebraska Test Number	None
Rear Tread, Adj. Range—Inches....	48-68
Front Tread—Inches	47.5
Height Overall—Inches	56
Length Overall—Inches	125.0
Wheelbase—Inches	75.5
Electric Starting—Std., Opt.	Std.
Cultivating Clearance—Inches	12
Hydraulic Power Unit	Opt.

Belt Pulley—P.T.O.—Engine

Pulley Diameter, Standard—Inches..	10.25
Pulley Face Width—Inches........	6.0
Pulley Speed, Loaded—rpm........	1190
Pulley Speed, Loaded—fpm	3193
Power Take-off—Std., Opt.	Opt.
Is Non Continuous PTO Available?..	Yes
Is Continuous PTO Available?......	Yes
PTO Cont. When Gearshifting?.....	Yes
Engine—Make ....(Diesel)	Cont.
(Gasoline Distillate & LP Gas)	Own
Engine—Model ....(Diesel)	GD157
(Gasoline Distillate & LP Gas)	G148
No. Cyl. & Displacement....(Diesel)	4-157
(Gasoline Distillate & LP Gas)	4-148
Rated rpm	1750

Brakes—Steering—Tires

Brakes, Type—Double Disc?	Yes
Brakes, Location—Diff. Side Gears?.	Yes
Steering Type—Worm & Gear, Cam & Lever..................	C & L
Power Steering—Std., Opt.	None
Tire Size—Rear—Inches	11x24
Tire Size—Front—Inches	6x16

Transmission of Power

Clutch—Wet or Dry Single Plate....	DSP
Clutch—O'center, Spring Loaded....	SL
Final Drive—Spur, Chain	Spur
High Gear Ratio ..(4 Speed Gearset)	19.2
(12 Speed Gearset)	11.5
Low Gear Ratio ..(4 Speed Gearset)	92.0
(12 Speed Gearset)	153.0
Speeds—Number Forward	4 or 12
Speeds—Number Reverse	1 or 3
Sliding or Constant Mesh Gear Change	SG

Case "310" Utility

J. I. CASE CO.
Racine, Wisconsin

General

	J. I. Case 301 311
Engine Type ....(301)	Diesel
(311)	Non Die.
Number and Size Plows.............	3-14
Type—Axle, Tricycle, Adj. Axle.....	T, AA
Shipping Wt., Max.—Lbs. ......(301)	3440
(311)	3300
Nebraska Test Number.............	None
Rear Tread, Adj. Range—Inches....	48-88
Front Tread, Adj. Range—In. (Tri.)	6.5-11.7
(Adj. Axle)	52-80
Height Overall—Inches	61
Length Overall—Inches .....(A. A.)	125
(Tricycle)	131
Wheelbase—Inches ......(Tricycle)	84.3
(Adjustable Axle)	79.7
Electric Starting—Std., Opt.	Std.
Cultivating Clearance—Inches	21.0
Hydraulic Power Unit	Std.

Belt Pulley—P.T.O.—Engine

Pulley Diameter, Standard—Inches..	10.25
Pulley Face Width—Inches	6
Pulley Speed, Loaded—rpm	1190
Pulley Speed, Loaded—fpm	3193
Power Take-off—Std., Opt.	Opt.
Is Non Continuous PTO Available?..	Yes
Is Continuous PTO Available?......	Yes
PTO Cont. When Gearshifting?......	Yes
Engine—Make ....(Diesel)	Cont.
(Gasoline, Distillate & LP Gas.)	Own
Engine—Model ....(Diesel)	GD157
(Gasoline, Distillate & LP Gas.)	G148
No. Cyl. & Displacement ...(Diesel)	4-157
(Gasoline, Distillate & LP Gas.)	4-148
Rated rpm	1750

Brakes—Steering—Tires

Brakes, Type—Disc, Internal Exp. ..	Disc
Brakes, Location—Diff. Side Gears?.	Yes
Steering Type—Worm & Wheel, Cam & Lever	C & L
Tire Size—Std. Rear—Inches.......	11x28
Tire Size—Std. Front—Inches......	5.5x16

Transmission of Power

Clutch—Dry Spring Loaded Plate?..	Yes
Final Drive—Spur, Chain	Spur
High Gear Ratio ..(4 Speed Gearset)	19.2
(12 Speed Gearset)	11.5
Low Gear Ratio ..(4 Speed Gearset)	92.0
(12 Speed Gearset)	153.0
Speeds—Number Forward	4 or 12
Speeds—Number Reverse	1 or 3

Case "311" General Purpose

J. I. CASE CO.
Racine, Wisconsin

General

	J. I. Case 402 412 Orch- ard	403 413 High- Clear.
Engine Type ....(402-403)	Diesel	
(412-413)	Non Diesel	
Number and Size Plows.............	4-14	4-14
Type—Axle, Adj. Axle, Tricycle......	Axle	Axle
Approximate Max. Weight, Std. Equip. .	RNA	RNA
Rear Tread, Adj. Range—Inches....	....	60-90
Front Tread, Adj. Range—Inches ...	....	54-79.7
Height Overall—Inches		108.8
Length Overall—Inches		142
Wheelbase—Inches		92.3
Electric Starting—Std., Opt.	Std.	Std.
Hydraulic Power Unit	None	Std.

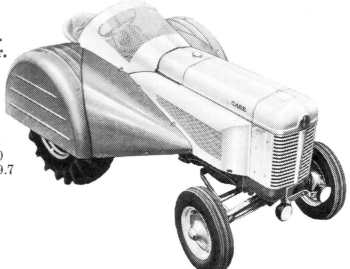

Case "402"

Belt Pulley—P.T.O.—Engine

Pulley Diameter, Standard—Inches...	10.5	10.5
Pulley Face Width—Inches	7.25	7.25
Pulley Speed, Loaded—rpm	1128	1128
Pulley Speed, Loaded—fpm	3100	3100
Engine—Make and Model	Own	Own
Number Cylinders & Displacement ..	4-251	4-251
Rated rpm	1450	1450

Brakes—Steering—Tires

Brakes Type—Double Disc?	Yes	Yes
Brakes Location—Diff. Shafts?	Yes	Yes
Steering Type—Worm & Gear?	Yes	Yes
Tire Size—Standard Rear—Inches...	13x26	12x38
Tire Size—Std. Front—Inches......	6x16	7.5x20

Transmission of Power

Clutch—Dry Single Plate?	Yes	Yes
Clutch—O'center, Spring Loaded	SL	SL
Final Drive—Spur, Chain	Spur	Spur
High Gear Ratio	RNA	RNA
Low Gear Ratio	RNA	RNA
Speeds—Number Forward	8	8
Speeds—Number Reverse	2	2
Sliding or Constant Mesh Gear Change.	S	S

Advertised Speeds, mph, With Std. Transmission
& Std. Tires—Models 402 & 412: 1.3, 1.9, 2.6, 4.3,
4.7, 6.7, 9.1, 15.3; reverse 1.7 & 6.0. Models 403 &
413: 1.4, 2.0, 2.8, 4.0, 5.0, 7.2, 9.9, 14.3; reverse
1.8 & 6.5.

RNA=Manufacturer declines to release the information.

Case "403"

J. I. CASE CO.
Racine, Wisconsin

1956

General

<table>
<tr><td></td><td colspan="2">J. I. Case
General
Purpose
400   401
410   411</td></tr>
<tr><td>Engine Type ....(400-401)</td><td colspan="2">Diesel</td></tr>
<tr><td>(410-411)</td><td colspan="2">Non Diesel</td></tr>
<tr><td>Number and Size Plows ....</td><td>4-14</td><td>4-14</td></tr>
<tr><td>Type—Axle, Tricycle ....</td><td>Axle</td><td>Tri.</td></tr>
<tr><td>Approximate Max. Weight, Std. Equip.</td><td>RNA</td><td>RNA</td></tr>
<tr><td>Nebraska Test Number ....</td><td>....</td><td>565, 566</td></tr>
<tr><td>Rear Tread, Adj. Range—Inches.....</td><td>52-68</td><td>52-88</td></tr>
<tr><td>Front Tread—Inches ....(A.A.)</td><td>52-58</td><td>53-82</td></tr>
<tr><td>(Tricycle)</td><td>....</td><td>9.1-15.1</td></tr>
<tr><td>Height Overall—Inches ....</td><td>89</td><td>93.5</td></tr>
<tr><td>Length Overall—Inches ...(Tricycle)</td><td>133</td><td>142.6</td></tr>
<tr><td>(Adj. Axle)</td><td>....</td><td>152</td></tr>
<tr><td>Wheelbase—Inches ......(Tricycle)</td><td>82</td><td>91.5</td></tr>
<tr><td>(Adj. Axle)</td><td>....</td><td>101</td></tr>
<tr><td>Electric Starting—Standard, Optional</td><td>Std.</td><td>Std.</td></tr>
<tr><td>Cultivating Clearance—Inches ......</td><td>17.3</td><td>24.2</td></tr>
<tr><td>Hydraulic Power Unit ....</td><td>Opt.</td><td>Std.</td></tr>
</table>

Case "410"

Belt Pulley—P.T.O.—Engine

Pulley Diameter, Standard—Inches..	10.5	10.5
Pulley Face Width—Inches.........	7.25	7.25
Pulley Speed, Loaded—rpm	1128	1128
Pulley Speed, Loaded—fpm	3100	3100
Power Take-off—Standard, Optional.	Opt.	Opt.
Is Power to P.T.O. Continuous?....	Yes	Yes
P.T.O. Cont. When Gearshifting?....	Yes	Yes
Engine—Make and Model	Own	Own
Number Cylinders & Displacement...	4-251	4-251
Rated rpm	1450	1450

Brakes—Steering—Tires

Brakes Type—Double Disc?.........	Yes	Yes
Brakes Location—Diff. Shafts?.....	Yes	Yes
Steering Type—Worm & Gear.......	Yes	Yes
Tire Size—Std. Rear—Inches.......	13x30	12x38
Tire Size—Std. Front—Inches.......	6x16	9x10 or
	....	6x16

Case "411"

Transmission of Power

Clutch—Dry Single Plate?..........	Yes	Yes
Clutch—O'center, Spg. Loaded.......	SL	SL
Final Drive—Spur, Chain...........	Spur	Spur
High Gear Ratio	RNA	RNA
Low Gear Ratio	RNA	RNA
Speeds—Number Forward	8	8
Speeds—Number Reverse	2	2
Sliding or Constant Mesh Gear Change.	S	S

Advertised Speeds, mph, With Std. Transmission & Std. Tires—Models 400 & 410: 1.3, 1.8, 2.5, 3.7, 4.6, 6.6, 9.0, 13.0; reverse 1.7 & 5.9. Models 401 & 411: 1.3, 1.9, 2.6, 3.7, 4.7, 6.7, 9.1, 13.2; reverse 1.7 & 6.0.

RNA=Manufacturer declines to release the information.

J. I. CASE CO.
Racine, Wisconsin

CATERPILLAR TRACTOR CO.
Peoria, Illinois

Caterpillar Diesel "D9"   1956

General

	Caterpillar D9
Number and Size Plows.............	RNA
Shipping Weight—Lbs.	57286
Standard Tread—Inches	90
Length Overall—Inches	214.7
Starting—Auxiliary Engine?	Yes
Cultivating Clearance—Inches	20.5
Hydraulic Power Unit..............	Opt.

Belt Pulley—P.T.O.—Engine

Engine—Make	Own
Engine—Model	D9
Number Cylinders & Displacement...	6-1473
Rated rpm	1200

Brakes—Steering—Tracks

Brakes, Type—Contracting Band?...	Yes
Brakes, Location— On Steering Clutches?...........	Yes
Steering Clutches, Type—Mult. Disc?.	Yes
Track Face Standard Width—Inches	27
Ground Contacting Area of Standard Tracks—Square Inches	7006

Transmission of Power

Clutch—Triple or Quadruple Plate ...	Quad.
Clutch—Dry, Wet	Wet
Clutch—Overcenter?	Yes
Final Drive—Spur, Chain...........	Spur
High Gear Ratio...................	21.3
Low Gear Ratio...................	89.0
Speeds—Number Forward..........	6
Speeds—Number Reverse..........	6

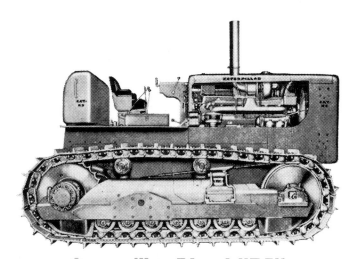

Caterpillar Diesel "D9"

CATERPILLAR TRACTOR CO.
Peoria, Illinois

DEERE & CO.
Moline, Illinois

John Deere "420" Hi-Crop	1956
John Deere "420" 2-Row Utility	1956
John Deere "420" Standard	1956
John Deere "420" Tricycle	1956
John Deere "420" Utility	1956
John Deere "420" Crawler	1956
John Deere "80" Diesel	1956

The New John Deere Research and Engineering Center Keeps Tractor Quality at Its Highest

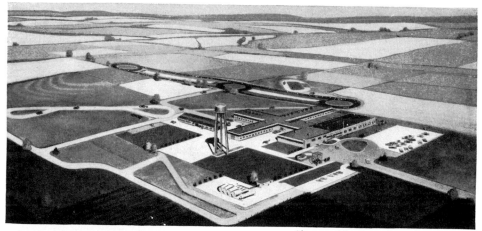

The new John Deere Research and Engineering Center near Waterloo, Iowa.

This obstacle course subjects test tractors to punishment far in excess of that encountered in normal field operations. Any weakness can be quickly spotted and corrective steps taken.

This mud bath, in which can be mixed varying amounts of sand and clay, enables John Deere engineers to check the effect of water and abrasives on wheel and axle bearings and oil seals.

QUALITY is a particularly precious commodity in the farm equipment industry. From quality stems the faith and subscription that make one manufacturer's product more acceptable than another's. Tractors are a good example. At John Deere, tractor quality is guarded with a vengeance. The words of the blacksmith, spoken more than a century ago, still ring loud and clear—"I'll never put my name on an implement that hasn't in it the best that is in me."

To this end, a year-'round program of research and testing is carried on in this modern John Deere Research and Engineering Center near Waterloo, Iowa. Here, through the media of the test tube and test track, with the aid of modern electronic and mechanical testing devices, the science of agricultural engineering and development pursues the goal of ever-higher tractor quality. The success of this program is evident by the growing number of John Deere Tractors that are a familiar part of every rural landscape. The important role played by the new Research and Engineering Center is another "built-in" feature that makes the John Deere dealer franchise the most valued in the farm equipment field.

JOHN DEERE
MOLINE, ILLINOIS

General

	John Deere 420 Hi-Crop	John Deere 420 2-R Util.
Number and Size Plows............	2, 3-14	2, 3-14
Type—Axle, Tricycle, Adj. Axle.....	AA	AA
Shipping Weight—Lbs.	3400	3000
Rear Tread, Adj. Range—In........	54-84	48-98
Front Tread, Minimum—In.	54	48, 56
Front Tread, Maximum—In.	84	80, 88
Height Overall—Inches	86	74.0
Length Overall—Inches	132	136.1
Wheelbase—Inches	80.7	85
Cultivating Clearance—In.	31.5	20.5
Hydraulic Power Unit	Std.	Std.

John Deere "420" Hi-Crop

Belt Pulley—P.T.O.—Engine

Pulley Diameter, Std.—Inches	9	9
Pulley Face Width—Inches.........	6	6
Pulley Speed, Loaded—rpm	1270	1270
Pulley Speed, Loaded—fpm........	3000	3000
Power Take-off—Std., Opt. .(Spec.)	Opt.	Opt.
Is Power to P.T.O. Continuous?...	No	No
Engine—Make	Own	Own
Number Cylinders & Displacement...	2-113	2-113
Rated rpm	1850	1850

Brakes—Steering—Tires

Brakes, Type—Double Disc?	Yes	Yes
Brakes, Location—Bull Pinion Shaft?	Yes	Yes
Steering Make	Ross	Ross
Steering Type—Cam & Lever?......	Yes	Yes
Tire Size—Std. Rear—In.	10x38	10x34
Tire Size—Std. Front—Inches	6.5x16	5x15

John Deere "420" 2-Row Utility

DEERE & COMPANY
Moline, Illinois

Transmission of Power

Clutch—Dry Disc Spring Loaded?...	Yes	Yes
Final Drive—Spur, Chain	Spur	Spur
High Gear Ratio (Std. Trans.)......	26.2	22.5
Low Gear Ratio (Std. Trans.)......	167.5	144.5
Speeds—Number Forward	4	4
Speeds—Number Reverse	1	1

General	John Deere 420 Std.	420 Tri.
Number and Size Plows.............	2, 3-14	2, 3-14
Type—Axle, Tricycle, Adj. Axle.....	AA	T, AA
Shipping Weight on Rubber—Lbs. ...	2750	3000
Nebraska Test Number	None	None
Rear Tread, Adj. Range—Inches....	38.7-54.2	48-96 ....
Front Tread, Minimum—In. ...(Tri.)	....	6.7
(Adj. Axle)	40.0	48, 68
Front Tread, Maximum—In. ..(Tri.)	....	11.7
(Adj. Axle)	55.0	80, 88
Height Overall—Inches	73.6	76.6
Length Overall—Inches	114.7	130.6
Wheelbase—Inches	70.0	82.2
Cultivating Clearance—Inches	21.0	21.0
Hydraulic Power Unit	Std.	Std.

Belt Pulley—P.T.O.—Engine

Pulley Diameter, Standard—Inches...	9	9
Pulley Face Width—Inches........	6	6
Pulley Speed, Loaded—rpm	1270	1270
Pulley Speed, Loaded—fpm	3000	3000
Power Take-off—Std., Opt.	Std.	Std.
Is Power to P.T.O. Continuous?....	No	No
Engine—Make	Own	Own
Number Cylinders & Displacement...	2-113	2-113
Rated rpm	1850	1850

John Deere "420" Standard

Brakes—Steering—Tires

Brakes, Type—Double Disc?........	Yes	Yes
Brakes, Location—Bull Pinion Shaft?	Yes	Yes
Steering Make	Ross	Ross
Steering Type—Cam & Lever?......	Yes	Yes
Tire Size—Standard Rear—Inches..	9x24	9x34
Tire Size—Standard Front—Inches ..	5x15	5x15

Transmission of Power

Clutch—Dry Disc Spring Loaded?...	Yes	Yes
Final Drive—Spur, Chain	Spur	Spur
High Gear Ratio	19.9	23.1
Low Gear Ratio	128.4	147.0
Speeds—Number Forward	4	4
Speeds—Number Reverse	1	1

John Deere "420" Tricycle

DEERE & COMPANY
Moline, Illinois

Advertised Speeds, mph, With Std. Transmission & Std. Tires—Models 420 Standard & 420 Tricycle: 1.6, 3.1, 4.2, 12.0; reverse, 2.5.

General	John Deere 420 Crawler	John Deere 420 Utility
Number and Size Plows..............	3, 4-14	2, 3-14
Type—Track, Tricycle, Adj. Axle....	Track	AA
Shipping Weight—Lbs. ....(4 Roller)	4210	2850
(5 Roller)	4825	....
Track Tread, Standard—Inches	36, 46	....
Track Tread, Optional—Inches	38, 44	....
Rear Tread, Adj. Range—Inches....	....	40.8-56.3
Front Tread, Adj. Range—Inches...	....	43-55
Height Overall—Inches	69	68.3
Length Overall—Inches	102	119.2
Wheelbase—Inches	....	77.7
Standard Starting—Electric?	Yes	Yes
Cultivating Clearance—Inches	12	11
Hydraulic Power Unit	Opt.	Opt.

Belt Pulley—P.T.O.—Engine

Pulley Diameter, Standard—Inches..	9	9
Pulley Face Width—Inches	6	6
Pulley Speed, Loaded—rpm	1270	1270
Pulley Speed, Loaded—fpm.........	3000	3000
Power Take-off—Std., Opt.	Opt.	Opt.
Is Power to P.T.O. Continuous?....	No	No
Is Continuous P.T.O. Available?....	No	No
Engine—Make	Own	Own
Number Cylinders & Displacement...	2-113	2-113
Rated rpm	1850	1850

John Deere "420" Crawler

Brakes—Steering—Tires—Tracks

Brakes, Type—Disc, Contracting ...	Con.	Disc
Brakes, Location—Steering Clutches, Bull Pinion Shafts	SC	BPS
Steering Type—Cam & Lever.......	....	C & L
Steering Clutches Type—Mult. Disc?	Yes	....
Track Face Width, Std.—Inches....	10	....
Tire Size—Standard Rear—Inches..	....	10x24
Tire Size—Standard Front—Inches..	....	5x15

Transmission of Power

Clutch—Single Plate	SP	SP
Clutch—Dry, Wet	Dry	Dry
Clutch—Spring Loaded, Overcenter..	SL	SL
Final Drive—Spur, Chain..........	Spur	Spur
High Gear Ratio..................	21.9	19.9
Low Gear Ratio..................	141.0	128.4
Speeds—Number Forward	4	4
Speeds—Number Reverse	1	1

John Deere "420" Utility

DEERE & COMPANY
Moline, Illinois

Advertised Speeds, mph, With Std. Transmission & Std. Tires or Tracks—Model 420 Crawler: 0.87, 2.25, 3.0, 5.25; reverse, 1.75, Model 420 Utility: 1.62, 3.12, 4.25, 12.0; reverse, 2.5.

General

	John Deere 80
Number and Size Plows	4, 5-14
Type—Adjustable Axle, Axle	Axle
Shipping Weight, Maximum—Lbs.	8028
Nebraska Test Number	567
Rear Tread, Adj. Range—Inches	64, 68
Front Tread, Adj. Range—Inches	56-59.7
Height Overall—Inches	82
Length Overall—Inches	137.6
Wheelbase—Inches	85.2
Starting—Aux. Engine, Electric	AE
Hydraulic Power Unit	Opt.

Belt Pulley—P.T.O.—Engine

Pulley Diameter, Standard—Inches	$12\frac{7}{32}$
Pulley Face Width—Inches	9
Pulley Speed, Loaded—rpm	1125
Pulley Speed, Loaded—fpm	3600
Power Take-off—Optional, Std.	Opt.
Is Continuous P.T.O. Available?	Yes
P.T.O. Cont. When Gearshifting?	Yes
Engine—Make	Own
Engine—Model	80
Number Cylinders & Displacement	2-471.5
Rated rpm	1125

Brakes—Steering—Tires

Brakes, Type—Internal Exp., Disc.	IE
Brakes, Location—Bull Pinion Shaft, Sep. Shafts Driven by Bull Gears	SS
Steering Make	Own
Steering Type—Cam & Lever, Worm & Gear	W&G
Tire Size—Std. Rear—In.	15x34
Tire Size—Std. Front—Inches	7.5x18

Transmission of Power

Clutch—Dry Disc Spring Loaded, Multiple Disc	MD
Final Drive—Spur, Chain	Spur
High Gear Ratio	14.71
Low Gear Ratio	77.83
Speeds—Number Forward	6
Speeds—Number Reverse	1

John Deere "80" Diesel

DEERE & COMPANY
Moline, Illinois

Where FAULT-FINDING
is a *Virtue*

NOW all of us know that fault-finding isn't the recommended short-cut to winning friends and influencing people. Still, there is a place for it—even an honored place—in industry. That's when fault-finding is the by-product of *fact-finding,* basic function of a practical Quality Control program.

We see it work every day at John Deere. Here, dozens upon dozens of "professional fact-finders" are stationed at strategic points throughout John Deere factories, charged—with the help of tens of thousands of instruments and gauges—to probe the vital statistics of manufactured parts, record them, and to expose fault where fault exists.

These men, of course, carry out but one phase—the inspection phase—of the John Deere Quality Control program—a program, incidentally, that embraces the entire scope of manufacturing. Others are just as busily engaged in tabulating these facts and translating them in terms of indicated manufacturing procedure.

The Quality Control program is John Deere's way of making sure that each unit leaving the assembly line stands, trim and efficient—a quality product—ready for the field and ready to serve the cause of better farming.

Here an operator is grinding the body diameter of a cotton-picker spindle. The control chart on this machine is designed to assist the operator and supervisor in maintaining tolerances.

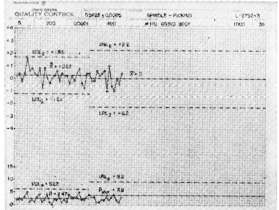

This chart is much like the one in the picture at the left and shows how statistical analysis is used to indicate the ability of the process to maintain established tolerances.

JOHN DEERE • Moline, Ill.
Quality Farm Equipment Since 1837

FORD MOTOR CO.
Tractor & Implement Division
Birmingham, Michigan

Ford Special Utility "620" 1956-1957
Ford Special Utility "630" 1956-1957
Ford Tricycle "740" 1956-1957
Ford Special Utility "820" 1956-1957
Ford Tricycle "950" 1956-1957
Ford Tricycle "960" 1956-1957

	Ford Special Utility 620 630	820
General		
Number and Size Plows	2-14	3-14
Type—Axle, Adjustable Axle	A.A.	A.A.
Shipping Weight—Lbs. ....(620)	2462	2637
(630)	2662	....
Rear Tread, Adj. Range—Inches	48-76	48-76
Front Tread, Adj. Range—Inches	52-80	52-80
Height Overall—Inches	55.2	55.5
Length Overall—Inches	113.6	113.6
Wheelbase—Inches	74.5	74.5
Cultivating Clearance—Inches	19.0	19.0
Hydraulic Power Unit ....(620)	None	Std.
(630)	Std.	....
Belt Pulley—P.T.O.—Engine		
Pulley Unit	None	None
Power Take-off—Std., Opt.	None	None
Engine—Make	Own	Own
Engine—Model	EAE	EAF
Number Cylinders & Displacement	4-134	4-172
Rated rpm	2000	2200
Brakes—Steering—Tires		
Brakes, Type—Internal Expanding Shoes, Contracting Band	IES	IES
Brakes, Location—Wheel Axle Shafts	WAS	WAS
Steering Type—Worm & Ball-Nut?	Yes	Yes
Tire Size—Standard Rear—Inches	10x28	10x28
Tire Size—Standard Front—Inches	5.5x16	6x16
Transmission of Power		
Clutch—Dry Single Disc?	Yes	Yes
Clutch—Spring Loaded?	Yes	Yes
Final Drive—Bevel, Spur Gear	Bevel	Bevel
High Gear Ratio	19.86	24.23
Low Gear Ratio	73.33	125.76
Speeds—Number Forward	4	5
Speeds—Number Reverse	1	1

Ford "630"

Ford "820"

**TRACTOR & IMPLEMENT DIVISION
FORD MOTOR CO.
Birmingham, Mich.**

Advertised Speeds, mph, at 2000 engine rpm, With Std. Transmission & Std. Tires—Models 620 & 630: 3.81, 4.89, 6.73, 14.05; reverse, 4.17. Model 820: 2.3, 3.66, 4.87, 6.72, 11.96; reverse, 3.93.

General

<table>
<tr><th></th><th>Ford
Tricycle
740</th><th>950
960</th></tr>
<tr><td>Number and Size Plows............</td><td>2-14</td><td>3-14</td></tr>
<tr><td>Type—Tricycle, Adjustable Axle....</td><td>Tri.</td><td>Tri.</td></tr>
<tr><td>Shipping Weight on Rubber—Lbs. ..</td><td>3079</td><td>3280</td></tr>
<tr><td>Rear Tread, Adj. Range—Inches....</td><td>56-80</td><td>56-80</td></tr>
<tr><td>Front Tread, Adj. Range—Inches...</td><td>8.3-16.3</td><td>8.3-16.3</td></tr>
<tr><td>Height Overall—Inches ....</td><td>65.07</td><td>65.8</td></tr>
<tr><td>Length Overall—Inches ....</td><td>132.1</td><td>132.6</td></tr>
<tr><td>Wheelbase—Inches ....</td><td>85.3</td><td>85.3</td></tr>
<tr><td>Cultivating Clearance—Inches .....</td><td>27.25</td><td>27.9</td></tr>
<tr><td>Hydraulic Power Unit.............</td><td>Std.</td><td>Std.</td></tr>
</table>

Belt Pulley—P.T.O.—Engine

<table>
<tr><td>Pulley Diameter, Standard—Inches..</td><td>9</td><td>9</td></tr>
<tr><td>Pulley Face Width—Inches........</td><td>6.54</td><td>6.54</td></tr>
<tr><td>Pulley Speed Loaded—rpm.........</td><td>1366</td><td>1366</td></tr>
<tr><td>Pulley Speed, Loaded—fpm........</td><td>3218</td><td>3218</td></tr>
<tr><td>Power Take-off—Std., Opt. ....</td><td>Std.</td><td>Std.</td></tr>
<tr><td>Is Std. P.T.O. Continuous?....(950)</td><td>No</td><td>No</td></tr>
<tr><td>(960)</td><td>....</td><td>Yes</td></tr>
<tr><td>P.T.O. Cont. When Gearshifting?...</td><td>No</td><td>Yes</td></tr>
<tr><td>Engine—Make ....</td><td>Own</td><td>Own</td></tr>
<tr><td>Engine—Model ....</td><td>EAE</td><td>EAF</td></tr>
<tr><td>Number Cylinders & Displacement..</td><td>4-134</td><td>4-172</td></tr>
<tr><td>Rated rpm ....</td><td>2000</td><td>2200</td></tr>
</table>

Brakes—Steering—Tires

<table>
<tr><td>Brakes, Type—Internal Expanding
Shoes, Contracting Band........</td><td>IES</td><td>IES</td></tr>
<tr><td>Brakes, Location—Wheel Axle Shaft</td><td>WAS</td><td>WAS</td></tr>
<tr><td>Steering Type—Worm & Sector.....</td><td>W&S</td><td>W&S</td></tr>
<tr><td>Tire Size—Standard Rear—Inches..</td><td>11x28</td><td>12x28</td></tr>
<tr><td>Tire Size—Standard Front—Inches.</td><td>6x16</td><td>6x16</td></tr>
</table>

Transmission of Power

<table>
<tr><td>Clutch—Dry Single Disc,
Dry Double Disc............(950)</td><td>DSD</td><td>DSD</td></tr>
<tr><td>(960)</td><td>....</td><td>DDD</td></tr>
<tr><td>Clutch—Spring Loaded? ....</td><td>Yes</td><td>Yes</td></tr>
<tr><td>Final Drive—Bevel, Spur Gear .....</td><td>Spur</td><td>Spur</td></tr>
<tr><td>High Gear Ratio..................</td><td>21.38</td><td>24.26</td></tr>
<tr><td>Low Gear Ratio..................</td><td>78.93</td><td>125.9</td></tr>
<tr><td>Speeds—Number Forward ....</td><td>4</td><td>5</td></tr>
<tr><td>Speeds—Number Reverse ....</td><td>1</td><td>1</td></tr>
</table>

Ford "960"

TRACTOR & IMPLEMENT DIVISION
FORD MOTOR CO.
Birmingham, Mich.

Advertised Speeds, mph, at 2000 engine rpm, With Std. Transmission & Std. Tires—Model 740: 3.54, 4.55, 6.26, 13.06; reverse, 3.87. Models 950 & 960: 2.3, 3.66, 4.86, 6.71, 11.95; reverse, 3.93.

FORD MOTOR CO.
Dagenham, England

Fordson Major Diesel 12	1956
Fordson Major Diesel 14	1956

	Fordson Major Diesel 12, 14
General	
Type—Axle, Adjustable Axle........	Axle
Shipping Weight on Rubber—Lbs.	5600
Nebraska Test Number.............	500
Rear Tread, Adj. Range—In. ....(12)	52-72
(14)	58-62
Front Tread, Adj. Range—Inches....	50.5-74
Height Overall—Inches	63.0
Length Overall—Inches	130.5
Wheelbase—Inches	80.0
Cultivating Clearance—Inches	19.5
Hydraulic Power Unit..............	Std.
Belt Pulley—P.T.O.—Engine	
Belt Pulley—Standard, Optional......	Opt.
Pulley Diameter, Standard—Inches...	8.5
Power Take-Off—Standard, Opt. ...	Std.
Is Power to P.T.O. Continuous?.....	No
Engine—Make	Own
Engine—Model	E1A-DDN
No. Cyl. & Displ.	4-220
Rated rpm	1600
Brakes—Steering—Tires	
Brakes, Type—Contracting Band, Internal Expanding Shoes........	IES
Brakes, Location—Planetary Drum & On Bull Pinion Shaft..............	BPS
Brake Units per Tractor..........	2
Steering Type—Steering Clutches & Brake, Worm & Ball Nut.........	W&BN
Tire Size—Std. Rear—Inches ...(14)	14x30
(12)	12x38
Tire Size—Standard Front—Inches..	7.5x16
Transmission of Power	
Clutch—Spring Loaded Double Plate, Spring Loaded Single Plate........	SLSP
Final Drive—Bevel, Spur Gear, Chain (Rear Wheels)	SG
(Front Wheels)	None
High Gear Ratio..................	19.3
Low Gear Ratio..................	123.0
Speeds—Number Forward	6
Speeds—Number Reverse	2

Fordson Major Diesel

**TRACTOR & IMPLEMENT DIVISION
FORD MOTOR CO.
Birmingham, Mich.**

INTERNATIONAL HARVESTER CO.
Chicago, Illinois

International Crawler "TD-24TC"	1956
International "Cab Lo-Boy"	1956
International "300 Utility"	1956-1957
International "W-400"	1956-1957
International "W-400" Diesel	1956-1957

General

	International Harvester TD-24TC
Engine Type—Diesel, Non-Diesel....	Diesel
Number and Size Size Plows........	20-14
Shipping Weight—Lbs.	42710
Nebraska Test Number...........	529
Tread, Standard—Inches	80
Height Overall—Inches	105.5
Length Overall—Inches	182.2
Ground Clearance—Inches	13.8
Electric Starting—Std. or Opt.	Std.
Hydraulic Power Unit	None

Belt Pulley—P.T.O.—Engine

Pulley Diameter, Standard—Inches..	None
Power Take-off—Standard, Opt. ..	[1]____
Is Power to P.T.O. Continuous?....	No
Engine—Make	Own
Engine—Model	D1091
Number Cylinders & Displacement..	6-1091
Rated rpm	1500

International Crawler "TD-24"
(TD-24TC is similar)

INTERNATIONAL HARVESTER CO.
Chicago, Illinois

Brakes—Steering—Tracks

Steering Type—Track Clutches, Hydraulic Planet Power?........	HPP
Steering Actuation—Manual, Hydraulic Power	HP
Brakes, Type—Contracting Band, Disc	Disc
Brakes Actuation—Manual, Hydraulic Power	M&HP
Track Face Width, Std.—Inches....	22
Ground Contacting Area of Standard Tracks—Square Inches	5159
(Optional)	5628

Transmission of Power

Clutch—Single or Double Plate?	SP
Clutch—Overcenter and Dry?......	Yes
Final Drive	Spur
Speeds—Number Forward..........	4
Speeds—Number Reverse..........	4
Torque Converter?	Yes

[1]For equipment combinations only.

General	I-H International Cub Lo-Boy	300 Utility
Number and Size Plows	1-12	3-14
Type—Adj. Axle, Axle, Tricycle	A.A.	A.A.
Shipping Wt., Max., on Rubber—Lbs.	1590	4140
Nebraska Test Number	....	539
Rear Tread, Adj. Range—Inches	40-56	48-76
Front Tread, Adj. Range—Inches	43-55	48-76
Height Overall—Inches	55	58
Length Overall—Inches	97	123
Wheelbase—Inches	62	75
Electric Starting—Std. or Opt.	Opt.	Std.
Cultivating Clearance—Inches	14	21
Hydraulic Power Unit	Opt.	Opt.

Belt Pulley—P.T.O.—Engine

Pulley Diameter, Standard—Inches	9	11
Pulley Face Width—Inches	4.5	7.5
Pulley Speed, Loaded—rpm	1485	1082
Pulley Speed, Loaded—fpm	3504	3115
Power Take-off—Std., Opt.	Opt.	Opt.
Is Power to P.T.O. Continuous?	No	Yes
P.T.O. Cont. When Gearshifting?	No	Yes
Engine—Make	Own	Own
Engine—Model	C-60	C-169
Number Cylinders & Displacement	4-60	4-169
Rated rpm	1800	2000

Brakes—Steering—Tires

Brakes, Type—Contracting Band, Disc	CB	Disc
Brakes, Location—Bull Pinion Shafts?	Yes	Yes
Steering, Type—Worm & Gear, Cam & Lever	W&G	C&L
Tire Size—Std. Rear—Inches	7x24	10x28
Tire Size—Std. Front—Inches	4x12	5.5x16

Transmission of Power

Clutch—Dry Disc Spring Loaded?	Yes	Yes
Final Drive—Spur, Chain	Spur	Spur
High Gear Ratio	26.8	16.8
Low Gear Ratio	80.5	161.0
Speeds—Number Forward	3	10
Speeds—Number Reverse	1	2

Advertised Speeds, mph, With Std. Transmission & Std. Tires—Model Cub Lo-Boy: 2.3, 3.1, 6.9; reverse, 2.6. Model 300 Utility: 1.75 & 2.60, 2.68 & 3.97, 3.61 & 5.36, 4.63 & 6.86, 11.30 & 16.74; reverse, 2.19 & 3.24.

International "Cub Lo-Boy"

International "300 Utility"

INTERNATIONAL HARVESTER CO.
Chicago, Illinois

General

	International W-400	W-400 Diesel
Number and Size Plows............	4-14	4-14
Type—Axle, Tricycle	Axle	Axle
Shipping Wt., Max., on Rubber—Lbs...	5940	6260
Nebraska Test Number............	533	535
Rear Tread, Min. & Max.—In.	60	60
Front Tread, Min. & Max.—In.	51	51
Height Overall—Inches	93	92
Length Overall—Inches	130	130
Wheelbase—Inches	82	82
Hydraulic Power Unit	Opt.	Opt.

International "W-400"

Belt Pulley—P.T.O.—Engine

Pulley Diameter, Standard—Inches...	11	11
Pulley Face Width—Inches.........	7½	7½
Pulley Speed, Loaded—rpm.........	899	899
Pulley Speed, Loaded—fpm.........	2588	2588
Power Take-Off—Std., Opt.	Opt.	Opt.
Is Power for P.T.O. Continuous?....	Yes	Yes
P.T.O. Cont. When Gearshifting?....	Yes	Yes
Engine—Make	Own	Own
Engine—Model	C-264	D-264
Number Cylinders & Displacement....	4-264	4-264
Rated rpm	1450	1450

Brakes—Steering—Tires

Brakes, Type—Disc.?	Yes	Yes
Brakes, Location—Bull Pinion Shafts?	Yes	Yes
Steering, Type—Cam & Lever?......	Yes	Yes
Tire Size—Standard Rear—Inches....	14x30	14x30
Tire Size—Standard Front—Inches..	6.5x18	6.5x18

International "W-400" Diesel

Transmission of Power

Clutch—Dry Disc Spring Loaded?....	Yes	Yes
Final Drive—Spur, Chain	Spur	Spur
High Gear Ratio	13.89	13.89
Low Gear Ratio	137.6	137.6
Speeds—Number Forward	10	10
Speeds—Number Reverse	2	2

Advertised Speeds, mph, With Std. Tires & Std. Transmission—Models International W-400 & W-400 Diesel: 1.63 & 2.42, 2.51 & 3.72, 3.15 & 4.67, 4.38 & 6.49, 10.9 & 16.15; reverse, 2.17 & 3.22.

INTERNATIONAL HARVESTER CO.
Chicago, Illinois

MASSEY-HARRIS-FERGUSON INC.
Massey-Harris Division

Racine, Wisconsin

Massey-Harris "333" RC	1956
Massey-Harris "333" Standard	1956
Massey-Harris "444" RC	1956
Massey-Harris "444" Standard	1956
Massey-Harris "MH-50" Standard	1956
Massey-Harris "MH-50" Tricycle High-Clearance	1956

General

	Massey-Harris 333 RC	333 Std.
Number and Size Plows	3-14	3-14
Type—Axle, Adj. Axle, Tricycle	AA & T	Axle
Front Tread, Adj. Range—In. (Tri.)	8.54	47.59
(Adj. Axle)	52.2-72.2	....
Wheelbase—Inches .....(Adj. Axle)	102.5	88.06
(Tricycle)	88.12	....
Hydraulic Power Unit	Opt.	Opt.

Belt Pulley—P.T.O.—Engine

Pulley Diameter, Std.—Inches	13.5	13½
Pulley Face Width—Inches	6.5	6.5
Pulley Speed, Loaded—rpm	876	876
Pulley Speed, Loaded—fpm	3097	3097
Power Take-off—Std., Opt.	Opt.	Opt.
Engine—Make	Own	Own
Engine—Model ....(Gasoline)	333	333
(Diesel)	333	333
Number Cylinders & Displacement	4-208	4-208
Rated rpm	1500	1500

Brakes—Steering—Tires

Steering—Make	Saginaw	Saginaw
Steering Type—Worm & Sector?	Yes	Yes
Tire Size—Std. Rear—Inches	11x38	12x28
Tire Size—Std. Front—Inches. (AA)	5.5x16	5.5x16
(Dual Wheel Tri.)	5.5x16	....
(Single Wheel Tri.)	9x10	....

Transmission of Power

Clutch—Dry Disc Spring Loaded?	Yes	Yes
Speeds—Number Forward	10	10
Speeds—Number Reverse	2	2

Advertised Speeds, mph, With Std. Transmission & Std. Tires—Model 33 RC: 1.43 & 2.44, 2.16 & 3.68, 2.87 & 4.83, 3.73 & 6.36, 7.97 & 13.60; reverse, 1.88 & 3.20.

Massey-Harris "333"

**MASSEY-HARRIS DIV.
MASSEY-HARRIS-FERGUSON INC.
Racine, Wisconsin**

General

	Massey-Harris 444 RC	444 Std.
Number and Size Plows	3,4-14	3,4-14
Type—Axle, Adj. Axle, Tricycle	AA, T	Axle
Front Tread, Adj. Range—In. (Tri.)	8.5-15.3	47.5
(Adj. Axle)	52.2-	....
	72.2	....
Wheelbase—Inches .....(Adj. Axle)	101.8	88.06
(Tricycle)	88.0	....
Hydraulic Power Unit	Opt.	Opt.

Belt Pulley—P.T.O.—Engine

Pulley Diameter, Std.—Inches	13.5	13.5
Pulley Face Width—Inches	6.5	6.5
Pulley Speed, Loaded—rpm	876	876
Pulley Speed, Loaded—fpm	3097	3097
Power Take-off—Std., Opt.	Opt.	Opt.
Engine—Make	Own	Own
Engine—Model ....(Gasoline)	444	444
(Diesel)	444	444
(LP-Gas.)	444	444
Number Cylinders & Displacement	4-277	4-277
Rated rpm	1500	1500

Massey-Harris "444"

Brakes—Steering—Tires

Steering Type—Worm & Sector?	Yes	Yes
Tire Size—Std. Rear—Inches	12x38	13x30
Tire Size—Std. Front—Inches (AA)	6.5x16	6.5x16
(Dual Wheel Tri.)	6.5x16	....
(Single Wheel Tri.)	9x10	....

Transmission of Power

Clutch—Dry Disc Spring Loaded?	Yes	Yes
Speeds—Number Forward	10	10
Speeds—Number Reverse	2	2

Advertised Speeds, mph, With Std. Transmission & Std. Tires—Model 444 RC: 1.43 & 2.44, 2.16 & 3.68, 2.87 & 4.88, 3.73 & 6.36, 7.97 & 13.60; reverse, 1.88 & 3.20.

MASSEY-HARRIS DIV.
MASSEY-HARRIS-FERGUSON INC.
Racine, Wisconsin

General	Massey-Harris MH-50 Std.	MH-50 Tricycle High-Clear.
Number and Size Plows...........	3-12 or 2-14	
Shipping Weight, Maximum.........	2961	3013
Nebraska Test Number...........	None	None
Rear Tread, Adj. Range—Inches....	48-76	48-76
Front Tread, Adj. Range—In. (Tri.)		17.7
(Axle & High-Clearance)	48-76	48-76
Height Overall—Inches	56.7	62.6
Length Overall—In. ..(High-Clear.)	119.9	124.5
(Single Wheel Tricycle)		128.9
(Dual Wheel Tricycle)		127.3
Cultivating Clearance—Inches	21.3	26.9
Hydraulic Power Unit..............	Std.	Std.

Belt Pulley—P.T.O.—Engine

Pulley Diameter, Standard—Inches..	9	9
Pulley Face Width—Inches........	6.5	6.5
Pulley Speed, Loaded—rpm........	1316	1316
Pulley Speed, Loaded—fpm........	3100	3100
Power Take-off—Std., Opt.	Std.	Std.
Is Power to P.T.O. Continuous?....	Yes	Yes
P.T.O. Cont. When Gearshifting?...	Yes	Yes
Engine—Make	Cont.	Cont.
Engine—Model	Z-134	Z-134
Number Cylinders & Displacement..	4-134	4-134
Rated rpm	2000	2000

Brakes—Steering—Tires

Brakes, Type—Internal Exp. Shoes?.	Yes	Yes
Brakes, Location—		
Wheel Axle Shafts?..............	Yes	Yes
Steering Make	Ross	Ross
Steering Type—Cam & Lever?.....	Yes	Yes
Power Steering—Standard, Optional.	Opt.	Opt.
Tire Size—Std. Rear—Inches......	11x28	10x38
Tire Size—Std. Front—In. ..(H-C)	5.5x16	5.5x16
(Single Wheel Tricycle)		7.5x10
(Dual Wheel Tricycle)		5.5x16

Massey-Harris "MH-50"

MASSEY-HARRIS DIV.
MASSEY-HARRIS-FERGUSON INC.
Racine, Wisconsin

Transmission of Power	Std.	Tri. H-C
Final Drive—Spur, Bevel..........	Bevel	Bevel
High Gear Ratio...(High Clearance)	18.7	20.2
Low Gear Ratio...(High Clearance)	205.5	222.0
Speeds—Number Forward	6	6
Speeds—Number Reverse	2	2

Advertised Speeds, mph, With Std. Transmission & Std. Tires—Standard Model: 1.33, 1.99, 3.64, 5.32, 7.96, 14.57; reverse, 1.77 & 7.09. Hi-Clearance Model: 1.45, 2.15, 3.98, 5.81, 8.69, 15.92; reverse, 1.93 & 7.75.

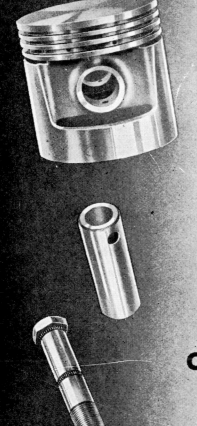
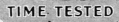

MINNEAPOLIS-MOLINE CO.

Minneapolis, Minnesota

Minneapolis-Moline 445 Universal	1956
Minneapolis-Moline 445 Utility	1956
Minneapolis-Moline "UB" Type U	1956-1957

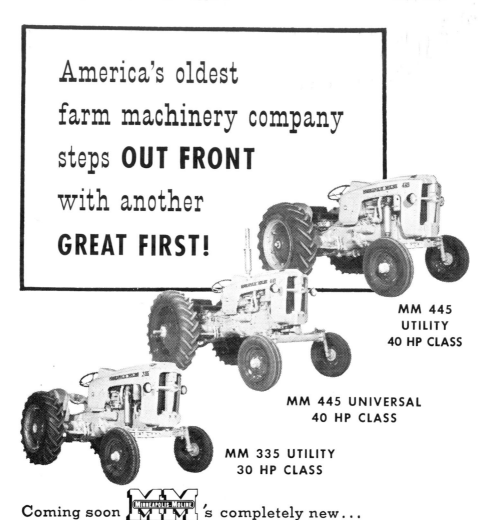

America's oldest
farm machinery company
steps **OUT FRONT**
with another
GREAT FIRST!

MM 445
UTILITY
40 HP CLASS

MM 445 UNIVERSAL
40 HP CLASS

MM 335 UTILITY
30 HP CLASS

Coming soon **MM** MODERN MACHINERY's completely new...

POWERLINED **TRACTORS**

Now . . . from the company that built the first all-purpose tractor, the Moline Universal; the famed "12-20", *first* really engineered farm tractor; the *first* factory-produced tractor with high-compression engine; the *first* Visionlined tractor; and *first* factory-produced tractor for LP Gas . . . comes a great *NEW* tractor advance! These are Minneapolis-Moline's completely new *POWERlined* tractors . . . out ahead in dynamic design, packed with blazing power and scores of exclusive new

MM advantages! Here's a revolutionary speed-power selector to boost power or speed in every gear; new power steering (available on 445 series), advanced hydraulic 3-point hitch; power-adjusted rear wheel tread (available on Utility Models), entirely new comfort and convenience, and a complete line of new power-matched MM machines to make *POWERlined* advantages pay off to the limit!

It's the *out ahead* look in power farming . . . coming your way soon!

MINNEAPOLIS-MOLINE MINNEAPOLIS 1, MINNESOTA

is on the march!

Minneapolis-Moline "445" Universal

General	Minneapolis-Moline 445 Universal	445 Utility
Type—Axle, Adj. Axle, Tricycle.....	AA&T	A.A.
Shipping Weight—Lbs. ...(Adj. Axle)	3900	3750
(Dual Wheel Tricycle)	3700	....
Rear Tread, Adj. Range—Inches....	56-88	56-84
Front Tread, Adj. Range—In. (A.A.)	56-84	50-78
(Dual Wheel Tricycle)	8-13	....
Height Overall—Inches.............	101	93.8
Length Overall, Maximum—Inches...	140.5	130.6
Wheelbase—Inches .....(Adj. Axle)	93.8	81.6
(Tricycle)	86.5	....
Cultivating Clearance—In. ...(A.A.)	22.5	20.1
(Tricycle)	25.5	....
Hydraulic Power Unit.............	Opt.	Opt.

Belt Pulley—P.T.O.—Engine

Pulley Diameter, Standard—Inches..	8⅜	8⅜
Pulley Face Width—Inches.........	6½	6½
Pulley Speed, Loaded—rpm........	1470	1470
Pulley Speed, Loaded—fpm........	3220	3220
Power Take-off—Standard, Opt. ..	Opt.	Opt.
Is Power to P.T.O. Continuous?....	Yes	Yes
P.T.O. Cont. When Gearshifting?...	Yes	Yes
Engine—Make	Own	Own
Engine—Model	206H-4	206H-4
Number Cylinders & Displacement..	4-206	4-206
Rated rpm	1550	1550

Minneapolis-Moline "445" Utility

MINNEAPOLIS-MOLINE COMPANY

Minneapolis, Minnesota

Brakes—Steering—Tires

Brakes, Type—Int. Exp., Disc......	Disc	Disc
Brakes, Location—Diff. Shafts?....	Yes	Yes
Steering Make	Own	Own
Steering, Type—Cam & Lever, Worm & Gear.................	W & G	W & G
Power Steering—Standard, Opt. ...	Opt.	Opt.
Tire Size—Std. Rear—In.	11x28	11x28
Tire Size—Std. Front—In. ..(A.A.)	5.5x16	5.5x16
(Single Wheel Tricycle)	7.5x10	....
(Dual Wheel Tricycle)	5.5x16	....

Transmission of Power

Clutch—Dry Double Disc..........	DDD	DDD
Clutch—Overcenter, Spring Loaded.	SL	SL
Final Drive—Spur Gear, Chain......	SG	SG
High Gear Ratio....(5-Speed Trans.)	16.65	14.57
(10-Speed Trans.)	31.71	27.7
Low Gear Ratio...(5-Speed Trans.)	92.1	80.5
(10-Speed Trans.)	175.4	153.5
Gearset Speeds—No. Forward (Std.)	5	5
(Planetary Unit)	10	10
Gearset Speeds—No. Reverse (Std.)	1	1
(Planetary Unit)	2	2

Advertised Speeds, mph, With Std. Tires—Model 445 Universal with Sliding Gear Transmission and Planetary Unit: 1.46 & 2.78, 2.23 & 4.26, 3.4 & 6.48, 5.28 & 10.05, 8.09 & 15.4; reverse, 2.23 & 4.26. Model 445 Universal with Sliding Gear Transmission only: 2.78, 4.26, 6.48, 10.05, 15.4; reverse, 4.26. Model 445 Utility with Sliding Gear Transmission and Planetary Unit: 1.41 & 2.69, 2.16 & 4.11, 3.29 & 6.26, 5.1 & 9.71, 7.81 & 14.88; reverse, 2.16 & 4.11. Model 445 Utility with Sliding Gear Transmission only: 2.61, 3.99, 6.08, 9.42, 14.44; reverse, 3.99.

General

Number and Size Plows 4-14
Type—Axle, Tri., Adj. Axle .... Tri.
Shipping Wt., Max., on Rubber—Lbs.... 5700
Nebraska Test Number 520, 522
Rear Tread, Minimum—Inches 54.5
Rear Tread, Maximum—Inches 84½
Front Tread, Adj. Range—Inches..... 8⅜-13
Height Overall—Inches.............. 78.5
Length Overall—Inches 133
Wheelbase—Inches 88
Hydraulic Power Unit.............. Opt.

Belt Pulley—P.T.O.—Engine

Pulley Diameter, Standard—Inches... 16
Pulley Face Width—Inches......... 7
Pulley Speed, Loaded—rpm......... 741
Pulley Speed, Loaded—fpm......... 3110
Power Take-Off—Standard, Optional. Opt.
Is Non Continuous P.T.O. Available?. Yes
Is Continuous P.T.O. Available?..... Yes
P.T.O. Cont. When Gearshifting?.... No
Engine—Make .... Own
Engine—Model ....(Gasoline & LPG) 283B
                        (Diesel) D283
Number Cylinders & Displacement... 4-283
Rated rpm 1300

Brakes—Steering—Tires

Brakes, Type—Disc? .... Yes
Brakes, Location—Bull Pin. Shafts?. Yes
Steering Make .... Own
Type—Cam & Lever, Worm & Sector? W&S
Tire Size—Standard Rear—Inches... 12x38
Tire Size—Standard Front—Inches... 6x16

Transmission of Power

Clutch—Dry Single Disc?.......... Yes
Clutch—Spring Loaded, Overcenter.. SL
Final Drive—Spur, Chain.......... Spur
High Gear Ratio 14.52
Low Gear Ratio 80.42
Speeds—Number Forward 5
Speeds—Number Reverse 1

Minneapolis-Moline
UB
Type
U

Minneapolis-Moline "UB" Type U

MINNEAPOLIS-MOLINE COMPANY
Minneapolis, Minnesota

THE OLIVER CORP.
Chicago, Illinois

Oliver "Super 99 GM"   1956

Oliver "Super 99 GM"

THE OLIVER CORPORATION
Chicago, Illinois

General

	Oliver Super 99 GM
Number and Size Plows	5, 6-14
Type—Axle, Track	Axle
Shipping Weight—Lbs.	7800
Nebraska Test Number	556
Rear Wheel Tread—Inches	62
Front Wheel Tread—Inches	59.2
Height Overall—Inches	90
Length Overall—Inches	136.8
Wheelbase—Inches	79.8
Cultivating Clearance—Inches	11.81
Hydraulic Power Unit	Opt.

Belt Pulley—P.T.O.—Engine

Pulley Diameter, Standard—Inches	12.25
Pulley Face Width—Inches	9
Pulley Speed, Loaded—rpm	980
Pulley Speed, Loaded—fpm	3207
Power Take-off—Std., Opt.	Opt.
Is Power to P.T.O. Continuous?	Yes
Engine—Make	G.M.
Engine—Model	3-71
Number Cyl. & Displacement	3-231
Rated rpm	1675

Brakes—Steering—Tires

Brakes, Type—	
Contracting Band, Disc	Disc
Brakes, Location—Differential Shaft	DS
Steering Make—Own, Saginaw	Sag.
Steering Type—Circulating Ball	CB
Tire Size—Std. Rear—Inches	15x34
Tire Size—Standard Front—Inches	7.5x18

Transmission of Power

Clutch—Single or Double Plate?	SP
Clutch—Spring Loaded?	Yes
Final Drive—Spur, Chain	Spur
High Gear Ratio	22.41
Low Gear Ratio	116.79
Speeds—Number Forward	6
Speeds—Number Reverse	2

INDEX

List of Manufacturers' Early Advertisements

(Not inclusive of all manufacturers contained herein or advertisements within the *Cooperative Tractor Catalog* and *Red Tractor Book*).